THE MOLECULAR ORBITAL THEORY
OF ORGANIC CHEMISTRY

McGRAW-HILL SERIES IN ADVANCED CHEMISTRY

AMDUR AND HAMMES   Chemical Kinetics: Principles and Selected Topics

BAIR   Introduction to Chemical Instrumentation

BALLHAUSEN   Introduction to Ligand Field Theory

BENSON   The Foundations of Chemical Kinetics

BIEMANN   Mass Spectrometry (Organic Chemical Applications)

DAVIDSON   Statistical Mechanics

DAVYDOV   (*Trans.* Kasha and Oppenheimer)   Theory of Molecular Excitons

DEAN   Flame Photometry

DEWAR   The Molecular Orbital Theory of Organic Chemistry

ELIEL   Stereochemistry of Carbon Compounds

FITTS   Nonequilibrium Thermodynamics

FRISTROM AND WESTENBERG   Flame Structure

HELFFERICH   Ion Exchange

HILL   Statistical Mechanics

HINE   Physical Organic Chemistry

JENSEN AND RICKBORN   Electrophilic Substitution of Organomercurials

KAN   Organic Photochemistry

KIRKWOOD AND OPPENHEIM   Chemical Thermodynamics

KOSOWER   Molecular Biochemistry

LAITINEN   Chemical Analysis

McDOWELL   Mass Spectrometry

MANDELKERN   Crystallization of Polymers

MARCH   Advanced Organic Chemistry: Reactions, Mechanisms, and Structure

MEMORY   Quantum Theory of Magnetic Resonance Parameters

PITZER AND BREWER   (*Revision of* Lewis and Randall)   Thermodynamics

POPLE, SCHNEIDER, AND BERNSTEIN   High-resolution Nuclear Magnetic Resonance

PRYOR   Free Radicals

PRYOR   Mechanisms of Sulfur Reactions

RAAEN, ROPP, AND RAAEN   Carbon-14

ROBERTS   Nuclear Magnetic Resonance

ROSSOTTI AND ROSSOTTI   The Determination of Stability Constants

SIGGIA   Survey of Analytical Chemistry

SOMMER   Stereochemistry, Mechanisms and Silicon

STREITWIESER   Solvolytic Displacement Reactions

SUNDHEIM   Fused Salts

WIBERG   Laboratory Technique in Organic Chemistry

THE MOLECULAR ORBITAL THEORY
OF ORGANIC CHEMISTRY

MICHAEL J. S. DEWAR, F.R.S.
ROBERT A. WELCH PROFESSOR OF CHEMISTRY
THE UNIVERSITY OF TEXAS

McGRAW-HILL BOOK COMPANY
NEW YORK
ST. LOUIS
SAN FRANCISCO
LONDON
SYDNEY
TORONTO
MEXICO
PANAMA

THE MOLECULAR ORBITAL THEORY
OF ORGANIC CHEMISTRY

PREFACE

The purpose of this book is to present an account of the molecular orbital theory of chemistry in general, and of organic chemistry in particular, in a form intelligible to organic chemists and illustrated by specific applications to problems of chemical interest.

Twenty years have elapsed since my first book‡ appeared. At that time few organic chemists had any knowledge of quantum mechanics or molecular orbital (MO) theory, and my object was to show that this could provide a much more satisfactory account of the subject than the then fashionable resonance approach. In 1949 the MO method was admittedly at a very early stage of development. Digital computers had barely begun to appear, and Roothaan and Pople had not yet published their classic papers on the self-consistent field (SCF) MO theory. Quantitative calculations had to be carried out by hand and were limited to the crude Hückel treatment; the only other way in which MO theory could be applied to chemical problems was in a rough, qualitative, and pictorial form based on simple ideas of orbitals and orbital overlap.

During the last twenty years the subject has changed out of recognition and these changes have in turn revolutionized organic chemistry. The three main developments in this respect have been (1) the introduction of digital computers, making possible calculations that would previously have been impracticably laborious; (2) the development of SCF MO theory, which has for the first time allowed one to think in terms of quantitative calculations of "chemical" accuracy; and (3) the realization that perturbation theory provides a particularly suitable approach to most chemical problems.

Progress of this kind must, however, be paid for, and the price to the organic chemist is a proper understanding of quantum organic chemistry. Twenty years ago practicing organic chemists could get by with a smattering of resonance theory, and ten years ago with a rudimentary knowledge of the Hückel method; now, however, any organic chemist who lacks a proper understanding of current developments in MO theory is already heavily handicapped, and unless he takes steps to counter this, he will in a few years time find himself left high and dry by the tide of theoretical organic chemistry and confined to routine studies of a classical nature.

The primary concern of chemistry is, as it has always been, the interpretation of the structures of molecules and the chemical reactions they undergo. This then should also be the primary concern of quantum chemistry, the branch of science that deals with the application of quantum mechanics to chemical problems. Since structure and reactivity are determined by the free energies of aggregates of atoms in their ground states, and since the main contribution, so far as chemistry is concerned, comes from the energy term rather than from entropy,§ the main object of quantum chemistry should likewise be to estimate the ground-state energies of

‡ Numbered references will be found in the list following Chap. 1.
§ The fact that theoretical organic chemistry is a feasible study is due to this, given that we cannot at present estimate theoretically the entropies of any but the very simplest molecules.

aggregates of atoms as a function of their geometrical arrangement in space. If the results are to be of practical value to chemists, it is moreover necessary that the energies be estimated with "chemical" accuracy, i.e., an accuracy at least of the order of ± 1 kcal/mole.

As can be seen at once from the agenda of any conference on quantum chemistry held during the last five years, this has not in fact been a primary concern of self-styled quantum chemists. Most of the papers presented at such meetings have been concerned with a priori calculations for small molecules, or with applications to nmr, esr, or ultraviolet-visible spectroscopy. The applications to spectroscopy are of obvious interest and importance to chemists, but these are nevertheless peripheral areas so far as chemistry proper is concerned; while the a priori calculations have either been limited to molecules so small as to be chemically trivial, or have been carried out by approximate methods inherently incapable of the accuracy that chemists require. Although, therefore, these studies are of great interest and importance in themselves, they are not of great significance to chemistry, and the average chemist could not for their sake alone feel justified in expending the time and effort needed to acquire the necessary expertise to take part in them.

Two developments have, however, altered the whole situation and made an understanding of quantum theory an urgent necessity for organic chemists. The first is the development of semiempirical SCF MO methods which for the first time seem capable of providing quantitative information concerning the energies and other properties of molecules in their ground states, with an accuracy sufficient for chemical purposes. The second is the development of the perturbational MO (PMO) approach mentioned above into a general theory of organic chemistry, no harder to apply in practice than resonance theory but infinitely more powerful and versatile. The PMO method is not in fact particularly new, having been presented in a series of rather indigestible papers no less than fifteen years ago (e.g. Ref. 2), however, no good account of it has yet appeared in book form and so it has been largely neglected by organic chemists. Here I have tried to remedy this omission and also to give a general introduction to SCF MO theory.

This book is concerned only with ground states of organic molecules, for four reasons. First, this is the field which has been most neglected in print, and the few available texts (e.g. Ref. 3) have been confined almost exclusively to the Hückel method, which must now be regarded as obsolete for any kind of quantitative work, or pay only very limited attention to the basic problems of chemistry proper. Secondly, several excellent texts have appeared in recent years dealing with inorganic chemistry (e.g. Ref. 4) and with the application of quantum mechanics to magnetic resonance spectroscopy and excited states (e.g. Ref. 5). Thirdly, any attempt to include such material would either have made this book excessively large, or would have reduced the coverage of ground states, or would have led to a compression of the theoretical derivations, thus making them harder to follow for those readers for whom it was mainly written. And fourthly, the material presented here should provide the interested reader with a very appropriate background for the accounts of transition-metal chemistry and excited states to which I have referred (e.g. Refs. 4 and 5) and which inevitably assume considerable theoretical knowledge on the part of the reader.

Because this book is concerned primarily with the application of quantum theory to the basic problems of chemistry, I have inevitably given a great deal of emphasis to the work of my own research group. The reasons for this should be evident from the previous paragraphs. Even today, few professional organic chemists are working in the area of quantum chemistry, while few theoreticians have the knowledge or inclination to pay much attention to purely chemical problems. It is indeed evident that further progress in this area is likely to depend on the activities of organic chemists rather than of professional theoreticians and the main purpose of this book is to increase the number of organic chemists working in the field.

I hope I have succeeded in presenting the subject in a form intelligible to a reader with little prior knowledge of quantum theory; I should be particularly well fitted to do this since I began my chemical career as a classical organic chemist at Oxford, and since most of the colleagues who have worked with me in this area have also been organic chemists who, in many cases, knew little about quantum theory when they arrived. Their collaboration has been one of the major pleasures I have derived from this work.

Our work in this field has been supported by the National Institutes of Health, and at present is being supported by the Air Force Office of Scientific Research and the Robert A. Welch Foundation. I would also like to thank my many chemical friends for their advice and criticism (especially the latter!) over the years, and Mrs. Wandeen Sakewitz, Mrs. Sondra Laemmle and Mrs. Patricia Cloud for their assistance in preparing the manuscript.

MICHAEL J. S. DEWAR

CONTENTS

THE MOLECULAR ORBITAL THEORY
OF ORGANIC CHEMISTRY

THE PRINCIPLES
OF QUANTUM
MECHANICS

1.1 INTRODUCTION

In classical mechanics we define a system of particles in terms of the position coordinates q_i and momenta p_i of the individual particles. Any measurable property of the system is represented by a *dynamic variable,* a function of the coordinates q_i and p_i. If we know all these coordinates at some instant in time, we can predict all the measurable properties of the system, both at that instant and for the whole of future time.

However this approach cannot be used for atomic and molecular systems; the Heisenberg uncertainty principle tells us that we cannot measure the positions and momenta of the particles involved in them accurately at the same time. If we cannot measure the coordinates q_i and p_i needed to define such a system in classical mechanics, we clearly cannot use classical mechanics to investigate its properties. To meet this situation it became necessary to devise an entirely new mathematical approach to the problem, i.e. quantum mechanics; in this chapter we shall examine the basic principles of this new‡ discipline partly in order to establish the terminology and symbolism that will be used throughout the rest of this book, and partly to familiarize the reader with the philosophy underlying quantum theory. This material is not usually included in the standard texts; yet without it quantum mechanics tends to become a dry and sterile mathematical exercise.

The treatment given here follows that given by Dirac.[6]§ The symbolism and terminology used by him have been widely adopted and anyone interested in the field now needs to be familiar with them.

1.2 THE BASIC PROBLEM

Figure 1.1 indicates a simple imaginary experiment which will illustrate all the essential principles of quantum theory. In this we allow a beam of light, plane-polarized at an angle θ to the vertical, to pass through a polarizer P, set to transmit vertically polarized light. A detector D measures the fraction of the light that passes through the polarizer.

‡ Perhaps it would be more correct to say moderately new.
§ Numbered references will be found at the end of each chapter.

In classical physics, where light was treated as a form of wave motion, the incident light was described by a wave function ψ which could be expressed as a combination of components ψ_V, ψ_H polarized vertically and horizontally respectively;

$$\psi = \psi_V \cos \theta + \psi_H \sin \theta \qquad (1.1)$$

The intensity of the transmitted beam is given by the square of the vertically polarized component; thus the intensity I of the transmitted beam is given in terms of that (I_0) of the incident beam by

$$I = I_0 \cos^2 \theta \qquad (1.2)$$

In quantum theory, however, a beam of light is treated as a stream of spinning particles (*photons*), a polarized light beam being composed of particles that are all spinning in the same direction. If the plane of polarization is vertical, each photon passes unchanged through the polarizer; if horizontal, each photon is rejected. In our experiment (Fig. 1.1), with an intermediate polarization, some of the photons pass through the analyzer while others are rejected; the only way we can interpret this is by saying that each photon has a definite chance of getting through the polarizer, the probability of this happening being given by $\cos^2 \theta$. However there is a further point to consider. Any light that does get through the polarizer is now vertically polarized. Our experiment therefore changes the nature of the photons, altering their plane of polarization from an angle θ to the vertical, to vertical. The polarizer in effect demands that each incident photon decide whether it is vertically or horizontally polarized; if the photons are polarized at an angle θ to the vertical, the chance that any given one will answer "vertical" to the polarizer and be let through is $\cos^2 \theta$.

The situation indicated by this experiment occurs in all measurements relating to atomic systems. The main points are as follows:

1   Any such measurement leads to one or other of a discrete set of possible results; in the polarized-light experiment there are just two answers to the polarizer's question—vertical or horizontal. In the general case there may be an infinite number of possible results—but the result of a given measurement is still restricted to one number of this set.

2   A system may be such that a given measurement leads to a definite result; thus in the polarized-light experiment we know for sure that every incident photon will pass through the polarizer if the incident light is polarized verti-

FIG. 1.1   Experiment illustrating principles of quantum mechanics.

cally, and that every incident photon will be rejected if the incident light is polarized horizontally.

3   If the system is in some intermediate state, then the measurement may lead to any one of the allowed results; however if the experiment is repeated a large number of times, the probability of getting one given result is found to have a definite fixed value.

Our basic problem is to develop a formalism consistent with these conditions, and then to establish some procedure for calculating the possible results of any given experiment, and for calculating the probability that a given measurement will lead to any one particular result.

1.3 THE FORMALISM OF QUANTUM THEORY

A given system may exist in any of a large (usually infinite) number of states. We may describe its condition by some suitable mathematical expression. Since we do not wish to commit ourselves to any particular kind of expression at this stage, we introduce a special term and symbol for this (as yet undetermined) expression describing a possible state of our system. Following Dirac[6] we call it a *ket*, symbolized thus: $|\ \rangle$. If we need to distinguish a particular ket, we can label it with one or more numbers a_i; viz. $|a_1 a_2 \cdots a_n\rangle$.

Any measurable property of the system is symbolized by a *dynamic operator.* An operator is a symbol implying some mathematical operation; $\sqrt{\ }$ and $\partial/\partial x$ are typical operators in simple algebra. We cannot of course express our operators in any explicit form as yet, since they are to operate on *kets*—and our kets are still undefined.

When a dynamic operator α acts on a ket, it converts it into another ket;

$$\alpha|a\rangle = |b\rangle \tag{1.3}$$

In certain special cases, the new ket may be simply a multiple of the old one;

$$\alpha|i\rangle = A_i|i\rangle \tag{1.4}$$

where A_i is an algebraic number. In this case $|i\rangle$ is termed an *eigenket* of α with *eigenvalue* A_i.

We know that a given measurement can lead only to one of a number of discrete possible values; we now assume that these are the eigenvalues of the corresponding dynamic operator α. The corresponding states of the system are of course symbolized by the corresponding eigenkets. Guided by the analogy of Eqs. (1.1) and (1.2), we now further assume that any possible state $|m\rangle$ of the system can be represented by a linear combination of the eigenkets of α;

$$|m\rangle = \sum_i a_{mi}|i\rangle \tag{1.5}$$

Here the a_{mi} are algebraic numbers, possibly complex; following again the classical analogy, we suppose that if the system is represented by $|m\rangle$, the probability P_i that the measurement α will lead to the result A_i is given by the square of the coefficient a_{mi} of the eigenket $|i\rangle$ —or since a_{mi} may be complex, by the absolute value of its square; i.e.

$$P_i = \bar{a}_{mi}a_{mi} \tag{1.6}$$

where $\bar{a}_{mi}$ is the complex conjugate of a_{mi}.

Three points now arise. First, Eqs. (1.5) and (1.6) can apply only if the eigenkets $|i\rangle$ are all linearly independent; thus if the kets $|i\rangle$ and $|j\rangle$ differed only by a numerical factor q, so that

$$|j\rangle = q|i\rangle \tag{1.7}$$

then one could not distinguish between the combination $a_{mi}|i\rangle + a_{mj}|j\rangle$ and other equivalent combinations such as $(a_{mi} + qa_{mj})|i\rangle$. This implies that an eigenket of a dynamic operator must be essentially unaffected when it is multiplied by some constant; in other words if $|i\rangle$ is an eigenket of α with eigenvalue A_i, so also is any multiple $q|i\rangle$ of $|i\rangle$. Thus:

$$\alpha(q|i\rangle) = A_{mi}(q|i\rangle) \tag{1.8}$$

Obviously this will be so only if

$$\alpha(q|i\rangle) = q\alpha|i\rangle \tag{1.9}$$

The operator α must therefore commute with the algebraic number q. This means that α must be a *linear operator*.‡

This brings us to our second point. In order to use Eqs. (1.5) and (1.6), we must in some way fix the scale of our kets. The third point is similar; we need some way of determining the coefficients a_{mi} in Eq. (1.5). Similar problems arise in vector analysis. If kets are regarded as generalized vectors of some kind, Eq. (1.5) would express an arbitrary ket in terms of components along the directions of the eigenkets of α. In order to do this, the eigenket vectors would be normalized to unit length.

The length A of a vector $\mathbf{A}$ is given by the square root of the scalar product of $\mathbf{A}$ with itself. In the general case where the components of $\mathbf{A}$ may be complex,

$$A^2 = \bar{\mathbf{A}} \cdot \mathbf{A} \tag{1.10}$$

where $\bar{\mathbf{A}}$ is the complex conjugate of $\mathbf{A}$.§ We need some analogous procedure for determining the "length" of our kets. To do this we introduce a complemen-

---

‡ An operator is termed linear if it obeys the distributive law, in this case $\alpha(|i\rangle + |j\rangle) = \alpha|i\rangle + \alpha|j\rangle$. Such an operator commutes with algebraic numbers. Not all operators are linear; thus the square-root operator $\sqrt{\ }$ is a nonlinear operator, $\sqrt{a+b} \neq \sqrt{a} + \sqrt{b}$.

§ In matrix notation, there is a further difference between the two vectors. A vector is a matrix with either one row or one column. If $\mathbf{A}$ is a row matrix, and $\bar{\mathbf{A}}$ a column matrix, Eq. (1.10) expresses A^2 as the (scalar) matrix product of $\bar{\mathbf{A}}$ by $\mathbf{A}$.

tary set of expressions which we shall term *bras*, denoted by the symbol $\langle\ |$. Each ket $|a\rangle$ has a corresponding bra $\langle\bar{a}|$; as the bar indicates, any numbers appearing in the bra are complex conjugates of those appearing in the corresponding ket. We now assume that:

1 The product of any bra $\langle\bar{a}|$ with any ket $|b\rangle$ is an algebraic number (scalar). This product is written as the complete bra(c)ket expression $\langle\bar{a}|b\rangle$; hence our use of the terms bra and ket for its components.

2 If $\langle\bar{i}|$ is the bra corresponding to an eigenket $|i\rangle$ of some dynamic operator α, and if $|j\rangle$ is some other eigenket of α, then

$$\langle\bar{i}|j\rangle = 0 \qquad i \neq j \tag{1.11}$$

The eigenbras and eigenkets of a dynamic operator thus form an *orthogonal* system, analogous to an orthogonal set of vectors. By analogy, the "length" of a given eigenket $|i\rangle$ is then the square root of the scalar product $\langle\bar{i}|i\rangle$. If this is equal to unity, the bra and ket are said to be *normalized*. From now on we shall assume that all eigenbras and eigenkets of dynamic operators are normalized, except where otherwise stated. If the bra $\langle\bar{a}|$ or ket $|a\rangle$ is not normalized, we can normalize it by multiplying it by $\langle\bar{a}|a\rangle^{-1/2}$.

The coefficients a_{mi} in Eq. (1.5) can now be found by a procedure analogous to a Fourier analysis. Consider the product of the ket $|m\rangle$ with an eigenbra $\langle\bar{i}|$ of α;

$$\langle\bar{i}|m\rangle = \langle\bar{i}|(\sum_j a_{mj}|j\rangle) = a_{mi}\langle\bar{i}|i\rangle = a_{mi} \tag{1.12}$$

(since the eigenkets $|j\rangle$ are orthogonal to the eigenbra $\langle\bar{i}|$, $\langle\bar{i}|j\rangle = 0$ unless $i = j$).

A further useful result follows from Eq. (1.6). The bra $\langle\bar{m}|$ corresponding to the ket $|m\rangle$ [Eq. (1.5)] can be expanded in terms of eigenbras of α;

$$\langle\bar{m}| = \sum_i \bar{a}_{mi}\langle\bar{i}| \tag{1.13}$$

Consider the function $\langle\bar{m}|\alpha|\bar{m}\rangle$. Using Eqs. (1.5) and (1.13), and the fact that α is a linear operator,

$$\langle\bar{m}|\alpha|\bar{m}\rangle = \sum_i \bar{a}_{mi}\langle\bar{i}|\alpha\sum_j a_{mj}|j\rangle$$

$$= \sum_i \bar{a}_{mi}\langle\bar{i}|\sum_j a_{mj}\alpha|j\rangle$$

$$= \sum_i \bar{a}_{mi}\langle\bar{i}|\sum_j a_{mj}A_j|j\rangle$$

$$= \sum_i \bar{a}_{mi}a_{mi}A_i\langle\bar{i}|i\rangle \qquad \text{from Eq. (1.4)}$$

$$= \sum_i a_{mi}a_{mi}A_i \qquad \begin{array}{l}\text{since the eigenbras and eigenkets}\\ \text{of } \alpha \text{ are normalized}\end{array}$$

$$= \sum_i P_iA_i \qquad \text{from Eq. (1.6)} \tag{1.14}$$

Now if the measurement α is repeated a large number of times, the average value A_{mean} obtained will be given by $\sum\limits_i P_i A_i$, when P_i is the probability that a given measurement will lead to the result A_i. Thus:

$$A_{\text{mean}} = \langle \overline{m} | \alpha | m \rangle \tag{1.15}$$

This result was obtained on the assumption that $\langle \overline{m} |$ and $| m \rangle$ are normalized. In some cases it may be convenient to use bras and kets that are not normalized; in that case we must normalize them before using Eq. (1.15); i.e.

$$A_{\text{mean}} = \frac{\langle \overline{m} | \alpha | m \rangle}{\langle \overline{m} | m \rangle} \tag{1.16}$$

This quantity, A_{mean}, is called the *expectation value* of the operator α, for the state represented by the ket $| m \rangle$.

Our formalism requires that a dynamic operator be linear, and that its eigenkets and eigenbras form an orthogonal set; a further restriction is placed by the physical consideration that the results of measurements appear as real, not complex, numbers. We do not measure weight in imaginary grams, or distance in complex centimeters. The eigenvalues of dynamic operators must therefore be real.

These three conditions can be combined into the statement that dynamic operators must be *hermitian*. An operator α is termed hermitian if for any bra $\langle \overline{m} |$, and any ket $| n \rangle$,

$$\langle \overline{m} | \alpha | n \rangle = \langle n | \overline{\alpha} | \overline{m} \rangle \tag{1.17}$$

Note that $\langle \overline{m} |$, $\langle n |$ are not the bras corresponding to $| \overline{m} \rangle$ and $| n \rangle$; they are the complex conjugates of those bras ($\langle m |$ and $\langle \overline{n} |$). The operator $\overline{\alpha}$ in Eq. (1.17) is the complex conjugate of α.

We shall now show that a linear operator with real eigenvalues and whose eigenfunctions form a complete set is necessarily hermitian; the converse is also true, but the proof will be left to the reader as an exercise.

The eigenfunctions and eigenvalues of $\overline{\alpha}$ are given by the complex conjugate of Eq. (1.4);

$$\overline{\alpha} | \overline{i} \rangle = \overline{A}_i | \overline{i} \rangle = A_i | \overline{i} \rangle \tag{1.18}$$

(the second equality follows since the eigenvalues of α are real). We can expand the bras and kets in Eq. (1.17) in terms of eigenbras and eigenkets of α and $\overline{\alpha}$;

$$\langle \overline{m} | = \sum_i \overline{a}_{mi} \langle \overline{i} | \qquad \langle n | = \sum_j b_{nj} \langle j |$$

$$| \overline{m} \rangle = \sum_i \overline{a}_{mi} | \overline{i} \rangle \qquad | n \rangle = \sum_j b_{nj} | j \rangle \tag{1.19}$$

Hence:

$$\langle \bar{m} | \alpha | n \rangle = \sum_i \bar{a}_{mi} \langle \bar{i} | \alpha \sum_j b_{nj} | j \rangle$$

$$= \sum_i \bar{a}_{mi} \langle \bar{i} | \sum_j b_{nj} \alpha | j \rangle \qquad \text{since } \alpha \text{ is linear}$$

$$= \sum_i \bar{a}_{mi} \langle \bar{i} | \sum_j A_j b_{nj} | j \rangle$$

$$= \sum_i \bar{a}_{mi} b_{ni} A_i \langle \bar{i} | i \rangle \qquad \text{since } \langle \bar{i} | j \rangle = 0 \text{ if } i \neq j$$

$$= \sum_i \bar{a}_{mi} b_{ni} A_i \qquad \begin{array}{l}\text{since the eigenbras and eigenkets} \\ \text{are normalized}\end{array} \qquad (1.20)$$

Likewise:

$$\langle \bar{n} | \bar{\alpha} | \bar{m} \rangle = \sum_j b_{nj} \langle j | \bar{\alpha} \sum_i \bar{a}_{mi} | \bar{i} \rangle$$

$$= \sum_j b_{nj} \langle j | \sum_i A_i \bar{a}_{mi} | \bar{i} \rangle$$

$$= \sum_i b_{ni} \bar{a}_{mi} A_i \langle i | \bar{i} \rangle = \sum_i b_{ni} \bar{a}_{mi} A_i \qquad (1.21)$$

Comparison of Eqs. (1.19) and (1.20) leads to Eq. (1.17).

1.4 DEGENERACY, SIMULTANEOUS MEASUREMENT, AND COMMUTATION RULES

If two or more eigenkets $|i(A)\rangle$ of a dynamic operator α correspond to the same eigenvalue A, the set of eigenkets is termed *degenerate*. Any linear combination of these degenerate eigenkets is also an eigenvalue of α, corresponding to the same eigenvalue; this can be seen at once:

$$\alpha \sum_i a_i | i(A) \rangle = \sum_i a_i A | i(A) \rangle = A \sum_i a_i | i(A) \rangle \qquad (1.22)$$

In this case our rule that different eigenkets of a given operator are orthogonal breaks down; thus if $|1(A)\rangle$ and $|2(A)\rangle$ are two degenerate eigenkets of α, the combination $|1(A)\rangle + |2(A)\rangle$ is different from, but not orthogonal to, either of the original kets. This result has a simple physical interpretation. The orthogonality of eigenkets corresponds to the fact that different states of a system are physically distinguishable. Now so far as the measurement α is concerned, the degenerate eigenstates are indistinguishable; the corresponding degenerate eigenkets need not therefore be orthogonal.

Why then do we need more than one eigenket to describe these degenerate states? The answer is that there are other properties of the system that can be measured, besides that corresponding to the operator α. The states that are degenerate to α need not be degenerate to the operators corresponding to other types of measurement.

This brings us to our next point. We know that a given measurement will give an unambiguous answer if a system is represented by an eigenket of the corresponding dynamic operator; under what conditions shall we simultaneously get exact results from two different measurements, corresponding to two different operators α, β? In other words, what is the condition that a system can be represented by a ket that is simultaneously an eigenket of α and eigenket of β?

Suppose that each eigenket $|i\rangle$ of α, with eigenvalue A_i, is also an eigenket of β, with eigenvalue B_i. We define the product $\alpha \cdot \beta$ of two operators by the statement that $\alpha \cdot \beta|m\rangle$ is the ket derived by first operating on $|m\rangle$ with β and then operating on the result of this with α. If we expand $|m\rangle$ in terms of the eigenkets $|i\rangle$ [Eq. (1.5)],

$$\alpha \cdot \beta|m\rangle = \alpha \sum_i a_{mi}\beta|i\rangle = \alpha \sum_i a_{mi}B_i|i\rangle = \sum_i a_{mi}A_iB_i|i\rangle \qquad (1.23)$$

Likewise:

$$\beta \cdot \alpha|m\rangle = \beta \sum_i a_{mi}\alpha|i\rangle = \beta \sum_i a_{mi}A_i|i\rangle = \sum_i a_{mi}A_iB_i|i\rangle \qquad (1.24)$$

Thus:

$$\alpha \cdot \beta|m\rangle = \beta \cdot \alpha|m\rangle \qquad (1.25)$$

Since $|m\rangle$ was a completely arbitrary ket, we can write this as an *operator equation*

$$\alpha \cdot \beta = \beta \cdot \alpha \qquad (1.26)$$

or

$$\alpha \cdot \beta - \beta \cdot \alpha = 0 \qquad (1.27)$$

(An equation of this kind implies that the equality will hold when each side of the equation operates on any suitable substrate, in this case any ket.)

Equation (1.27) shows that with our definition of multiplication, the operators α and β commute. Algebraic numbers of course necessarily obey the commutative law of multiplication, but this is not true of other mathematical quantities. For instance matrices do not, and neither do many simple algebraic operators. A good example is provided by the operators $\partial/\partial x$ and $x \cdot$ (that is multiply by x). If y is some function of x,

$$\frac{\partial}{\partial x}x \cdot y = x\frac{\partial y}{\partial x} + y \qquad (1.28)$$

From this we see that the operators $\partial/\partial x$ and $x \cdot$ obey the *commutation rule*

$$x\frac{\partial}{\partial x} - \frac{\partial}{\partial x}x = -1 \qquad (1.29)$$

It is easily shown that if two dynamic operators α, β commute, then any eigenket of one is also an eigenket of the other. The only complication arises in cases of degeneracy. Thus if $|i(A)\rangle$ ($i = 1, 2, \ldots, n$) is an n-fold-degenerate set of eigenkets of α with eigenvalue A, the individual eigenkets need not be eigenkets of β. However we can always select a set of n orthogonal combinations of the $|i(A)\rangle$ that *are* eigenkets of β. Physically this corresponds to the fact that the states do differ as regards the measurement β; this measurement therefore removes the ambiguity attached to a set of degenerate eigenstates, and so removes the degeneracy of the corresponding eigenkets.

In this book we shall be concerned only with systems in steady states, i.e. systems that are isolated from their surroundings and so neither absorb nor emit energy. The law of conservation of energy requires such a system to have a definite unchanging energy, regardless of the instantaneous positions of the particles in it; such a system must therefore be represented by an eigenket of the operator corresponding to the total energy of the system. Now the quantity in classical mechanics corresponding to the total energy of a system is called the *hamiltonian function* and is written as H; the corresponding dynamic operator in quantum mechanics is therefore called the *hamiltonian operator* and is written as **H**.

Two other properties of an isolated system are likewise independent of the instantaneous positions of the particles, viz. the total angular momentum of the system and any one component of the angular momentum. Since these properties are independent of the positions of the particles, their constancy should not be affected by the uncertainty principle; one would expect them still to be *constants of the motion* in quantum mechanics and to have unambiguous values. This means that the corresponding dynamic operator must commute with the hamiltonian operator. The two operators used to define these quantities are the operator corresponding to the square of the total angular momentum, written as **M**^{2}, and the operator corresponding to angular momentum along one of the coordinate axes, usually the z axis, written as $\mathbf{m}_z$.

Other properties of the system (e.g. the positions, momenta, or energies of individual particles) are not constants of the motion; they vary with time as the positions of the particles change. Since the uncertainty principle prevents us from following the motions of individual particles exactly, operators corresponding to quantities of this kind do not commute with the hamiltonian. Our next problem then is to determine the commutation rules for such operators.

These commutation rules cannot be fixed by a priori reasoning, any more than the laws of motion could in classical mechanics. The commutation rules indeed play the same role in quantum mechanics that Newton's laws of motion played in classical mechanics; their choice is likewise made on purely empirical grounds. A semi-intuitive derivation will be found in Dirac's book;[6] here we shall simply state the results.

In classical mechanics a system is determined by a set of coordinates q_i, three for each particle, defining the positions of the particles in it, and by a set of conjugate momenta p_i, p_i representing the momentum due to change in the position coordinate q_i. Thus if q_i is one cartesian coordinate of a particle of mass m, then:

$$p_i = m \frac{\partial q_i}{\partial t} \qquad (1.30)$$

Any measurable property of the system is expressed by a *dynamic variable*, which in turn can be written as a function of the q's and p's.

In quantum mechanics, we shall have a corresponding set of *dynamic operators*, $\mathbf{q}_i$, $\mathbf{p}_i$, representing the measurement of the coordinates and momenta of the individual particles. We shall also have dynamic operators corresponding to the other classical dynamic variables. The commutation rules for these are fixed by the following assumptions:

1   If a dynamic variable in classical mechanics is given by a function $f(q_i, p_i)$ of the position and momentum coordinates, the corresponding dynamic operator in quantum mechanics is given by the *same* function of the operators $\mathbf{q}_i$, $\mathbf{p}_i$.

2   The commutation rules for the position and momentum operators are:

$$\mathbf{q}_i \mathbf{q}_j - \mathbf{q}_j \mathbf{q}_i = 0 \qquad (1.31)$$

$$\mathbf{p}_i \mathbf{p}_j - \mathbf{p}_j \mathbf{p}_i = 0 \qquad (1.32)$$

$$\mathbf{q}_i \mathbf{p}_j - \mathbf{p}_j \mathbf{q}_i = 0 \qquad i \neq j \qquad (1.33)$$

$$\mathbf{q}_i \mathbf{p}_i - \mathbf{p}_i \mathbf{q}_i = i\hbar \qquad (1.34)$$

where
$$\hbar = \frac{h}{2\pi} \qquad (1.35)$$

h being Planck's constant.

This completes our exposition of quantum mechanics; from here everything can be derived by rigorous mathematical reasoning, just as the whole of classical mechanics can be derived once Newton's laws of motion are assumed.

At first sight this seems an amazing statement; for we have not yet even given a definite mathematical form to our bras, kets, and operators. It turns out, however, that we do not need to do this in order to find the eigenvalues of dynamic operators. *The commutation rules alone are sufficient to determine the eigenvalues of dynamic operators.* Since the result of any possible physical measurement is equal to one of the eigenvalues of the corresponding dynamic operator, we have therefore all the information we need to construct a complete theory of the universe.

One example may be given, to convince the reader and to indicate the way in which eigenvalues can be found solely by using the commutation rules.

1.5 THE ONE-DIMENSIONAL SIMPLE HARMONIC OSCILLATOR

The simple one-dimensional harmonic oscillator is a system in which a particle of mass m moves to and fro along a line, being attracted to a point on that line by a force proportional to its distance from it (Fig. 1.2). The total energy H of the system is given in classical mechanics by:

$$H = T + V = \frac{p^2}{2m} + \frac{1}{2}kq^2 \tag{1.36}$$

when T, V are respectively the kinetic and potential energy of the particle, q is its distance from the origin, k is the *force constant*, and p the momentum [given in this case by Eq. (1.30)]. The corresponding hamiltonian operator is then given by:

$$\mathbf{H} = \frac{\mathbf{p}^2}{2m} + \frac{1}{2}k\mathbf{q}^2 \tag{1.37}$$

Since the system is supposed to be in a steady state, its energy must be one of the eigenvalues E_i of $\mathbf{H}$;

$$\mathbf{H}|i\rangle = E_i|i\rangle \tag{1.38}$$

For convenience we introduce an operator $\mathbf{H}'$, defined by:

$$\mathbf{H}' = 2m\mathbf{H} \tag{1.39}$$

Hence:

$$\mathbf{H}'|i\rangle = 2m\mathbf{H}|i\rangle = 2mE_i'|i\rangle \tag{1.40}$$

Thus the eigenkets of $\mathbf{H}$ are also eigenkets of $\mathbf{H}'$, the eigenvalues of $\mathbf{H}$ being $(2m)^{-1}$ times those of $\mathbf{H}'$. Now:

$$\mathbf{H}' = 2m\mathbf{H} = \mathbf{p}^2 + mk\mathbf{q}^2 = \mathbf{p}^2 + a^2\mathbf{q}^2 \tag{1.41}$$

where $\qquad a^2 = mk \tag{1.42}$

We now introduce two new operators, ω and $\bar{\omega}$, defined by:

$$\omega = \mathbf{p} + ia\mathbf{q} \tag{1.43}$$

$$\bar{\omega} = \mathbf{p} - ia\mathbf{q} \tag{1.44}$$

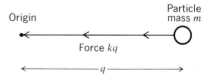

FIG. 1.2   The simple harmonic oscillator.

Consider the product $\omega\bar{\omega}$:

$$\omega\bar{\omega} = (\mathbf{p} + ia\mathbf{q})(\mathbf{p} - ia\mathbf{q}) = \mathbf{p}^2 + a^2\mathbf{q}^2 + ia(\mathbf{qp} - \mathbf{pq})$$
$$= \mathbf{H}' - a\hbar \tag{1.45}$$

[The last step follows from Eqs. (1.34) and (1.41)]. Likewise:

$$\bar{\omega}\omega = (\mathbf{p} - ia\mathbf{q})(\mathbf{p} + ia\mathbf{q}) = \mathbf{H}' + a\hbar \tag{1.46}$$

We can now construct the product $\omega\bar{\omega}\omega$ in two different ways, either by multiplying Eq. (1.45) from the right, or Eq. (1.46) from the left, by ω.‡   Thus:

$$\omega\bar{\omega}\omega = (\mathbf{H}' - a\hbar)\omega \qquad \text{from Eq. (1.45)}$$
$$= \mathbf{H}'\omega - a\hbar\omega \tag{1.47}$$
$$\omega\bar{\omega}\omega = \omega(\mathbf{H}' + a\hbar) \qquad \text{from Eq. (1.46)}$$
$$= \omega\mathbf{H}' + a\hbar\omega \tag{1.48}$$

Equating the two expressions:

$$\mathbf{H}'\omega = \omega\mathbf{H}' + 2a\hbar\omega \tag{1.49}$$

Likewise we can construct two expressions for $\bar{\omega}\omega\bar{\omega}$, by multiplying Eq. (1.45) from the left, or Eq. (1.46) from the right, by $\bar{\omega}$; equating these, we find:

$$\mathbf{H}'\bar{\omega} = \bar{\omega}\mathbf{H}' - 2a\hbar\bar{\omega} \tag{1.50}$$

Let us operate with Eq. (1.49) on an eigenket $|i\rangle$ of $\mathbf{H}$.

$$\mathbf{H}'(\omega|i\rangle) = \omega\mathbf{H}'|i\rangle + 2a\hbar\omega|i\rangle$$
$$= (2mE_i + 2a\hbar)(\omega|i\rangle) \tag{1.51}$$

Thus $\omega|i\rangle$ is also an eigenket of $\mathbf{H}'$, with eigenvalue $2mE_i + 2a\hbar$. Likewise $\omega^2|i\rangle$ is an eigenket of $\mathbf{H}'$ with eigenvalue $2mE_i + 4a\hbar$. Repeating this, we obtain a whole series of eigenkets of $\mathbf{H}'$, spaced at intervals of $2a\hbar$. Likewise by operating with Eq. (1.50) on $|i\rangle$, we find that $\bar{\omega}|i\rangle$ is an eigenket of $\mathbf{H}'$ with eigenvalue $2mE_i - 2a\hbar$, and repeating this we again obtain a series of decreasing eigenvalues of $\mathbf{H}'$, spaced once more by $2a\hbar$.

This second series must, however, terminate; for since $\mathbf{H}'$ is a sum of squared terms, its eigenvalues must be positive.§   There is just one flaw in the reasoning we have given; $\bar{\omega}|i\rangle$ is an eigenfunction of $\mathbf{H}'$ with eigenvalue $2mE_i - 2a\hbar$, *unless* $\bar{\omega}|i\rangle$ vanishes. The eigenket obeying this relation, which we may write as $|0\rangle$, is then the eigenket corresponding to the lowest eigenvalue E_0' of $\mathbf{H}'$. We have:

---

‡ Note that since Eqs. (1.45) and (1.46) are operator equations, and since operators do not necessarily commute, and since ω is an operator, we must multiply each side of the equation *from the same direction,* i.e. from the left or from the right.

§ The proof of this is left to the reader.

$$\bar{\omega}|0\rangle = 0 \tag{1.52}$$

Hence:

$$\omega\bar{\omega}|0\rangle = 0 \tag{1.53}$$

Using Eq. (1.49),

$$(\mathbf{H}' - a\hbar)|0\rangle = (E_0' - a\hbar)|0\rangle = 0 \tag{1.54}$$

Thus:

$$E_0' = a\hbar \tag{1.55}$$

The remaining eigenvalues are all spaced from this by multiples of $2a\hbar$; thus:

$$E_n' = 2a\hbar(n + \tfrac{1}{2}) \tag{1.56}$$

where n is an integer. The eigenvalues of $\mathbf{H}$ are thus given by:

$$E_n' = \frac{a\hbar}{m}(n + \tfrac{1}{2}) = \left(\frac{h}{2\pi}\sqrt{\frac{k}{m}}\right)(n + \tfrac{1}{2}) \tag{1.57}$$

$$E_n' = h\nu(n + \tfrac{1}{2}) \tag{1.58}$$

where ν is the classical frequency of vibration for the system. This is the usual result, derived in most textbooks by much more complicated reasoning, based on a solution of the corresponding Schrödinger equation. We have derived it with just two assumptions; first, that the hamiltonian operator $\mathbf{H}$ is the same function of the position $\mathbf{q}$ and momentum $\mathbf{p}$ operators that the classical hamiltonian function is of the corresponding position and momentum coordinates; secondly, that $\mathbf{q}$ and $\mathbf{p}$ obey the commutation rule of Eq. (1.34).

1.6 REPRESENTATIONS; THE SCHRÖDINGER REPRESENTATION

Any problem in quantum mechanics can in principle be solved in a manner similar to that used in Sec. 1.5; the eigenvalues of the angular-momentum operators $\mathbf{M}^2$ and $\mathbf{M}_z$ are often derived in this way, and recently a complete solution for the hydrogen atom has been given. In most cases, however, this direct approach is too difficult and a simpler alternative is preferred.

We have seen that the eigenvalues of dynamic operators are determined entirely by their commutation rules. We have assumed a procedure for constructing these operators from the position and momentum operators $\mathbf{q}_i$, $\mathbf{p}_i$ by analogy with classical mechanics. The eigenvalues of operators are thus determined by the commutation rules for the position and momentum operators [Eqs. (1.31) to (1.34)]. Consequently we are free to substitute *any* mathematical expressions we please for the position and momentum operators, provided these obey the required commutation rules. At the same time we also introduce explicit forms for the bras and kets. Now we can represent the bras and kets describing any possible state of a system in terms of the eigenbras and eigenkets of any dynamic operators; it is usual to select one such *basis set* of bras and kets, in terms of which all others can then be expressed [compare Eq. (1.5)]. The use of such explicit forms for dynamic operators, and for the corresponding bras and kets, is called a *representation;* by having explicit forms for the dynamic operators, we can greatly simplify the problem of finding their eigenvalues.

The representation that has proved most useful in chemistry is the so-called *Schrödinger representation*. In this the position and momentum operators assume the following forms:

$$\mathbf{q}_i \equiv q_i \qquad \text{that is multiply by } q_i \tag{1.59}$$

$$\mathbf{p}_i \equiv - i\hbar \frac{\partial}{\partial q_i} \tag{1.60}$$

Equation (1.29) shows that the operators defined in this way do obey the commutation rules of Eqs. (1.31) to (1.34). To complete this representation, we need to select one set of eigenbras and eigenkets, in terms of which all the others will be expressed; we select for this purpose the eigenbras and eigenkets of the position operators $\mathbf{q}_i$.

First let us consider a very simple case, a one-dimensional system with a single position coordinate $\mathbf{q}$. We intend to represent all kets for this system in terms of eigenkets $|i\rangle$ of the operator $\mathbf{q}$; in the Schrödinger representation these will be functions of q, obeying the eigenvalue equation:

$$q|i\rangle = A_i|i\rangle \tag{1.61}$$

Now in order to satisfy this equation, $|i\rangle$ must be a very unusual function; it must vanish for all values of q except at the one point where $q = A_i$. Figure 1.3 shows a plot of this; the plot is a horizontal line except for a single spike (of zero width) at $q = A_i$. This function is called the *Dirac delta function;* we write it as $\delta(q - A_i)$, implying a function of q that vanishes everywhere except at the point $q = A_i$.

Let us now consider an arbitrary ket $|m\rangle$, representing a possible state of our system. We can expand this in terms of the eigenkets of $\mathbf{q}$;

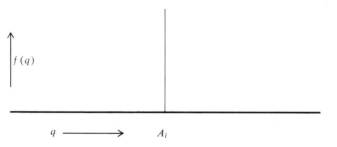

FIG. 1.3 The Dirac delta function $\delta(q - A_i)$.

$$|m\rangle = \sum_i a_{mi}|i\rangle \qquad (1.62)$$

Since the eigenkets are delta functions covering the whole range of values of q from $-\infty$ to $+\infty$, we may write this as:

$$|m\rangle = f(q)\delta(q) \qquad (1.63)$$

where $f(q)$ is some function of q, its value at $q = A_i$ being a_{mi}. The corresponding bra $\langle\overline{m}|$ will then be:

$$\langle\overline{m}| = \sum_i \bar{a}_{mi}\langle\bar{\imath}| = \bar{f}(q)\delta(q) \qquad (1.64)$$

when $\bar{f}(q)$ is the complex conjugate of the function $f(q)$.

A problem now arises in connection with the normalization of the eigenkets $|i\rangle$. Consider the product of the bra $\langle\overline{m}|$ and the ket $|m\rangle$. We know this must be a finite algebraic number; however from Eqs. (1.62) and (1.64) it is given by the infinite sum:

$$\langle\overline{m}|m\rangle = \sum_i \bar{a}_{mi}a_{mi}\langle\bar{\imath}|i\rangle \qquad (1.65)$$

If we set each $\langle\bar{\imath}|i\rangle$ equal to unity, the value of this sum would be infinite unless the coefficients a_{mi} were infinitesimal; clearly we must choose some other criterion for normalizing the eigenkets $|i\rangle$.

We can do this in the following way. Consider the set of eigenkets $|i\rangle$ of **q** lying in the range from q to $q + \delta q$. We adopt as our normalization condition the relation:

$$\sum_q^{q+\delta q} \langle\bar{\imath}|i\rangle = \delta q + O(\delta q)^2 \qquad (1.66)$$

In the limit, when δq is very small, the value of $\bar{a}_{mi}a_{mi}$ in Eq. (1.65) will be effectively the same over the range from q to $q + \delta q$, being equal to $\bar{f}(q)f(q)$; in this limit we then have:

$$\langle\overline{m}|m\rangle = \lim_{\delta q \to 0} \Sigma \bar{f}(q)f(q)\,\delta q = \int\bar{f}(q)f(q)\,dq \qquad (1.67)$$

The last result follows from the definition of an integral as the limit of a sum. This suggests that we can identify bras and kets with simple functions of q if we define multiplication of a bra by a ket to conform with Eq. (1.67); in other words if $\langle\overline{m}|$ and $|n\rangle$ are represented respectively by the functions $\bar{f}_1(q)$ and $f_2(q)$, the product $\langle\overline{m}|n\rangle$ is defined by:

$$\langle\overline{m}|n\rangle = \int\bar{f}_1(q)f_2(q)\,dq \qquad (1.68)$$

where the integration extends over the whole range of the variable q. Under these conditions we call the functions f_1, f_2 *wave functions* or *state functions* for the system.

Our next problem is to generalize this result to a system specified by n different position coordinates q_t. This is a simple matter. Since the operators $\mathbf{q}_t$ all commute with one another [Eq. (1.31)], we can choose a set of kets that are simultaneously eigenkets of all the $\mathbf{q}_t$. Such an eigenket $|i\rangle$ will have to obey the n simultaneous eigenvalue equations

$$\mathbf{q}_t|i\rangle = A_{ti}|i\rangle \quad t = 1, 2, \ldots, n \tag{1.69}$$

The solution of each of these equations is a delta function $\delta(q_t - A_{ti})$ which is a function of one variable only. How can we combine these? We can do so by applying a general and very important principle which we shall use again in other connections. Consider an operator α with an eigenket $|k\rangle$;

$$\alpha|k\rangle = A_k|k\rangle \tag{1.70}$$

Consider now the product of $|k\rangle$ with any function G that commutes with α;

$$\alpha(G|k\rangle) = G\alpha|k\rangle = GA_k|k\rangle = A_k(G|k\rangle) \tag{1.71}$$

The product $G|k\rangle$ is thus still an eigenket of α with the same eigenvalue A_k. We can therefore multiply an eigenket of α by any function whatsoever without altering its eigenvalue properties, so long as this function commutes with α. Now any function of q_t will commute with any function of an independent variable q_n; we see then that the solution of Eqs. (1.69) can be written in the form:

$$|i\rangle = \delta(q_1 - A_{1i})\delta(q_2 - A_{2i})\cdots\delta(q_n - A_{ni}) \tag{1.72}$$

From analogy with the one-dimensional case, we can then write any ket $|m\rangle$ in the form:

$$|m\rangle = \sum_i a_{mi}|i\rangle = f(q_1, q_2, \ldots, q_n)\delta(q_1)\delta(q_2)\cdots\delta(q_n) \tag{1.73}$$

where f is a function of the coordinates $q_1, q_2, \ldots, q_n$. From the definition of f, it must of course be a one-valued function of these coordinates; for its value at the point $(A_{1i}, A_{2i}, \ldots, A_{ni})$ is simply the coefficient a_{mi} of the eigenket $|i\rangle$ in the expansion of $|m\rangle$ in terms of eigenkets of the position operators.

An argument precisely similar to that used in the one-dimensional case then shows that we can identify kets with the corresponding wave functions $f(q_1, q_2, \ldots, q_n)$, provided that we define the product of a bra $\langle \overline{m}|$ and a ket $|n\rangle$ in a manner analogous to Eq. (1.68); i.e. if

$$\langle \overline{m}| = f_1(q_1, q_2, \ldots, q_n); \quad |n\rangle = f_2(q_1, q_2, \ldots, q_n) \tag{1.74}$$

then:

$$\langle \overline{m}|n\rangle = \smallint\smallint\cdots\smallint\overline{f_1}f_2\, dq_1\, dq_2\, \cdots\, dq_n \tag{1.75}$$

where the integrations are over the whole range of each of the n variables. This is often written in the shorthand form:

$$\langle \overline{m}|n \rangle = \smallint \overline{f}_1 f_2 \, d\tau \tag{1.76}$$

where $d\tau \, (= dq_1 \, dq_2 \cdots dq_n)$ is a volume element in the n-dimensional space spanned by the coordinates q_i.

Wave functions are commonly represented by Greek letters toward the end of the Greek alphabet, in particular ψ, ϕ, or ξ.

With these definitions, the eigenvalue equation for an operator α becomes:

$$\alpha\psi = A\psi \tag{1.77}$$

Since operators in the Schrödinger representation are constructed from the space coordinates ($\mathbf{q} \equiv q \cdot$) and partial differentials with respect to them ($\mathbf{p} \equiv -i\hbar\partial/\partial q$), Eq. (1.77) is a partial differential equation. This is a major advantage of the Schrödinger representation; for an immense amount of work has been channeled into the solution of such equations in view of their general importance in physics and engineering. We have therefore a vast background of mathematical knowledge and techniques to draw on in dealing with problems of this kind.

The normalization condition for a state function ψ can of course be written at once:

$$\smallint \overline{\psi}\psi \, d\tau = 1 \tag{1.78}$$

From this we see that the function ψ is not an unrestricted function of the coordinates; for this integral must have a finite value. We say that ψ must have an integrable square.

A further restriction on ψ is placed by the consideration that we must be able to calculate expectation values of operators. If our system is represented by ψ, the expectation value of an operator α is given [compare Eq. (1.15)] by:

$$A_{\text{mean}} = \frac{\smallint \overline{\psi}\alpha\psi \, d\tau}{\smallint \overline{\psi}\psi \, d\tau} \tag{1.79}$$

In order to calculate A_{mean}, we must be able to evaluate the integral in the numerator, and we must be able to do this for all possible dynamic operators α. Consider the operator $\mathbf{p}_i$. In the Schrödinger representation, this is given by $-i\hbar\partial/\partial q_i$. The expectation value for the momentum p_i is then given by:

$$(p_i)_{\text{mean}} = \frac{-i\hbar\smallint \overline{\psi}(\partial\psi/\partial q_i) \, d\tau}{\smallint \overline{\psi}\psi \, d\tau} \tag{1.80}$$

Now the integral in the numerator of this expression can be evaluated only if ψ is a continuous function of q_i; for if there were a discontinuity at any point, the integrand $\overline{\psi}(\partial\psi/\partial q_i)$ would be indeterminate there. Extension of this argument shows that ψ must be a continuous function of the n coordinates q_i.

A final restriction on ψ is placed by a similar consideration of the expectation value of the ith component of the kinetic energy T_i. In classical mechanics,

$$T_i = \frac{p_i{}^2}{2\mu_i} \tag{1.81}$$

where μ_i is a generalized mass. The corresponding Schrödinger operator is then given by:

$$\mathbf{T}_i = \frac{(-i\hbar\partial/\partial q_i)^2}{2\mu_i} = -\frac{\hbar^2}{2\mu_i}\frac{\partial^2}{\partial q_i} \tag{1.82}$$

The expectation value for this for the function ψ is then:

$$\begin{aligned} (T_i)_{\mathrm{mean}} &= \frac{-(\hbar^2/2\mu_i)\int\overline{\psi}(\partial^2\psi/\partial q_i{}^2)\,d\tau}{\int\overline{\psi}\psi\,d\tau} \\ &= \frac{-(\hbar^2/2\mu_i)\int\overline{\psi}(\partial/\partial q_i)(\partial\psi/\partial q_i)\,d\tau}{\int\overline{\psi}\psi\,d\tau} \end{aligned} \tag{1.83}$$

The argument used above indicates that the integral in the numerator will have a definite value only if $\partial\psi/\partial q_i$ is a continuous function of q_i. Here, however, there is a loophole. A discontinuity in $\partial\psi/\partial q_i$ may not matter if it occurs at a point where ψ (and so also $\overline{\psi}$) vanishes; for the integrand will then normally vanish.

The various restrictions on the form of a possible state function ψ are then the following: ψ must be one-valued and continuous and have an integrable square, and its first derivative with respect to each of the position coordinates must also be continuous, except at points when ψ vanishes. A function conforming to these restrictions is called a *well-behaved function*.

1.7   THE SCHRÖDINGER EQUATION AND ITS SOLUTION

We have seen that the ket describing a system in a steady state must be an eigenket of the hamiltonian operator; we shall now examine the procedure involved in determining such eigenkets in the Schrödinger representation.

Consider a *conservative* system of particles. A conservative system is one in which the (classical) potential energies of the particles depend only on their position coordinates q_i and not on their momenta p_i; atoms and molecules can be regarded as conservative systems if we are willing to neglect magnetic interactions—a legitimate assumption in the case of light atoms, and molecules derived from them, since here the magnetic forces are very small compared with the electrostatic forces between the particles (electrons and nuclei). If the system contains n particles, $3n$ coordinates will be needed to describe their positions; we shall take them to be the $3n$ cartesian coordinates of the particles, the coordinates of particle i being (x_i, y_i, z_i).

The total energy of the system is given in classical mechanics by the hamiltonian function H, which in this case is a simple sum of the kinetic energies T_i of the particles and of the potential energy V. Since the system is conservative, V is a function of the position coordinates only.

The kinetic energy of particle i is given by:

$$T_i = \tfrac{1}{2}m_i(V_{xi}^2 + V_{yi}^2 + V_{zi}^2) \tag{1.84}$$

where V_{xi}, V_{yi}, V_{zi} are the three components of the velocity along the coordinate axes. Since the three components P_{xi}, P_{yi}, P_{zi} of the momentum are given by m_iV_{xi}, m_iV_{yi}, and m_iV_{zi} respectively,

$$T_i = \frac{1}{2m_i}(P_{xi}^2 + P_{yi}^2 + P_{zi}^2) \tag{1.85}$$

Thus the hamiltonian function is given by:

$$H = \sum_i T_i + V = \sum_i \frac{1}{2m_i}(P_{xi}^2 + P_{yi}^2 + P_{zi}^2) + V \tag{1.86}$$

The hamiltonian operator **H** is found by replacing the position and momentum coordinates in Eq. (1.86) by the operators of Eqs. (1.59) and (1.60);

$$\mathbf{H} = \sum_i \frac{1}{2m_i}\left[\left(-i\hbar\frac{\partial}{\partial x_i}\right)^2 + \left(-i\hbar\frac{\partial}{\partial y_i}\right)^2 + \left(-i\hbar\frac{\partial}{\partial z_i}\right)^2\right] + V\cdot$$

$$= \sum_i\left[-\frac{\hbar^2}{2m_i}\left(\frac{\partial^2}{\partial x_i^2} + \frac{\partial^2}{\partial y_i^2} + \frac{\partial^2}{\partial z_i^2}\right)\right] + V\cdot \tag{1.87}$$

The function V in Eq. (1.86) is here replaced by the operator $V\cdot$ (multiply by the *same* function V), since V contains only position coordinates, and the operator corresponding to coordinate q_i is simply the operation "multiply by q_i." Equation (1.87) is usually written in the form:

$$\mathbf{H} = \sum_i\left(-\frac{\hbar^2}{2m_i}\nabla_i^2\right) + V \tag{1.88}$$

where the laplacian operator ∇_i^2 (pronounced del squared) is defined by:

$$\nabla_i^2 = \frac{\partial^2}{\partial x_i^2} + \frac{\partial^2}{\partial y_i^2} + \frac{\partial^2}{\partial z_i^2}$$

The possible wave functions and total energies for the system are then given by the eigenvalue equation:

$$\mathbf{H}\psi_i = E_i\psi_i \tag{1.89}$$

This equation, the eigenvalue equation for the hamiltonian operator in the Schrödinger representation, is called the *Schrödinger equation*. It is a partial differential equation of second degree in $3n$ variables, and the solutions are restricted by the condition that ψ_i must be a well-behaved function. It is easy to write down the Schrödinger equation for any chemical problem; in this sense chemistry has been reduced to the straightforward mathematical problem of solving the appropriate Schrödinger equations.

Unfortunately this problem is straightforward only in principle; in practice there are no general methods known for solving equations of this kind. The equations cannot be solved even by numerical integration; even three-variable equations are outside the reach of present digital computers—and a three-variable Schrödinger equation would refer to a system with but a single particle!

Although these criticisms seem damning at first sight, the situation is not in fact as bad as it seems. It is true that the Schrödinger equation can be solved exactly only for very simple systems, where subtle tricks can be used to get round the mathematical obstacles; however its true virtue lies in the facility with which approximate solutions can be obtained for complex systems. This is the main advantage of using a representation, and in particular the Schrödinger representation; it is very much easier to devise approximate methods in the Schrödinger representation than it would be in an abstract treatment, where no specific mathematical form was ascribed to operators and kets.

The Schrödinger representation has one final advantage, crucial to chemists; it leads to a simple physical picture of atomic systems. Consider for example a system composed of a single particle moving along the x axis, and in a state represented by the wave function $\psi(x)$. The probability that the x coordinate of the particle will have some value a is given, apart from a normalizing factor, by the absolute square of the coefficient A_a of the corresponding eigenket $|a\rangle$ of x. Since this eigenket is a delta function, $\delta(x - a)$, A_a is given by:

$$A_a = \psi(x)\delta(x - a) = \psi(a) \tag{1.90}$$

Apart from a normalizing factor, the required probability is then $\bar{\psi}(a)\psi(a)$.

To find this factor, we assume first that the function ψ has been normalized, i.e. that

$$\int \bar{\psi}\psi \, dx = 1 \tag{1.91}$$

and secondly that the delta functions have been normalized in accordance with Eq. (1.66). In this case we can see at once that the probability p_x that the coordinate of our particle lies in the range from x to $(x + dx)$, dx being small, is given by:

$$p_x = \bar{\psi}(x)\psi(x) \, dx \tag{1.92}$$

Thus the value of the square of the wave function at any point is a measure of the probability that the particle will be found there. This treatment can be extended at once to many-dimensional wave functions; thus the square of the function $\psi(q_1, q_2, \ldots, q_n)$ is a measure of the probability that the first coordinate has the value q_1, the second q_2, and so forth; in the case of a system of particles where the q_i are coordinates of individual particles, ψ becomes a measure of the probability of finding the particles at various points in space. These probability distributions can be visualized and represented in diagrams; such pictorial representations have been of decisive assistance to chemists in applying quantum theory to chemical problems.

The possibility of such a pictorial representation arises solely because in the Schrödinger treatment kets are represented in terms of eigenkets of the position operators; no other representation would offer this advantage.

PROBLEMS

1.1 Prove that the eigenvalues of a linear hermitian operator are real, and that its eigenkets are mutually orthogonal or, in the case of degeneracy, can be expressed in mutually orthogonal form.

1.2 Prove that if two operators commute, they must have a common set of eigenkets.

1.3 Derive the commutation rule for the operators $\mathbf{p}^2$ and $\mathbf{q}^2$, $\mathbf{p}$ and $\mathbf{q}$ being conjugate momentum and position operators.

1.4 In classical mechanics, the three components of angular momentum of a particle about the origin are given by

$$M_x = yp_z - zp_y \qquad M_y = zp_x - xp_z \qquad M_z = xp_y - yp_x$$

The total angular momentum M^2 is given by

$$M^2 = M_x^2 + M_y^2 + M_z^2$$

Deduce the commutation rules for the corresponding operators $\mathbf{M}_x$, $\mathbf{M}_y$, $\mathbf{M}_z$, $\mathbf{M}^2$, and $\mathbf{M}_x^2 + \mathbf{M}_y^2$.

1.5 Using the results from the preceding exercise, deduce‡ the eigenvalues of $\mathbf{M}_z$ and $\mathbf{M}^2$.

REFERENCES§

1 Dewar, M. J. S.: "The Electronic Theory of Organic Chemistry," Oxford University Press, Fair Lawn, N.J., 1949.

2 Dewar, M. J. S.: *J. Am. Chem. Soc.* **74**, 3341, 3345, 3350, 3353, 3355, 3357 (1952).

3 Streitwieser, A.: "Molecular Orbital Theory for Organic Chemists," John Wiley & Sons, Inc., New York, 1961.

‡ This example is worked out in detail in Dirac.[6] Two new operators ω and $\bar{\omega}$ are introduced, defined by $\omega = \mathbf{M}_x + i\mathbf{M}_y$, $\bar{\omega} = \mathbf{M}_x - i\mathbf{M}_y$. Using an argument similar to that for the simple harmonic oscillator (Sec. 1.5), the eigenvalues of $\mathbf{M}_z$ are found to form a series, spaced by $i\hbar$; this has to terminate at either end; for since $\mathbf{M}_z$ is a component of M, the eigenvalues of M_z must be less than the square root of the corresponding eigenvalue of $\mathbf{M}^2$.

§ This list includes references for the Preface and Chap. 1.

4 Griffith, J. S.: "Theory of Transition Metal Ions," Cambridge University Press, New York, 1961; C. J. Ballhausen: "Ligand Field Theory," McGraw-Hill Book Company, New York, 1962.

5 Pople, J. A., W. G. Schneider, and H. J. Bernstein: "High-resolution Nuclear Magnetic Resonance," McGraw-Hill Book Company, New York, 1959; A. Carrington and A. D. McLachlan: "Introduction to Magnetic Resonance," Harper & Row, Publishers, Incorporated, New York, 1967; C. P. Slichter: "Principles of Magnetic Resonance," Harper & Row, Publishers, Incorporated, New York, 1963; C. Sandorfy: "Electronic Spectra and Quantum Chemistry," Prentice-Hall, Inc., Englewood Cliffs, N.J., 1964.

6 Dirac, P. A. M.: "Quantum Mechanics," 4th ed., Oxford University Press, Fair Lawn, N.J., 1957.

CHAPTER TWO

EXACT AND
APPROXIMATE SOLUTIONS
OF THE SCHRÖDINGER
EQUATION

2.1 THE SCHRÖDINGER EQUATION FOR THE HYDROGEN ATOM

We shall first consider a very simple problem which will illustrate the methods used to obtain exact solutions of the Schrödinger equation for simple systems, and which will also tell us why exact solutions cannot be obtained in other cases. We shall discuss the hydrogen atom, a system of two particles, proton and electron, moving under their mutual coulomb attraction. For simplicity we shall first assume that the atom is stationary with the proton fixed at the origin of our coordinate system; later we shall consider the modifications that must be introduced if we allow the atom to move freely (see Fig. 2.1).

Since the proton is fixed, we have in effect a system of one particle (the electron) of mass m, attracted to the origin by a force $-e^2/r^2$, e being the electronic charge and r the distance of the electron from the origin. The potential energy V is given by $-e^2/r$, so the hamiltonian operator [Eq. (1.87)] becomes:

$$\mathbf{H} = -\frac{\hbar^2}{2m}\nabla^2 - \frac{e^2}{r} \tag{2.1}$$

The corresponding Schrödinger equation is then a partial differential equation of second degree in three variables; such equations cannot be solved by existing methods. How then shall we proceed? The answer is provided by the arguments embodied in Eq. (1.71).

Suppose we can find an operator α that commutes with $\mathbf{H}$ and is a function of only one variable q_1. The eigenfunctions ϕ of α are then functions of one variable only. However α and $\mathbf{H}$ commute, so any eigenfunction ψ of $\mathbf{H}$ is necessarily an eigenfunction of α, and conversely; yet the eigenfunctions of $\mathbf{H}$ are functions of three variables which we can write as q_1, q_2, q_3. How can we reconcile these statements? The solution is provided by an argument similar to that embodied in Eq. (1.71). If ψ is of the form:

Proton:
mass M,
charge $+e$

Electron:
mass m,
charge $-e$

FIG. 2.1 The hydrogen atom.

$$\psi = f_1(q_1)F(q_2,q_3) \tag{2.2}$$

where f_1 is one of the eigenfunctions of α with eigenvalue A and F is a function of q_2 and q_3, then ψ will also be an eigenfunction of α with the same eigenvalue A. This follows since F, being a function only of q_2 and q_3, commutes with α, which is a function of q_1 only. Thus:

$$\alpha\psi = \alpha f_1 F = F\alpha f_1 = FAf_1 = Af_1F = A\psi \tag{2.3}$$

If this expression for ψ is substituted into the Schrödinger equation, it then reduces to a partial differential equation in two variables only, solution of which gives the function F. If further we can find a second operator β that commutes both with $\mathbf{H}$ and with α and is a function of only one of the two remaining coordinates q_2, q_3, the problem can be still further simplified. Suppose for instance that β is a function of q_1 and q_2, but not q_3. Its eigenfunctions θ will then be functions of q_1 and q_2 only. However these eigenfunctions must also be eigenfunctions of α; it follows that:

$$\theta = \phi(q_1)\chi(q_2) \tag{2.4}$$

where χ is a function only of q_2. Introducing this into the eigenvalue equation for β,

$$\beta\theta = B\theta \tag{2.5}$$

the equation reduces to a simple differential equation for χ which can be solved without difficulty. We now see that the eigenfunction ψ must be of the form:

$$\psi = \phi(q_1)\chi(q_2)\omega(q_3) \tag{2.6}$$

where ω is a function only of q_3. Substituting this in the Schrödinger equation, we get a third simple differential equation, this time for the remaining function ω. Solution of this equation at the same time gives us the possible values of the total energy E.

This procedure can be applied to the hydrogen atom, if we transform the Schrödinger equation into spherical polar coordinates. In this coordinate system‡ the hamiltonian operator becomes:

$$\mathbf{H} = -\frac{\hbar^2}{2m}\left(\frac{1}{r^2}\frac{\partial}{\partial r}r^2\frac{\partial}{\partial r} + \frac{1}{r^2\sin\theta}\frac{\partial}{\partial\theta}\sin\theta\frac{\partial}{\partial\theta} + \frac{1}{r^2\sin^2\theta}\frac{\partial^2}{\partial\phi^2}\right) - \frac{e^2}{r} \tag{2.7}$$

Now we have seen that the total angular momentum of any isolated system is a constant of the motion, and so also is any one component of it; the corresponding operators should commute with $\mathbf{H}$. This is the case here. The operator $\mathbf{M}^2$, corresponding to the square of the total angular momentum, and the operator $\mathbf{M}_z$,

‡ The transformation of the laplacian operator ∇^2 into spherical polar coordinates can be found in most standard texts of quantum theory, e.g. Ref. 1.

corresponding to the angular momentum about the polar axis, are given[1] in spherical polar coordinates by:

$$\mathbf{M}^2 = -\hbar^2\left(\frac{1}{\sin\theta}\frac{\partial}{\partial\theta}\sin\theta\frac{\partial}{\partial\theta} + \frac{1}{\sin^2\theta}\frac{\partial^2}{\partial\phi^2}\right) \tag{2.8}$$

$$\mathbf{M}_z = -i\hbar\frac{\partial}{\partial\phi} \tag{2.9}$$

We can then write $\mathbf{H}$ and $\mathbf{M}^2$ in the form:

$$\mathbf{H} = -\frac{\hbar^2}{2mr^2}\frac{\partial}{\partial r}r^2\frac{\partial}{\partial r} - \frac{\mathbf{M}^2}{2mr^2} - \frac{e^2}{r} \tag{2.10}$$

$$\mathbf{M}^2 = -\frac{\hbar^2}{\sin\theta}\frac{\partial}{\partial\theta}\sin\theta\frac{\partial}{\partial\theta} + \frac{(\mathbf{M}_z)^2}{\sin^2\theta} \tag{2.11}$$

Obviously $\mathbf{M}^2$ commutes with $\mathbf{H}$; for $\mathbf{M}^2$ is a function of θ and ϕ only, and these variables appear in $\mathbf{H}$ only in the form of $\mathbf{M}^2$ itself. A similar argument shows that $\mathbf{M}_z$ commutes with both $\mathbf{M}^2$ and $\mathbf{H}$.

Now $\mathbf{M}_z$ is a function of ϕ only, and $\mathbf{M}^2$ of θ and ϕ; the arguments of the last section then show that the eigenfunctions ψ of $\mathbf{H}$ must be of the form:

$$\psi = \xi_1(r)\xi_2(\theta)\xi_3(\phi) \tag{2.12}$$

The eigenfunctions ξ_3 and eigenvalues M_z of $\mathbf{M}_z$ can be found at once by solving a simple differential equation in one variable ϕ; it turns out that M_z is restricted to certain definite values by the condition that ξ_3 must be a well-behaved function. We can then substitute one of these functions ξ_3 in the eigenvalue equation for $\mathbf{M}^2$; since the arguments given above show that the eigenfunctions of $\mathbf{M}^2$ must be of the form $\xi_2(\theta)\xi_3(\phi)$, this equation becomes:

$$\begin{aligned}
\mathbf{M}^2(\xi_2\xi_3) &= -\frac{\hbar^2}{\sin\theta}\frac{\partial}{\partial\theta}\sin\theta\frac{\partial}{\partial\theta}(\xi_2\xi_3) + \frac{M_z^2(\xi_2\xi_3)}{\sin^2\theta} \\
&= -\frac{\hbar^2}{\sin\theta}\frac{\partial}{\partial\theta}\sin\theta\frac{\partial}{\partial\theta}(\xi_2\xi_3) + \frac{M_z^2(\xi_2\xi_3)}{\sin^2\theta} = M^2(\xi_2\xi_3)
\end{aligned} \tag{2.13}$$

Here we have used the fact that ξ_3 is an eigenfunction of $\mathbf{M}_z$ with eigenvalue M_z; hence $\mathbf{M}_z^2\xi_3 = M_z^2\xi_3$. We can now cancel out the function ξ_3 from both sides of Eq. (2.13); this leaves a simple differential equation in one variable for the functions ξ_2 and the eigenvalues M^2.

Substituting the appropriate functions ξ_2 and ξ_3 in Eq. (2.12), and substituting this value for ψ in the Schrödinger equation $\mathbf{H}\psi = E\psi$, this equation reduces to:

$$-\frac{\hbar^2}{2mr^2}\frac{\partial}{\partial r}r^2\frac{\partial\xi_1}{\partial r} - \frac{M^2\xi_1}{2mr^2} - \frac{e^2\xi_1}{r} = E\xi_1 \tag{2.14}$$

This again is a simple differential equation in one variable r, solution of which gives the functions ξ_1 and eigenvalues E.

In this way we have reduced the original intractable problem of solving a partial differential equation in three variables to the relatively trivial one of solving three separate simple differential equations. The solutions of these are given in all the standard texts; we need not reproduce them here since the procedures are of no general value in quantum chemistry. The results are summarized at the end of this section; however we must first clear up one final point. In the treatment given above we made the artificial assumption that the proton was fixed in space; what happens if we remove this arbitrary restriction?

If we do this, we must then treat the hydrogen atom as a two-particle system. The hamiltonian operator for this can be written [compare Eq. (1.87)];

$$\mathbf{H} = -\frac{\hbar^2}{2M}\nabla_n{}^2 - \frac{\hbar^2}{2m}\nabla_e{}^2 - \frac{e^2}{r} \tag{2.15}$$

Here $\nabla_n{}^2$ is the laplacian operator for the proton, $\nabla_e{}^2$ that for the electron, and r is the distance between the two particles. $\mathbf{H}$ is now a function of six variables, and so also will be the Schrödinger equation; we shall be able to solve this only if we can reduce it to an equivalent set of six simple differential equations. By an obvious extension of the arguments used earlier in this section, we can see that this will be possible if, and only if, we can find five dynamic operators that commute with each other and with $\mathbf{H}$. We already have two such operators, $\mathbf{M}_z$ and $\mathbf{M}^2$; we need three more. Now the law of conservation of energy tells us that there are indeed three other constants of the motion for an isolated hydrogen atom in classical mechanics, i.e. the three components of kinetic energy of the center of gravity. If the cartesian coordinates of the center of gravity are (X, Y, Z), the corresponding dynamic operators are [compare Eq. (1.87)]:

$$\mathbf{T}_X = -\frac{\hbar^2}{2(m+M)}\frac{\partial^2}{\partial X^2} \tag{2.16}$$

$$\mathbf{T}_Y = -\frac{\hbar^2}{2(m+M)}\frac{\partial^2}{\partial Y^2} \tag{2.17}$$

$$\mathbf{T}_Z = -\frac{\hbar^2}{2(m+M)}\frac{\partial^2}{\partial Z^2} \tag{2.18}$$

We can now transform the hamiltonian operator $\mathbf{H}$ to a coordinate system in which the six coordinates are X, Y, Z and spherical polar coordinates (r, θ, ϕ) centered on the proton. $\mathbf{H}$ then becomes[1]:

$$\mathbf{H} = -\frac{\hbar^2}{2(m+M)}\left(\frac{\partial^2}{\partial X^2} + \frac{\partial^2}{\partial Y^2} + \frac{\partial^2}{\partial Z^2}\right) - \frac{\hbar^2}{2\mu}\nabla^2 - \frac{e^2}{r} \tag{2.19}$$

where ∇^2 is the laplacian operator for the "internal" coordinates (r, θ, ϕ) and μ is the reduced mass,

$$\mu = \frac{mM}{m+M} \tag{2.20}$$

We can then write **H** in the form:

$$\mathbf{H} = \mathbf{T}_X + \mathbf{T}_Y + \mathbf{T}_Z + \mathbf{H}_{\text{int}} \tag{2.21}$$

$$\mathbf{H}_{\text{int}} = -\frac{\hbar^2}{2\mu}\nabla^2 - \frac{e^2}{r} \tag{2.22}$$

where $\mathbf{H}_{\text{int}}$ is an operator representing the internal energy of the atom, due to the mutual coulomb attraction of the particles and to their motion about their common center of gravity. Obviously **H** commutes with $\mathbf{T}_X$, $\mathbf{T}_Y$, and $\mathbf{T}_Z$ and also with $\mathbf{H}_{\text{int}}$; further, since $\mathbf{H}_{\text{int}}$ is identical in form with the simple hamiltonian of Eq. (2.7), except in that the electronic mass m has now been replaced by the reduced mass μ, $\mathbf{H}_{\text{int}}$ clearly commutes with $\mathbf{M}^2$ and $\mathbf{M}_z$. The eigenfunctions ψ and eigenvalues E of **H** are thus of the form:

$$\psi = f_1(r)f_2(\theta)f_3(\phi)f_4(X)f_5(Y)f_6(Z) \tag{2.23}$$

$$E = E_{\text{int}} + T_X + T_Y + T_Z = E_{\text{int}} + T \tag{2.24}$$

where the functions f_1, f_2, f_3 and the eigenvalues E_{int} are the same as in our simple treatment (except in that the electronic mass m is everywhere replaced by μ), and where T is the total translational kinetic energy of the atom.

The "internal" eigenvalues E_{int}, M^2, and M_z have the following forms:

$$E_{\text{int}} = \frac{\mu e^4}{2n^2\hbar^2} \qquad \text{with } n \text{ a positive integer (} principal \text{ } quantum \text{ } number) \tag{2.25}$$

$$M^2 = l(l+1)\hbar^2 \qquad \text{with } l \text{ an integer (} azimuthal \text{ } quantum \text{ } number) \text{ and } 0 < l < n \tag{2.26}$$

$$M_z = m\hbar \qquad \text{with } m \text{ an integer (} magnetic \text{ } quantum \text{ } number) \text{ and } -l \leq m \leq +l \tag{2.27}$$

The radial eigenfunctions $f_1(r)$ are of the following form:

$$f_1(r) = \left(\frac{2r}{na_0}\right)^l e^{-r/na_0} L_{n+l}^{2l+1} \frac{2r}{na_0} \tag{2.28}$$

where $L_a^b(x)$ is a polynomial function of x, known as the associated *Laguerre polynomial*, and a_0 is the radius of the smallest orbit in the Bohr model of the atom:

$$a_0 = \frac{\hbar^2}{\mu e^2} \tag{2.29}$$

The functions listed in Eq. (2.28) are not normalized; the normalizing factors, which are quite complicated, will be found in any standard text.[1]

The angular eigenfunctions, also in unnormalized form, are given by:

$$f_2(\theta) = P_l^{|m|}(\cos\theta) \tag{2.30}$$

$$f_3(\phi) = e^{im\phi} \tag{2.31}$$

where $P_a^b(x)$ is another polynomial known as the *associated Legendre polynomial*.

The product $f_2 f_3$ of the angular functions is termed a *spherical harmonic*, since these functions first appeared in classical mechanics in the theory of vibrations of spheres; spherical harmonics are usually designated by the symbol $Y(l,m)$, l and m being respectively the azimuthal and magnetic quantum numbers corresponding to the particular function in question.

The wave functions for hydrogen are therefore complex, containing the factor $e^{im\phi}$; the only exceptions to this are the states with $m = 0$, where $f_3(\phi)$ reduces to unity. It will also be noticed that the functions appear in degenerate sets; for the energies depend only on the value of the principal quantum number n, so that states with the same value for n, but different l and/or m, are degenerate. Moreover the functions all appear in pairs, with equal and opposite values for m; the two functions in such a pair are complex conjugates of each other, one containing the factor $e^{im\phi}$, the other $e^{-im\phi}$.

Now we know that if a solution of the Schrödinger equation is degenerate, then any linear combination of the degenerate functions will also be a solution belonging to the same eigenvalue. We can therefore replace the pair of degenerate solutions of the form $f_1(r)f_2(\theta)e^{\pm im\phi}$ by the combinations:

$$f_1(r)f_2(\theta)e^{im\phi} + f_1(r)f_2(\theta)e^{-im\phi} = 2f_1(r)f_2(\theta) \cos m\phi \qquad (2.32)$$

$$f_1(r)f_2(\theta)e^{im\phi} - f_1(r)f_2(\theta)e^{-im\phi} = 2if_1(r)f_2(\theta) \sin m\phi \qquad (2.33)$$

Of these the first is real, the second a pure imaginary. Since a wave function is not intrinsically affected if we multiply it by any algebraic number, we can multiply the second function by i and so obtain an equivalent wave function which is real. Thus the original pairs of complex wave functions can be replaced by equivalent pairs of wave functions which are real.

Most textbooks of chemistry now contain pictures of the hydrogen wave functions or *orbitals* as they are commonly termed, from analogy with the orbits of the Bohr model for the hydrogen atom. These pictorial orbitals correspond to the real wave functions discussed above. They differ from the "correct" wave functions only in one respect; they are eigenfunctions of $\mathbf{H}$ and $\mathbf{M}^2$, but not of $\mathbf{M}_z$. Thus the set of $2p$ orbitals ($n = 2, l = 1, m = +1, 0, -1$) have the "correct" form:

$$2p(+1) = f(r) \sin \theta \, e^{i\phi} \qquad (2.34)$$

$$2p(0) = f(r) \cos \theta \qquad (2.35)$$

$$2p(-1) = f(r) \sin \theta \, e^{-i\phi} \qquad (2.36)$$

where
$$f(r) = re^{-r/2a_0} \qquad (2.37)$$

Of these only the function $2p(0)$ is real; this corresponds to the $2p_z$ orbital pictured in books. The other pictorial orbitals, $2p_x$, $2p_y$, correspond to combinations of $2p(+1)$ and $2p(-1)$; viz.

$$2p_x = \tfrac{1}{2}[2p(+1) + 2p(-1)] = f(r) \sin \theta \cos \phi \qquad (2.38)$$

$$2p_y = -\frac{i}{2}[2p(+1) - 2p(-1)] = f(r) \sin \theta \sin \phi \qquad (2.39)$$

The orbital $2p_z$ is thus a "correct" wave function for the hydrogen atom, being an eigenfunction of $\mathbf{H}$, $\mathbf{M}^2$, and $\mathbf{M}_z$; the orbitals $2p_x$ and $2p_y$ are eigenfunctions of $\mathbf{H}$ and $\mathbf{M}^2$, but not of $\mathbf{M}_z$. So long as we are concerned only with properties of the atom that depend only on its energy, or its total angular momentum, the real orbitals $2p_x$ and $2p_y$ are entirely equivalent to the "correct" orbitals $2p(+1)$ and $2p(-1)$. If, however, we are concerned with measurements involving some component of the angular momentum, then we must be careful to use only the "correct" orbitals.

2.2 REAL AND COMPLEX WAVE FUNCTIONS
The last paragraphs of Sec. 2.1 raise an important point. We shall now prove the following theorem:

Theorem 2.1 Solution of any Schrödinger equation gives wave functions which are either real or occur in degenerate pairs which are complex conjugates of one another.

The hamiltonian operator for a conservative system of particles [Eq. (1.87)] is real; for the laplacian operator is a real operator, and physical considerations require the potential function V to be real. Consider then the Schrödinger equation

$$\mathbf{H}\psi = E\psi \qquad (2.40)$$

The complex conjugate of this equation must also hold;

$$\overline{\mathbf{H}}\overline{\psi} = \overline{E}\overline{\psi} \qquad (2.41)$$

Since $\overline{\mathbf{H}}$ is a real operator, and since the eigenvalue E is also real, $\mathbf{H} = \overline{\mathbf{H}}$ and $E = \overline{E}$; hence:

$$\mathbf{H}\overline{\psi} = E\overline{\psi} \qquad (2.42)$$

Thus $\overline{\psi}$ is also an eigenfunction of $\mathbf{H}$, belonging to the same eigenvalue E as ψ, so either ψ and $\overline{\psi}$ are a pair of different degenerate functions, or they are identical in which case of course ψ is real. This proves the theorem.

If ψ and $\overline{\psi}$ are degenerate, we can replace them by any linear combinations we please. Now the combination $\psi \pm \overline{\psi}$ is either real or a pure imaginary function [compare Eqs. (2.32) and (2.33)], and a pure imaginary function can be converted to a real function by multiplying it by an algebraic number i. We can therefore replace the complex functions ψ, $\overline{\psi}$ by two equivalent functions which are real. It follows that *the eigenfunctions of a hamiltonian operator are either real or can be expressed equivalently in real form.* Therefore so long as we are concerned only with those properties of a system that are determined by the hamiltonian rather than by operators such as $\mathbf{M}^2$ or $\mathbf{M}_z$—and this will be true of nearly all the problems with which we shall be concerned in this book—we can without loss of generality assume that all our wave functions are real. Since this is a useful simplification, and costs us nothing, we shall adopt it from now on.

2.3 MANY-PARTICLE SYSTEMS

The hamiltonian operator for an n-particle system is, in the Schrödinger representation, a partial differential operator in $3n$ variables [Eq. (1.87)]; the corresponding Schrödinger equation is then a partial differential equation, also in $3n$ variables. As we have seen (Sec. 2.1), such an equation can be solved only if it can be reduced to an equivalent set of simple differential equations, each involving one variable only; such a reduction is in turn possible only if we can find a set of $3n - 1$ suitable operators that commute with one another and with $\mathbf{H}$. These operators must moreover satisfy the conditions restricting the form of a dynamic operator; apart from unlikely coincidences, the $3n - 1$ operators must therefore themselves be dynamic operators. Now a dynamic operator will commute with the hamiltonian if, and only if, the corresponding dynamic variable in classical mechanics is a constant of the motion; whether or not we can solve a given Schrödinger equation by direct integration therefore depends on whether the system in question contains enough suitable dynamic variables.

As a rule, there are only five such variables which are constants of the motion in classical mechanics; these are the three components of translational kinetic energy of the system as a whole, the total angular momentum of the system, and any one component of the total angular momentum. If the particles attract or repel one another, as is true for any pair of particles in an atom or molecule, the energies, momenta, and angular momenta of the individual particles will vary with time, and so will not be constants of the motion; for the forces will lead to an interchange of energy and angular momentum so that although the atom (or molecule) as a whole has a fixed energy and a fixed angular momentum, the way these are partitioned between the individual particles varies with time.

These five constants of the motion are enough to reduce the Schrödinger equation for a system of at most two particles; indeed, this was the approach used in Sec. 2.1 to reduce the Schrödinger equation for the hydrogen atom, treated as a two-particle system. We cannot extend the treatment to a three-particle system (e.g. the helium atom) even by the expedient of fixing one particle (the nucleus) at the origin of our coordinate system; for in that case the atom will be fixed in space so that we lose three of our constants of the motion [i.e. the components of translational kinetic energy; compare Eqs. (2.16) to (2.18)].

The remaining constants of the motion M^2, M_z are insufficient to reduce the six-variable Schrödinger equation for the two electrons.

Nearly all chemical problems unfortunately involve systems containing three or more particles; as these arguments indicate, we cannot treat them by rigorous solution of the corresponding Schrödinger equations. If then we wish to apply quantum theory to chemical problems, we must devise some alternative procedure, possibly involving approximate solutions of the Schrödinger equations; the rest of this chapter will be concerned with approaches of this kind.

2.4 THE HARTREE SCF METHOD

We shall start with a simplifying assumption, that the nucleus (in the case of an atom) or the nuclei (in the case of a molecule) occupy fixed position(s) in space. In the case of atoms, this can make little difference; for even in the case of hydrogen, where the errors would be greatest, they are in fact small. In the case of molecules, the corresponding assumption (known as the *Born-Oppenheimer approximation*) depends on the fact that electrons, being much lighter than nuclei, move much faster, so that the behavior of the electrons in a molecule at any instant differs but imperceptibly from what it would be if the nuclei were "frozen" at the positions they then occupy. Our problem consequently reduces to that of calculating the wave functions and energies of a set of n electrons, moving in the field due to one or more nuclei.

The corresponding hamiltonian operator can be derived immediately from the general expression of Eq. (1.88);

$$\mathbf{H} = \sum_i \left(-\frac{\hbar^2}{2m} \nabla_i^2 \right) - \sum_i \sum_m \frac{Z_m e^2}{r_{im}} + \sum_{i<j} \frac{e^2}{r_{ij}} \tag{2.43}$$

The first sum represents the kinetic energies of the electrons, the second their potential energies due to the attraction of the nuclei (r_{im} being the distance of electron i from nucleus m, whose atomic number is Z_m), and the third the mutual repulsion of the electrons (r_{ij} being the distance between electrons i, j). We can write this in the form:

$$\mathbf{H} = \sum_i \mathbf{H}_i' + \sum_{i<j} \frac{e^2}{r_{ij}} \tag{2.44}$$

where $\mathbf{H}_i'$ is a *one-electron operator*, being a function of the coordinates of a single electron;

$$\mathbf{H}_i' = -\frac{\hbar^2}{2m} \nabla_i^2 - \sum_m \frac{Z_m e^2}{r_{im}} \tag{2.45}$$

Suppose we could neglect the final sum in Eq. (2.44); in that case $\mathbf{H}$ would obviously commute with each $\mathbf{H}_i'$. The $\mathbf{H}_i'$ would also commute with one another, being functions of different variables. The arguments of Sec. 2.1 lead immediately to the conclusion that the solutions of the overall Schrödinger equation,

$$\mathbf{H}\psi = E\psi \tag{2.46}$$

would then be of the form:

$$\psi = \psi_1'\psi_2' \cdots \psi_n' \tag{2.47}$$

$$E = E_1' + E_2' + \cdots + E_n' \tag{2.48}$$

where ψ_i is a function of the coordinates of electron i only, being a solution of the one-electron equation:

$$\mathbf{H}_i'\psi_i' = E_i'\psi_i' \tag{2.49}$$

In this way the original $3n$-variable Eq. (2.46) could be reduced to an equivalent set of n three-variable Eq. (2.49).

However we cannot just neglect the interelectronic repulsions in an atom or molecule because they are by no means small; for instance the total interelectronic repulsion in benzene is of the order of 1,000 ev or 20,000 kcal/mole. Can we perhaps make some allowance for these repulsions without destroying the simplification achieved by neglecting them?

The solution of this problem was first indicated by Hartree. The trouble with the interelectronic terms in Eq. (2.44) is that each of them depends on the coordinates of two different electrons. Hartree pointed out that if this repulsion were averaged over all positions of one of the two electrons, the resulting quantity would be a function of the coordinates of the other electron alone. We can then set up a series of one-electron hamiltonians $\mathbf{H}_i$, given by:

$$\mathbf{H}_i = -\frac{\hbar^2}{2m}\nabla_i^2 - \sum_m \frac{Z_m e^2}{r_{im}} + \sum_j \left(\frac{e^2}{r_{ij}}\right)_{\text{av over } j} \tag{2.50}$$

where $(e^2/r_{ij})_{\text{av over } j}$ is the repulsion between electrons i and j, averaged over all positions of electron j, and is therefore a function only of the coordinates of electron i.

Now consider the operator $\mathbf{H}'$, given by

$$\mathbf{H}' = \sum_i \mathbf{H}_i \tag{2.51}$$

The eigenfunctions ψ' and eigenvalues E' of $\mathbf{H}'$ are:

$$\psi' = \psi_1\psi_2 \cdots \psi_n \tag{2.52}$$

$$E' = E_1 + E_2 + \cdots + E_n \tag{2.53}$$

where ψ_i, E_i are solutions of the one-electron equation

$$\mathbf{H}_i\psi_i = E_i\psi_i \tag{2.54}$$

FIG. 2.2   Calculation of $(e^2/r_{ij})_{\text{av over } j}$.

From the form of $\mathbf{H}_i$, we see that

$$E_i = (\text{KE of electron } i) + (\text{PE of electron } i \text{ due to attraction}$$
$$\text{of nuclei}) + (\text{av PE of electron } i \text{ due to repulsion of all other}$$
$$\text{electrons}) \tag{2.55}$$

Thus E' is a sum of the kinetic energy of all the electrons, of their total potential energy due to the attraction of all the nuclei, and of *twice* their average mutual-repulsion energy.   The last statement follows since we have counted the repulsion between two electrons, say electrons i and j, twice over; once as $(e^2/r_{ij})_{\text{av over } j}$ in $\mathbf{H}_i$, once as $(e^2/r_{ij})_{\text{av over } i}$ in $\mathbf{H}_j$.   The total energy E of the atom (or molecule) is then:

$$E = E' - \text{total interelectronic repulsion} \tag{2.56}$$

$$E = E' - \sum_{i<j}\sum \left(\frac{e^2}{r_{ij}}\right)_{\text{av over } i, j} \tag{2.57}$$

The hamiltonian operator is consequently given by:

$$\mathbf{H} = \mathbf{H}' - \sum_{i<j}\sum \left(\frac{e^2}{r_{ij}}\right)_{\text{av over } i, j} \tag{2.58}$$

Since this last sum is independent of the coordinates of the electrons, having been averaged over all possible positions of the electrons, $\mathbf{H}$ also commutes with each of the one-electron operators $\mathbf{H}_i$.

The average repulsion energies are easily calculated.   Consider for example the term $(e^2/r_{ij})_{\text{av over } j}$.   Suppose electron j is in a small volume element $d\tau_j$ (Fig. 2.2).   If the distance between electron i and j is then r_{ij}, the mutual-repulsion energy is e^2/r_{ij}.   The probability P_i that electron j is in $d\tau_j$ is given‡ by

$$P_j = \psi_j^2 \, d\tau_j \tag{2.59}$$

The repulsion, averaged over all positions of electron j, is then:

$$\left(\frac{e^2}{r_{ij}}\right)_{\text{av over } j} = \int \frac{\psi_j^2 e^2 \, d\tau_j}{r_{ij}} \tag{2.60}$$

By an obvious extension of this argument, we can at once calculate the double average in Eq. (2.57); these are called *coulomb integrals*, and are written as J_{ij}.

‡ Remember that we are now assuming all wave functions to be real; see Sec. 2.2.

Thus:

$$J_{ij} = \left(\frac{e^2}{r_{ij}} \right)_{\text{av over } i,\, j} = \iint \frac{\psi_i^2 e^2 \psi_j^2 \, d\tau_i \, d\tau_j}{r_{ij}} \tag{2.61}$$

Consequently we only need to solve the one-electron equation (2.54), using Eq. (2.60) to find the necessary average repulsions; however several difficulties immediately arise.

In the first place, the one-electron equations are still equations in three variables; such equations cannot be solved by existing methods. We can progress only if the individual one-electron equations can themselves be reduced. This is possible only in the case of atoms, and then only if the total electron distribution in the atom is spherically symmetrical. If so, the potential energy of the electron depends only on its distance from the nucleus; the forces acting on it are therefore directed toward the nucleus, and its angular momentum about the nucleus must be conserved. The operators $\mathbf{M}_i^2$ and $\mathbf{M}_{zi}$ must then commute with $\mathbf{H}_i$ and can be used to reduce the one-electron Schrödinger equation (2.54). This can be seen at once if we write a one-electron hamiltonian for an electron whose potential energy is some function $V(r)$ of its distance from the origin;

$$\mathbf{H}_i = -\frac{\hbar^2}{2m} \nabla_i^2 + V(r) \tag{2.62}$$

Comparison with Eqs. (2.7) to (2.14) shows that $\mathbf{H}_i$ commutes with the operators $\mathbf{M}_i^2$ and $\mathbf{M}_{zi}$ and also that the eigenfunctions ψ_i are of the form:

$$\psi_i = Y_i(lm) f_i(r) \tag{2.63}$$

where $Y(lm)$ is a spherical harmonic and $f_i(r)$ is a solution of the simple differential equation:

$$-\frac{\hbar^2}{2mr^2} \frac{\partial}{\partial r} r^2 \frac{\partial}{\partial r} f_1(r) - \frac{l(l+1)\hbar^2}{2mr^2} f_1(r) - V(r) f_1(r) = E_i f_i(r) \tag{2.64}$$

Equation (2.64) is of course much more complicated than its counterpart for the hydrogen atom (2.14) and has to be solved by numerical integration; this, however, is a trivial matter now that digital computers are freely available.

In the case of molecules, the one-electron Schrödinger equations cannot be reduced. The potential energy of each electron depends on its distances from two or more different nuclei; the force acting on the electron is no longer directed toward a single center, and so its angular momentum is no longer constant. The Hartree method cannot therefore be applied to molecules.

A second difficulty arises even in the case of atoms. In order to solve the one-electron Schrödinger equation (2.54), we have to set up the corresponding operators $\mathbf{H}_i$; to do this we need to calculate the average electron repulsions $(e^2/r_{ij})_{\text{av over } j}$. These in turn can be calculated only if we know the one-electron functions ψ_j [see Eq. (2.60)]; in other words we have to know the solutions to our equations before we can solve them! This kind of difficulty turns up again and again in the quantum theory of atoms and molecules; it is met by the following general procedure. We start by assuming values for the n functions ψ_i; let us denote these *zero-order approximations* by $\psi_i{}^0$. Using them, we set up the corresponding hamiltonian operators $\mathbf{H}_i{}^0$ and solve the resulting set of one-electron equations, obtaining a new set of functions, $\psi_i{}^1$. These in turn are used to set up a new set of operators $\mathbf{H}_i$. The process is repeated until the functions obtained in one cycle are identical (or almost identical) with the functions that had been used to set up the one-electron equations; the resulting functions form a self-consistent set of solutions to the problem in that if they are used to construct the operators $\mathbf{H}_i$, the same functions are obtained by solving the resulting set of equations.

This general procedure is known as the *self-consistent field* (SCF) method; the particular application indicated above was first introduced by Hartree. It should be added that SCF calculations are by no means foolproof; for there is never any guarantee either that the iterative procedures involved in them will converge to a definite solution, or that the solution, in cases where they do converge, is the correct one. However no other method is available for solving problems of this kind, and as a rule neither of the theoretical specters materializes. Usually one finds a reasonably rapid convergence to the required solution.

2.5 THE ORBITAL APPROXIMATION

The Hartree method cannot of course give exact values for the wave functions and energies of atoms or molecules, since the Hartree hamiltonian (2.57) is not the same as the true hamiltonian (2.44). Our next problem is to consider the physical significance of the approximation involved in using averaged values for interelectronic repulsions.

Consider the probability that in our n-electron system, electron 1 occupies a volume element $d\tau_1$, electron 2 $d\tau_2$, and so on. If the wave function is ψ, the probability P is given by:

$$P = \psi^2 \, d\tau_1 \, d\tau_2 \cdots d\tau_n \qquad (2.65)$$

In the Hartree approximation, the corresponding probability P' is given by:

$$P' = (\psi')^2 \, d\tau_1 \, d\tau_2 \cdots d\tau_n = (\psi_1\psi_2 \cdots \psi_n)^2 \, d\tau_1 \, d\tau_2 \cdots d\tau_n$$
$$= (\psi_1{}^2 \, d\tau_1)(\psi_2{}^2 \, d\tau_2) \cdots (\psi_n{}^2 \, d\tau_n) = P_1 P_2 \cdots P_n \qquad (2.66)$$

where P_i is the probability that an electron, represented by the wave function ψ_i, will be found in the volume element $d\tau_i$. Equation (2.66) implies that P' can be expressed as a product of these individual probabilities; this in turn implies that the probability of finding electron i in a volume element $d\tau_i$ has the same fixed value $\psi_i{}^2\, d\tau_i$, *no matter what the positions of the other* $n - 1$ *electrons may be.* This is obviously incorrect. Consider for example a helium atom. The probability of finding the first electron in a small volume element $d\tau_1$ will obviously be less if the other electron is almost exactly in the same position than it will be if the other electron is far away; for the electrons repel each other, and so will tend to keep apart. The probability of finding electron 1 in $d\tau_1$ therefore depends on the position of the other electron; in other words the electrons in helium tend to synchronize their motions about the nucleus in such a way as to keep apart as much as possible, a good analogy being provided by two men circling a very attractive $(+2e)$ girl. This phenomenon, the tendency of electrons to keep apart, is known as *electron correlation;* the Hartree method neglects this.

Having thus pinpointed the physical principles underlying the Hartree method, we can now arrive at a more general formulation. If we neglect electron correlation, then the probability of finding a given electron in a given volume element must be independent of the positions of the other electrons. Reversing the arguments used above, we conclude that it must be possible to factorize the overall wave function of the system into a product of one-electron functions ψ_i. Hence our object is to choose n one-electron functions ψ_i in such a way that their product is as good an approximation as possible to the true wave function for the system, this being one in which electron correlation is taken into account. It can be shown that the functions satisfying this condition are in fact solutions of the Hartree equations; however the present formulation is more general than Hartree's in that it envisages other procedures for arriving at the functions ψ_i.

The alternative approach also leads to a definite physical picture. If the probability of finding electron i in $d\tau_i$ is independent of the positions of the other electrons, this must mean that the electrons are moving quite independently of one another. The motion of electron i is specified by a definite one-electron function ψ_i, just as is the motion of the single electron in a one-electron system such as the hydrogen atom. We therefore term these one-electron functions *orbitals, atomic orbitals* (AO) in the case of an atom, *molecular orbitals* (MO) in the case of a molecule, and we term this whole general approach the *orbital approximation.*

2.6   THE VARIATION METHOD

The situation that faces us in the case of many-particle systems is a common one in the physical sciences. We know in principle how to solve a given problem, but our mathematical resources are insufficient to do this exactly; we therefore have to content ourselves with approximate solutions. One possible line of approach is to introduce enough simplifying assumptions to allow the problem to be solved theoretically; another is to use an empirical curve-fitting approach in which we try to fit some arbitrary function to the experimental data, by adjusting parameters in it.   Here we shall consider the quantum-mechanical analog of this second procedure; in particular we shall derive a criterion by which parameters in such a function can be adjusted.

Consider the Schrödinger equation:

$$\mathbf{H}\psi_i = E_i\psi_i \tag{2.67}$$

Our problem is to adjust the parameters a_i in a *trial eigenfunction* ψ in such a way as to make ψ as good an approximation as possible to one of the eigenfunctions ψ_i.   How good an approximation we can get will of course depend on how cleverly we select our trial eigenfunction; this choice is a matter of intuition, instinct, or common sense, rather than mathematics; for if we knew the exact form of ψ_i, we would not be reduced to expedients of this kind.   However we can at least make sure that our parameters are chosen as efficiently as possible, and this we can do rigorously by making use of the following theorem, known as the *variation theorem*.

Theorem 2.2   The expectation value of $\mathbf{H}$ for an arbitrary well-behaved function ψ is not less than the lowest eigenvalue E_0 of $\mathbf{H}$.

The expectation value E is given by:

$$E = \frac{\int \psi \mathbf{H}\psi \, d\tau}{\int \psi^2 \, d\tau} \tag{2.68}$$

In order to make ψ as good an approximation as possible to the eigenfunction ψ_0, corresponding to the eigenvalue E_0, we need but chose the parameters a_i to make E as small as possible; for the variation theorem tells us that $E > E_0$, so the best approximation to E_0 is given by minimizing E.   A necessary condition for this is that:

$$\frac{\partial E}{\partial a_1} = \frac{\partial E}{\partial a_2} = \cdots = \frac{\partial E}{\partial a_n} = 0 \tag{2.69}$$

Equations (2.69) are a set of simultaneous equations for the coefficients a_i; solution of these equations therefore solves our problem.‡   This curve-fitting approach to the problem of solving Schrödinger equations is called the *variation method*.

To prove the variation theorem, we expand ψ in terms of the eigenfunctions ψ_i of $\mathbf{H}$; this can of course be done exactly since the ψ_i form a *complete set* (Eq. 1.5);

$$\psi = \sum_i c_i\psi_i \tag{2.70}$$

---

‡ It is true that Eqs. (2.69) may have more than one solution and also that a given solution may correspond to a *maximum* rather than a minimum in E.   However these potential difficulties hardly ever cause trouble in practice and they are usually ignored.

Substituting this expression in Eq. (2.68),

$$E = \frac{\int \left(\sum_i c_i \psi_i\right) \mathbf{H} \left(\sum_j c_j \psi_j\right) d\tau}{\int \left(\sum_i c_i \psi_i\right) \left(\sum_j c_j \psi_j\right) d\tau}$$

$$= \frac{\sum_i \sum_j c_i c_j \int \psi_i \mathbf{H} \psi_j \, d\tau}{\sum_i \sum_j c_i c_j \int \psi_i \psi_j \, d\tau}$$

$$= \frac{\sum_i \sum_j c_i c_j E_j \int \psi_i \psi_j \, d\tau}{\sum_i c_i^2} = \frac{\sum_i c_i^2 E_i}{\sum_i c_i^2} \tag{2.71}$$

since the ψ_1 form an orthonormal set, and since ψ_j is an eigenfunction of $\mathbf{H}$ with eigenvalue E_j. Now by assumption, $E_i > E_0$ $(i \neq 0)$, since E_0 is the lowest eigenvalue of $\mathbf{H}$; hence:

$$E \geq \frac{\sum_i c_i^2 E_0}{\sum_i c_i^2} = E_0 \tag{2.72}$$

This proves the theorem; it is also evident that the equality sign arises only if $c_0 = 1$, $c_i = 0$ $(i \neq 0)$; in that case the trial eigenfunction ψ is *identical* with the lowest eigenfunction ψ_0 of $\mathbf{H}$.

The same procedure can be extended to other eigenfunctions of $\mathbf{H}$. Consider for example a trial eigenfunction ψ' which is orthogonal to the lowest eigenfunction ψ_0 of $\mathbf{H}$;

$$\int \psi' \psi_0 \, d\tau = 0 \tag{2.73}$$

If we expand ψ' in terms of the ψ_i,

$$\psi' = \Sigma c_i' \psi_i \tag{2.74}$$

Eq. (2.73) becomes:

$$\int \psi_0 \left(\sum_i c_i' \psi_i\right) d\tau = \sum_i c_i' \int \psi_0 \psi_i \, d\tau = c_0 = 0 \tag{2.75}$$

The expectation value for ψ' [compare Eq. (2.71)] then becomes:

$$E' = \frac{\sum_{i \neq 0} c_i^2 E_i}{\sum_{i \neq 0} c_i^2} \geq E_1 \tag{2.76}$$

where E_1 is the next but lowest eigenvalue of $\mathbf{H}$. In this case minimizing E' makes ψ' an approximation to the corresponding eigenfunction ψ_1.

An obvious extension of this procedure can be used to find other eigenfunctions and eigenvalues; thus a trial eigenfunction ψ'' orthogonal to ψ_0 and ψ_1 can be used to approximate the next eigenvalue E_2 and eigenfunction ψ_2. The trouble is that we do not know the true eigenfunctions $\psi_0, \psi_1, \ldots$ and so we cannot make our trial eigenfunctions orthogonal to them; the best we can do is to make them orthogonal to our approximations to the true functions. Thus having made ψ as good an approximation as possible to ψ_0, by adjusting the parameters in it through use of Eq. (2.69), we can pick a second trial eigenfunction ψ' that is orthogonal to ψ. Minimizing the corresponding expectation value E' will then make ψ' an approximation to ψ_1. Here, however, we cannot be sure that $E'_1 \geq E_1$; for ψ' will not be truly orthogonal to ψ_0, except in the unlikely event that we hit the jackpot with our first approximation so that the optimized form of ψ happened to be identical with ψ_0. Moreover the errors due to this will accumulate, so that progressively less reliance can be placed on approximations to higher eigenvalues and eigenfunctions of $\mathbf{H}$.

In order to use the variation method, we must of course be able to evaluate the integrals in Eq. (2.68). This immediately places restrictions on the forms of trial eigenfunctions that we can use; for these functions contain unknowns (the parameters a_i), and clearly one cannot use numerical methods to determine integrals involving unknown parameters. We can of course choose our trial eigenfunction in such a way that the integrals can be expressed in analytical form; this, however, is much too restrictive. The alternative is to arrange things so that the integrals appear as products of the parameters with integrals that are parameter-free, and an obvious way to do this is to use a *linear trial eigenfunction* of the form:

$$\psi = \sum_i a_i \phi_i \tag{2.77}$$

Here the a_i are real algebraic numbers, while the ϕ_i form a set of arbitrary real well-behaved functions which we call the *basis set* for our problem; our object is to choose the parameters a_i in such a way as to make ψ approximate as closely as possible to ψ_0. This version of the variation method bears an obvious resemblance to Fourier analysis, except that here we are free to choose the functions ϕ_i in any way we please, guided by intuition, prayer, or any other suitable source of inspiration. With this trial eigenfunction, the integrals in Eq. (2.68) reduce to integrals over the basis functions ϕ_i; i.e.

$$E = \frac{\int \left(\sum_i a_i \phi_i \, \mathbf{H} \right) \left(\sum_j a_j \phi_j \right) d\tau}{\int \left(\sum_i a_i \phi_i \right) \left(\sum_j a_j \phi_j \right) d\tau} = \frac{\sum_i \sum_j a_i a_j H_{ij}}{\sum_i \sum_j a_i a_j S_{ij}} = \frac{f_1}{f_2} \tag{2.78}$$

where the integrals H_{ij}, S_{ij} are integrals over the functions ϕ_i, and do not involve the parameters a_i;

$$H_{ij} = \int \phi_i \mathbf{H} \phi_j \, d\tau \tag{2.79}$$

$$S_{ij} = \int \phi_i \phi_j \, d\tau \tag{2.80}$$

The variation equations (2.69) for the coefficients become:

$$\frac{\partial E}{\partial a_i} = \frac{1}{f_2} \frac{\partial f_1}{\partial a_i} - \frac{f_1}{f_2^2} \frac{\partial f_2}{\partial a_i} = 0 \qquad i = 1, 2, \ldots, n \tag{2.81}$$

Canceling f_2, and using Eq. (2.78),

$$\frac{\partial E}{\partial a_i} = \frac{\partial f_1}{\partial a_i} - E \frac{\partial f_2}{\partial a_i}$$

$$= \sum_j 2a_j H_{ij} - E \sum_j 2a_j S_{ij} = 0 \qquad i = 1, 2, \ldots, n \tag{2.82}$$

We can write this equivalently in the form:

$$\sum_j a_j (H_{ij} - ES_{ij}) = 0 \qquad i = 1, 2, \ldots, n \tag{2.83}$$

For any given value of E, Eq. (2.83) is a set of n homogeneous linear equations in n variables a_i. Since the equations are homogeneous, they can give only the $n - 1$ ratios of the a_i to one another; for if we have a set of values $a_1, a_2, \ldots, a_n$ that satisfy the equations, so also will multiples of the a's by any algebraic number A (that is $Aa_1, Aa_2, \ldots, Aa_n$). These $n - 1$ ratios can be found from the first $n - 1$ equations of the set; however the values so found will not as a rule satisfy the nth equation. The difficulty can be seen clearly from a simple example, involving two variables x, y; the following simultaneous equations have no solution other than the trivial one, $x = y = 0$, since the ratio x/y found from Eq. (2.84) fails to satisfy Eq. (2.85).

$$x - 3y = 0 \tag{2.84}$$

$$2x + 5y = 0 \tag{2.85}$$

This difficulty can, however, be avoided in the case of Eqs. (2.83); for if we choose the value of E properly, we can make the equations self-consistent. According to a standard theorem in algebra, the required condition is that the determinant of the coefficients of the a_i should vanish; i.e.

$$\begin{vmatrix} H_{11} - ES_{11} & H_{12} - ES_{12} & \cdots & H_{1n} - ES_{1n} \\ H_{21} - ES_{21} & H_{22} - ES_{22} & \cdots & H_{2n} - ES_{2n} \\ \vdots & \vdots & & \vdots \\ H_{n1} - ES_{n1} & H_{n2} - ES_{n2} & \cdots & H_{nn} - ES_{nn} \end{vmatrix} = 0 \tag{2.86}$$

Equation (2.86) can conveniently be written:

$$|H_{ij} - ES_{ij}| = 0 \tag{2.87}$$

the left-hand side of this equation representing a determinant in which the element occupying the ith row and jth column is $H_{ij} - ES_{ij}$. Expansion of the determinant gives a polynomial of nth degree in E; the resulting equation has therefore n roots. Substituting any of these n values in Eq. (2.83), we can then find a corresponding set of coefficients a_i.

At first sight it may seem embarrassing that we have ended up with not one, but n, solutions of our problem! However it can easily be shown that the n functions ψ corresponding to these n solutions are orthogonal to one another; it follows that they must be approximations to the first n solutions of the Schrödinger equation. Thus we have an unexpected bonus; we set out to find an approximation to the wave function corresponding to the lowest eigenvalue E_0 of Eq. (2.67), and we have ended up with approximations to $n - 1$ other eigenfunctions as well.

The determinantal equation (2.87) is called a *secular equation* from analogy with classical mechanics, where similar equations appeared in the solution of secular problems, i.e. those concerned with periodic motion. Note that the *secular determinant* in Eq. (2.87) is a symmetrical determinant; for since ϕ_i and ϕ_j are real, $S_{ij} = S_{ji}$, and since moreover $\mathbf{H}$ is a real hermitian operator,

$$H_{ij} = \int \phi_i \mathbf{H} \phi_j \, d\tau = \overline{\int \phi_j \mathbf{H} \phi_i \, d\tau} = \int \phi_j \mathbf{H} \phi_i \, d\tau = H_{ji} \tag{2.88}$$

This is an important point; for it can be shown that the roots of a secular equation are real if the determinant is symmetrical. Since the roots of Eq. (2.87) are supposed to be approximations to the first n eigenvalues of $\mathbf{H}$, it would be embarrassing if any of them were complex or imaginary.

Since no restrictions whatsoever have been placed on the form of the functions ϕ_1, other than that they should be well-behaved, there is no reason why they should be orthogonal [see Eq. (2.80); S_{ij} need not vanish if $i \neq j$]. If, however, we choose an orthonormal set of functions ϕ_i as our basis set, Eqs. (2.83) and (2.87) are greatly simplified. In this case

$$S_{ij} = \int \phi_i \phi_j \, d\tau = \delta_{ij} \tag{2.89}$$

where the quantity δ_{ij} (*Kronecker delta*) vanishes if $i \neq j$, and is equal to unity if $i = j$. Equations (2.83) and (2.87) then become:

$$\sum_j a_j (H_{ij} - e\delta_{ij}) = 0 \qquad i = 1, 2, \ldots, n \tag{2.90}$$

$$|H_{ij} - E\delta_{ij}| = 0 \tag{2.91}$$

The unknown E now appears only in the diagonal elements of the secular determinant; this makes the secular equation much easier to solve.

Limiting ourselves to the use of orthonormal basis sets does not in fact involve any loss of generality; for it can easily be shown that if ϕ_i ($i = 1, 2, \ldots, n$) are a set of well-behaved functions which are not mutually orthogonal, then one can always construct n linear combinations ϕ_i',

$$\phi_i' = \sum_j c_{ij}\phi_j \qquad i = 1, 2, \ldots, n \tag{2.92}$$

such that the ϕ_i' form an orthogonal set. Since the existence of Eq. (2.92) implies the existence of the reverse transformation,

$$\phi_j = \sum_i c_{ij}'\phi_i' \tag{2.93}$$

we can express any linear combination of the original functions ϕ_j as a linear combination of the orthogonal functions ϕ_i'. We therefore arrive at exactly the same solution by using as our trial eigenfunction a linear combination of the orthogonal functions ϕ_i', the coefficients being given by Eqs. (2.90) and (2.91), as we do by using a linear combination of the nonorthogonal functions ϕ_j, the coefficients being given by Eqs. (2.83) and (2.87).

Procedures for finding the coefficients c_{ij} in Eq. (2.92) are given in all the standard texts[1] and need not be repeated here; there are in fact an infinite number of possible sets of coefficients leading to different (but equivalent) sets of orthogonal functions ϕ_i'.

One particularly important example of the use of an orthogonal basis set is that where the functions ϕ_i are the eigenfunctions of some dynamic operator $\boldsymbol{\alpha}$;

$$\boldsymbol{\alpha}\phi_i = A_i\phi_i \tag{2.94}$$

The eigenfunctions of any dynamic operator not only are orthogonal, but also form a complete set; we can therefore express any eigenfunction of $\mathbf{H}$ *exactly* as a linear combination of the eigenfunctions ϕ_i of $\boldsymbol{\alpha}$. A variation treatment using a linear combination of all these functions ϕ_i, together with Eqs. (2.90) and (2.91), should therefore lead to an exact solution of the Schrödinger equation (2.67). This is not feasible in practice, since the functions ϕ_i are infinite in number; even the latest digital computers quail at handling equations containing an infinite number of variables! Nevertheless this approach has important implications which will be discussed in the two following sections. Note the distinction between a treatment of this kind using a *complete basis set*, such as the set of eigenfunctions of some dynamic operator, and approximate solutions based on the use of *finite* or *incomplete basis sets*.

2.7 MATRIX REPRESENTATION

Treatments of the kind indicated in the last section can be stated more concisely and elegantly in matrix notation. While this is not essential, the use of matrices has become so general that it is difficult to follow the quantum-chemical literature without some basic understanding of it. Here we shall outline the use of matrix methods, and the corresponding terminology, in problems involving the use of linear variation functions.‡

A matrix is a rectangular array of numbers (real or complex) in rows and columns, like a determinant, except that the array need not be square. The symbol $[a_{ij}]$ denotes a matrix in which a_{ij} is the element in the ith row and jth column; the use of brackets distinguishes it from a determinant (for example $|a_{ij}|$). A *vector* is a matrix with either a single row (*row vector,* represented as $[a_i]$) or a single column (*column vector,* which we shall represent as $\{a_i\}$ to distinguish it from a row vector). We shall be concerned only with row and column vectors, and with *square matrices,* in which the numbers of rows and columns are the same.

Addition, subtraction, and equality are defined for matrices only if they are of the same size and shape; in that case:

$$[a_{ij}] = [b_{ij}] \qquad \text{if } a_{ij} = b_{ij} \text{ for all } i, j \tag{2.95}$$

$$[a_{ij}] \pm [b_{ij}] = [a_{ij} \pm b_{ij}] \tag{2.96}$$

The product $[a_{ij}][b_{ij}]$ of two matrices is defined only if the number of columns in $[a_{ij}]$ is the same as the number of rows in $[b_{ij}]$; in that case:

$$[a_{ij}][b_{ij}] = [c_{ik}] \qquad \text{where } c_{ik} = \sum_j a_{ij} b_{jk} \tag{2.97}$$

Thus the product $[a_{ij}]\{b_j\}$ of a matrix with a column vector is a column vector, $\left\{\sum_j a_{ij} b_j\right\}$, and the product $[a_i][b_{ij}]$ of a row vector with a matrix is a row vector, $\left[\sum_i a_i b_{ij}\right]$; the product of a matrix with a row vector, or of a column vector with a matrix, is not defined. The product of two vectors is defined if one is a row vector and the other a column vector;

$$[a_i]\{b_i\} = \sum_i a_i b_i \qquad \text{a single number or } scalar \tag{2.98}$$

$$\{a_i\}[b_i] = [a_i b_j] \qquad \text{a square matrix} \tag{2.99}$$

Two conclusions follow from this. First, matrices do not necessarily obey the commutative law of multiplication. Thus the product $[b_{ij}][a_{ij}]$ is given by:

$$[b_{ij}][a_{ij}] = [d_{ik}] \qquad \text{when } d_{ik} = \sum_j b_{ij} a_{jk} \tag{2.100}$$

Comparison with Eq. (2.97) shows that this is not in general the same as the product $[a_{ij}][b_{ij}]$.

Secondly, we can associate with any square matrix $[a_{ij}]$ a corresponding de-

‡ A good introduction to matrix algebra will be found in Ref. 2. For a very readable general account see Ref. 3.

terminant $|a_{ij}|$. Since the rules for multiplying determinants are identical with those for multiplying matrices, it follows that the determinant of the product of two matrices is equal to the product of the two individual determinants. One difference should be noted, however; since a determinant can be multiplied out to give a single scalar number, determinants, unlike matrices, commute. Thus the determinants of the matrices $[c_{ik}][d_{ik}]$ in Eqs. (2.97) and (2.100) are equal;

$$|a_{ij}||b_{ij}| - |b_{ij}||a_{ij}| = 0 \qquad (2.101)$$

The *null matrix* [0], or 0, is a matrix in which every element is zero; obviously

$$0[a_{ij}] = [a_{ij}]0 = 0 \qquad (2.102)$$

A *diagonal matrix* is a square matrix in which all the elements a_{ij} vanish unless $i = j$; the surviving elements lie along the leading diagonal. The *unit matrix I* or $[\delta_{ij}]$ is a diagonal matrix in which each diagonal element is unity; evidently,

$$I[a_{ij}] = [\delta_{ij}][a_{ij}] = [a_{ij}] = [a_{ij}][\delta_{ij}] = [a_{ij}]I \qquad (2.103)$$

The null matrix and unit matrix therefore commute with other matrices.

The product of a scalar A with a matrix is defined by:

$$A[a_{ij}] = [a_{ij}]A = [Aa_{ij}] \qquad (2.104)$$

It will be seen that a scalar A is equivalent to a diagonal matrix in which each diagonal element is A; for

$$A[a_{ij}] = AI[a_{ij}] = [A\delta_{ij}][a_{ij}] \qquad (2.105)$$

The matrix $[A\delta_{ij}]$ is one in which each off-diagonal element vanishes, while each diagonal element is equal to A. Such a matrix may be written as $[A]$, the use of an unsubscripted capital letter distinguishing it from a row vector.

We are now ready to translate the variation equations into matrix form. Equations (2.90) can be written:

$$\sum_j H_{ij}a_j = Ea_i \qquad i = 1, 2, \ldots, n \qquad (2.106)$$

Since two column vectors are equal only if all corresponding pairs of elements in them are equal, this set of equations can be replaced by the single vector equation:

$$\{H_{ij}a_j\} = E\{a_i\} = [E]\{a_i\} \qquad (2.107)$$

Using Eq. (2.97), we can write the left-hand side of this equation as a product of the matrix $[H_{ij}]$ with the column vector $\{a_i\}$;

$$[H_{ij}]\{a_i\} = [E]\{a_i\} \qquad (2.108)$$

or
$$([H_{ij}] - [E])\{a_i\} = [H_{ij} - E\delta_{ij}]\{a_i\} = 0 \qquad (2.109)$$

Now let us multiply Eq. (2.109) from the right by an arbitrary row vector $[b_j]$;

$$[H_{ij} - E\delta_{ij}]\{a_i\}[b_j] = [H_{ij} - E\delta_{ij}][a_ib_j] = 0 \qquad (2.110)$$

From the correspondence between square matrices and determinants, it follows that the product of the determinants $|H_{ij} - E\delta_{ij}|$ and $|a_ib_j|$ is equal to the determinant of the null matrix; i.e.

$$|H_{ij} - E\delta_{ij}||a_ib_j| = |0| = 0 \qquad (2.111)$$

Since the vector $[b_j]$ was arbitrary, we can choose it in such a way that $|a_ib_j| \neq 0$; hence:

$$|H_{ij} - E\delta_{ij}| = 0 \qquad (2.112)$$

This of course is just the secular equation (2.91), which is alternatively called the *characteristic equation* for the matrix $[H_{ij}]$.

The matrix $[H_{ij}]$ is called the *energy matrix* for the basis set ϕ_i; however this term is usually restricted to the case where we are using a complete basis set. Here the solutions of the secular equation (2.112) are the eigenvalues of the operator **H**; we can write Eq. (2.107) in the form:

$$[H_{ij}]\{a_i\} = E_i\{a_i\} \qquad (2.113)$$

the solutions E_i being *eigenvalues* of the matrix $[H_{ij}]$, with corresponding *eigenvectors* $\{a_i\}$.

Since the eigenvalues of the energy matrix are the same as the eigenvalues of the operator **H**, the matrix $[H_{ij}]$ must have the same eigenvalues *no matter what basis set we use to construct the matrix elements H_{ij}* (provided of course that the set is complete). Indeed, we need not even use the Schrödinger representation to construct the energy matrix; it is easily shown that if $\langle \bar{i}|, |i\rangle$ are eigenbras and eigenkets of any dynamic operator α, then the matrix $[H_{ij}]$, whose matrix elements are given by

$$H_{ij} = \langle \bar{i}|\mathbf{H}|j\rangle \qquad (2.114)$$

again has eigenvalues identical with those of the operator **H**.

This suggests the possibility of a matrix representation of quantum mechanics in which the fundamental dynamic operators are replaced by *dynamic matrices*, the bras by row vectors, and the kets by column vectors; such a representation is not only possible, but it was one of the forms in which quantum theory was first developed (*Heisenberg representation*). The fact that matrices do not obey the commutative law of multiplication, and that the eigenvalue properties of dynamic matrices are independent of the representation used to construct their matrix elements, suggests that the eigenvalues of such matrices may be determined by their commutation rules; this again is true. Moreover the commutation rules for dynamic matrices are the same as for the corresponding operators;

for instance the matrices $[q_{ij}{}^m]$, $[p_{ij}{}^m]$, corresponding to a position variable q_m and the conjugate momentum p_m, obey the same commutation rule as that [Eq. (1.34)] for the operators $\mathbf{q}_m$, $\mathbf{p}_m$; i.e.

$$[q_{ij}{}^m][p_{ij}{}^m] - [p_{ij}{}^m][q_{ij}{}^m] = i\hbar I \qquad (2.115)$$

Let us now consider the relationship between the various different forms of a given dynamic matrix $[H_{ij}]$. To do this, we first need to define the *reciprocal* of a matrix. If the reciprocal $[c_{ij}]^{-1}$ of the matrix $[c_{ij}]$ exists, it is defined by:

$$[c_{ij}][c_{ij}]^{-1} = I \qquad (2.116)$$

Since this is an equation involving only square matrices, it must hold if the matrices are replaced by determinants; this will be true only if neither determinant vanishes. The reciprocal of a square matrix therefore exists only if the corresponding determinant differs from zero; a matrix whose determinant vanishes is called a *singular matrix*. Let us now consider the matrix $[A_{ij}]$ derived from $[H_{ij}]$ by the following *similarity transformation*, $[c_{ij}]$ being an arbitrary nonsingular matrix;

$$[A_{ij}] = [c_{ij}][H_{ij}][c_{ij}]^{-1} \qquad (2.117)$$

The eigenvalues A and eigenvectors $\{a_i\}$ of $[A_{ij}]$ are determined by the eigenvalue equation:

$$[A_{ij}]\{a_i\} = A\{a_i\} \qquad (2.118)$$

or $\qquad\qquad ([A_{ij}] - AI)\{a_i\} = 0 \qquad\qquad (2.119)$

Now since the unit matrix I commutes with other matrices,

$$[c_{ij}]I[c_{ij}]^{-1} = I[c_{ij}][c_{ij}]^{-1} = I \qquad (2.120)$$

From Eqs. (2.117) to (2.120),

$$[c_{ij}]\{[H_{ij}] - AI\}[c_{ij}]^{-1}\{a_i\} = [c_{ij}][H_{ij} - A\delta_{ij}][c_{ij}]^{-1}\{a_i\} = 0 \qquad (2.121)$$

Using the same argument as before, we find that the values of A are given by the characteristic equation:

$$|c_{ij}||H_{ij} - A\delta_{ij}||c_{ij}|^{-1} = 0 \qquad (2.122)$$

However $|c_{ij}| \neq 0$, since $[c_{ij}]$ is by definition a nonsingular matrix; hence:

$$|H_{ij} - A\delta_{ij}| = 0 \qquad (2.123)$$

Comparison of Eqs. (2.112) and (2.123) shows that the eigenvalues of $[A_{ij}]$ and $[H_{ij}]$ are identical. Thus *the eigenvalues of a matrix are unchanged if we submit the matrix to a similarity transformation.* Conversely, it can be shown that if two matrices have identical eigenvalues, then they can be interconverted by a similarity transformation. The different forms of a given dynamic matrix must then be related in this way.

Using Eq. (2.114) and the fact that dynamic operators are hermitian [compare Eq. (1.17)],

$$H_{ij} = \langle \bar{i}|\mathbf{H}|j\rangle = \langle j|\mathbf{H}|i\rangle = \langle \overline{j|\mathbf{H}|i}\rangle = \overline{H}_{ji} \qquad (2.124)$$

It follows that the diagonal elements H_{ii} of the energy matrix are real (since $H_{ii} = \overline{H}_{ii}$), while each off-diagonal element H_{ij} is the complex conjugate of its mirror image H_{ji} in the leading diagonal. Such a matrix is termed *hermitian;* for it is easily seen that if $[H_{ij}]$ is a hermitian matrix, and $[a_i]$, $\{b_j\}$ are any two vectors, then

$$[a_i][H_{ij}]\{b_j\} = [b_i][\overline{H}_{ij}][a_j] \qquad (2.125)$$

an equation identical in form with Eq. (1.17). An important corollary of this parallel is that *the eigenvalues of a hermitian matrix are real.*

It can be shown that any hermitian matrix $[H_{ij}]$ can be transformed into a diagonal matrix by a suitably chosen similarity transformation; the diagonal elements are then the eigenvalues E_i of $[H_{ij}]$. In other words there is a nonsingular matrix $[c_{ij}]$ such that

$$[c_{ij}][H_{ij}][c_{ij}]^{-1} = [E_i\delta_{ij}] \qquad (2.126)$$

The process of determining the eigenvalues of a given dynamic matrix is therefore commonly described as *diagonalizing* the matrix. Likewise the process of solving the variation equations (2.90) and (2.91) is often described as *extracting the eigenvalues and eigenvectors* of the corresponding matrix; for the solutions a_i of Eq. (2.90) are clearly the components of one eigenvector of the matrix $[H_{ij}]$ [compare Eq. (2.108)].

2.8 PERTURBATION THEORY

Suppose that we have a system designated in the Schrödinger representation by the hamiltonian operator $\mathbf{H}'$. Suppose that there is a very similar system, with hamiltonian operator $\mathbf{H}$, for which the solutions of the Schrödinger equation are known:

$$\mathbf{H}\psi_i = E_i\psi_i \qquad (2.127)$$

Is there any way in which the eigenvalues and eigenfunctions of $\mathbf{H}'$ can be approximated in terms of the eigenfunctions and eigenvalues of $\mathbf{H}$? *Perturbation theory* provides the solution of this problem.

Since the two systems are similar, so also must be their hamiltonian operators. We can then write $\mathbf{H}'$ in the form

$$\mathbf{H}' = \mathbf{H} + \mathbf{P} \qquad (2.128)$$

where the *perturbation* $\mathbf{P}$ represents the small difference between $\mathbf{H}$ and $\mathbf{H}'$. A good example of this procedure is provided by the helium atom. As we have seen [Eq. (2.44)], the hamiltonian operator $\mathbf{H'}$ for this can be written:

$$\mathbf{H'} = \mathbf{H}_1 + \mathbf{H}_2 + \frac{e^2}{r_{12}} \tag{2.129}$$

If the term e^2/r_{12} were omitted, the Schrödinger equation could be solved exactly; for the hamiltonian operator $\mathbf{H}$ would then be a sum of two one-electron hydrogenlike operators $\mathbf{H}_1$, $\mathbf{H}_2$. The operator $\mathbf{H'}$ thus fits our scheme exactly, the perturbation here being the term e^2/r_{12}.

Our object is to solve the Schrödinger equation,

$$\mathbf{H'}\psi_i' = E_i'\psi_i' \tag{2.130}$$

To do this, let us use the variation method, taking the eigenfunctions ψ_i of the unperturbed hamiltonian $\mathbf{H}$ as our basis set. The eigenfunctions of $\mathbf{H'}$ will then be of the form:

$$\psi_i' = \sum_j a_{ij}\psi_j \tag{2.131}$$

where the coefficients a_{ij} are found by solving the set of simultaneous equations:

$$\sum_j a_{mj}(H_{ij}' - E_m\delta_{ij}) = 0 \qquad i = 1, 2, \ldots \tag{2.132}$$

Here E_m is a root of the secular equation

$$|H_{ij}' - E\delta_{ij}| = 0 \tag{2.133}$$

The matrix elements H_{ij}' are as follows:

$$H_{ij}' = \int\psi_i\mathbf{H'}\psi_j\,d\tau = \int\psi_i\mathbf{H}\psi_j\,d\tau + \int\psi_i\mathbf{P}\psi_j\,d\tau = E_j\delta_{ij} + P_{ij} \tag{2.134}$$

since ψ_j is an eigenfunction of $\mathbf{H}$ with eigenvalue E_j, and since the eigenfunctions ψ_i form an orthonormal set. Here P_{ij} is a *matrix element* for the perturbation operator $\mathbf{P}$, using the basis set ψ_i.

Using this expression, Eq. (2.132) becomes:

$$a_i(E_i + P_{ij} - E) + \sum_{j\neq i} a_{ij}P_{ij} = 0 \qquad i = 1, 2, \ldots \tag{2.135}$$

The secular equation (2.133) is of the form:

$$\begin{vmatrix} E_1 + P_{11} - E & P_{12} & P_{13} & \cdots \\ P_{21} & E_2 + P_{22} - E & P_{23} & \cdots \\ P_{31} & P_{32} & E_3 + P_{33} - E & \cdots \\ & & & \cdots \\ \vdots & \vdots & \vdots & \cdots \\ & & & \cdots \end{vmatrix} = 0 \tag{2.136}$$

As we have seen, equations of this type cannot as a rule be solved exactly since the number of eigenfunctions ψ_i of $\mathbf{H}$ will usually be infinite. However since $\mathbf{P}$ is assumed to be small, so also must be the matrix elements P_{ij}; this suggests that we may be able to find the roots of Eq. (2.136) by a method of successive approximations, expanding the secular determinant and keeping only terms involving less than a certain number of elements P_{ij}.

When $\mathbf{P} \to 0$, the secular determinant approximates to a diagonal determinant which can be expanded immediately;

$$\begin{vmatrix} E_1 - E & 0 & 0 & \cdots \\ 0 & E_2 - E & 0 & \cdots \\ 0 & 0 & E_3 - E & \cdots \\ \vdots & \vdots & \vdots & \cdots \\ & & & \cdots \end{vmatrix} = \prod_i (E_i - E) = 0 \qquad (2.137)$$

The roots of this equation are the unperturbed energies E_i, as they must be, since as $\mathbf{P} \to 0$, $\mathbf{H}' \to \mathbf{H}$. If $\mathbf{P}$ is small, the roots of the perturbed equation must then still be close to the roots of the unperturbed equation.

Consider first the case where all the eigenvalues E_i of $\mathbf{H}$ are different. If we are interested in the root of Eq. (2.136) that lies close to the unperturbed eigenvalue E_m, we need to know the value of the secular determinant when $E \approx E_m$. In this case the diagonal element $E_m + P_{mm} - E$ will be small, of the same order of magnitude as the off-diagonal elements P_{ij}, but the other diagonal elements will be large. If then we expand the determinant in the usual way, the term obtained by multiplying together all the elements along the leading diagonal will be of order P_{ij}. As we shall see presently, the other terms in the expansion are all smaller than this, of order P_{ij}^2 or less; the secular equation can therefore be written in the form:

$$\prod_i (E_i + P_{ii} - E) + O(P_{ij}^2) = 0 \qquad (2.138)$$

Since the choice of root E_m was arbitrary, it follows that the solutions of the secular equation are given to a first approximation by Eq. (2.138) with the terms in P_{ij}^2 omitted; i.e. by:

$$E = E_m + P_{mm} \qquad i = 1, 2, \ldots \qquad (2.139)$$

This result has a simple physical significance. If we calculate the energy of a system whose wave function is ψ_m, and whose hamiltonian is $\mathbf{H}'$, we arrive at Eq. (2.139). First-order perturbation theory thus corresponds to the approximation of assuming the wave functions for the perturbed system to be the same as those for the unperturbed system. This is very reasonable; for the wave functions ψ_m of a given system are chosen in such a way as to make the expression for the energy (that is $\int \psi_m \mathbf{H} \psi_m \, d\tau$) a minimum. Any small change in a given wave function will therefore have only a second-order effect on the energy. Since first-order perturbation theory neglects second-order effects, it will neglect any contributions due to changes in the wave function.

The other terms in the expansion of the secular determinant are derived from the largest one by replacing one or more of the diagonal elements in it by off-diagonal elements. Since the off-diagonal elements are all of order P_{ij}, it will clearly be best to replace in this way the one small diagonal element, that is $E_m + P_{mm} - E$. Suppose we replace this by the off-diagonal element P_{mn}. Then since P_{mn} is an element from the nth column of the determinant, and since each term in the expansion consists of a product of elements of which only one is taken from each column, it follows that we must also omit the diagonal element $E_n + P_{nn} - E$. In order to avoid having to omit any more of the (large) diagonal elements, we must then replace this with the off-diagonal element P_{nm}; for if we replaced it by some other element P_{nk}, the same argument would show that the diagonal element $E_k + P_{kk} - E$ would also have to be omitted. In this way we obtain a series of terms in the expansion that are of order $P_{ij}{}^2$, each being of the form:

$$- \frac{P_{mn} P_{nm} \prod_i (E_i + P_{ii} - E)}{(E_m + P_{mm} - E)(E_n + P_{nn} - E)} \tag{2.140}$$

The term is negative, since it requires one interchange of columns of the determinant (columns m and n) to bring all the component elements onto the leading diagonal. Combining the first-order term [Eq. (2.138)] with the second-order terms [Eq. (2.140)], the secular equation becomes:

$$\prod_i (E_i + P_{ii} - E)\left[1 - \sum_{n \neq m} \frac{P_{mn} P_{nm}}{(E_m + P_{mm} - E)(E_n + P_{nn} - E)}\right] = 0 \tag{2.141}$$

It is easily seen that any other terms in the expansion of the determinant are of order P relative to the ones included in Eq. (2.141). By an obvious manipulation, Eq. (2.141) becomes:

$$E = E_m + P_{mm} + \sum_{n \neq m} \frac{P_{mn} P_{nm}}{E - E_n - P_{nn}} \tag{2.142}$$

Now since we are considering the perturbed root corresponding to the unperturbed E_m,

$$E = E_m + P_{mm} + O(P^2) \tag{2.143}$$

Substituting this in Eq. (2.142), and neglecting terms of order P^3, we find:

$$E = E_m + P_{mm} + \sum_{n \neq m} \frac{P_{mn} P_{nm}}{E_m - E_n} \tag{2.144}$$

The sum in Eq. (2.144) is called the *second-order perturbation*.   Note that $\mathbf{P}$ is a real hermitian operator, being the difference between two real hermitian operators $\mathbf{H}'$ and $\mathbf{H}$; if the basis-set functions ψ_i are real, as we suppose to be the case, then

$$P_{mn} = P_{nm} \qquad (2.145)$$

Next we must find an approximation to the perturbed eigenfunctions ψ_i', by solving the set of Eqs. (2.135).   Consider any equation from this set, with $i \neq m$. Since we are interested in the solution corresponding to the perturbed root E_m', the coefficient of a_i may be written as $E_i + P_{ii} - E_m - P_{mm} + O(P^2)$; since $E_i \neq E_m$, this is large compared with the P's.   On the other hand the coefficients P_{ij} of all the other a_j are small.   It follows that the term involving a_i must also be of order P; hence:

$$a_i \approx P \qquad (2.146)$$

The only terms in the equation which are of order P are therefore those involving a_i and a_m; for the product $a_j P_{ij}$ is of order P^2 unless $j = m$.   Neglecting quantities of order P^2 or smaller, we have then:

$$a_i(E_i - E_m) + a_m P_{mi} = 0 \qquad (2.147)$$

or
$$a_i = \frac{P_{mi}}{E_m - E_i} a_m \qquad (2.148)$$

Our approximation to the perturbed eigenfunction ψ_m', corresponding to the unperturbed function ψ_m, is then given by:

$$\psi_m' = a_m\left(\psi_m + \sum_{n \neq m} \frac{P_{mn}}{E_m - E_n}\psi_n\right) \qquad (2.149)$$

Equations (2.142) and (2.149) therefore provide us with a second approximation to the eigenvalues of $\mathbf{H}'$ and a first approximation to its eigenfunctions; higher approximations can easily be obtained by retaining higher powers of P in our expansions of Eqs. (2.135) and (2.136), but they are rarely of interest and we shall not need them here.   However one very important question does remain to be considered; what happens if the unperturbed equation (2.127) has a degenerate solution?

Suppose that the n eigenvalues $E_1, E_2, \ldots , E_n$ of $\mathbf{H}$ are identical, having a common value E_0.   The corresponding eigenvalues of $\mathbf{H}'$ will then differ from E_0 only by small amounts.   If then we are looking for roots of Eq. (2.136) that correspond to the unperturbed levels $E_1 - E_n$, so that $E \approx E_0$, all elements in the first n rows of the secular determinant, and *all* elements in the first n columns, will be of order P.   Every term in the expansion of the determinant will then be of order P^n or smaller.   The largest terms will then be those in which we retain all the diagonal elements $E_i + P_{ii} - E$ other than the first n; for these alone are large.   A first approximation to the levels $E_1', E_2', \ldots , E_n'$ is then given by:

$$\begin{vmatrix} E_1 + P_{11} - E & P_{12} & P_{13} & \cdots & P_{1n} \\ P_{21} & E_2 + P_{22} - E & P_{23} & \cdots & P_{2n} \\ \vdots & \vdots & \vdots & \cdots & \vdots \\ P_{n1} & P_{n2} & P_{n3} & \cdots & E_n + P_{nn} - E \end{vmatrix}$$
$$\times \prod_{i>n} (E_i + P_{ii} - E) = 0 \quad (2.150)$$

or

$$\begin{vmatrix} E_0 + P_{11} - E & P_{12} & \cdots & P_{1n} \\ P_{21} & E_0 + P_{22} - E & \cdots & P_{2n} \\ \vdots & \vdots & \cdots & \vdots \\ P_{n1} & P_{n2} & \cdots & E_0 + P_{nn} - E \end{vmatrix} = 0 \quad (2.151)$$

Solution of this equation gives the first-order approximations to the set of n-degenerate unperturbed roots. The physical significance of this can be seen if we rewrite the matrix elements in Eq. (2.151), in terms of the quantities H'_{ij} of Eq. (2.134);

$$\begin{vmatrix} H'_{11} - E & H'_{12} & \cdots & H'_{1n} \\ H'_{21} & H'_{22} - E & \cdots & H'_{2n} \\ & & \cdots & \\ \vdots & \vdots & \cdots & \vdots \\ & & \cdots & \\ H'_{n1} & H'_{n2} & \cdots & H'_{nn} - E \end{vmatrix} = 0 \quad (2.152)$$

It will be seen [compare Eq. (2.91)] that this is the secular equation for a variation treatment of Eq. (2.130), using as trial eigenfunction a linear combination of the n-degenerate functions $\psi_1, \psi_2, \ldots, \psi_n$. The corresponding coefficients of these functions are then given by the set of simultaneous equations [compare Eq. (2.90)],

$$\sum_{j=1}^{n} a_j(H'_{ij} - E\delta_{ij}) = 0 \quad i = 1, 2, \ldots, n \quad (2.153)$$

where E is one root of Eq. (2.152).

In this case all the coefficients a_i are comparable in magnitude; this is a different situation from that where all the eigenvalues E_i of $\mathbf{H}$ differ [see Eq. (2.149)]. The reason is that whereas the n roots $E_1, E_2, \ldots, E_n$ of Eq. (2.127) are degenerate, the corresponding roots of Eq. (2.130) are not. *Any* linear combination of the ψ_i ($i = 1, 2, \ldots, n$) will satisfy Eq. (2.127); however only certain definite combinations will correspond to the unambiguous solutions of Eq. (2.130). In other words, since the perturbation removes the degeneracy, we must pick the correct combination of the n-degenerate eigenfunctions if we want a set of n functions that approximate closely to the eigenfunctions ψ'_i of $\mathbf{H}'$.

This argument can be extended to the case where $\mathbf{H}$ has two or more sets of degenerate eigenfunctions; each set will lead to a separate secular equation (2.152), and to a separate set of equations (2.153) for the coefficients a_i. We can of course go on to find higher-order corrections to the energies and wave functions; these higher-order perturbations are very rarely needed.

2.9 THE ORIGINAL PAULI PRINCIPLE

If the Hartree method is applied to atoms with three or more electrons, the results bear no relation to experiment. Although the variation theorem tells us that no approximate wave function can lead to lower energies than the true ground state, the ground-state energies calculated by the Hartree method are far lower than those observed experimentally.

The reason for this is that the Hartree method ignores the *Pauli principle*, which, in its most naïve form, states that not more than two electrons can occupy a given orbital; in the simple Hartree method all the electrons in any atom are predicted to occupy a single, nodeless, spherical orbital analogous to the $1s$ orbital of hydrogen.

While the Hartree method can be patched up by insisting that not more than two electrons occupy a given orbital, this is clearly a makeshift; for the orbital picture of an atom is a gross approximation, and the Pauli principle, as originally stated, could be applied only to systems where the electrons move independently of one another and so can be regarded as occupying orbitals. Our problem is to restate the Pauli principle in some more fundamental form; to do this we must first consider some additional principles guiding the behavior of atomic systems.

2.10 ELECTRON SPIN

Electrons are now known to behave as if they were spinning about some axis; as a result of this they possess angular momentum ($\pm\hbar/2$) and behave like tiny magnets. The quantum restrictions on angular momentum require each electron to align itself in a magnetic field, so that its component of angular momentum along the field is either $+\hbar/2$ or $-\hbar/2$. We can represent measurements of these angular momenta in the usual way; S^2 is an operator representing the square of the total spin angular momentum of an electron, or set of electrons, while S_z represents the component of angular momentum along the applied magnetic field (taken to be the z axis). Each electron can then exist in two distinct *spin states*, represented by *spin eigenfunctions* α, β; thus:

$$S_z\alpha = \tfrac{1}{2}\hbar\alpha \tag{2.154}$$

$$S_z\beta = -\tfrac{1}{2}\hbar\beta \tag{2.155}$$

When we wish to denote the spin function of an electron without specifying whether it is α or β, we shall use the symbol σ. We can regard α and β as being functions of some unspecified spin coordinate; however we do not need to know what this is, or what the mathematical forms of α and β may be.

Since electrons behave like magnets, they can interact with the magnetic fields inside atoms and molecules, set up by the spins of other particles (electrons or nuclei) or by the orbital motions of electrons. In light atoms ($Z < 10$) these interactions are, however, small, so that the energy of such a system depends little on the spin functions of the individual electrons. If we are prepared to neglect these small interactions, we can then write a hamiltonian operator that depends only on the spatial coordinates of the individual electrons. This is the procedure which we shall adopt here; it is a sufficiently good approximation for chemical purposes, although it must of course be abandoned in fields when we are directly interested in the spins of individual particles (e.g. magnetic-resonance spectroscopy).

Our orbital picture of atoms and molecules must now be modified to allow for electron spin. Each orbital must be replaced by a *spin-orbital*, this being a function of three space coordinates and the (unspecified) spin coordinate. Since, however, the one-electron hamiltonian operators contain only space coordinates, they must commute with the spin operators S^2 and S_z; it follows that each spin-orbital Ψ_i must be a product of a function ψ_i of the space coordinates and of a spin function σ_i (which of course can only have one of the two possible values, α or β);

$$\Psi_i = \psi_i \sigma_i \tag{2.156}$$

The spatial function ψ_i is an eigenfunction of the corresponding one-electron hamiltonian $\mathbf{H}_i$;

$$\mathbf{H}_i \psi_i = E_i \psi_i \tag{2.157}$$

In the orbital approximation, we must construct our atomic or molecular wave function from some combination of component spin-orbitals.

2.11 MOLECULAR SYMMETRY

Consider a molecule which has a plane, or center, or n-fold axis, of symmetry; a simple example is ammonia, NH_3, which has a threefold axis of symmetry running through the nitrogen atom. If we carry out an appropriate *symmetry operation* on such a molecule, e.g. rotate NH_3 through $120°$ about its threefold axis, the final state of the molecule is indistinguishable from the first. It follows at once that the hamiltonian operator $\mathbf{H}$ must be unchanged by, or *invariant* to, such a symmetry operation; for the hamiltonian operator for the electrons in a molecule depends only on the nuclear field in which the electrons move and the symmetry operation leaves this unchanged.

Let us denote such a symmetry operation for a given molecule by σ, and let us consider the effect of σ on the Schrödinger equation $\mathbf{H}\psi = E\psi$; we have

$$(\sigma\mathbf{H})(\sigma\psi) = E(\sigma\psi) \tag{2.158}$$

Since $\mathbf{H}$ is invariant to σ, this becomes:

$$\mathbf{H}(\sigma\psi) = E(\sigma\psi) \tag{2.159}$$

Thus $\sigma\psi$ is an eigenfunction of $\mathbf{H}$, belonging to the same eigenvalue E as ψ. If this is a nondegenerate eigenfunction, then $\sigma\psi$ must be a simple multiple of σ;

$$\sigma\psi = s\psi \tag{2.160}$$

when s is an algebraic number. Now if we repeat σ a sufficient number of times, we shall return our molecule to its original state; if for example we rotate NH_3 three times through $120°$ about its threefold axis, the molecule ends up in exactly the same position that it started. This means that:

$$\sigma^n\psi = s^n\psi = \psi$$

so

$$s^n = 1 \tag{2.161}$$

Hence operating on ψ with σ has the effect of multiplying ψ by an nth root of unity. In the particular case of a twofold symmetry, e.g. a plane or center or twofold axis, $n = 2$, so that:

$$\sigma\psi = \pm\psi \tag{2.162}$$

In this case we can divide the eigenfunctions of $\mathbf{H}$ into two classes, depending on whether they are symmetric, or antisymmetric, with respect to the symmetry operation σ; symmetric functions remain unchanged, while antisymmetric functions change sign, when subjected to the symmetry operation.

2.12   THE TRUE PAULI PRINCIPLE; SLATER DETERMINANTS

One particular symmetry operation common to all electronic systems is an interchange of two electrons in it. Obviously such an interchange can have no effect on the physical properties of the system, since electrons are indistinguishable; such an "interchange" must indeed be regarded as a purely artificial process, involving an interchange of the suffixes we use to distinguish the electrons in our mathematical treatment. If we repeat the interchange, then of course we restore the system to its original state; the interchange symmetry is therefore a twofold symmetry, and the wave function for an electronic system must therefore be symmetric, or antisymmetric, for interchange of any pair of electrons in it.

The Pauli exclusion principle, in its correct form, states that any electronic wave function is antisymmetric for the interchange of any pair of electrons. This is a new principle, and not merely a deduction from the basic laws of quantum mechanics; we could equally well visualize a world in which electronic wave functions were symmetric for interchange, or in which symmetric and antisymmetric wave functions occurred impartially. The Pauli principle is a statement of an experimental fact, that no electronic systems are known which are symmetric for interchange of electrons.

Let us now reconsider our formulation of many-electron wave functions. As we have seen, we can formulate such a wave function only in terms of the orbital approximation; however the simple product function of Eq. (2.52) fails to meet our new specification since it does not have the right symmetry properties. Consider for example a simple two-electron function ψ, given by

$$\psi = \phi_a(1)\phi_b(2) \tag{2.163}$$

where ϕ_a is a function (spin-orbital) of the coordinates of electron 1, and ϕ_b of electron 2. Suppose we interchange the two electrons. Electron 1 now occupies orbital ϕ_b, and electron 2 ϕ_a; the new wave function ψ' is then given by:

$$\psi' = \phi_a(2)\phi_b(1) \tag{2.164}$$

Clearly:

$$\psi' \neq \pm\psi \tag{2.165}$$

Thus neither of the two functions ψ, ψ' can satisfactorily represent the system in question.

A further difficulty arises. The functions ψ, ψ' are different, yet they must correspond to states of the system having identical energies; for the hamiltonian operator is invariant to any symmetry operation and interchange meets this condition. We have then two different wave functions corresponding to the same eigenvalue of $\mathbf{H}$; this would imply that the state in question is degenerate, which it clearly is not if the Schrödinger equation has but one solution corresponding to that particular eigenenergy.

However, this second difficulty in fact provides us with an escape from our dilemma; for we can replace degenerate wave functions by arbitrary linear combinations without affecting their eigenvalue properties [compare Eq. (1.22)]. We can then combine ψ and ψ' into two equivalent combinations ξ_s, ξ_a which are respectively symmetric and antisymmetric for exchange of the two electrons:

$$\xi_s = \psi + \psi' = \phi_a(1)\phi_b(2) + \phi_a(2)\phi_b(1) \tag{2.166}$$

$$\xi_a = \psi - \psi' = \phi_a(1)\phi_b(2) - \phi_a(2)\phi_b(1) \tag{2.167}$$

The Pauli principle excludes the symmetric combination ξ_s; we are therefore left with a single nondegenerate wave function ξ_a to describe our system.

This idea can at once be extended to many-electron systems. Consider such a system in an orbital representation, where N electrons occupy the N spin-orbitals $\psi_i\sigma_i$ ($i = 1,2, \ldots, N$). We can construct $N!$ product functions of the form

$$[\psi_1\sigma_1(a)][\psi_2\sigma_2(b)]\cdots[\psi_n\sigma_n(t)] \tag{2.168}$$

in which the N electrons are permuted in every possible way among the N spin-orbitals. Our problem is to construct a linear combination of these $N!$ functions that will be antisymmetric for interchange of *any* pair of the N electrons.   The solution of this problem was given by Slater, who showed that the following determinant, Ψ, known as the *Slater determinant* for the N spin-orbitals $\psi_i\sigma_i$, has the correct properties;

$$\Psi = \begin{vmatrix} \psi_1\sigma_1(1) & \psi_1\sigma_1(2) & \psi_1\sigma_1(3) & \cdots & \psi_1\sigma_1(N) \\ \psi_2\sigma_2(1) & \psi_2\sigma_2(2) & \psi_2\sigma_2(3) & \cdots & \psi_2\sigma_2(N) \\ & & & \cdots & \\ \vdots & \vdots & \vdots & \cdots & \vdots \\ & & & \cdots & \\ \psi_N\sigma_N(1) & \psi_N\sigma_N(2) & \psi_N\sigma_N(3) & \cdots & \psi_N\sigma_N(N) \end{vmatrix} \qquad (2.169)$$

Each term in the expansion of Ψ is a product of spin-orbitals of the required form [Eq. (2.168)], while interchange of two electrons is equivalent to interchange of two columns of the determinant—and interchanging two columns of a determinant has the effect of changing its sign, though not its magnitude.   Consequently the wave function Ψ satisfies the Pauli principle, being antisymmetric for exchange of any pair of electrons.

It is easily shown that the Slater determinant is the *only* function of this kind that has the required properties; the solution is therefore unique.   Equation (2.167) is a special case of this; the function ξ_a is simply the expansion of the corresponding Slater determinant with two rows and columns.   We can also see the reason for the simple form of the Pauli principle quoted above; for if two of the spin-orbitals $\psi_i\sigma_i$ were identical, two rows of the determinant Ψ would be identical, and a determinant with two identical rows vanishes.   We cannot therefore write a wave function in the orbital approximation that will obey the Pauli principle if two of the orbitals (or more correctly, spin-orbitals) are the same. However the Pauli principle in its proper form can of course also be applied to the more general case of a many-electron system which cannot be dissected into contributions by individual spin-orbitals.

2.13   THE HARTREE-FOCK METHOD

We are now ready to replace the Hartree method by a more rigorous treatment in which the resulting many-electron wave function obeys the Pauli principle; this treatment was first introduced by Fock, and it is therefore called the *Hartree-Fock method*.   In it we write a many-electron wave function as a Slater determinant of a set of spin-orbitals $\psi_i\sigma_i$; we then adjust the spatial parts of these to make the energy of the system a minimum.   For convenience we shall henceforth refer to these spatial parts ψ_i of spin-orbitals $\psi_i\sigma_i$ as *orbitals*; for reasons that will appear presently, we shall also assume that the orbitals we use form an orthonormal set.

The total energy E of the system is then given by

$$E = \frac{\iint \Psi \mathbf{H} \Psi \, d\tau \, d\sigma}{\iint \Psi^2 \, d\tau \, d\sigma} \tag{2.170}$$

where Ψ is the same Slater determinant as in Eq. (2.169) and the integrations are over both space $d\tau$ and spin $d\sigma$ coordinates. Let us first consider the denominator of Eq. (2.170), this being the square of the normalizing factor for the determinantal wave function Ψ. We have:

$$\iint \Psi^2 \, d\tau \, d\sigma = \iint \cdots \int |\psi_i \sigma_i(j)| |\psi_k \sigma_k(l)| \, d\tau_1 \, d\tau_2 \cdots d\tau_N \, d\sigma_1 \, d\sigma_2 \cdots d\sigma_N \tag{2.171}$$

Consider one particular term from the expansion of the left-hand determinant in this expression; the resulting set of integrals can be written:

$$\iint \cdots \int [\psi_1 \sigma_1(a)][\psi_2 \sigma_2(b)] \cdots [\psi_N \sigma_N(t)] \Sigma(\pm 1)[\psi_1 \sigma_1(f)][\psi_2 \sigma_2(g)]$$
$$\cdots [\psi_N \sigma_N(u)] \, d\tau_1 \, d\tau_2 \cdots d\tau_N \, d\sigma_1 \, d\sigma_2 \cdots d\sigma_N \tag{2.172}$$

The sign depends on the sign of the term taken from the expansion of the second determinant in Eq. (2.171). Since the spin-orbitals are functions of the coordinates of one electron only, and since each spin-orbital is a product of an orbital, containing only space coordinates, and a spin function, containing only a spin coordinate, we can factorize the multiple integrals of Eq. (2.172) into products of one-electron integrals;

$$\Sigma(\pm 1) \int \psi_1(a)\psi_1(f) \, d\tau_1 \int \sigma_1(a)\sigma_1(f) \, d\sigma_1 \cdots \int \psi_N(t)\psi_N(u) \, d\tau_N \int \sigma_N(t)\sigma_N(u) \, d\sigma_N \tag{2.173}$$

But the spin functions α, β are orthogonal, and so too by assumption are the orbitals ψ_i; all the integrals in Eq. (2.172) therefore vanish, except when

$$\begin{array}{ll} \psi_1(a) = \psi_1(f) & \sigma_1(a) = \sigma_1(f) \\ \psi_2(b) = \psi_2(g) & \sigma_2(b) = \sigma_2(g) \end{array} \tag{2.174}$$

etc. Since the spin-orbitals in Ψ must all be different, the conditions can be met only if

$$a = f \quad b = g \quad \cdots \quad t = u \tag{2.175}$$

In other words the only integral which does not vanish is that corresponding to a situation where we select from the expansion of the second determinant in Eq. (2.171) a term *identical* with the one we chose from the expansion of the first determinant. Moreover in this case all the one-electron integrals of Eq. (2.172) are equal to unity; for we assume our spin-orbitals to be normalized. The sum of all the integrals in (2.172) is therefore equal to unity, and the same argument will apply no matter which term we choose from the expansion of the first determinant in Eq. (2.171); since there are $N!$ such terms, it follows that

$$\iint \Psi^2 \, d\tau \, d\sigma = N! \tag{2.176}$$

The normalized form of Ψ is then given by

$$\Psi(\text{normalized}) = (N!)^{-1/2}|\psi_i\sigma_i(j)| \qquad (2.177)$$

We are now ready to evaluate the numerator of (2.170). The hamiltonian operator $\mathbf{H}$ can be written as a sum of one-electron terms $\mathbf{H}_i$ and two-electron terms e^2/r_{ij} [see Eq. (2.44)]:

$$\mathbf{H} = \sum_i \mathbf{H}_i + \sum\sum_{i<j} \frac{e^2}{r_{ij}} \qquad (2.178)$$

Here $\mathbf{H}_i$ is a function only of the coordinates of electron i. We can then divide the integral in the numerator of Eq. (2.170) into two parts, corresponding to the one- and two-electron terms in $\mathbf{H}$. Let us first consider one of the one-electron integrals, corresponding to the one-electron operator $\mathbf{H}_i$. We have:

$$\iint \Psi \mathbf{H}_i \Psi \, d\tau \, d\sigma = \iint \cdots \int |\psi_i\sigma_i(j)|\mathbf{H}_i|\psi_k\sigma_k(l)| \, d\tau_1 \cdots d\tau_N \, d\sigma_1 \cdots d\sigma_N \quad (2.179)$$

As before, let us consider a single term from the expansion of the left-hand determinant;

$$\iint \cdots \int [\psi_1\sigma_1(a)][\psi_2\sigma_2(b)]\cdots[\psi_N\sigma_N(t)]\mathbf{H}_i\Sigma(\pm)[\psi_1\sigma_1(f)][\psi_2\sigma_2(g)]$$
$$\cdots[\psi_N\sigma_N(u)] \, d\tau_1 \cdots d\tau_N \, d\sigma_1 \cdots d\sigma_N \qquad (2.180)$$

Since $\mathbf{H}_i$ contains only the spatial coordinates of electron i, we can again dissect this multiple integral into a product of one-electron integrals:

$$\Sigma(\pm)\int\psi_1(a)\psi_1(f) \, d\tau_1 \int\sigma_1(a)\sigma_1(f) \, d\sigma_1 \cdots \int\psi_m(i)\mathbf{H}_i\psi_n(i) \, d\tau_1 \int\sigma_m(i)\sigma_n(i) \, d\sigma_1$$
$$\cdots\int\psi_N(t)\psi_N(u) \, d\tau_N \int\sigma_N(t)\sigma_N(u) \, d\sigma_N \qquad (2.181)$$

As before, the integrals over all the electrons other than i vanish unless the spin-orbitals match exactly; the one remaining pair of spin-orbitals, housing electron i, must then also match, by elimination. Since all the orbitals and spin functions are normalized, the sum of integrals in Eq. (2.181) reduces to a single term,

$$\int\psi_m(i)\mathbf{H}_i\psi_m(i) \, d\tau_i = E_m \qquad (2.182)$$

where E_m represents the sum of the kinetic energy and the potential energy due to attraction by the nuclei of an electron occupying the orbital ψ_m.

If we now replace the single operator $\mathbf{H}_i$ in Eqs. (2.180) and (2.181) by other operators $\mathbf{H}_j$, we shall then obtain a series of terms of the form of Eq. (2.182), one for each electron in the system. It follows at once that the sum of these integrals is equal to $\sum_m E_m$. Moreover the same result will follow, no matter which term we choose in passing from Eq. (2.179) to Eq. (2.180); since these are $N!$ such terms in the expansion of Ψ, it follows that:

$$\iint\Psi\left(\sum_i\mathbf{H}_i\right)\Psi \, d\tau \, d\sigma = N!\sum_m E_m \qquad (2.183)$$

Let us next consider a typical two-electron term from the integral in the numerator of Eq. (2.170), e.g. the integral V_{ij} representing the repulsion between electrons i, j;

$$V_{ij} = \int\int \Psi \frac{e^2}{r_{ij}} \Psi \, d\tau \, d\sigma = \int\int \cdots \int |\psi_i \sigma_i(j)| \frac{e^2}{r_{ij}} |\psi_k \sigma_k(l)| \, d\tau_1 \cdots d\tau_N \, d\sigma_1 \cdots d\sigma_N \quad (2.184)$$

As before, let us consider the integrals arising from one term in the expansion of the first determinant; e.g.

$$\int\int \cdots \int [\psi_1 \sigma_1(a)] \cdots [\psi_m \sigma_m(i)][\psi_n \sigma_n(j)] \cdots [\psi_N \sigma_N(t)] \frac{e^2}{r_{ij}} \Sigma(\pm)$$

$$[\psi_1 \sigma_1(f)] \cdots [\psi_g \sigma_g(i)][\psi_h \sigma_h(j)] \cdots [\psi_N \sigma_N(u)] \, d\tau_1 \cdots d\tau_N \, d\sigma_1 \cdots d\sigma_N \quad (2.185)$$

As before, the integrals vanish unless all the spin-orbitals match, except those occupied by electrons i, j. These must occupy the two remaining spin-orbitals, that is $\psi_m \sigma_m$ and $\psi_n \sigma_n$. In this case, however, *two* integrals may have nonvanishing values; for there are two terms in the expansion of the second determinant that meet this specification, the term in which electron i occupies the spin-orbital $\psi_m \sigma_m$, and j occupies $\psi_n \sigma_n$, and the term in which these electrons are interchanged. Thus the sum of integrals in Eq. (2.185) reduces to:

$$\int\int\int\int [\psi_m \sigma_m(i)][\psi_n \sigma_n(j)] \frac{e^2}{r_{ij}} [\psi_m \sigma_m(i)][\psi_n \sigma_n(j)] \, d\tau_i \, d\tau_j \, d\sigma_i \, d\sigma_j$$

$$- \int\int\int\int [\psi_m \sigma_m(i)][\psi_n \sigma_n(j)] \frac{e^2}{r_{ij}} [\psi_n \sigma_n(i)][\psi_m \sigma_m(j)] \, d\tau_i \, d\tau_j \, d\sigma_i \, d\sigma_j \quad (2.186)$$

The minus sign arises from the fact that the term from the expansion of the second determinant in Eq. (2.184) differs from the first in that one suffix is interchanged; the terms therefore have opposite signs, so their product is negative.

Since the spin functions are normalized, we can integrate them out of the first of these expressions; the remaining integral is then seen to be:

$$\int\int \psi_m(i)\psi_m(i) \frac{e^2}{r_{ij}} \psi_n(j)\psi_n(j) \, d\tau_i \, d\tau_j \equiv J_{mn} \quad (2.187)$$

This integral represents the mean coulomb repulsion between two electrons, one occupying the orbital ψ_m, the other occupying ψ_n [compare Eq. (2.61)].

The second integral in (2.186) vanishes unless $\sigma_m = \sigma_n$, because the spin functions α, β are orthogonal to one another. If $\sigma_m = \sigma_n$, then this integral reduces to:

$$\int\int \psi_m(i)\psi_n(i) \frac{e^2}{r_{ij}} \psi_m(j)\psi_n(j) \, d\tau_i \, d\tau_j \equiv K_{mn} \quad (2.188)$$

K_{mn} is called an *exchange integral,* because it arises from a product of terms in the expansion of the determinants of Eq. (2.184) that differ from one another only in that electrons i, j have exchanged orbitals.

We can now proceed as before, replacing the single two-electron operator e^2/r_{ij} in Eq. (2.186) by the complete sum of two-electron operators from Eq. (2.187). Each operator e^2/r_{ij} leads to a term J_{mn}, or a pair of terms $J_{mn} - K_{mn}$, depending on the relative spins of the electrons in the spin-orbitals occupied by the electrons i, j; the complete set of integrals therefore reduces to:

$$\sum_{m<n}\sum J_{mn} - \overset{\uparrow\;\uparrow}{\sum_{m<n}\sum} K_{mn} \tag{2.189}$$

The arrows imply summation over spin-orbitals m, n that have identical spin functions (that is $\sigma_m = \sigma_n$), and the summations are restricted ($m < n$) in order to avoid counting any interactions twice over.

As before, we obtain the same set of integrals (2.189) from each term in the expansion of the first determinant in Eq. (2.184), replacing e^2/r_{ij} by the sum of two-electron terms. The total contribution of these terms to E is then given by:

$$\iint \Psi \left(\sum_i \sum_j \frac{e^2}{r_{ij}}\right)\Psi\, d\tau\, d\sigma = N!\left(\sum_{m<n}\sum J_{mn} - \overset{\uparrow\;\uparrow}{\sum_{m<n}\sum} K_{mn}\right) \tag{2.190}$$

Collecting together Eqs. (2.170), (2.176), (2.178), (2.182), and (2.190),

$$E = \sum_m E_m + \sum_{m<n}\sum J_{mn} - \overset{\uparrow\;\uparrow}{\sum_{m<n}\sum} K_{mn} \tag{2.191}$$

The first sum in this expression represents the total kinetic energy of the electrons plus the total potential energy due to the attractions between them and the nuclei. The second sum represents the total mean repulsion between the electrons, assuming them to move independently of each other in individual orbitals ψ_m. The sum of these two expressions is identical with the total energy given by the Hartree method, where the effects of electron spin and the Pauli principle were neglected. The final sum in Eq. (2.191) then represents a correction to the total interelectronic repulsion due to inclusion of these additional factors.

Much has been made of the mysterious nature of the so-called *exchange energy* comprised in the terms K_{mn}; in fact they have a very simple physical significance and are not at all difficult to understand. The situation can be seen most clearly from a specific example; a two-electron system, whose wave function is a function $f(x_1,y_1,z_1,\sigma_1;x_2,y_2,z_2,\sigma_2)$ of the eight coordinates (six space coordinates and two spin coordinates) of the two electrons. This function has to be antisymmetric for interchange of the two electrons; thus:

$$f(x_1,y_1,z_1,\sigma_1;x_2,y_2,z_2,\sigma_2) = -f(x_2,y_2,z_2,\sigma_2;x_1,y_1,z_1,\sigma_1) \tag{2.192}$$

If $\sigma_1 \neq \sigma_2$, that is if the electrons have opposite spins, this places no restriction on the form of the spatial part of the wave function. However if $\sigma_1 = \sigma_2 = $ (say) α, then:

$$f(x_1,y_1,\alpha;x_2,y_2,z_2,\alpha) = -f(x_2,y_2,z_2,\alpha;x_1,y_1,z_1,\alpha) \tag{2.193}$$

It follows that if

$$x_1 = x_2 \qquad y_1 = y_2 \qquad z_1 = z_2 \qquad\qquad (2.194)$$

then:

$$f(x_1,y_1,z_1,\alpha;x_1,y_1,z_1,\alpha) = -f(x_1,y_1,z_1,\alpha;x_1,y_1,z_1,\alpha) = 0 \qquad (2.195)$$

Thus the two electrons can never occupy the same position in space if they have parallel spins.

Consider now the behavior of f for fixed values of (x_1,y_1,z_1), the position coordinates of the first electron, for example the variation in f with variation of the x coordinate (x_2) of the second electron. When $x_2 = x_1$, $f = 0$; therefore there is a node in the wave function for $x_2 = x_1$. Since the wave function f must be a continuous function of x_2, a plot of f vs. x_2 must have the form indicated in Fig. 2.3a. The corresponding probability function f^2 must then have a cusp at $x_2 = x_1$ (Fig. 2.3b). Thus not only is there no chance at all of finding both electrons simultaneously at the same point in space, but even the probability of finding them very near to each other is also reduced in comparison with an otherwise similar system where the electrons have opposite spins. This situation is indicated in Fig. 2.3b; the full line shows the probability function for electrons with parallel spins, the dotted line a corresponding function which differs only in that the electrons have opposite spins. The probability distribution of electron 2 has a hole (the *Fermi hole*) round the point where electron 1 is positioned; the probability of finding the electrons within a certain small distance of each other is less than it would be if the electrons had opposite spins.

The repulsion between two electrons occupying orbitals ψ_m, ψ_n and moving entirely independently of each other is given [compare Eq. (2.61)] by

$$J_{mn} = \iint [\psi_m(1)]^2 \frac{e^2}{r_{ij}} [\psi_n(2)]^2 \, d\tau_1 \, d\tau_2 \qquad (2.196)$$

This expression holds if the electrons have opposite spins. If, however, the elec-

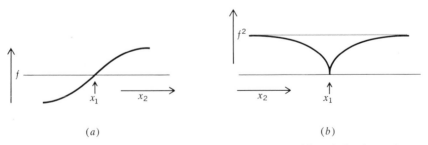

(a)   (b)

FIG. 2.3 Variation in (a) wave function and (b) its square with variation in x_2, for two electrons moving in one dimension with electron 1 at $x = x_1$.

trons have parallel spins, we must include a weighting factor to allow for the reduced probability of the electrons' ever being very close together. Now the probability of this happening will clearly be greater, the more the two orbitals ψ_m, ψ_n overlap in space; if the orbitals do not overlap, then of course the chance that the electrons occupying them are at the same place at the same time is zero. The repulsion between two electrons of parallel spin is therefore less than J_{mn}, and the difference should vary qualitatively as the overlap between the orbitals ψ_m, ψ_n; the difference between the two repulsion energies is the so-called exchange energy K_{mn}, and Eq. (2.188) shows that it does in fact have the anticipated dependence on the overlap between the two orbitals.

This argument can at once be extended to many-electron systems; here the repulsion between any pair of electrons occupying orbitals ψ_m, ψ_n and having antiparallel spins is given by the coulomb integral J_{mn}; if, however, the electrons have parallel spins, the repulsion between them is decreased by an amount equal to the exchange energy K_{mn}.

Evidently we are now including an allowance for *correlation* of the motions of electrons occupying different orbitals; how can we reconcile this with our statement (Sec. 2.5) that the orbital approximation neglects correlation? The answer to this is that there are two distinct kinds of correlation. First, there is the correlation between the motions of electrons of like spin, due to the Pauli principle (*exchange correlation*); secondly, there is the correlation due to mutual coulomb repulsion of pairs of electrons (*coulomb correlation*), an effect which operates for *all* pairs of electrons, regardless of their spins. This second type of correlation is indeed neglected in the orbital approximation; however exchange correlation is automatically taken into account in any treatment which uses wave functions that satisfy the Pauli principle.

It should also be emphasized that the decreased repulsion between electrons of parallel spin is in no way due to the operation of some mysterious "exchange force" between them. It arises from a physical law which prohibits the electrons from being close together. A similar effect would be observed if electrons had finite diameters (a cm); two electrons would then be unable to approach within a certain distance, simply because they would bounce apart. In this case the mean repulsion between electrons occupying the orbitals ψ_m, ψ_n would again be less than J_{mn}, the difference here being the overall contribution to the integral J_{mn} of configurations where the centers of the electrons are less than a cm apart. One could describe this difference in energy as "exclusion energy" and treat it in a manner as mystifying as "exchange energy" in normal quantum theory; the true situation would, however, be precisely analogous and equally easy to understand.

We are now ready to replace the Hartree one-electron equations by an analogous set of equations in which the exchange energy is taken into account. The statements embodied in Eqs. (2.54) and (2.55) still stand; the one-electron energy ε_m [compare Eq. (2.55)] is now given by

ε_m = (KE of electron occupying spin-orbital $\psi_m \sigma_m$) + (PE of electron occupying $\psi_n \sigma_m$ due to attraction of all the nuclei) + (mean PE of electron in $\psi_m \sigma_m$ due to repulsion of all other electrons) (2.197)

Using Eqs. (2.182) and (2.191), and the arguments associated with them,

$$\varepsilon_m = E_m + \sum_{n \neq m} J_{mn} - \overset{\uparrow\uparrow}{\sum_{n \neq m}} K_{mn} \tag{2.198}$$

Now we can see at once from Eqs. (2.188) and (2.196) that

$$J_{mm} = K_{mm} \tag{2.199}$$

We can therefore add $J_{mm} - K_{mm}$ to the right-hand side of Eq. (2.198), and so reduce it to a more symmetrical form:

$$\varepsilon_m = \varepsilon_m + \sum_{n} J_{mn} - \overset{\uparrow\uparrow}{\sum_{n}} K_{mn} \tag{2.200}$$

In this form, ε_m is seen to represent the total energy of an electron occupying the orbital ψ_m, due to its motion (kinetic energy), to the attraction of all the nuclei, and to the repulsion of all the electrons in the system *including itself.* The quantity ε_m is called the *Hartree-Fock energy* of the orbital ψ_m. The one-electron hamiltonian in Eq. (2.54) will now be of the form:

$$\mathbf{H}_i = -\frac{\hbar^2}{2m} \nabla_i^2 - \sum_{m} \frac{Z_m e^2}{r_{im}} + V_i \tag{2.201}$$

where V_i is a common potential function for *all* the electrons in the system. Thus all the one-electron operators have *identical mathematical forms,* a most important simplification in comparison with the Hartree method, where the one-electron operators for different orbitals are different.

It is a simple matter to write the form of this one-electron operator and so find the set of one-electron Schrödinger equations that corresponds to the basic equations in the Hartree method; however these equations can be solved only for atoms, not for molecules, since, as in the original Hartree method, it is only in the case of atoms that the one-electron Schrödinger equations can be reduced to sets of simple differential equations. For our purpose the resulting *Hartree-Fock* method is therefore of little value and we are forced to adopt a more approximate approach described below (Sec. 2.16).

2.14 CLOSED-SHELL MOLECULES

The large majority of stable molecules have *closed-shell* structures, i.e. they have singlet ground states with equal numbers of electrons having α and β spin, and they can be approximated by an orbital description in which each orbital is either doubly occupied or empty. The occupied spin-orbitals therefore occur in pairs, $\psi_m\alpha$ and $\psi_m\beta$, the space parts of the two spin-orbitals being identical (ψ_m).

A convenient shorthand notation is commonly used for Slater determinants; in this we list the orbitals occupied by the electrons, distinguishing spin-orbitals of α and β spin by writing a bar over the orbitals associated with β spin. Thus the spin-orbitals $\psi\alpha$, $\psi\beta$ are written as ψ, $\bar{\psi}$. The Slater determinant Ψ for a closed-shell configuration can be written in this notation as:

$$\Psi = |\psi_1\bar{\psi}_1\psi_2\bar{\psi}_2\cdots\psi_n\bar{\psi}_n| \tag{2.202}$$

Let us now consider the expression for the total energy of a closed-shell molecule. Equation (2.192) shows that this includes a J integral between each pair of occupied spin-orbitals and a K integral between each pair associated with parallel spins. Consider the integral J_{mn}. This arises from interactions between spin-orbitals $\psi_m\alpha$ or $\psi_m\beta$ with spin-orbitals $\psi_n\alpha$ or $\psi_n\beta$. In the case of a closed-shell molecule, all four spin-orbitals are occupied; the term J_{mn} therefore appears four times, corresponding to the interactions $\psi_m\alpha - \psi_n\alpha$, $\psi_m\alpha - \psi_n\beta$, $\psi_m\beta - \psi_n\alpha$, $\psi_m\beta - \psi_n\beta$. The term K_{mn} will likewise appear twice: $\psi_m\alpha - \psi_n\alpha$, $\psi_m\beta - \psi_n\beta$. In this case the integral J_{mm} will also appear once, being the repulsion between the two electrons occupying the orbital ψ_m. Equation (2.192) thus becomes:

$$E = 2\sum_m E_m + \sum_m J_{mm} + 4\sum_{m<n}\sum J_{mn} - 2\sum_{m<n}\sum K_{mn}$$
$$= 2\sum_m E_m + \sum_m J_{mm} + \sum_{m\neq n}\sum (2J_{mn} - K_{mn}) \tag{2.203}$$

[The second line is equivalent to the first; J_{mn} still appears four times, twice as J_{mn} and twice as J_{nm}, and K_{mn} likewise appears twice, once as K_{mn} and once as K_{nm}. Obviously $J_{mn} = J_{nm}$, and $K_{mn} = K_{nm}$, from the definitions of these integrals; see Eqs. (2.187) and (2.188).] Equation (2.203) can be written in a more symmetrical form by adding to it $\sum_m (J_{mm} - K_{mm})$ [compare Eqs. (2.198) to (2.200)];

$$E = 2\sum_m E_m + \sum_m\sum_n (2J_{mn} - K_{mn}) \tag{2.204}$$

The expressions for the Hartree-Fock energies ε_m [Eq. (2.200)] likewise become:

$$\varepsilon_m = E_m + \sum_n (2J_{mn} - K_{mn}) \tag{2.205}$$

2.15 SLATER-ZENER ORBITALS

The Hartree-Fock method provides the best possible approximation to the solution of Schrödinger equations in terms of orbitals; in practice, however, it has been little used, mainly for two reasons. First, the one-electron equations can be solved only for atoms, and then only with the assumption that the overall distribution of electrons is spherically symmetrical; secondly, even when such a solution is possible, it can be achieved only by numerical integration, so that the resulting orbitals appear in tabular form rather than as analytical functions of the coordinates. Suppose we wish to estimate some property of an atom other than its energy; the expectation value of this is given [compare Eq. (1.15)] by $\int \psi \alpha \psi \, d\tau$, where α is the corresponding dynamic operator and ψ the wave function of the atom. Integrals of this kind cannot be evaluated if we know ψ only as a table of its values for various values of the coordinates; we cannot therefore make any practical use of the Hartree-Fock solutions even in cases where it is feasible to determine them. We must therefore resign ourselves to accepting some less exact solution of the orbital problem in return for having the orbitals expressed as analytical functions that can be used conveniently in subsequent calculations. The following argument leads to a simple solution of this problem that has been extensively employed.

Consider one of the electrons i in an atom, which at some instant is at a distance r_i from the nucleus. In the orbital approximation, we suppose electron i to be moving in a field due to the attraction of the nucleus and to repulsion by a cloud of negative charge representing the time-average distribution of the electrons; in the case of an atom, we may assume this cloud of negative charge to have spherical symmetry. Now we know from classical electrostatics that the field produced by a spherical cloud of total charge qe at some point outside it is the same as that produced by an equal charge qe concentrated at the center of the sphere; we also know that the potential inside a uniform spherical charged shell is zero. The potential energy v of our electron is therefore given by

$$v = -\frac{Ze^2}{r_{ij}} + \frac{qe^2}{r_{ij}} = -\frac{Z'e^2}{r_{ij}} \tag{2.206}$$

where $$Z' = Z - q \tag{2.207}$$

The effect of the other electrons on electron i is therefore to *screen* part of the charge of the nucleus, so that the motion of electron i will be the same at that instant as if it were the sole electron moving in the field of a nucleus of charge Z'.

Of course Z' will vary with the distance r_{ij} of electron i from the nucleus; for q is the average number of electrons that lie inside a sphere of radius r_{ij}. Hartree-Fock orbitals are thus solutions of a hydrogenlike problem in which the nuclear charge Z' varies with the distance of the electron from the nucleus. However this argument suggests that we may get a fair approximation to the true Hartree-Fock orbital by assuming that Z' has some fixed mean value $\overline{Z}'$; the resulting one-electron function ψ_i will then be a hydrogenlike function for a nuclear charge $\overline{Z}'e$; from Eq. (2.28), this is seen to be given in unnormalized form by:

$$\psi_i = r^l e^{-r/n\overline{Z}'a_0} L_{n+1}^{2l+1}\left(\frac{2r}{n\overline{Z}'a_0}\right) Y(l,m) \tag{2.208}$$

where L is an associate Laguerre polynomial.   The wave function for the atom can then be written as a Slater determinant of such hydrogenlike orbitals; in the case of the ground state, the orbitals are chosen in such a way as to make the total energy a minimum.

Each orbital is distinguished, as in hydrogen, by three quantum numbers, n, l, and m, and, as in hydrogen, the orbital energies are in general greater, the greater n.   However there is one important difference.   Consider the screening constant $\bar{q}$ corresponding to a given orbital ψ_i.   The value of $\bar{q}$ is equal to the average number of electrons that, at any instant, are nearer to the nucleus than is an electron occupying the orbital ψ_i.   The value of $\bar{q}$ is therefore greater, the greater the mean radius $\bar{r}_i$ of the orbital ψ_i; since $\bar{r}_i$ will vary from one orbital to another, $\bar{q}$, and so also the *effective nuclear charge* $\bar{Z}'$, will vary likewise.   As we shall see later (Chap. 4), $\bar{r}_i$ varies not only with changes in n but also with changes in l; consequently the energies of our orbitals depend on the values of both the principal and the azimuthal quantum numbers, unlike the energies of true hydrogenlike orbitals that depend only on the principal quantum number m.

The value of $\bar{Z}'$ for the individual orbitals can of course be found by the variation method; detailed calculations of this kind were first carried out by Zener,[4] and Slater subsequently showed that his results could be matched by values calculated using a few simple rules[5] (see Chap. 4).   Slater and Zener also introduced a still simpler form of orbital in which the associated Laguerre polynomial L in Eq. (2.208) is replaced by its leading term; these *Slater-Zener orbitals* (SZO) are given, apart from a normalizing factor, by the following expression:

$$\text{SZO} = \psi = r^l e^{-r/nZ'a_0} Y(l,m) \tag{2.209}$$

SZOs are easier to handle than the full hydrogenlike AOs of Eq. (2.208), and they are accurate enough for many purposes; problems arise, however, in cases where we are concerned with electrons in different quantum levels, because SZOs with the same values of l and m, but different n, are not orthogonal to one another.   In the case of hydrogen, the orthogonality of such orbitals is of course assured by the fact that the associated Laguerre polynomials form an orthogonal set.

2.16   THE ROOTHAAN METHOD

Although the use of SZOs provides a convenient and simple description of atoms, this description is a poor approximation to the exact Hartree-Fock solution of the orbital problem; furthermore it is of no help at all in dealing with molecules.   Therefore our next problem is to find some more general, and more accurate, approximation to the Hartree-Fock solution in which the orbitals still appear in analytical form.

The obvious procedure here is to use the variation method, choosing suitable trial eigenfunctions to represent the individual orbitals and adjusting the parameters in them to make them approximate as closely as possible to the true Hartree-Fock orbitals. For reasons indicated above, the best choice of trial eigenfunction will be a linear variation function, each orbital ψ_μ being written as a linear combination of functions ϕ_i forming a suitable basis set;

$$\psi_\mu = \sum_i a_{\mu i}\phi_i \tag{2.210}$$

(Note that henceforth we shall use Greek subscript letters to denote orbitals, roman subscript letters to denote basis-set functions.) The coefficients $a_{\mu i}$ are the variation parameters which are to be adjusted to make ψ_μ as good an approximation as possible to one of the Hartree-Fock orbitals. The procedure for doing this was first developed by Roothaan,[6] and this treatment should therefore properly be described as the *Roothaan method*.

As we have seen, the one-electron operators in the Hartree-Fock treatment are all of identical form $\mathbf{H}'$. Each Hartree-Fock orbital χ_μ is therefore one of the eigenfunctions of a single one-electron Schrödinger equation,

$$\mathbf{H}'\chi_\mu = E_\mu \chi_\mu \tag{2.211}$$

The coefficients $a_{\mu i}$ in Eq. (2.210) are therefore to be chosen in such a way as to make ψ_μ approximate as closely as possible to a solution of this equation. According to the variation theorem, the coefficients must then be chosen in such a way as to minimize the expectation value $\bar{E}_\mu$ for the energy, $\bar{E}_\mu$ being given by:

$$\bar{E}_\mu = \frac{\int \psi_\mu \mathbf{H}' \psi_\mu \, d\tau}{\int \psi_\mu^2 \, d\tau} \tag{2.212}$$

From Eqs. (2.83) and (2.87), we see that the coefficients must then satisfy the following set of simultaneous equations,

$$\sum_j a_{\mu i}(F_{ij} - E_\mu S_{ij}) = 0 \qquad i = 1, 2, \ldots, M \tag{2.213}$$

where M is the total number of basis-set functions and E_μ is one solution of the secular equation:

$$|F_{ij} - ES_{ij}| = 0 \tag{2.214}$$

The elements F_{ij} of the F matrix $[F_{ij}]$ are given by:

$$F_{ij} = \int \phi_i \mathbf{H}' \phi_j \, d\tau \tag{2.215}$$

The secular equation (2.214) is an equation for the eigenvalues of the F matrix, while the sets of coefficients $a_{\mu i}$ found by solving Eq. (2.213) are its eigenvectors. Of course this problem will have to be solved by an iterative procedure, analogous to that used in the Hartree-Fock method; for we need to know the orbitals before we can construct the Hartree-Fock operator $\mathbf{H}'$. We shall then start with a set of assumed zero-order approximations $\psi_\nu{}^0$ to the molecular orbitals, written as linear combinations of the basis-set functions;

$$\psi_\nu{}^0 = \sum_i a_{\nu i}{}^0 \phi_i \tag{2.216}$$

Using these, we construct the corresponding Hartree-Fock operator $\mathbf{H}'$; we then solve our variation equations (2.213) and (2.214) to find a new set of orbitals $\psi_\mu{}^1$ and orbital coefficients $a_{\mu i}{}^1$, and we repeat the cycle until the orbital energies and orbital coefficients converge sufficiently closely to a limit—which we take as our approximation to the true solutions of the Hartree-Fock equations.

Two points should be noted. First, the number of solutions of the variation equations (2.213) and (2.214) is equal to the number M of basis functions ϕ_i; this is normally greater than the number N of orbitals occupied by electrons. In constructing $\mathbf{H}'$, we use only the N solutions with lowest energies, just as in the Hartree-Fock method. Secondly, since our operator $\mathbf{H}'$ is constructed from approximations to the true Hartree-Fock orbitals, it can be at best an approximation to the true Hartree-Fock operator. The equation we are trying to solve approximately by our variation method is therefore but an approximation to the true Hartree-Fock equation.

In order to carry out this program, we must of course be able to determine the matrix elements F_{ij}. We can do this by calculating the Hartree-Fock energy ε_μ for a given orbital ψ_μ, in terms of the matrix elements F_{ij}, and comparing this expression with the one given earlier [Eq. (2.205)]. In terms of the Hartree-Fock operator $\mathbf{H}'$ [see Eq. (2.201)],

$$\varepsilon_\mu = \int \psi_\mu \mathbf{H}' \psi_\mu \, d\tau = \sum_i \sum_j a_{\mu i} a_{\mu j} F_{ij} \tag{2.217}$$

In terms of our earlier treatment [Eq. (2.200)],

$$\varepsilon_\mu = E_\mu + \sum_v (2J_{\mu v} - K_{\mu v}) \tag{2.218}$$

where E_μ represents a sum of the kinetic energy of an electron in the MO ψ_μ and of its potential energy due to attraction by the nuclei, while the sum represents an average value of the repulsion between the electron in ψ_μ and all the electrons in the molecule. In calculating these repulsions, we assume the electrons to occupy a set of given orbitals $\psi_\nu{}^0$; in the first iteration, these are the initial set of orbitals that we assume at the start of our SCF procedure; in subsequent iterations, the ψ_ν are the solutions obtained in the preceding iteration.

As before, we can divide the operator $\mathbf{H}'$ into two parts, one $(\mathbf{H}^c)$ representing a sum of kinetic energy and attraction by the nuclei, the other $(\Sigma e^2/r_{ij})$ representing the mutual repulsions of pairs of electrons. The core contribution E_μ is then given by:

$$E_\mu = \int \psi_\mu \mathbf{H}^c \psi_\mu \, d\tau = \int \left(\sum_i a_{\mu i} \phi_i \right) \mathbf{H}^c \left(\sum_j a_{\mu j} \phi_j \right) d\tau$$

$$= \sum_i \sum_j a_{\mu i} a_{\mu j} H_{ij}{}^c \tag{2.219}$$

where
$$H_{ij}{}^c = \int \phi_i \mathbf{H}^c \phi_j \, d\tau \tag{2.220}$$

The coulomb integral $J_{\mu\nu}$ represents the average repulsion between our electron occupying the MO ψ_μ and an electron occupying the orbital $\psi_\nu{}^0$; this is given [see Eq. (2.187)] by:

$$J_{\mu\nu} = \iint \psi_\mu(1)\psi_\mu(1) \frac{e^2}{r_{12}} \psi_\nu{}^0(2)\psi_\nu{}^0(2) \, d\tau_1 \, d\tau_2 \tag{2.221}$$

Expanding the ψ's in terms of the basis-set functions ϕ,

$$J_{\mu\nu} = \iint \left[\sum_i a_{\mu i}\phi_i(1) \right]\left[\sum_j a_{\mu j}\phi_j(1) \right] \frac{e^2}{r_{12}} \left[\sum_k a_{\nu k}{}^0\phi_k(2) \right]\left[\sum_l a_{\nu l}{}^0\phi_l(2) \right] d\tau_1 \, d\tau_2$$

$$= \sum_i \sum_j \sum_k \sum_l a_{\mu i} a_{\mu j} a_{\nu k}{}^0 a_{\nu l}{}^0 (ij,kl) \tag{2.222}$$

where $a_{\nu k}{}^0$, $a_{\nu l}{}^0$ are coefficients of basis-set functions in the assumed orbital $\psi_\nu{}^0$, and where

$$(ij,kl) = \iint \phi_i(1)\phi_j(1) \frac{e^2}{r_{12}} \phi_k(2)\phi_l(2) \, d\tau_1 \, d\tau_2 \tag{2.223}$$

Likewise the exchange integral $K_{\mu\nu}$ is given by:

$$K_{\mu\nu} = \iint \psi_\mu(1)\psi_\nu{}^0(1) \frac{e^2}{r_{12}} \psi_\mu(2)\psi_\nu{}^0(2) \, d\tau_1 \, d\tau_2$$

$$= \iint \left[\sum_i a_{\mu i}\phi_i(1) \right]\left[\sum_k a_{\nu k}{}^0\phi_k(1) \right] \frac{e^2}{r_{12}} \left[\sum_j a_{\mu j}\phi_j(2) \right]\left[\sum_l a_{\nu l}{}^0\phi_l(2) \right] d\tau_1 \, d\tau_2$$

$$= \sum_i \sum_j \sum_k \sum_l a_{\mu i} a_{\mu j} a_{\nu k}{}^0 a_{\nu l}{}^0 (ik,jl) \tag{2.224}$$

Note that we have reserved the suffixes i, j for summations involving ψ_μ, and k, l for those involving $\psi_\nu{}^0$; as a result, the integrals over the basis-set functions have one index transposed in passing from Eq. (2.222) to (2.223) [(ij,kl) vs. (ik,jl)].

Using Eqs. (2.219), (2.223), and (2.224), Eq. (2.218) becomes:

$$\varepsilon_\mu = \sum_i \sum_j a_{\mu i} a_{\mu j} H_{ij}{}^c + \sum_\nu \sum_i \sum_j \sum_k \sum_l a_{\mu i} a_{\mu j} a_{\nu k}{}^0 a_{\nu l}{}^0 [2(ij,kl) - (ik,jl)] \tag{2.225}$$

Now since the coefficients $a_{\nu k}{}^0$ have fixed values, being coefficients of basis-set functions in our assumed orbitals $\psi_\nu{}^0$, we can conveniently introduce the abbreviation:

$$2\sum_{\nu} a_{\nu k}{}^0 a_{\nu l}{}^0 = P_{kl} \tag{2.226}$$

Equation (2.225) then becomes:

$$\varepsilon_\mu = \sum_i \sum_j a_{\mu i} a_{\mu j} \left\{ H_{ij}{}^c + \sum_k \sum_l P_{kl}[(ij,kl) - \tfrac{1}{2}(ik,jl)] \right\} \tag{2.227}$$

This must be identical with the earlier expression for ε_μ [Eq. (2.217)] for all values of the coefficients $a_{\mu i}$; hence:

$$F_{ij} = H_{ij}{}^c + \sum_k \sum_l P_{kl}[(ij,kl) - \tfrac{1}{2}(ik,jl)] \tag{2.228}$$

Equations (2.213) and (2.214), with F_{ij} given by Eq. (2.228), are called the *Roothaan equations*.

An alternative procedure for deriving these equations, and one which Roothaan followed in his original paper,[6] is to apply the variation method directly to the expression for the total energy [Eq. (2.204)]. We can expand E in terms of integrals involving the functions ϕ_i, and then vary the parameters $a_{\mu i}$ to make E a minimum. The difficulty here is that the expression for E [Eq. (2.204)] was derived on the assumption that all the orbitals ψ_μ are mutually orthogonal; in varying the parameters, we must do so only in such a way that the orbitals remain orthogonal. The resulting treatment is rather complicated.

There is, however, a simple relation between the two treatments. Consider a small variation $\delta\psi_\mu$ in one of the orbitals ψ_μ such that the orbital still remains orthogonal to all the other orbitals. Let the corresponding changes in the integrals E_μ, $J_{\mu\nu}$, and $K_{\mu\nu}$ be δE_μ, $\delta J_{\mu\nu}$, and $\delta K_{\mu\nu}$. Then from Eq. (2.204),

$$\delta E = 2\delta E_\mu + \sum_\nu (4\delta J_{\mu\nu} - 2\delta K_{\mu\nu}) \tag{2.229}$$

Note that $J_{\mu\nu}$ appears four times in the expression for E; hence $\delta J_{\mu\nu}$ appears four times in the expression for δE. Likewise from Eq. (2.205):

$$\delta\varepsilon_\mu = \delta E_\mu + \sum_\nu (2\delta J_{\mu\nu} - \delta K_{\mu\nu}) \tag{2.230}$$

Hence:

$$\delta\varepsilon_\mu = \tfrac{1}{2}\delta E \tag{2.231}$$

The condition that the set of functions ψ_μ should approximate as closely as possible to the true Hartree-Fock orbitals is that δE should be zero for all variations in the ψ_μ, subject to the condition that the ψ_μ remain orthogonal. Equation (2.231) shows that the orbitals satisfying this condition are also those that minimize the individual orbital energies ε_μ, subject to the same orthogonality restrictions. The functions ψ_μ given by solving Eqs. (2.213) and (2.214) automatically satisfy these requirements; consequently these equations must be identical with the ones derived by Roothaan through minimizing the total energy E.

2.17   CHOICE OF BASIS-SET FUNCTIONS; THE LCAO APPROXIMATION

The following argument suggests that SZOs should provide the best basis-set functions for a Roothaan treatment of atoms.   In the first place, an orbital treatment of atoms using SZOs is surprisingly successful; clearly the differences between SZOs and Hartree-Fock SCF AOs are not very great.   Secondly, our derivation of the SZO treatment suggests that orbitals of this type are seriously in error only near the nucleus, where the "correct" value of Z' is much greater than the assumed average value $\overline{Z}'$, and far out from the nucleus, where the correct value of Z' is much less than the average value.   In the intermediate region, where most of the orbital is concentrated, the SZO should be a good approximation to a Hartree-Fock SCF AO.   The use of a constant average value $\overline{Z}'$ will therefore make the orbital density of the SZO too small near the nucleus, and will also tend to underestimate the orbital density at relatively large distances from the nucleus; however it should give a reasonable approximation in the intermediate region, where most of the orbital is in any case concentrated. This argument suggests that one might obtain an even better approximation to the "true" Hartree-Fock AO by using a linear combination of SZOs, one with a high value of $\overline{Z}'$ to approximate the region near the nucleus, one with a "normal" intermediate value of $\overline{Z}'$ to approximate the region of maximum orbital density, and one with a low value of $\overline{Z}'$ to approximate the region far out from the nucleus.   Clementi[7] has indeed found that one can obtain very good approximations to the "true" Hartree-Fock solutions for atoms by using a Roothaan treatment in which each AO is approximated by a linear combination of three SZOs, with different and optimized effective nuclear charges.

In the case of molecules, a similar intuitive argument can be used to select a good set of basis-set functions.   Consider an electron occupying the MO ψ_μ of a neutral molecule, at some instant when the electron is near nucleus i.   The potential field in this region is due mainly to the nucleus of atom i and other electrons in its vicinity; for since the molecule is neutral, the attraction between our electron and some other nucleus j will be more or less balanced by the repulsion between our electron and the electrons in the vicinity of that nucleus. The motion of our electron will therefore be much the same as it would be if all other atoms were removed; in an orbital representation, the MO ψ_μ must therefore approximate in the vicinity of nucleus i to one of the AOs ϕ_i of that atom. Extension of this argument suggests that ψ_μ must, in the vicinity of the nucleus of each atom j, approximate to an AO ϕ_j of that atom; since AOs are large only in the vicinity of their own nuclei, we should then be able to get a satisfactory approximation to ψ_μ by writing it as a linear combination of AOs of the individual atoms, i.e.

$$\psi_\mu = \sum_i a_{\mu i}\phi_i \tag{2.232}$$

Comparison of Eqs. (2.210) and (2.232) implies that the best basis set for a Roothaan treatment of molecules is a linear combination of AOs of the individual atoms. This approach to the treatment of molecules, i.e. the use of an orbital approximation in which the individual MOs are written as linear combinations of AOs, is termed the *LCAO MO approximation* (*l*inear *c*ombinations of *a*tomic *o*rbitals).

For reasons indicated above it is not practical to use "true" Hartree-Fock orbitals for this purpose; the next best choice is to use the analytical approximations to these orbitals given by the Roothaan method. Calculations of this kind have been carried out by Roothaan and his collaborators.‡ The evidence suggests that the wave functions obtained do approximate closely to those that would be given by a rigorous Hartree-Fock treatment, were this feasible.

Calculations of this kind are, however, limited at present to very simple systems, either diatomic molecules or linear triatomic molecules, derived from atoms in the first part of the periodic table. The difficulty here lies in the evaluation of the integrals (ij,kl). Not only are there an enormous number of these to be evaluated, the number increasing roughly as the fourth power of the number of functions in the basis set, but also their evaluation in cases where the functions ϕ_i, ϕ_j, ϕ_k, ϕ_l are orbitals of three or four different atoms presents technical difficulties. A further objection to this approach lies in the inherent limitations of the SCF method, due to its neglect of electron correlation. The Hartree-Fock method, even in its exact form, cannot give electronic binding energies with an accuracy better than 1 percent. From the standpoint of chemistry, an error of this magnitude is quite unacceptable. Even in the case of a relatively small molecule, such as benzene, it amounts to hundreds of *kilocalories* per mole—and energy differences of even a few hundred *calories* per mole can have significant chemical consequences.

This may seem an alarming conclusion; for we have already decided that the Roothaan method represents the best we can possibly hope to achieve at present. How then shall we proceed? The answer lies in abandoning attempts to carry out rigorous a priori calculations. Instead, we shall introduce parameters into our treatment; the resulting approach will of course no longer be a priori, but rather semiempirical, given that the parameters will have to be fixed by reference to experiment. This, however, is a hardship we can easily bear if the results are accurate and reliable enough to be of practical value. A further advantage lies in the possibility of simplifying the theoretical approach; a very approximate

‡ For reviews see Ref. 8.

parametric treatment can often be more successful than a much more rigorous one where everything has to be calculated from first principles.

In Chap. 4 we shall discuss various semiempirical versions of the Roothaan method that have been used to treat molecules.

2.18   ORBITAL ENERGIES AND IONIZATION POTENTIALS; KOOPMAN'S THEOREM

The emphasis so far has been entirely on the calculation of total energies, or total electronic energies, of molecules; orbitals and orbital energies were introduced only as a stepping stone to this end.   However the Hartree-Fock energies ε_μ of individual orbitals do have a real physical significance, as we shall now see.

Consider a closed-shell atom or molecule with total energy E, given as before in an orbital approximation by:

$$E = 2\sum_\mu E_\mu + \sum_\mu \sum_\nu (2J_{\mu\nu} - K_{\mu\nu}) \tag{2.233}$$

Suppose we remove one electron from the orbital ψ_ρ.   What will be the corresponding change $\delta E(\rho)$ in E?   Physically this process will correspond to an ionization of the atom or molecule; the energy change will therefore correspond to one of its ionization potentials.   We shall now show that to a first approximation,

$$\delta E(\rho) = -\varepsilon_\rho \tag{2.234}$$

The Hartree-Fock energies of orbitals therefore give approximations to atomic or molecular ionization potentials.   This result is often described as Koopman's theorem.[9]

We can prove this result very simply by using first-order perturbation theory. Removal of one electron from the molecule has the same effect on the total energy as would removal of mass and charge from that electron; the corresponding first-order perturbation can be found by assuming that the wave function remains unchanged, the energy of the perturbed system being calculated using the unperturbed function.

If an electron in the orbital ψ_ρ loses its mass and charge, the following terms in the expression for E [Eq. (2.233)] will vanish: E_ρ (since this represents a sum of the kinetic energy of the electron and its potential energy due to attraction by the nucleus or nuclei), $J_{\rho\mu}$ and $K_{\rho\mu}$ (which represent interactions between the electron and electrons in the orbital ψ_ν).   Hence from Eq. (2.233),

$$\delta E(\rho) = -\left[E_\rho + \sum_\nu (J_{\rho\nu} - K_{\rho\nu})\right] = -\varepsilon_\rho \tag{2.235}$$

from Eq. (2.205).   This proves our theorem.

PROBLEMS

2.1 Carry out the transformation indicated in passing from Eq. (2.15) to Eq. (2.19).

2.2 Obtain an approximate solution of the Schrödinger equation defined by Eq. (2.7), using as trial eigenfunction e^{ar^2}, a being the parameter.   Compare the calculated energy with the exact value.

2.3 The potential function for the simple harmonic oscillator (see Sec. 1.5) is $\frac{1}{2}kx^2$, x being the displacement from equilibrium and k the force constant. In the Schrödinger representation, the normalized eigenfunctions for the two lowest levels (with eigenvalues $\frac{1}{2}\hbar$ and $\frac{3}{2}\hbar$) are given by:

$$\psi_0 = \left(\frac{\beta}{\pi}\right)^{1/4} e^{-\beta x^2/2} \qquad \psi_1 = \left(\frac{\beta}{\pi}\right)^{1/4} 2^{1/2} x e^{-\beta x^2/2} \qquad \text{where } \beta = \frac{(mk)^{1/2}}{\hbar}$$

Use first-order perturbation theory to deduce approximately the first two energy levels of an analogous anharmonic oscillator where the potential energy is given by

$$V = \tfrac{1}{2}kx^2 + \lambda x^4$$

λ being small.   (*Note:* The necessary integrals can be found in standard lists, e.g. the "Handbook of Chemistry and Physics," published annually by the Chemical Rubber Co., Cleveland, Ohio.)

2.4 Deduce an expression for the third-order perturbation to a nondegenerate root, using the procedure of Sec. 2.8.

2.5 In LCAO form, the ground-state MO for H_2 is given by $(\phi_1 + \phi_2)(1 + S)^{-1/2}$, where ϕ_1 and ϕ_2 are $1s$ AOs of the two hydrogen atoms and S is the overlap integral,

$$S = \int \phi_1 \phi_2 \, d\tau$$

(*a*) Work out in full the Roothaan expression for the total energy of the electrons.   (*b*) Using values for the integrals given by C. A. Coulson in *Trans. Faraday Soc.* **33**, 1479 (1937) and *Proc. Cambridge Phil. Soc.* **34**, 204 (1938), calculate the total energy of the electrons; find the total energy of H_2 by adding to this the internuclear repulsion (bond length, 0.7461 Å).   (*c*) Hence deduce the bond energy in H_2.

REFERENCES

1 Eyring, H., J. Walter, and G. E. Kimball: "Quantum Chemistry," John Wiley & Sons, Inc., New York, 1944.

2 Margenau, H., and F. M. Murphy: "The Mathematics of Physics and Chemistry," D. Van Nostrand Company, Inc., Princeton, N.J., 1943.

3   Littlewood, D. E.: "A University Algebra," William Heinemann, Ltd., London, 1950.

4   Zener, C.: *Phys. Rev.* **36,** 51 (1930).

5   Slater, J. C.: *Phys. Rev.* **36,** 57 (1930).

6   Roothaan, C. C. J.: *Rev. Mod. Phys.* **23,** 69 (1951).

7   Clementi, E.: *J. Chem. Phys.* **38,** 996, 1001, 2248 (1963); **39,** 175 (1963); **41,** 295, 303 (1964).

8   Ransil, B. J.: *Rev. Mod. Phys.* **32,** 245 (1960); E. Clementi: *J. Chem. Phys.* **36,** 33 (1962); E. Clementi and A. D. McLean: *ibid.* 45, 563, 745.

9   Koopman, T.: *Physica* **1,** 104 (1933).

SEMIEMPIRICAL
LCAO MO
METHODS

3.1 INTRODUCTION; PHYSICAL INTERPRETATION
OF THE ROOTHAAN METHOD

While the Roothaan expression for the total energy of a molecule may look somewhat forbidding [see Eq. (2.227)], all the terms in it are in fact capable of simple
physical interpretations. Not only does this provide an easily visualized picture,
but it will also help us in devising and understanding simplified versions of the
Roothaan method that can be used conveniently in the analysis of large molecules.

In the orbital approximation, each electron is supposed to move independently
of the rest; the total energy is a sum of the average attraction between each electron and the nuclei and of the average repulsions between pairs of electrons.
Now we can look at these contributions in a different but equivalent way. Consider an electron occupying the orbital ψ. So far we have regarded an electron
as a particle moving in such a way that the probability of finding it at any instant
in a given volume element $d\tau$ is $\psi^2 \, d\tau$. If the potential energy of the electron is
given in terms of its position by some function $V(\tau)$ of the coordinates τ, then
the average potential energy, averaged over all possible positions of the electron,
is given by $\int \psi^2 V \, d\tau$. However we could alternatively regard the electron statistically, as a cloud of negative charge whose density at any position is given by
ψ^2; the potential energy of the small fragment of this cloud contained in the
volume element $d\tau$ will then be $\psi^2 V \, d\tau$. The total potential energy of the whole
electron is given by summing all these infinitesimal contributions; the resulting
sum is of course given by the same integral $\int \psi^2 V \, d\tau$ as in the previous treatment.
The two pictures are entirely equivalent; in the orbital approximation we can
conveniently regard electrons occupying orbitals as corresponding clouds of
negative charge, rather than as moving charged particles. Consider now an
electron occupying a MO ψ_μ, which we write as a linear combination of AOs ϕ_i;

$$\psi_\mu = \sum_i a_{\mu i} \phi_i \tag{3.1}$$

The density distribution $\psi_\mu{}^2$ is given by:

$$\psi_\mu{}^2 = \left(\sum_i a_{\mu i} \phi_i \right) \left(\sum_j a_{\mu j} \phi_j \right) = \sum_i \sum_j a_{\mu i} a_{\mu j} \phi_i \phi_j \tag{3.2}$$

We can thus regard the overall density distribution $\psi_\mu{}^2$ as a sum of a number of
component parts $\phi_i \phi_j$. These in turn can be divided into two groups, the parts
$\phi_i{}^2$, which are identical in form with the density distributions of individual AOs ϕ_i,

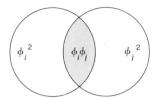

FIG. 3.1 Dissection of the MO density distribution function Ψ_μ^2 into contributions by AOs (ϕ_i^2) and overlap between AOs (ϕ_i, ϕ_j).

and contributions $\phi_i\phi_j$, from regions where pairs of AOs overlap (Fig. 3.1). The factors $a_{\mu i}a_{\mu j}$ are then measures of the extent to which these individual distributions contribute to the particular MO ψ_μ.‡

The overall density distribution D of the electrons in the molecule can be written as a sum of contributions ψ_μ^2 by individual electrons; in the case of a closed-shell molecule, where each MO is either doubly occupied or empty,

$$D = 2\sum_\mu^{\text{occ}} \psi_\mu^2 = 2\sum_\mu^{\text{occ}}\sum_i\sum_j a_{\mu i}a_{\mu j}\phi_i\phi_j = \sum_i\sum_j P_{ij}\phi_i\phi_j \qquad (3.3)$$

using the definition of P_{ij} in Eq. (2.226). The quantities P_{ij} in the Roothaan equations are thus seen to be measures of the extent to which the various distributions $\phi_i\phi_j$ contribute to the overall density distribution of the molecule.

The total electronic energy of the molecule is a sum of the kinetic energy of the electrons and their mean potential energy due to the attraction of the nuclei, represented by the core operator $\mathbf{H}^c$, and the mean potential energy due to their mutual repulsions. In our present picture, we wish to write these interactions in terms of contributions by the individual charge clouds $\phi_i\phi_j$. Now the core contribution E_μ by an electron occupying the MO ψ_μ is given [see Eq. (2.219)] by

$$E_\mu = \sum_i\sum_j a_{\mu i}a_{\mu j}H_{ij}^c \qquad (3.4)$$

with H_{ij}^c given by Eq. (2.220). If we sum this over all the electrons, the resulting expression for the total core energy E^c is seen to be:

$$E^c = 2\sum_\mu^{\text{occ}} E_\mu = \sum_i\sum_j P_{ij}H_{ij}^c \qquad (3.5)$$

‡ Note that the MO distribution function ψ_μ^2 is not a sum of the AO distribution functions ϕ_i^2; it contains also contributions from the "overlap clouds" $\phi_i\phi_j$. This is a quantum-mechanical effect, analogous to the interference of waves. If the AOs ϕ_i, ϕ_j overlap in phase, the orbital density is greater in the overlap region than just a sum of the two AO overlap densities ϕ_i^1, ϕ_j^2; if they overlap out of phase, the density in this region is less. The difference, given by the term in $\phi_i\phi_j$, will be positive in the first case, and negative in the second. The treatment is indeed mathematically analogous to the treatment of interference, and it is this analogy which gives rise to the apparent "wavelike" behavior of fundamental particles such as electrons.

Comparing this with Eq. (3.2), we see that $H_{ij}{}^c$ can be identified as the core energy of the electron cloud represented by the function $\phi_i\phi_j$, as one might have expected intuitively from the argument given at the beginning of this section.

Let us now consider the repulsion between the two clouds of charge $P_{ij}\phi_i\phi_j$ and $P_{kl}\phi_k\phi_l$. The amount of the first cloud in a small volume element $d\tau_1$ is given by:

$$eP_{ij}\phi_i(1)\phi_j(1)\ d\tau_1 \tag{3.6}$$

where the symbols (1) are introduced to show that this element refers to the first of our electron clouds. Likewise the amount of the second cloud in a volume element $d\tau_2$ is given by:

$$eP_{kl}\phi_k(2)\phi_l(2)\ d\tau_2 \tag{3.7}$$

If the volume elements are at a distance r_{12} apart, the potential energy dV due to their mutual repulsion is given by:

$$dV = [eP_{ij}\phi_i(1)\phi_j(1)\ d\tau_1][eP_{kl}\phi_k(2)\phi_l(2)\ d\tau_2]\frac{1}{r_{12}} \tag{3.8}$$

The total repulsion V between the two clouds is found by summing these contributions over the whole of each of the two charge clouds; this of course is equivalent to integrating the expression over the whole of space. Thus:

$$V = \int dV = \iint [eP_{ij}\phi_i(1)\phi_j(1)\ d\tau_1][eP_{kl}\phi_k(2)\phi_l(2)\ d\tau_2]\frac{1}{r_{12}}$$

$$= P_{ij}P_{kl}(ij,kl) \tag{3.9}$$

from Eq. (2.223).

The total repulsion between the various clouds of charge into which we have dissected the overall electron distribution [Eq. (3.2)] can then be found by summing the various contributions given by Eq. (3.9). However there is a complication. Since we are dealing with a closed-shell molecule, half the electrons will have α spin, half β spin, and the same will be true of the electron clouds representing the individual contributions $\phi_i\phi_j$. Now the repulsion between two electron clouds will be given by the "classical" expression of Eq. (3.9) *only* if they correspond to electrons of opposite spin; otherwise there will be an "exchange" correction. The arguments given in Sec. 2.13 show that in the case of the two electron clouds $\phi_i\phi_j$ and $\phi_k\phi_l$, corresponding to electrons with parallel spin, the total correction will be given not by (ij,kl) but by:

$$(ij,kl) - (ik,jl) \tag{3.10}$$

In our molecule, half the cloud $P_{ij}\phi_i\phi_j$ will correspond to electrons of α spin, and the same will be true for those of the cloud $P_{kl}\phi_k\phi_l$; the exchange correction to their mutual repulsion will then be given by:

$$(\tfrac{1}{2}P_{ij})\,(\tfrac{1}{2}P_{kl})\,(ik,jl)\tag{3.11}$$

There will likewise be a corresponding exchange correction to the repulsion between the remaining (β-spin) halves of the two clouds. The net repulsion between the two clouds V' is then given by:

$$
\begin{aligned}
V' &= P_{ij}P_{kl}(ij,kl) - 2(\tfrac{1}{2}P_{ij})\,(\tfrac{1}{2}P_{kl})\,(ik,jl)\\
&= P_{ij}P_{kl}[(ij,kl) - \tfrac{1}{2}(ik,jl)]
\end{aligned}\tag{3.12}
$$

Summing this expression over all pairs of electron clouds, the total electron repulsion energy E^{el} is given by:

$$E^{el} = \frac{1}{2}\sum_i\sum_j\sum_k\sum_l P_{ij}P_{kl}[(ij,kl) - \tfrac{1}{2}(ik,jl)]\tag{3.13}$$

(The overall factor $\tfrac{1}{2}$ is introduced to avoid counting the repulsion between the clouds $\phi_i\phi_j$ and $\phi_k\phi_l$ twice over.)   Combining Eqs. (3.5) and (3.13), the total electronic energy E is found to be:

$$E = \sum_i\sum_j P_{ij}\left\{H_{ij}^c + \tfrac{1}{2}\sum_k\sum_l P_{kl}[(ij,kl) - \tfrac{1}{2}(ik,jl)]\right\}\tag{3.14}$$

This is precisely the expression we get if we substitute the Roothaan values for E_μ, $J_{\mu\nu}$, and $K_{\mu\nu}$ from Eqs. (2.219), (2.222), and (2.224) into the orbital expression for the total energy, Eq. (2.204).

The Roothaan expression for the orbital energy ε_μ of an electron occupying the MO ψ_μ [Eq. (2.227)] can also be derived in the way indicated above, by calculating the total interaction between the components $a_{\mu i}a_{\mu j}\phi_i\phi_j$ into which the electron distribution ψ_μ^2 can be dissected; this derivation is left to the reader as an exercise.

3.2   THE MULLIKEN APPROXIMATIONS FOR INTEGRALS

The electron repulsion integrals (ij,kl) appearing in the Roothaan treatment can be divided into four categories, depending on the number of atoms contributing to the four AOs ϕ_i, ϕ_j, ϕ_k, ϕ_l. The *one-center* integral (ii,ii) and the *two-center* integrals (ii,jj), (ij,jj), and (ij,ij) are easily calculated in terms of SZOs, or the analytical approximations to SCF AOs given by the Roothaan method. The same is true of integrals involving three or four different orbitals, that is (ij,kk), (ij,ik), and (ij,kl), provided that these refer to AOs of at most two different atoms; however if three or four different atoms are involved (*three-* and *four-center* integrals), the integrations become exceedingly difficult, and methods for evaluating them have only recently been devised. Much use has therefore been made of the following approximate method for calculating such integrals, due originally to Mulliken.

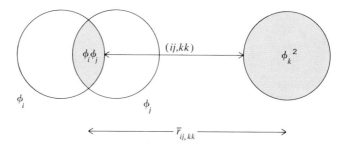

FIG. 3.2   The Mulliken approximation for the integral (ij,kk).

Consider the integral (ij,kk).   This represents (Fig. 3.2) the repulsion between the overlap cloud $\phi_i\phi_j$ between the AOs ϕ_i, ϕ_j and the cloud $\phi_k{}^2$ representing an electron occupying the AO ϕ_k.   This integral is given by the expression:

$$(ij,kk) = \iint \phi_i(1)\phi_j(1) \frac{e^2}{r_{12}} \phi_k{}^2(2)\, d\tau_1\, d\tau_2 \tag{3.15}$$

where r_{12} is the distance between the two volume elements $d\tau_1$, $d\tau_2$, representing respectively small fragments of the two electron clouds $\phi_i\phi_j$ and $\phi_k{}^2$.

The integrals will not be greatly changed if we replace r_{12} in Eq. (3.15) by its mean value, $\bar{r}_{ij,kk}$, the subscript implying that this is a mean distance between volume elements in the two charge clouds $\phi_i\phi_j$ and $\phi_k{}^2$.   In that case:

$$(ij,kk) \approx \iint \phi_i(1)\phi_j(1) \frac{e^2}{\bar{r}_{ij,kk}} \phi_k{}^2(2)\, d\tau_1\, d\tau_2$$

$$= \frac{e^2}{\bar{r}_{ij,kk}} \int \phi_i(1)\phi_j(1)\, d\tau_1 \int \phi_k{}^2(2)\, d\tau_2 = \frac{e^2}{\bar{r}_{ij,kk}} S_{ij} \tag{3.16}$$

S_{ij} being the overlap integral between the AOs ϕ_i and ϕ_j, and it being assumed, as usual, that the AOs are normalized (so that $\int \phi_k{}^2\, d\tau = 1$).

Next let us apply the same approximation to the two-center integrals (ii,kk) and (jj,kk), representing respectively the repulsion between charge clouds $\phi_i{}^2$, $\phi_k{}^2$ and $\phi_j{}^2$, $\phi_k{}^2$.   Using the same notation as above,

$$(ii,kk) = \iint \phi_i{}^2(1) \frac{e^2}{r_{12}} \phi_k{}^2(2)\, d\tau_1\, d\tau_2 \approx \iint \phi_i{}^2(1) \frac{e^2}{\bar{r}_{ii,kk}} \phi_k{}^2(2)\, d\tau_1\, d\tau_2$$

$$= \frac{e^2}{\bar{r}_{ii,kk}} \int \phi_i{}^2(1)\, d\tau_1 \int \phi_k{}^2(2)\, d\tau_2 = \frac{e^2}{\bar{r}_{ii,kk}} \tag{3.17}$$

Likewise:

$$(jj,kk) = \frac{e^2}{\bar{r}_{jj,kk}} \tag{3.18}$$

Since the cloud $\phi_i\phi_j$ lies halfway between the two clouds $\phi_i{}^2$ and $\phi_j{}^2$, it is reasonable to assume that the mean distance $\bar{r}_{ij,kk}$ is some kind of average of the mean distances $r_{ij,kk}$ and $r_{jj,kk}$; assuming that

$$\frac{1}{\overline{r}_{ij,kk}} = \frac{1}{2}\left(\frac{1}{\overline{r}_{ii,kk}} + \frac{1}{\overline{r}_{jj,kk}}\right)$$ (3.19)

and using Eqs. (3.15) to (3.18), we find:

$$(ij,kk) \simeq \tfrac{1}{2}S_{ij}[(ii,kk) + (jj,kk)]$$ (3.20)

This argument can be extended at once to the other type of three-center integral (ij,ik), and to the four-center integral (ij,kl); we find:

$$(ij,ik) \simeq \tfrac{1}{4}S_{ij}S_{ik}[(ii,ii) + (ii,kk) + (jj,ii) + (jj,kk)]$$ (3.21)

$$(ij,kl) \simeq \tfrac{1}{4}S_{ij}S_{kl}[(ii,kk) + (ii,ll) + (jj,kk) + (jj,ll)]$$ (3.22)

In this way the difficult three- and four-center integrals can be found approximately in terms of simple one- and two-center integrals of the type (ii,ii) or (ii,jj).

Mulliken has also introduced a somewhat similar approximation for calculating the core integrals $H_{ij}{}^c$, ϕ_i and ϕ_j being different AOs. This integral represents a sum of the kinetic energy of the charge cloud $\phi_i\phi_j$ and its potential energy due to attraction by the nuclei. From its form [Eq. (2.220)], one might expect it to be proportional to the mean of the integrals $H_{ii}{}^c$ and $H_{jj}{}^c$, which represent the corresponding energies of the charge clouds ϕ_i and ϕ_j. One might also expect $H_{ij}{}^c$ to run parallel to the total charge of the cloud $\phi_i\phi_j$, which is given by:

$$\int e\phi_i\phi_j\, d\tau = eS_{ij}$$ (3.23)

These arguments suggest the approximation:

$$H_{ij}{}^c \simeq CS_{ij}(H_{ii}{}^c + H_{jj}{}^c)$$ (3.24)

where C is a constant. In this case one would not expect C to be necessarily one-half because these integrals are more complicated than those involving electron repulsion; the core operator $\mathbf{H}^c$ is a differential operator, containing the kinetic-energy expression $(h^2/2\overline{m})\nabla^2$. In practice C is found to be much greater than one-half, usually being of the order of unity.

3.3 THE POPLE METHOD

Although the Mulliken approximation simplifies the problem of estimating individual three- and four-center integrals, it does not solve the other problem inherent in any attempts to use the Roothaan method for large molecules, i.e. the enormous number of such integrals that have to be evaluated and stored during a computation. Furthermore, even if these difficulties could be overcome, the results would not be of much use to us in our attempts to interpret chemistry since, as we have seen, the Roothaan method is inherently too inaccurate. Our next object therefore is to introduce some parameters into the treatment, in the hope that we may in this way improve its accuracy.

We must also find some way of simplifying the Roothaan method, because although we can avoid the difficult quadratures involved in it by treating the repulsion integrals as parameters, we are still faced with the problem of their number, which varies roughly as the fourth power of the number of orbitals used in the basis set. The number of orbitals that can be conveniently handled with the largest available computers is therefore quite limited. The way out of this impasse was first shown by Pople,[1] who introduced a simplified version of the Roothaan SCF LCAO MO treatment that is commonly known as the *Pople method* or *Pople approximation*.

In his original derivation, Pople solved the problem of the three- and four-center integrals in the Roothaan treatment by the cavalier procedure of simply ignoring them. In mathematical terms, the Pople method rests on the assumption that the AOs ϕ_i nowhere overlap in space, i.e. that if ϕ_i, ϕ_j are two different AOs, then:

$$\phi_i \phi_j \, d\tau = 0 \tag{3.25}$$

for all volume elements $d\tau$. With this assumption, the integral (ij,kl) clearly vanishes unless $i = j$ and $k = l$; the remaining two-center integrals (ii,kk) are much easier to evaluate than those involving three- and four-centers—although this is a matter of little concern; for these integrals are in any case to be treated as parameters, to be evaluated by some more or less empirical procedure. This approximation [i.e. Eq. (3.25)] is known as *neglecting differential overlap*. Obviously if Eq. (3.25) holds, then the overlap integrals between different AOs ϕ_i, ϕ_j will vanish;

$$S_{ij} = \int \phi_i \phi_j \, d\tau = 0 \qquad \text{if } i \neq j \tag{3.26}$$

since the integrand vanishes everywhere. Note that while Eq. (3.25) implies that Eq. (3.26) must hold, the converse is not true; the integral S_{ij} can vanish even if the integrand $\phi_i \phi_j$ remains finite, provided the overall contributions of regions where $\phi_i \phi_j$ is positive and where it is negative cancel. In certain cases LCAO MO calculations have been carried out using the approximation of Eq. (3.26) rather than (3.25); this is known as *neglecting overlap*, as opposed to neglecting differential overlap.

If Eq. (3.25) holds, then logically the core integral $H_{ij}{}^c$ should also vanish, in cases where $i \neq j$; however it is found in practice that the Pople method gives unsatisfactory results if this is assumed to be the case. These integrals, which are described as *resonance integrals* and written as $\beta_{ij}{}^c$, are therefore assumed to have finite values; they are usually treated as parameters, to be determined empirically. The reason for this apparent lack of logical self-consistency in the Pople method will be discussed presently (Sec. 3.4).

With these assumptions, the matrix elements F_{ij} [see Eq. (2.228)] assume the following form:

$$F_{ii} = H_{ii}{}^c + \sum_k P_{kk}[(ii,kk) - \tfrac{1}{2}(ik,ik)]$$

$$= H_{ii}{}^c + \sum_k P_{kk}(ii,kk) - \tfrac{1}{2}P_{ii}(ii,ii)$$

$$= H_{ii}{}^c + \tfrac{1}{2}P_{ii}(ii,ii) + \sum_{j \neq i} P_{jj}(ii,jj) \tag{3.27}$$

$$F_{ij} = H_{ij}{}^c - \tfrac{1}{2}P_{ij}(ii,jj) \qquad i \neq j \tag{3.28}$$

All the other terms in Eq. (2.228) vanish, since by assumption,

$$(ij,kl) = 0 \qquad \text{if } i \neq j \text{ or } k \neq l \tag{3.29}$$

The procedure for solving the Pople equations follows the same pattern as that used to solve the Roothaan equations. We start with a set of assumed MOs $\psi_\mu{}^0$ given by Eq. (2.216); we use these to calculate the quantities P_{ij} in Eqs. (3.27) and (3.28) and so obtain the corresponding F matrix; diagonalization of this gives a set of eigenvectors $a_{\mu i}{}^1$ corresponding to a set of MOs $\psi_\mu{}^1$,

$$\psi_\mu{}^1 = \sum_i a_{\mu i}\phi_i{}^1 \tag{3.30}$$

These are used to construct a new set of P_{ij} and so a new F matrix, and the cycle is repeated until the P_{ij}, and the eigenvalues and eigenvectors of the F matrix, converge to a limit. This is then taken to be the required solution. The calculations require the use of a reasonably large digital computer; a CDC 1604 or IBM 7090 can handle problems involving a basis set with 50 AOs, the time required for 10 iterations (usually sufficient) being about half an hour.

3.4 MORE DETAILED ANALYSIS OF THE POPLE METHOD

The original derivation of the Pople equations, outlined above, is logically unsatisfactory in two respects. In the first place, AOs of different atoms do not satisfy the condition expressed in Eq. (3.25), and the same is true of any other set of functions that could serve satisfactorily as a basis set in the Roothaan treatment. Secondly, as we have already remarked, Eq. (3.25) logically requires us to set the core integrals $H_{ij}{}^c$ ($\equiv \beta_{ij}$) equal to zero; yet if we do this, the method fails to give satisfactory results. In this section we shall therefore examine the basis of the Pople method in more detail to see if anything can be done to make it more acceptable.

In the SCF method, the total electronic energy E of a closed-shell molecule is given by [see Eq. (2.204)]:

$$E = 2 \sum_\mu^{occ} E_\mu + \sum_\mu^{occ} \sum_\nu^{occ} (2J_{\mu\nu} - K_{\mu\nu}) \tag{3.31}$$

Here the terms in E_μ represent the core contribution, those in $J_{\mu\nu}$ and $K_{\mu\nu}$ the interelectronic repulsions. Let us now compare the total interelectronic repulsions calculated for a given molecule by the Roothaan and Pople methods.

Using Eqs. (2.222), (2.224), and (3.25), the corresponding repulsion energies E_R and E_P are given by:

$$E_R = \sum_\mu^{occ} \sum_\nu^{occ} \sum_i \sum_j \sum_k \sum_l a_{\mu i} a_{\mu j} a_{\nu k} a_{\nu l} [2(ij,kl) - (ik,jl)] \tag{3.32}$$

$$E_P = \sum_\mu^{occ} \sum_\nu^{occ} \sum_i \sum_k (2a_{\mu i}^2 a_{\nu k}^2 - a_{\mu i} a_{\mu k} a_{\nu i} a_{\nu k})(ii,kk) \tag{3.33}$$

Comparing these expressions, we see that:

$$E_R = E_P + \sum_\mu^{occ} \sum_\nu^{occ} \left[2\sum_{i \neq j} \sum_{k \neq l} a_{\mu i} a_{\mu j} a_{\nu k} a_{\nu l} (ij,kl) - \sum_{i \neq k} \sum_{j \neq l} a_{\mu i} a_{\mu j} a_{\nu k} a_{\nu l} (ik,jl) \right] \tag{3.34}$$

Therefore it seems at first sight that the Pople method must greatly underestimate the interelectronic repulsions, given that the three- and four-center integrals are by no means negligible if we use any kind of AOs (either SCF AOs or SZOs) as our basis set.

However there is another factor to be considered. The energy expressions of Eqs. (3.32) and (3.33) presuppose the MOs ψ_μ to be normalized; the conditions for normalization are different in the Roothaan method, where overlap integrals are included, from those in the Pople method, where overlap is neglected [Eq. (3.26)]. The conditions are:

Roothaan: $$\sum_i \sum_j a_{\mu i} a_{\mu j} S_{ij} = \sum_i a_{\mu i}^2 + \sum_{i \neq j} a_{\mu i} a_{\mu j} S_{ij} = 1 \tag{3.35}$$

Pople: $$\sum_i \sum_j a_{\mu i} a_{\mu j} S_{ij} = \sum_i a_{\mu i}^2 = 1 \tag{3.36}$$

The numerical values of the coefficients are thus systematically greater in the case of the Pople method; as a result, the quantity E_P in Eq. (3.34) will be less than the total repulsion energy calculated by the Pople method, and this difference could well balance the extra terms in Eq. (3.36).

To explore this possibility further, let us examine the values for one of the individual integrals, say $J_{\mu\nu}$, in the Roothaan and Pople approximations, using identical (unnormalized) expressions for the individual MOs ψ_μ and ψ_ν; i.e.

$$\psi_\mu = \sum_i A_{\mu i} \phi_i \qquad \psi_\nu = \sum_j A_{\nu j} \phi_j \tag{3.37}$$

Using Eq. (2.222), the Roothaan expression $J_{\mu\nu}{}^R$ for $J_{\mu\nu}$ is then seen to be:

$$J_{\mu\nu}{}^R = \frac{\displaystyle\sum_i\sum_j\sum_k\sum_l A_{\mu i}A_{\mu j}A_{\nu k}A_{\nu l}(ij,kl)}{\left(\displaystyle\sum_i\sum_j A_{\mu i}A_{\mu j}S_{ij}\right)\left(\displaystyle\sum_k\sum_l A_{\nu k}A_{\nu l}S_{kl}\right)}$$ (3.38)

The corresponding Pople expression $J_{\mu\nu}{}^P$ is derived from this by omitting terms in the numerator when $i \neq j$, or $k \neq l$, and with

$$S_{ij} = 0 \qquad i \neq j \qquad S_{ii} = 1$$ (3.39)

Hence:

$$J_{\mu\nu}{}^P = \frac{\displaystyle\sum_i\sum_k A_{\mu i}{}^2 A_{\nu k}{}^2 (ii,kk)}{\left(\displaystyle\sum_i A_{\mu i}{}^2\right)\left(\displaystyle\sum_k A_{\nu k}{}^2\right)}$$ (3.40)

It will be seen at once that the number of terms in the numerator, and the number of terms in the denominator, is the same in each of these expressions for $J_{\mu\nu}$; this certainly supports the idea that the greater number of terms in the Roothaan expression $J_{\mu\nu}{}^R$ may be balanced by a corresponding increase in the normalizing factor. As a further check, let us use the Mulliken approximation [Eqs. (3.20) to (3.22)] for the integrals in Eq. (3.38). We then find:

$$J_{\mu\nu}{}^R \approx \frac{\frac{1}{4}\displaystyle\sum_i\sum_j\sum_k\sum_l A_{\mu i}A_{\mu j}A_{\nu k}A_{\nu l}S_{ij}S_{kl}[(ii,kk) + (ii,ll) + (jj,kk) + (jj,ll)]}{\displaystyle\sum_i\sum_j\sum_k\sum_l A_{\mu i}A_{\mu j}A_{\nu k}A_{\nu l}S_{ij}S_{kl}}$$ (3.41)

The parallel between the numerator and denominator is now complete. And finally, let us make the further simplifying assumption that the individual two-center integrals in Eq. (3.41) can be replaced by their mean value $\overline{V}$. Equation (3.41) then immediately reduces to:

$$J_{\mu\nu}{}^R \approx \overline{V}$$ (3.42)

If we make the same simplifying assumption in Eq. (3.40), we find:

$$J_{\mu\nu}{}^P = \overline{V}$$ (3.43)

Any differences between the two estimates for $J_{\mu\nu}$ therefore depend only on the weighting factors of individual integrals, and the effect of these is likely to average out in the case of systems containing any appreciable number of electrons.

This argument provides a different—and valid—justification for neglecting the contributions of three- and four-center integrals to $J_{\mu\nu}$; it can be shown in a similar way that the contributions of such integrals to $K_{\mu\nu}$ can also be neglected, as a good first approximation. However the same argument also indicates that the one-electron resonance integrals $H_{ij}{}^c$ *cannot* be neglected; their contribution to the total energy would be compensated by neglecting overlap [compare Eqs. (3.35) and (3.36)] only if they were given approximately by the expression:

$$H_{ij}^c = \tfrac{1}{2}S_{ij}(H_{ii}^c + H_{jj}^c) \tag{3.44}$$

In the Mulliken approximation, however, H_{ij}^c is given by a multiple C of this, where C is usually in the range 1.5 to 2.0. In the Pople treatment, we must therefore retain a term representing the difference between H_{ij}^c and the value given by Eq. (3.44). This difference is the quantity β_{ij} that appears in the Pople equations, and is usually described as a resonance integral. This argument shows very clearly why integrals of this type have to be retained in the Pople treatment; it also indicates that they must *not* be equated to the true core integrals H_{ij}^c. In the Pople treatment the resonance integrals are treated as parameters, to be determined empirically.

While these arguments provide a good justification for the use of the Pople method as a semiempirical treatment of molecules, there is one serious exception to them. The arguments justify the neglect of three- and four-orbital repulsion integrals (ij,kk), (ij,ik), and (ij,kl) only in cases where ϕ_i, ϕ_j, ϕ_k, and ϕ_l are AOs of different atoms. Consider for example the integral (ij,kk), where ϕ_i and ϕ_j are two different AOs of one single atom. This integral could be neglected only if it were compensated by a corresponding change in the normalizing factor [see Eqs. (3.35) and (3.36)]. Here, however, there is no such change; for since AOs of a given atom are mutually orthogonal, the corresponding term involving S_{ij} in Eq. (3.35) vanishes. We must therefore be prepared to retain three- and four-orbital integrals in the Pople treatment if the overlapping orbitals are AOs of the same atom; i.e.

(ij,kk) where ϕ_i, ϕ_j are AOs of the same atom

(ij,ik) where ϕ_i, ϕ_j, ϕ_k are AOs of the same atom   (3.45)

(ij,kl) where ϕ_i, ϕ_j are AOs of one atom, and ϕ_k, ϕ_l are AOs of a single atom which may or may not be the same as the first

Apart from these theoretical considerations, there is also an important practical objection to neglecting these integrals.[2] If they are neglected, the results of a Pople treatment may not be invariant for rotation of the coordinate axes, a situation which would clearly be quite unacceptable. The truth of this statement can be seen at once from a simple example. Consider a system of MOs containing an s AO (s) of one atom A, and P_x and P_y AOs (x and y respectively) of a second atom B. We first choose our coordinates so that atoms A and B lie along the x axis (Fig. 3.3a); we shall then rotate the axes through an angle θ (Fig. 3.3b) and examine the Pople equations to see what effect, if any, this rotation will have. If the equations are significantly altered, this will indicate that the results of a Pople treatment will not be invariant for rotation of the coordinate axes.

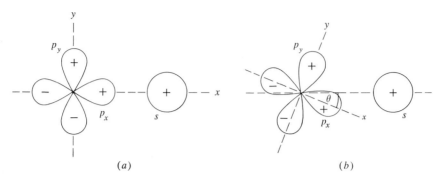

FIG. 3.3 The effect of a rotation of the coordinate axes on the Pople equations for a molecule.

For simplicity, let us assume that the charge densities q_x, q_y in the AOs x, y are each unity.   Now it is very easily seen from the expressions for p AOs [Eqs. (2.34) to (2.39)] that the sum of these two charge distributions represents an overall distribution which is axially symmetrical about the z axis; if we dissect this into any two mutually perpendicular p AOs, the total charge density in each will therefore also be unity.   The charge densities q'_x, q'_v in the skewed p AOs x', y' of Fig. 3.2b are therefore each equal to unity.

Consider now the F-matrix element F_{ss} in each of these cases.   Neglecting contributions by other AOs, and neglecting overlap between AOs of different atoms, the two expressions for F_{ss} are:

$$F_{ss} = \alpha_s + \tfrac{1}{2}q_s(ss,ss) + q_x(ss,xx) + q_y(ss,yy) + 2p_{xy}(ss,xy)$$

$$= \alpha_s + \tfrac{1}{2}q_s(ss,ss) + (ss,xx) + (ss,yy) + 2p_{xy}(ss,xy) \qquad (3.46)$$

$$F'_{ss} = \alpha_s + \tfrac{1}{2}q_s(ss,ss) + (ss,x'x') + (ss,y'y') + 2p'_{xy}(ss,x'y') \qquad (3.47)$$

Consider the integral (ss,xy).   This is given by:

$$(ss,xy) = \iint s(1)s(1)\frac{e^2}{r_{12}}x(2)y(2)\, d\tau_1\, d\tau_2 \qquad (3.48)$$

Suppose we invert the coordinate system in the xz plane, i.e. replace the coordinate y by $-y$.   Since the AOs x and s are symmetric for reflection in the xz plane, this replacement will leave them unchanged; on the other hand the AO y, being antisymmetric, will change sign.   The integrand of Eq. (3.48), and so the whole integral, will therefore change sign if we replace y by $-y$.   Now this integral represents the coulomb energy of repulsion between two fixed clouds of charge, a quantity whose value must clearly be independent of the coordinate system used in calculating it.   Since we have shown that (ss,xy) has equal and opposite values in two different but equivalent coordinate systems, it follows that the integral must vanish.   We can therefore rewrite Eq. (3.46) in the form:

$$F_{ss} = \alpha_s + \tfrac{1}{2}q_s(ss,ss) + (ss,xx) + (ss,yy) \qquad (3.49)$$

This is the expression that would be given by a "normal" Pople treatment in which *all* three- and four-orbital integrals are neglected, including in particular (ss,xy). However this is so simply because of a symmetry effect, due to the fact that the coordinate axes were chosen in such a way that s lay on the axis of one of the p AOs of atom B. In the rotated system of Fig. 3.2b, such is no longer the case, and the integral $(ss,x'y')$ therefore does *not* vanish. Unless we retain this integral in our calculations, the value of F_{ss}, and so also the orbitals and energies calculated by the Pople method, will be different in the two cases—and these correspond to two different arbitrary choices of coordinate axes.

This difficulty has been discussed in detail by Pople, Santry, and Segal,[2] who have pointed out two alternative procedures for meeting it. The simpler of these is to assume that integrals of the type (ii,jj) are invariant for rotation of the coordinate axes; thus the expressions F_{ss} and F'_{ss} in Eqs. (3.46) and (3.47) would be identical if we neglect the three-center integral $(ss,x'y')$ but at the same time assume that:

$$(ss,xx) = (ss,yy) = (ss,x'x') = (ss,y'y') \tag{3.50}$$

Equation (3.50) is equivalent to assuming that the charge distribution represented by any AO can be treated as spherically symmetrical, so that the repulsion between it and the charge distribution represented by some other AO is independent of the mutual orientations of the two AOs in space. Pople et al.[2] have called this the *CNDO approximation* (complete neglect of differential overlap).

The second approach is the one outlined above [Eq. (3.46)], in which all repulsion integrals are included that involve overlap of pairs of orbitals of the same atom; integrals involving overlap between AOs of different atoms are still neglected. Pople et. al[2] have called this the *NDDO approximation* (neglect of diatomic differential overlap).

The problems involved in applying these methods in practice will be discussed in detail in Chap. 10, where some intermediate approximations will also be described.

3.5 THE GOEPPERT-MAYER–SKLAR POTENTIAL

In the two preceding sections we have considered the physical significance of all the terms in the Roothaan and Pople equations except the one-electron core integrals of the type $H_{ii}{}^c$, an integral which represents the attraction between the core of the molecule and an electron occupying the AO ϕ_i; viz.

$$H_{ii}{}^c = \int \phi_i \mathbf{H}^c \phi_i \, d\tau \tag{3.51}$$

Let us consider in more detail the nature and physical significance of integrals of this kind.

The core operator $\mathbf{H}^c$ is written:

$$\mathbf{H}^c = \mathbf{T} + \sum_q \mathbf{V}_q \tag{3.52}$$

where **T** is the kinetic-energy operator and V_q represents the potential energy due to interaction with the core of atom q. The core integral H_{ii}^c is written:

$$H_{ii}^c = \int \phi_i \mathbf{T} \phi_i \, d\tau + \sum_q V_{iq} \tag{3.53}$$

where V_{iq} represents the potential energy of an electron in the AO ϕ_i due to attraction by the core of atom q.

Let us first consider an integral V_{iq}, where q is an atom other than that (p) of which ϕ_i is an AO. Suppose now that we fill up the AOs ϕ_k of atom q with enough electrons to make it neutral, the total number of electrons in the AO ϕ_k being written as c_k. Denote by (ii,q) the total energy of the electron occupying the AO ϕ_i due to interaction with the neutral atom q. This (see Fig. 3.4) can be written as a sum of the attraction between the electron in ϕ_i and the core of atom q (that is V_{iq}) and of the repulsion between the same electron and the various electrons occupying the AOs ϕ_k of atom q. Since the mean repulsion between an electron in the AO ϕ_i and one in the AO ϕ_k is given by the integral (ii,kk), it follows that:

$$(ii,q) = V_{iq} + \sum_k^{(q)} c_k(ii,kk) \tag{3.54}$$

where the sum is over AOs ϕ_k of atom q. Hence:

$$V_{iq} = (ii,q) - \sum_k^{(q)} c_k(ii,kk) \tag{3.55}$$

This method of estimating V_{iq} was introduced by Goeppert-Mayer and Sklar, and the corresponding expression [Eq. (3.53)] is commonly described as the *Goeppert-Mayer–Sklar potential*; the quantity (ii,q) is called a *penetration integral*.

The reader will probably have noticed one obvious loophole in this argument; the repulsion between an electron in the AO ϕ_i and one in the AO ϕ_k is equal to (ii,kk) only if the electrons have opposite spins; otherwise an exchange correction should be included, given by the integral (ik,ik). However as long as we are prepared to neglect differential overlap between AOs of different atoms, integrals of this type will vanish and so the simple potential of Eq. (3.53) will suffice.

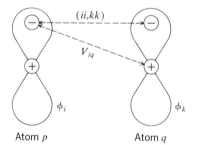

Atom p Atom q

FIG. 3.4   The Goeppert-Mayer–Sklar potential.

Next let us consider the remaining term V_{ip} in Eq. (3.53), representing the attraction between an electron in ϕ_i and the core of atom p, of which ϕ_i is an AO. This can be estimated in a manner similar to that used for the other terms V_{iq}. We shall again neglect differential overlaps between the relevant AOs even though in this case they are AOs of the same atom p; if necessary, they can easily be estimated by the procedure outlined in the latter part of Sec. 3.4.

Consider an electron occupying the AO ϕ_i of an isolated, neutral atom p. The binding energy, or ionization potential W_i, of this electron can be written as a sum of three parts; its kinetic energy T_i, which is given by the first term in Eq. (3.53); its potential energy due to attraction by its own nucleus, given by V_{ip}; and the potential energy due to repulsion between it and the electrons occupying other AOs ϕ_i of atom j. Thus:

$$W_i = \int \phi_i \mathbf{T}\phi_i \, d\tau + V_{ip} + \sum_{j \neq i}^{(p)} c_j(ii,jj) \tag{3.56}$$

when c_j is the number (0, 1, or 2) of electrons occupying the AO ϕ_j, and the summation is over AOs of atom p. Combining Eqs. (3.53) to (3.56),

$$H_{ii}{}^c = W_i - \sum_{j \neq i} c_j(ii,jj) + \sum_{q \neq p} (ii,q) \tag{3.57}$$

when the first summation is now over all the AOs of all the atoms, other than the AO ϕ_i itself.

Since the penetration integrals (ii,q) are quite small, and since their omission should be largely compensated in a semiempirical treatment by the presence of adjustable parameters, it is usual in the Pople calculation to neglect them. If this is done, and if all three- and four-center integrals are neglected, then the Pople equation (3.27) for the diagonal matrix element F_{ii} becomes:

$$F_{ii} = W_i + \tfrac{1}{2}P_{ii}(ii,ii) + \sum_{j \neq i} (P_{jj} - c_j)(ii,jj) \tag{3.58}$$

3.6 CHARGE DENSITIES AND BOND ORDERS

In the Pople treatment, a simple significance can be given to the quantities P_{jj} that appear in the diagonal elements of the F matrix. The MO ψ_μ is here represented as a sum of contributions by nonoverlapping AOs ϕ_i. Suppose we have an electron in the MO ψ_μ, and suppose we try to calculate the probability $P(\mu j)$ that it will at any instant be found in the domain of the AO ϕ_j. Clearly:

$$P(\mu j) = \int^j \left(\sum_i a_{\mu i}\phi_i \right)^2 d\tau = \sum_i a_{\mu i}{}^2 \int^j \phi_i{}^2 \, d\tau \tag{3.59}$$

where the integral is over the domain of ϕ_j; the other integrals vanish since the product $\phi_i\phi_j \, d\tau$ ($i \neq j$) vanishes everywhere [Eq. (3.25)]. In the domain ϕ_j, all other ϕ_i vanish; all terms in the sum of Eq. (3.59) therefore vanish except that with $i = j$. Moreover the integral for $i = j$ is equal to unity; for we suppose the AOs ϕ_i to be normalized, and the whole orbital ϕ_i is within the range of the integration. Thus:

$$P(\mu j) = a_{\mu j}{}^2 \tag{3.60}$$

If then we represent our electron in ψ_μ statistically as a cloud of "electron gas," the total fraction of the cloud that falls in the domain ϕ_j is $a_{\mu j}{}^2$. If we sum this quantity over all the occupied MOs in the molecule, the resulting quantity, q_j, will then be a measure of the total average number of electrons in the domain ϕ_j. Thus:

$$q_j = 2 \sum_\mu^{\text{occ}} a_{\mu j}{}^2 \tag{3.61}$$

From Eq. (2.226)

$$q_j \equiv P_{jj} \tag{3.62}$$

Thus the quantity P_{jj} in the Pople treatment is a measure of the total electron density q_j in the AO ϕ_j; it is called the *charge density*.

In the Pople method, the quantities P_{ij} $(i \neq j)$ are usually written with lowercase p's (p_{ij}) and are termed *bond orders;* thus:

$$p_{ij} = P_{ij} = 2 \sum_\mu^{\text{occ}} a_{\mu i} a_{\mu j} \tag{3.63}$$

With this notation, and using the Goeppert-Mayer–Sklar potential with neglect of penetration integrals, we arrive at the following expressions for the elements of the Pople F matrix:

$$F_{ii} = W_i + \tfrac{1}{2} q_i (ii,ii) + \sum_{j \neq i} (q_j - c_j)(ii,jj) \tag{3.64}$$

$$F_{ij} = \beta_{ij}{}^c - \tfrac{1}{2} p_{ij}(ii,jj) \tag{3.65}$$

[see Eqs. (3.27), (3.28), (3.56), (3.60), and (3.63)].

3.7 THE HÜCKEL (HMO) METHOD

Although the Pople method was formulated as early as 1953, it has only recently been applied at all extensively. The reason for this is simple; although the calculations involved are much lighter than those in the Roothaan method, they still require the use of a digital computer, and a fairly large one at that (of the order of a CDC 1604 or IBM 7090). Computers of this type have only recently become generally available; in the past it was therefore necessary to use still simpler and cruder treatments if we wished to undertake numerical calculations for typical organic molcules.

For these reasons most of the quantum-chemical work in this field has been carried out by the *Hückel (HMO) method,* introduced originally by Hückel in 1931.[3]

The original derivation given by Hückel, and reproduced in most texts, is as follows. In the orbital representation, the individual MOs of a molecule are eigenfunctions of the corresponding one-electron Hartree-Fock operator $\mathbf{H}$;

$$\mathbf{H}\psi_\mu = \epsilon_\mu\psi_\mu \tag{3.66}$$

Instead of solving this equation, we approximate the MOs by using the variation method, with an LCAO trial eigenfunction;

$$\psi_\mu = \sum_i a_{\mu i}\phi_i \tag{3.67}$$

Assuming neglect of differential overlap, and using the same notation as in previous sections, the corresponding variation equations are:

$$|H_{ij} - \epsilon\delta_{ij}| = 0 \tag{3.68}$$

$$\sum_j a_{\mu j}(H_{ij} - \epsilon_\mu\delta_{ij}) = 0 \qquad i = 1, 2, \ldots, N \tag{3.69}$$

where
$$H_{ij} = \int\phi_i\mathbf{H}\phi_j \, d\tau \tag{3.70}$$

Instead of calculating the integrals H_{ij}, we treat them as parameters. The diagonal element H_{ii} is called a *coulomb integral* and is supposed to have a value α_i characteristic of the AO ϕ_i and the atom of which it is an AO, and independent of the rest of the molecule, while the off-diagonal element H_{ij}, written as β_{ij} and called a *resonance integral,* is likewise assumed to have a value characteristic only of the AOs ϕ_i, ϕ_j.   It is usually assumed that:

$$\beta_{ij} = 0 \qquad \text{\small unless ϕ_i, ϕ_j are AOs of two atoms} \atop \text{\small that are linked by a covalent bond} \tag{3.71}$$

On the basis of various intuitive arguments, it is also assumed that if ϕ_i is an AO of an atom p, then

$$\alpha_i = \text{ionization potential of an electron occupying}$$
$$\text{the AO } \phi_i \text{ of an isolated atom } p \qquad [\equiv W(\phi_i)] \tag{3.72}$$

The ground state of a closed-shell molecule is supposed to correspond to a situation where the $2N$ electrons are placed in pairs in the N MOs of lowest energy; the total binding energy E_T of the molecule is then equated to the total orbital energy of the electrons, i.e.

$$E_T = 2\sum_\mu^{\text{occ}} \epsilon_\mu \tag{3.73}$$

The energy E_p of an atom p is likewise equated to the total orbital energy of its electrons; i.e.

$$E_p = \sum_i^{(p)} n_i\alpha(\phi_i) \tag{3.74}$$

where the sum is over AOs ϕ_i of atom p, and where n_i is the number of electrons occupying the AO ϕ_i. Thus the heat of formation of the molecule for atoms ΔH is given by

$$\Delta H = E_T - \sum_p E_p = 2 \sum_{\mu}^{occ} \epsilon_{\mu} - \sum_i n_i \alpha(\phi_i) \qquad (3.75)$$

This derivation and the assumptions involved in it are dubious, to say the least. The expressions for the total energies [Eqs. (3.73) and (3.74)] are definitely incorrect. In an orbital representation, the total electronic energy is *not* a sum of the orbital energies; one has both to subtract from this total the average interelectronic repulsion [see Eqs. (2.204) and (2.205)] and to add the total internuclear repulsion. The assumption that the matrix elements H_{ii}, H_{ij} have fixed values independent of the rest of the molecule is also hard to justify except on the basis of intuition; as we shall see presently, intuition here is a dangerous guide since it can equally be used to support the assumption implied in Eq. (3.72)—which again is incorrect. And finally, the Hückel method is usually presented in terms of the spin-free Hartree SCF picture; in this, however, the one-electron operators $\mathbf{H}^i$ for the individual electrons are *not* all the same. The standard derivation is therefore self-inconsistent; it neglects electron spin, yet uses a form of the one-electron hamiltonian that can be justified only if electron spin is taken into account (that is $\mathbf{H}$ must be a Hartree-Fock hamiltonian, not a Hartree hamiltonian; see Sec. 2.13).

The most unfortunate thing about this naïve and unsatisfactory derivation is its failure to give any clear idea of the real nature of the approximations on which the Hückel method rests. Many chemists have as a result tended to use the method blindly, without really knowing what they were doing; this has become all the easier now that digital computers, and Hückel programs, are freely available. The previous discussion has put us in a position to remedy this; our analysis will show that the Hückel method is not in fact nearly as bad as the foregoing paragraphs would suggest; at the same time it will indicate rather clearly the serious pitfalls that lie in wait for the unwary user.

Comparison of Eqs. (3.68) to (3.72) with Eqs. (2.213), (2.214), (3.64), and (3.65) reveals the true basis of the Hückel method rather clearly. It is a simplified version of the Pople method in which the elements of the F matrix are treated as parameters, with the assumption that the element F_{ij} is a function only of the atom (or atoms) of which ϕ_i and ϕ_j are AOs, being independent of the rest of the molecule. Our first problem is to see if there is any justification for this clearly drastic assumption.

Consider first the diagonal element F_{ii}, using the simplified Pople treatment embodied in Eq. (3.64). In this W_i represents the attraction between electron i and the core of its own atom, while the sum of terms

$$\sum_k^{(q)} (q_k - c_k)(ii,kk) \qquad (3.76)$$

represents the net interaction between an electron in the AO ϕ_i, and the core and electrons of atom q.   In the case of a neutral molecule, it is likely that the individual atoms will be more or less neutral; if so, the sum in Eq. (3.76) will vanish.   A similar argument shows that if atom p is neutral, the corresponding sum over the AOs of atom p will also vanish.   Making these simplifying assumptions, Eq. (3.64) becomes:

$$F_{ii} = W_i + \tfrac{1}{2}q_i(ii,ii) \tag{3.77}$$

Here W_i is an atomic property, independent of the molecule of which atom p forms a part.   Moreover the arguments indicated above suggest that atom p should be more or less neutral, in which case q_i should be approximately equal to the number of electrons (one or two) occupying the AO ϕ_i of an isolated atom p.   If so, F_{ii} will have a constant value, characteristic of the AO ϕ_i and independent of the molecule of which atom p forms a part.   This of course is equivalent to the Hückel assumption that α_i is a constant.   It is, however, wrong to identify the Hückel parameter α_i with the ionization potential W_i; the two quantities differ by $\tfrac{1}{2}(ii,ii)$ or by (ii,ii), depending on the number of electrons that occupy the AO ϕ_i in an isolated atom p.

Thus as long as the atoms in a molecule are essentially neutral, the Hückel method should be a reasonable approximation, so far as the diagonal elements of the F matrix are concerned.   However the assumptions inherent in it break down completely in the case of polar molecules or ions; obviously we must be extremely careful about applying the Hückel method to systems of this kind.

Considerations of a somewhat similar kind apply to the off-diagonal elements F_{ij} [Eq. (3.65)].

In the Pople treatment,

$$F_{ij} = \beta_{ij}{}^c - \tfrac{1}{2}p_{ij}(ii,jj) \tag{3.78}$$

If the atoms of which ϕ_i, ϕ_j are AOs are linked by a covalent bond, the distance between them will usually have a value characteristic of the bond and independent of the molecule in which it occurs.   The overlap cloud between the AOs will then have a constant size (see Fig. 3.1).   Since the field in the region between the two nuclei will be more or less independent of the rest of the molecule, it is therefore reasonable to suppose that $\beta_{ij}{}^c$ will have a fixed value, characteristic of the AOs ϕ_i and ϕ_j, and independent of the molecule in which this bond occurs.

The integral (ii,jj) will of course also fulfill this condition; if p_{ij} is also constant, then F_{ij} will have a constant value characteristic of the AOs ϕ_i, ϕ_j and independent of the rest of the molecule.

The Hückel assumption, that F_{ij} has a constant value β_{ij}, is therefore defensible if ϕ_i, ϕ_j are AOs of two atoms that are covalently linked.   Even if the length of the bond varies, one would at least expect β_{ij} to be a one-valued function of bond length; for all the quantities in Eq. (3.69) would be expected to have this property.   This is obvious for $\beta_{ij}{}^c$ and (ii,jj); while the argument outlined in

Sec. 3.9, implying that the strength of a bond is a function of the term $p_{ij}\beta_{ij}$, suggests that p_{ij} is also a one-valued function of bond strength and bond length. (This point will be elaborated in later sections of this book so we need not pursue it further at this point.)

There is, however, a major discrepancy between the Pople and Hückel methods. If the AOs ϕ_i, ϕ_j belong to nonadjacent atoms in a molecule, it is very reasonable to suppose that the core resonance integral $\beta_{ij}{}^c$ will be small. However the matrix element F_{ij} also contains a contribution $-\frac{1}{2}p_{ij}(ii, jj)$, arising from the molecular exchange integrals $K_{\mu\nu}$; this does not vanish even if the AOs ϕ_i, ϕ_j do not overlap. The reason for this is simple. Such integrals represent a correction to the interelectronic repulsion energy of the molecule to allow for the fact that electrons of opposite spin are held apart by the Pauli principle. Consider two electrons occupying MOs ψ_μ, ψ_ν, with parallel spins. Suppose the first electron is at some instant located in the AO ϕ_i. The probability of finding the second electron in some nearby AO ϕ_j will then be less than one would expect if the electrons moved independently; for the Pauli hole round the first electron will encompass surrounding parts of the MO ψ_μ and so will include AOs of other nearby atoms, even if these are not covalently linked to the atom of which ϕ_i is an AO. In other words the term $-\frac{1}{2}p_{ij}(ii, jj)$ arises from the overlap between the MOs ψ_μ and ψ_ν; whether or not the individual AOs ϕ_i, ϕ_j overlap is irrelevant.

This of course invalidates the Hückel assumption, that β_{ij} is a one-valued function of the AOs ϕ_i and ϕ_j; for if these are AOs of nonadjacent atoms, the bond order p_{ij} may have any value. Not only will the matrix element F_{ij} then differ from zero, but its value will also vary with the molecule in which the AOs ϕ_i, ϕ_j appear.

Here again it is impossible to estimate in advance how serious will be the errors introduced in this way into the Hückel method. As long as the geometrical environment of each atom is the same, we may reasonably hope that the contributions of matrix elements F_{ij} between nonbonded atoms may be sufficiently uniform for their effects to be compensated by adjusting the β's. We cannot, however, extrapolate from one type of molecule to another; the fact that a given choice of Hückel parameters works well for one set of compounds cannot be taken as a justification for using them indiscriminately for compounds of other kinds.

The last—and most disturbing—assumption in the Hückel method is that embodied in Eqs. (3.73) to (3.75), i.e. that the total energy of a molecule can be equated to the sum of the orbital energies E_μ of the electrons in it. This is obviously incorrect in principle; for the Hückel orbital energies E_μ are supposed to be approximations to the true Hartree-Fock SCF orbital energies, and the sum of these is certainly not equal to the total energy.

As we have seen (Sec. 2.13), the total electronic energy of a closed-shell molecule, in the SCF approximation, is given by taking the sum of the individual orbital energies and subtracting from it the mean value of the total energy of interelectronic repulsion.   This, however, still does not give us the total energy of the molecule; for the electrons move in the field of a number of positively charged nuclei, or cores of atoms, and the latter will repel each other.   The total energy E of the molecule is a sum of the total electronic energy and the core repulsion.   Thus if the orbital energies are ϵ_μ,

$$E = 2 \sum_{\mu}^{occ} \epsilon_\mu - \text{(total interelectronic repulsion)} + \text{(core repulsion)} \tag{3.79}$$

$$E = 2 \sum_{\mu}^{occ} \epsilon_\mu - \sum_{\mu} \sum_{\nu} (2J_{\mu\nu} - K_{\mu\nu}) + \text{(core repulsion)} \tag{3.80}$$

If the molecule is neutral, and if the atoms in it are more or less neutral, then the coulomb repulsion of the cores of two atoms should be more or less balanced by the coulomb repulsion of the electrons attached to those two cores.   We are, however, still left with the terms in Eq. (3.80) representing the exchange correction to the coulomb repulsion.

If we assume that the core repulsion balances the terms J_{mn} in Eq. (3.80), we can write this equation in the form:

$$E = 2 \sum_{\mu}^{occ} \epsilon_\mu + \sum_{\mu} \sum_{\nu} K_{\mu\nu} \tag{3.81}$$

If we expand ϵ_μ and $K_{\mu\nu}$ in terms of AOs, and use the definitions of charge density and bond order of Eqs. (3.61) and (3.63), we find:

$$E = \sum_i q_i[W_i + \tfrac{1}{2}q_i(ii,ii)] + \sum_{i \neq j} \sum p_{ij}[\beta_{ij}^c - \tfrac{1}{2}p_{ij}(ii,jj)] + \frac{1}{4} \sum_{i \neq j} \sum p_{ij}^2(ii,jj)$$

$$= \sum_i q_i[W_i + \tfrac{1}{2}q_i(ii,ii)] + \sum_{i \neq j} \sum p_{ij}[\beta_{ij}^c - \tfrac{1}{4}p_{ij}(ii,jj)] \tag{3.82}$$

The corresponding expression for the total energy E^H in the Hückel treatment is given [see Eqs. (3.68) to (3.75)] by:

$$E^H = \sum_i q_i\alpha_i + \sum_{i \neq j} \sum p_{ij}\beta_{ij} \tag{3.83}$$

The two expressions, Eqs. (3.82) and (3.83), will be identical if:

$$W_i + \tfrac{1}{2}q_i(ii,ii) \equiv \alpha_i = \text{const} \tag{3.84}$$

$$\beta_{ij}^c - \tfrac{1}{4}p_{ij}(ii,jj) \equiv \beta_{ij} = \text{const} \tag{3.85}$$

The arguments given earlier in this section show that these conditions may well hold as a first approximation in the case of neutral, nonpolar molecules.

The Hückel method is therefore not nearly as bad as it seems at first sight, or from the thoroughly unsatisfactory derivations given in all the standard texts. Provided that our assumptions about the q_i and p_{ij} hold, it represents a very plausible simplification of the Pople treatment.   The neglect of off-diagonal matrix elements between nonbonded AOs is admittedly hard to justify; however it is reasonable to hope that so long as we confine our attention to molecules of very similar type, we may be able to allow for these by empirical adjustment of the parameters β_{ij}. The effect of polarity will clearly be much more serious; yet even here we may be able to make some allowance for the presence of small charges on the atoms of polar molecules by adjusting the parameters α_i. However this is all very tenuous and uncertain; we certainly cannot be sure that the values that fit one series of compounds will necessarily be suitable for another. Much of the misuse of the Hückel method derives from the erroneous assumption that "Hückel parameters" established for one series of compounds will carry over to other series. A still more serious error is concerned with the application of the Hückel method to ions; here the basic assumption, that the total interelectronic and internuclear repulsion cancel, is clearly incorrect. The Hückel method cannot be used in such cases without great circumspection.

These considerations suggest that the Hückel method is essentially useless for quantitative work. If the parameters α, β do not have constant values for compounds of all types—and they certainly do not—then we can get quantitative results only by multiplying the number of parameters to an absurd extent. The extensive literature on attempts to determine "best values" for Hückel parameters must be regarded as representing a waste of print and computer time.

The main value of the Hückel method lies in the facility with which it can be used to generalize chemical phenomena in a qualitative, or even semiquantitative, manner. As we shall see presently, we can in this way develop a general theory of organic chemistry which represents a major advance over the earlier treatments. For accurate work, however, it is necessary to use some more refined approach.

3.8 ATTEMPTS TO IMPROVE THE HÜCKEL METHOD
Various attempts have been made to improve the Hückel (HMO) method; since none of these has proved useful or satisfactory, we need not consider them in any great detail.

One obvious modification is to abandon the neglect of overlap; such a treatment bears the same relationship to the Roothaan LCAO treatment as the normal HMO method does to the Pople method. The HMO parameters α_i, β_{ij} now stand for elements of the Roothaan LCAO F matrix [compare Eqs. (3.84) and (3.85)]. The modified HMO equations then become:

$$|F_{ij} - ES_{ij}| = 0 \qquad (3.86)$$

$$\sum_j a_{mj}(F_{ij} - \epsilon_m S_{ij}) = 0 \qquad i = 1, 2, \ldots, N \qquad (3.87)$$

where
$$F_{ii} = \alpha_i \qquad \text{characteristic of AO } \phi_i \qquad (3.88)$$

and
$$F_{ij} = \beta_{ij} \qquad \text{characteristic of AOs } \phi_i, \phi_j \qquad (3.89)$$

The overlap integrals are usually calculated directly, using Slater AOs:

$$S_{ij} = \int \phi_i \phi_j \, d\tau \tag{3.90}$$

This treatment is little more complicated than the usual HMO treatment, and the corresponding equations (3.86) and (3.87) can be solved without difficulty using digital computers. However the arguments given above suggest that this is rather a pointless exercise. We have reached the conclusion that there would be no advantage in including overlap in the Pople method, given that we are treating it in a semiempirical fashion. The same must hold all the more forcibly for the still cruder HMO method; introducing overlap into this must be a useless refinement. The available evidence indeed suggests, first, that introduction of overlap offers no practical advantages; secondly, that the treatment thus modified is still useless for quantitative calculations; and thirdly, that in certain cases the effect of including overlap is positively disadvantageous (see Chap. 5).

A second modification, designed to allow for molecular polarity, was first introduced by Wheland and Mann[4] and has since been used extensively by Streitwieser.[5] We have seen that if the atoms in a molecule are neutral, so that in the notation of Sec. 3.7,

$$q_i = c_i \tag{3.91}$$

then the Hückel assumption, that H_{ii} has a constant value α_i, can be justified, assuming that the net interaction between an electron in the AO ϕ_i and some other neutral atom p is negligible. If we first make this assumption, and then allow the charge densities q_i to vary, we can write the diagonal matrix element F_{ii} in the form [compare Eqs. (3.64) and (3.84)]:

$$F_{ii} = \alpha_i + \tfrac{1}{2}(q_i - c_i)(ii,ii) + \sum_{j \neq i}(q_j - c_j)(ii,jj) \tag{3.92}$$

The one-center integral (ii,ii) is larger than the other integrals, since it represents the mutual repulsion between two electrons in the *same* AO ϕ_i; if we neglect the other terms in Eq. (3.92), we can write:

$$F_{ii} \approx \alpha_i + \tfrac{1}{2}(q_i - c_i)(ii,ii) \tag{3.93}$$

We can then allow for the variations in F_{ii} by using an alternative procedure. We first solve the HMO equations, using "normal" values for the coulomb integrals; from the resulting sets of orbital coefficients $a_{\mu i}$ we then calculate charge densities q_i; we use these to calculate new values for the diagonal elements F_{ii} (H_{ii}); and we repeat the cycle of operations until the q_i converge to a limit.

In practice the integral (ii,ii) in Eq. (3.93) is treated as a parameter; i.e.

$$F_{ii} = \alpha_i + \omega(q_i - c_i) \tag{3.94}$$

where ω is chosen to give the best fit with experiment. Streitwieser has called this procedure the ω *technique* after the symbol used by Wheland and Mann for the parameter.

At the time when Wheland and Mann introduced this treatment, the basis of the Hückel method was still uncertain and computations had still to be carried out by hand. Under these circumstances the method represented a valuable improvement over the simple Hückel approach. Now, however, there no longer seems much point in using it; for although it allows for one factor that leads to variations in values of the matrix elements, it neglects other terms of comparable magnitude. Thus while it is true that repulsion integrals (ii, jj) between electrons in different AOs are less than the one-center integrals (ii, ii), terms of the former type appear in Eq. (3.92) with twice the weight of the one-center term. Moreover a treatment of this type pays no attention to the equally serious errors involved in the Hückel assumption that the off-diagonal matrix elements have constant values. A final serious error appears in the calculation of molecular energies; our justification for the HMO method, which at best was tenuous, rested on the assumption that the atoms in a molecule are neutral. If this is not the case, then we cannot hope to calculate molecular energies, even within the limited context of the Hückel procedure.

There might still be some point in carrying out calculations of this kind if they were notably simpler than the ones using the Pople method and so used appreciably less computer time, but this is not the case. The slowest step in any HMO or Pople program is that involving the diagonalization of secular determinants. The Hückel method is faster than any process involving an iterative procedure because the secular equation has to be solved only once. Both the Wheland-Mann and Pople methods involve solution of one secular equation per iteration; the number of iterations required to reach a given degree of self-consistency is more or less the same for each method. The only difference lies in the time required to construct the successive F matrices; in the Roothaan treatment this is a major factor, but in the much simpler Pople method the time required is negligible compared with the time required for diagonalization. Therefore although it takes less time to construct the F matrices for the Wheland-Mann method than it does to do so for the Pople method, the difference is insignificant.

3.9 PHYSICAL SIGNIFICANCE OF BOND ORDERS

The arguments of Sec. 3.7 lead to a simple physical interpretation of the bond orders p_{ij} in the Pople and HMO treatments. If we are dealing with neutral molecules in which the simplifying assumptions that led to the HMO method hold, then the total energy E will be given approximately by:

$$E = 2 \sum_{\mu}^{occ} \epsilon_{\mu} = 2 \sum_{\mu}^{occ} \psi_{\mu} \mathbf{H}^{SCF} \psi_{\mu} \, d\tau = 2 \sum_{\mu}^{occ} \left(\sum_{i} a_{\mu i} \phi_{i} \right) \mathbf{H}^{SCF} \left(\sum_{j} a_{\mu j} \phi_{j} \right) d\tau$$

$$= 2 \sum_{\mu}^{occ} \sum_{i} \sum_{j} a_{\mu i} a_{\mu j} F_{ij}$$

$$= 2 \sum_{\mu}^{occ} \sum_{i} a_{\mu i}^{2} \alpha_{i} + 2 \sum_{\mu}^{occ} \sum_{i} \sum_{j} a_{\mu i} a_{\mu j} \beta_{ij}$$

$$= \sum_{i} q_{i} \alpha_{i} + 2 \sum_{i<j} \sum p_{ij} \beta_{ij} \tag{3.95}$$

Consider now the energy required to dissociate the molecule into widely separated atoms, i.e. the energy of atomization ΔE. In the Hückel treatment, the energy of the dissociated atoms will be given by a sum $\sum_{i} \alpha_{i}$ for the electrons in them. In a neutral molecule, the individual atoms will be almost neutral; this sum will be almost the same as the first sum in Eq. (3.95). Hence:

$$\Delta E \approx 2 \sum_{i<j} \sum p_{ij} \beta_{ij} \tag{3.96}$$

The sum consists of a number of terms, each referring to AOs of one pair of atoms; it is natural to associate the term associated with one pair of AOs, ϕ_{i} and ϕ_{j}, with the corresponding contribution to the total bonding in the molecule. This in turn is proportional to the bond order p_{ij}, which therefore emerges as a measure of the strength of the bond due to contributions by the AOs ϕ_{i} and ϕ_{j}. Suppose for example that we can dissect ΔE into contributions ΔE_{ij} due to the "bonds" formed through pairs of valence-shell AOs;

$$\Delta E = \sum_{i,j} \Delta E_{ij} \tag{3.97}$$

Suppose now we calculate the change in ΔE when one of the "bonds" tu changes in length by an amount δr_{tu}, using first-order perturbation theory. In this approximation, we assume that the wave function remains unchanged; hence all the bond orders p_{ij} in Eq. (3.96) remain unchanged. From the definitions of β_{ij} [Eq. (3.85)] and ΔE_{ij}, it is evident that all these quantities also remain unaffected, except β_{tu} and ΔE_{tu}. Hence:

$$\delta \Delta E = \delta \Delta E_{tu} = \frac{\partial \Delta E_{tu}}{\partial r_{tu}} \delta r_{tu}$$

$$= \delta(2 p_{tu} \beta_{tu}) = 2 p_{tu} \frac{\partial \beta_{tu}}{\partial r_{tu}} \delta r_{tu} \tag{3.98}$$

Thus:

$$\frac{\partial \Delta E_{tu}}{\partial r_{tu}} = 2 p_{tu} \frac{\partial \beta_{tu}}{\partial r_{tu}} \tag{3.99}$$

Integrating, and using Eqs. (3.96) and (3.97),

$$\Delta E_{tu} = 2p_{tu}\beta_{tu} \tag{3.100}$$

While this discussion has been given only in terms of the HMO method, and for a very simple case, it can easily be extended to the Pople approximation and generalized.   For a detailed discussion, see Ruedenberg.[6]

3.10   CONFIGURATION INTERACTION

The orbital approximation cannot give an exact value for the energy of a molecule because it neglects electron correlation due to the mutual coulomb repulsion of the electrons.   As we shall see (Chap. 5), some allowance may be made for this in a semiempirical treatment by adjustment of parameters, but this at best seems something of a makeshift expedient.   If we are to circumvent the difficulty, we must abandon our approximation of writing the wave function for a many-electron system as a Slater determinant of one-electron functions or orbitals.

One way to do this is to write the total wave function Ψ as a linear combination of two or more individual Slater determinants Φ_κ:

$$\Psi = \sum_\kappa A_\kappa \Phi_\kappa \tag{3.101}$$

The coefficients A_κ can as usual be found by the variation method, by choosing them in such a way as to minimize the total energy.   A function of this kind no longer corresponds to electrons moving independently of one another; in other words we can in this way include electron correlation in our treatment.   Indeed, by using a sufficient number of different functions Φ_κ, we can make Ψ approach as closely as we like to the true molecular wave function; here we are using the variation method to find an approximation to the true molecular wave function, whereas the Roothaan method merely provides an approximation to an approximation (i.e. to the true Hartree-Fock representation).

The individual determinants in a treatment of this kind are called *configurations;* the treatment itself is described as *configuration interaction* (CI).

In order to use this approach, we must first devise some way of amassing a collection of suitable determinantal functions Φ_κ.   Most of the work in this field has made use of the following procedure.   When we carry out a Roothaan, or Pople, or Hückel calculation, we normally use as our basis set a set of AOs which are at least equal in number to the total number of electrons.   Now the number of MOs obtained from such a calculation is clearly equal to the number N of basis functions; for the secular equation is an equation of Nth degree and so has N solutions.   At most half these are required to accommodate the N electrons; in the ground-state determinant or configuration Φ_0, half these MOs remain unused.   We can construct a large number of alternative determinants Φ_κ by distributing the N electrons in alternative ways among the N MOs; the resulting set of determinants forms a convenient basis set for our CI treatment.   This basis set is particularly convenient in that the determinantal functions Φ_κ are mutually orthogonal.   This can be seen at once from the argument used to calculate the normalizing factor for a Slater determinant [see Eqs. (2.171) to (2.176)]; the integral $\int \Phi_\mu \Phi_\nu \, d\tau$ vanishes if the determinants differ even by one orbital, given that the orbitals form an orthogonal set.

Using the variation treatment for a linear combination of basis-set functions, the coefficients A_κ and corresponding total energy $\mathcal{E}$ are given by:

$$|H_{\kappa\lambda} - \mathcal{E}\delta_{\kappa\lambda}| = 0 \tag{3.102}$$

$$\sum_\kappa A_{\mu\kappa}(H_{\kappa\lambda} - \mathcal{E}_\mu \delta_{\kappa\lambda}) = 0 \tag{3.103}$$

where

$$H_{\kappa\lambda} = \int \Phi_\kappa \mathbf{H} \Phi_\lambda \, d\tau \tag{3.104}$$

$\mathbf{H}$ being the correct hamiltonian operator for the molecule [Eq. (2.43)].

The necessary matrix elements $H_{\kappa\lambda}$ can be found in a straightforward way, using the same procedures as in Eqs. (2.171) to (2.188); a detailed description will be found in a monograph by Daudel, LeFebvre, and Moser.[7]   As, however, for reasons that will appear presently, we do not intend to use this kind of treatment, we need not go into details.

In applying configuration interaction to molecules, we must of course use the LCAO approximation; the individual orbitals ψ_μ are then expressed as linear combinations of AOs ϕ_i, the coefficients $a_{\mu i}$ being found by one of the standard procedures outlined above.   We can thus superimpose a CI treatment on either the Roothaan, or Pople, or Hückel LCAO MO methods.

The main difficulty in using CI lies in the number of configurations that can be constructed from a given set of MOs ψ_μ.   However it is easy to show that if we are interested in the ground-state wave function of the molecule, then only the lower energy configurations are likely to be important.

In the Hartree-Fock method, we write the total hamiltonian operator $\mathbf{H}^{\text{SCF}}$ for a molecule as a sum of one-electron operators $\mathbf{H}^i$;

$$\mathbf{H}^{\text{SCF}} = \sum_i \mathbf{H}^i \tag{3.105}$$

The various configurations built up from the corresponding Hartree-Fock MOs ψ_μ are eigenfunctions of $\mathbf{H}^{\text{SCF}}$.   Since the Hartree-Fock method gives a reasonable approximation to the ground-state energy, the true hamiltonian $\mathbf{H}$ must differ only slightly from $\mathbf{H}^{\text{SCF}}$; i.e.

$$\mathbf{H} = \mathbf{H}^{\text{SCF}} + \mathbf{P} \tag{3.106}$$

where $\mathbf{P}$ is small.   We can then use perturbation theory to find the eigenfunction of $\mathbf{H}$ from those of $\mathbf{H}^{\text{SCF}}$; in other words, we can carry out a kind of CI treatment using perturbation theory to find the coefficients A_μ in Eq. (3.105).   If the configuration of lowest energy is Φ_0, the approximation Φ_0' to the ground state will then be given by:

$$\Phi_0' = \Phi_0 + \sum_\mu \frac{P_{0\mu}}{E_0 - E_\mu}\Phi_\mu \qquad (3.107)$$

where
$$P_{0\mu} = \int\Phi_0 P\Phi_\mu\, d\tau \qquad (3.108)$$

The contribution of a given configuration will therefore in general be less, the greater the difference between its energy E_μ and that E_0 of the ground state.

Configurations can be described as singly, doubly, etc., excited depending on the number of spin-orbitals by which they differ from the ground state. It is easily shown that the energy of a configuration increases rapidly with the degree of excitation; we would expect interactions between configurations of similar excitation to be large, between configurations differing by 1 in excitation to be small, by 2 smaller still, and so forth.

Now it is very easily shown that the matrix element $H_{0\mu}$ between the ground state and an excited state Φ_μ vanishes, if Φ_μ is a singly excited state.[8] Since matrix elements of the type

$$H_{\mu\nu}{}^{\mathrm{SCF}} \equiv \int\Phi_\mu \mathbf{H}^{\mathrm{SCF}}\Phi_\nu\, d\tau \qquad (3.109)$$

necessarily vanish, Φ_μ and Φ_ν being different eigenfunctions of $\mathbf{H}^{\mathrm{SCF}}$, it follows that if $H_{\mu\nu}$ vanishes, so also does $P_{\mu\nu}$. Equation (3.107) then indicates that singly excited configurations do not mix with the ground state. Since doubly excited structures have energies far above that of the ground state, their contribution to the ground state must be small. This suggests that a CI treatment of the ground state may have little to offer; any gain will be offset by a great increase in complexity, the number of doubly excited configurations being unreasonably large even in the case of quite simple molecules.‡

These arguments were developed for a treatment based on rigorous Hartree-Fock orbitals; however the conclusions apply equally to the results of any SCF treatment, provided that we use it consistently. Thus if we use Pople MOs, we must neglect differential overlap in calculating the matrix elements between configurations. If we do this, we shall again find that matrix elements between the ground state and singly excited states vanish.

It seems then that CI is not very attractive for problems involving ground states; any advantages it can offer in the way of increased accuracy can probably be at least duplicated by using a parametric treatment involving single determinants. Further arguments supporting this idea will be found in Chap. 5. However the situation is entirely different in the case of excited states. All the determinants corresponding to singly excited states can combine with one an-

---

‡ The number of doubly excited configurations derived from a set of $2N$ orbitals and $2N$ electrons is $\frac{1}{4}N(N-1)$; for a molecule containing 42 electrons, e.g. benzene, this amounts to 88,200. No existing computer could begin to diagonalize a matrix with 88,200 rows and columns.

other, and since all have the same degree of excitation, the interactions should be large. We cannot therefore hope to get any kind of reasonable description of excited states in terms of single determinants; here we *must* introduce configuration interaction.

If we are interested in the light absorption of molecules, or in the chemistry of photoexcited states, we must then proceed very warily. Only in special circumstances will it be possible to describe these processes in terms of a simple orbital picture. Conversely, it is incorrect in principle to assess a theoretical treatment of ground states by its efficiency for calculating excitation energies; the two problems are entirely distinct.

3.11   THE PARISER-PARR AND RUEDENBERG METHODS

Two CI treatments deserve special mention since they follow a rather different philosophy. The first of these is known as the Pariser-Parr method, after its originators;[9] this is based on a CI treatment, using Slater determinants constructed from Hückel orbitals. At the time this method was devised, computers were not yet available, but it was already recognized that the Hückel method was inadequate for quantitative calculations of molecular properties; Pariser and Parr suggested that these inadequacies might be countered by introducing configuration interaction, if differential overlap is neglected. The interconfigurational matrix elements $H_{\kappa\lambda}$ [Eq. (3.104)] can be calculated without much difficulty, and the method thus becomes a feasible procedure, using ordinary desk calculating machines.

Since the basis MOs have not been determined by a SCF procedure, the matrix elements between the ground-state configuration and singly excited configurations no longer vanish. This approach is therefore better than the Hückel method for ground states of molecules; even the ground state benefits from configuration interaction. Nevertheless the method is less satisfactory in this connection than the semiempirical Pople treatment; the deficiencies of the Hückel method are in general too serious to be covered up in this way.

The situation is, however, entirely different for excited states; here the Pariser-Parr method gives very satisfactory results, particularly in the case of conjugated molecules. This is true even of a simplified treatment[10] in which only a very limited number of configurations is included; indeed, this "poor man's Pariser-Parr method" is not only much superior to any treatments in which excited states are represented by single determinants but it is almost as good as the full treatment. This emphasizes the point made above, that CI is *essential* in treatments of excited states.

The second approach, due to Ruedenberg,[6] is similar; here, however, the basic MOs are calculated by a Hückel procedure in which overlap between bonded atoms is included. The main purpose of these calculations has been to estimate electronic spectra of conjugated molecules; in this it has again been very successful.

For chemical purposes, however, where we are primarily interested in the properties of ground states, the semiempirical Pople method still seems to offer by far the most promising line of attack. Correspondingly, for qualitative purposes, the Hückel method suffices without the various complications and refinements that have been introduced into it at various times.

PROBLEMS

3.1 Examine the correctness of the arguments in Sec. 3.4 by comparing the Pople and Roothaan expressions for the total energy of H_2. *Note:* The occupied MO ψ is determined by symmetry; in unnormalized form, $\psi = \phi_1 + \phi_2$, where ϕ_1 and ϕ_2 are $1s$ AOs of the hydrogen atoms.

3.2 Carry out Hückel calculations for H_2, and for H_3 with the nuclei at the corners of an equilateral triangle. Should H_3 be stable?

3.3 What changes must be made in the Hückel method to allow for overlap? That is, repeat the simple derivation of the Hückel equations, Sec. 3.7, using the general form of the variation method where overlap is included; see Sec. 2.6.

3.4 Repeat the calculations of Prob. 3.2, including overlap. Does inclusion of overlap alter your conclusions concerning the stability of H_3? *Hint:* In order to solve the secular equations, introduce a new variable x, given by

$$x = \frac{\alpha - \epsilon}{\beta - S\epsilon}$$

where S is the overlap integral.

3.5 Consider a closed-shell system represented by the Slater determinant $|\phi_1\bar\phi_1\phi_2\bar\phi_2\cdots\phi_\mu\bar\phi_\mu|$, where ϕ_λ is the λth MO of energy ϵ_λ. Consider the states of the molecule corresponding to excitation of an electron from the MO ϕ_μ to an empty MO ϕ_ν. Four Slater determinants of this kind can be written:

$$\psi_1 = |\phi_1\bar\phi_1\phi_2\bar\phi_2\cdots\phi_\mu\phi_\nu| \qquad \psi_2 = |\phi_1\bar\phi_1\phi_2\bar\phi_2\cdots\bar\phi_\mu\phi_\nu|$$
$$\psi_3 = |\phi_1\bar\phi_1\phi_2\bar\phi_2\cdots\phi_\mu\bar\phi_\nu| \qquad \psi_4 = |\phi_1\bar\phi_1\phi_2\bar\phi_2\cdots\bar\phi_\mu\bar\phi_\nu|$$

(*a*) Calculate the energies of the individual configurations (compare Sec. 2.13). (*b*) Calculate the matrix elements S_{ij} and H_{ij} between the configurations ψ_1 to ψ_4 where

$$S_{ij} = \int\psi_i\psi_j\,d\tau \qquad H_{ij} = \int\psi_i\mathbf{H}\psi_j\,d\tau$$

(c) Using these matrix elements, carry out a configuration-interaction treatment for the excited states, using a linear combination of the functions ψ_1 to ψ_4. (d) Hence deduce the singlet and triplet transition energies corresponding to the transition $\phi_\mu \rightarrow \phi_\nu$.

REFERENCES

1   Pople, J. A.: *Trans. Faraday Soc.* **49,** 1375 (1953); *Proc. Roy. Soc.* (*London*) **A233,** 233 (1955); *J. Phys. Chem.* **61,** 6 (1957); A. Brickstock and J. A. Pople: *Trans. Faraday Soc.* **50,** 901 (1954).

2   Pople, J. A., D. P. Santry, and G. A. Segal: *J. Chem. Phys.* **43,** S129 (1965); J. A. Pople and G. A. Segal: *ibid.,* S136; **44,** 3289 (1966).

3   Hückel, E.: *Z. Physik* **70,** 204 (1931).

4   Wheland, G. W., and D. E. Mann: *J. Chem. Phys.* **17,** 264 (1949).

5   Streitwieser, A., Jr.: *J. Am. Chem. Soc.* **82,** 4123 (1960); A. Streitwieser, Jr., and P. M. Nair: *Tetrahedron* **5,** 149 (1959).

6   Ruedenberg, K.: *J. Chem. Phys.* **34,** 1861, 1878, 1884, 1892, 1897, 1907 (1961); *Rev. Mod. Phys.* **34,** 326 (1962).

7   Daudel, R., R. LeFebvre, and C. Moser: "Quantum Chemistry," Interscience Publishers, Inc., New York, 1959.

8   Pople, J. A.: *Proc. Phys. Soc.* (*London*) **68,** 81 (1955).

9   Pariser, R., and R. G. Parr: *J. Chem. Phys.* **21,** 466, 767 (1953).

10   Weltin, E., J. P. Weber, and E. Heilbronner: *Theoret. Chim. Acta* **2,** 114 (1964).

ATOMS AND
SIMPLE MOLECULES

4.1 THE ORBITAL PICTURE OF ATOMS

The best picture of atoms that current theory can provide is that given by an orbital approach using Hartree-Fock orbitals or the close approximations to these afforded by the Roothaan method. Here each electron is supposed to move independently of the others in a central field of force, i.e. one in which the force acting on the electron is directed toward the nucleus and the magnitude of the force depends only on the distance of the electron from the nucleus. When the electron is at a distance r from the nucleus, this force is given by $Z'e^2/r^2$, where Z' is a number which decreases with r and is equal to Z (the atomic number of the atom) when r is zero. As we have seen, the resulting orbitals ψ are of the form:

$$\psi = F(r)\, Y(l,m) \tag{4.1}$$

where $Y(l,m)$ is a spherical harmonic and F a function only of r. The general shapes of the orbitals are thus similar to those of hydrogen, the difference between the two lying in the nature of the radial function F.

The picture given by this kind of approach must correspond quite closely to reality; for the Hartree-Fock binding energies agree with experiment to better than 1 percent. This suggests that one might get a sufficiently good picture if one used hydrogenlike AOs instead of Hartree-Fock AOs, the variable number Z' in the potential function being replaced by some mean value $\overline{Z}$. Such indeed is the philosophy underlying the Slater-Zener treatment; in practice the results given by a treatment of this kind are in surprisingly good agreement with experiment, the errors in the calculated binding energies being still on the order of 1 percent. One might therefore expect there to be a very close correspondence between the orbitals given by rigorous Hartree-Fock calculations and the hydrogenlike orbitals corresponding to fixed mean values of Z'; this indeed is the case. The orbitals are similar both in shape and in the number of radial nodes; they differ (see Sec. 2.17) only in that the SCF orbitals have a higher density in the region near the nucleus (where $Z' > \overline{Z}$) and are more diffuse (since in the outer regions of the atom, $Z' < \overline{Z}$). We can therefore legitimately discuss the structure of atoms in terms of an orbital approximation using hydrogenlike orbitals.

In the Slater-Zener method, both the effective nuclear charge $\overline{Z}$ and the principal quantum number n of each orbital are treated as parameters, their values being adjusted to minimize the total energy of the atom. However for atoms in the first half of the periodic table, the values of n turn out to be integers; since the angular part of each orbital is the same as that of a hydrogen AO [Eq. (4.1)], each orbital can therefore be characterized by the same three quantum numbers n, l, m as a corresponding orbital of hydrogen, and the same nomenclature can be used for them.

In the case of a hydrogenlike atom, each orbital corresponds to motion in the field of a fixed charge $\overline{Z}e$. Our orbitals will be similar to these, representing motion in the field of a fixed charge $\overline{Z}e$, but here $\overline{Z}e$ will not be the same for different orbitals. As we have seen (Sec. 2.15), $\overline{Z}$ represents the effective nuclear charge seen by our electron, part of the attraction of the nucleus being screened by electrons that lie closer to it than does the electron we are considering. The average number of such electrons is then $Z - \overline{Z}$. This number will clearly be less, and so $\overline{Z}$ greater, the smaller the size of our orbital. Since the size of hydrogenlike orbitals normally increases with increasing n, $\overline{Z}$ should decrease correspondingly; since the energy E_h of a hydrogenlike orbital is given by

$$E_h = \frac{mZ^2e^4}{n^2h^2} \tag{4.2}$$

and since Z decreases as n increases, the energies of our orbitals should be greater, the greater the principal quantum number n, just as for the orbitals of a hydrogen atom.

Differences arise, however, in the case of orbitals with the same n but different values for the azimuthal and magnetic quantum numbers l and m. If Z is fixed, all these orbitals have the same energy (compare Sec. 2.1); in the case of atoms with many electrons, however, the value of $\overline{Z}$ depends on l, and so this degeneracy no longer holds.

The reason for this is simple. Consider for example an s orbital and a corresponding p orbital of hydrogen, both with the same principal quantum number n. The corresponding radial functions R_s, R_p, are of the form:

$$R_s = (A_0 + A_1 r + \cdots)e^{-a_0 r/n} \qquad R_p = (B_1 r + B_2 r^2 + \cdots)e^{-a_0 r/n} \tag{4.3}$$

where the terms in parentheses represent the corresponding associated Laguerre polynomials (see Sec. 2.1). As $r \to 0$, the leading term in the polynomial for the s AO is a constant (A_0), but that for the p AO is a term in r; while therefore the s AO has a finite density near the origin, the p AO does not. (This difference of course corresponds to the fact that a p AO, unlike an s AO, has a radial node passing through the nucleus.) Consequently an electron occupying an s AO is much more likely to be found in the region near the nucleus than one in a p AO. Now in the case of a many-electron atom, the region near the nucleus is one where an electron is exposed to the full, almost unscreened, field of the nucleus; since an s electron spends more time there than a corresponding p electron does, the effective nuclear charge $\overline{Z}_s$ of the s AO must be greater than that $(\overline{Z}_p)$ of the p AO, and the binding energy of the s AO must likewise be greater.

The same argument can be applied to comparisons of corresponding p and d AOs. The leading term in the associated Laguerre polynomial for a d orbital is a term in r^2; such an orbital therefore vanishes even more effectively in the vicinity of the nucleus than a corresponding p orbital does, so the effective nuclear charge $\overline{Z}_d$ and binding energy are correspondingly less.

Therefore in heavier atoms the degeneracy of orbitals with the same n but different l disappears. The orbitals now differ in energy, the energy being less, the smaller l. The order of orbital energies is then $s < p < d < f < \cdots$. The spread of energies due to this effect is indeed so great that it can lead to orbitals with a high value of n but low value of l lying below orbitals with a smaller value of n but a greater value of l. Thus the $4s$ orbitals in elements of the first transition series lie below the $3d$ orbitals in energy, while the $4f$ orbitals in the rare earths lie below the $5s$, $5p$, and even the $6s$ orbitals.

Orbitals with the same value of n and l but different values of m still retain their degeneracy, in this approximation; for such orbitals can be interconverted merely by a rotation of the coordinate axes.

The ground state of our atom is to be represented by a Slater determinant constructed from these hydrogenlike orbitals. The orbitals are to be selected in such a way as to minimize the total energy. Now the total energy of an atom, in the orbital approximation, is given by a sum of the orbital energies of the electrons *less* the total interelectronic repulsion. The choice of orbitals cannot therefore be made solely on the basis of their orbital energies; for it might be profitable to place electrons in an orbital of higher energy if the interelectronic repulsions were correspondingly decreased. In practice, however, the interelectronic repulsions between electrons in different orbitals do not differ sufficiently to outweigh the differences in orbital energy; other things being equal, we can therefore use an *aufbau* principle in selecting orbitals, placing our electrons in pairs in the orbitals of lowest energy available to them.

As will be familiar from textbooks of inorganic chemistry, this principle does in fact hold very well; problems arise only when we are assigning electrons to a group of orbitals of identical energy, i.e. orbitals all of which have the same values for the quantum numbers n and l; here the choice *is* determined by differences in interelectronic repulsion, as will become clear in the following section.

4.2 THE VECTOR MODEL AND HUND'S RULES

The order of orbitals in the first segment of the periodic table is:

$$1s < 2s < 2p < 3s < 3p \tag{4.4}$$

Following the aufbau principle, the configurations of the first five elements are then:

H:	$1s$	
He:	$(1s)^2$	
Li:	$(1s)^2(2s)$	(4.5)
Be:	$(1s)^2(2s)^2$	
B:	$(1s)^2(2s)^2(2p)$	

Carbon, however, presents an ambiguity. Here two electrons must be assigned to the $2p$ level; will these occupy the same p AO, in which case of course their spins must be antiparallel, or will they occupy different AOs, and if so, will their spins be parallel or antiparallel?

The choice between these three possibilities presents no difficulties. All these states have identical total orbital energies; any differences between them must be due to differences in the total electronic repulsion. Now the repulsion between a given p electron and the "core," composed of the nucleus together with the "inner shells" of $1s$ and $2s$ electrons, will obviously be the same for a p electron in any one of the three possible $2p$ AOs ($m = 1, 0, -1$); for these orbitals are equivalent. Any differences must then arise from differences in the mutual repulsion between the two $2p$ electrons. The repulsion between two electrons will clearly be less if they occupy different $2p$ AOs than if they occupy the same one, since they will then on an average be further apart in space; moreover, other things being equal, the repulsion between two electrons of parallel spin will be less than that between electrons of antiparallel spin, since in the former case the mutual interelectronic repulsion is reduced by an "exchange correction." The lowest state of the carbon atom must then be one with the two $2p$ electrons occupying different orbitals and with parallel spins. This argument can obviously be generalized; other things being equal, the lowest state of an atom will be one in which as many electrons as possible occupy different orbitals with parallel spins, a generalization known as *Hund's first rule.*

To progress further, we must look into the situation in more detail. The arguments of Sec. 1.4 show that the total angular momentum of an atom is a constant of the motion. The angular momentum of an atom is built up from three main parts, the orbital angular momentum of the electrons, the spin angular momentum of the electrons, and the spin angular momentum of the nuclei. In light atoms there is very little coupling between these three components; consequently there is little interchange of angular momentum between them, and so, to a good approximation, the total angular momentum of each component is a constant of the motion. Atoms which obey this condition are said to have *Russell-Saunders coupling;* most "organic" atoms fall into this category.

In such an atom, the total orbital angular momentum and any one component of it are constants of the motion. Let us then consider one component of the angular momentum, i.e. that about the z axis. We know that the z component of angular momentum of a given electron, in the orbital approximation, is given by $m\hbar$, where m is its magnetic quantum number, and the total z component of angular momentum is given by summing the contributions of the individual electrons. We can therefore represent the z component of the total angular momentum by a quantum number M, given by:

$$M = \sum_i m_i \tag{4.6}$$

where m_i is the magnetic quantum number of the ith electron.

The total angular momentum of any system is, we know, given by an expression of the form:

$$L\hbar^2(L + 1) \tag{4.7}$$

where L is an overall quantum number equivalent to the azimuthal quantum number of a single electron. In this case, however, L cannot be expressed in any simple way in terms of the quantum numbers l_i of the individual electrons, because angular momentum is a vector quantity; the total electronic angular momentum of an atom is a *vector* sum of the angular momenta of the individual electrons, and this depends on the mutual orientation of the vectors as well as on their magnitude.

Suppose for example that the two $2p$ electrons in carbon have their angular momenta directed at right angles. Then when the component of one of them along the z axis is $\hbar$, that of the other is zero (Fig. 4.1). There is no way in which we can arrive at a situation where both electrons have their vectors simultaneously pointing along the z axis; consequently although $l = 1$ for each electron, the maximum value of M, i.e. the value of L, is unity and not 2.

This intuitive argument can be put very simply into mathematical terms. Consider the operator $\mathbf{M}_z$, representing the z component of the total angular momentum of the electrons in an atom. It is easily shown that:

$$\mathbf{M}_z = \sum_i \mathbf{M}_{zi} \tag{4.8}$$

where $\mathbf{M}_{zi}$ is the operator for the z component of the angular momentum of the ith electron. An argument similar to that used in Sec. 2.12 then shows that if ψ is a Slater determinant of such AOs,

$$\mathbf{M}_z\psi = M\psi = \left(\sum_i m_i\right)\psi \tag{4.9}$$

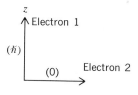

FIG. 4.1 Vector addition of angular momenta; the numbers in parentheses are the components of angular momenta of the p electrons ($l = 1$) along the z axis.

where m_i is the magnetic quantum number for the ith electron.   Each such Slater determinant is therefore automatically an eigenfunction of $\mathbf{M}_z$.   The same is not true, however, of the operator $\mathbf{L}^2$ corresponding to the square of the total electronic angular momentum of the atom. $\mathbf{L}^2$ cannot be written as a simple combination of the one-electron operators $\mathbf{L}_i{}^2$, and ψ will not necessarily be an eigenfunction of $\mathbf{L}^2$.   We can, however, get round this difficulty in the following way.   We know that any state of the atom, with total angular momentum $L(L + 1)\hbar^2$ [Eq. (4.7)], will have $2L + 1$ substates, in which M adopts all possible integral values from $+L$ to $-L$.   We also know that each possible state of the atom is represented by a function that is an eigenfunction of $\mathbf{M}_z$, and that any Slater determinant of our set of orbitals is such a function.   If there is only a single function with a given value of M, this must then also be an eigenfunction of $\mathbf{L}^2$; for all our possible wave functions must be eigenfunctions of both $\mathbf{L}^2$ and $\mathbf{M}_z$, and if there is only *one* determinant corresponding to a given value of M, this must be one of the substates arising from the level corresponding to some given value of L.   If, however, there are two or more substates with a given value of M, this argument no longer holds; for any linear combination of those functions will be equally an eigenfunction of $\mathbf{M}_z$.   However we must then be able to replace the individual functions by a set of linear combinations which *are* eigenfunctions of $\mathbf{L}^2$; this is a typical case of degeneracy with respect to one physical measurement being removed by introducing another (Sec. 1.4).

Consider again our carbon atom.   Each of the two $2p$ electrons can have three different values of m, viz. 1, 0, or -1.   There are therefore nine possible configurations, listed in Table 4.1.   We see that there are two configurations which are unique, with $M = \pm 2$; these must also be eigenfunctions of $\mathbf{L}^2$.   The corresponding state is termed a D state from analogy with the hydrogen atom, the square of its orbital momentum being $2\hbar^2(2 + 1)$.   The states with $M = \pm 2$ are two of the five possible substates of this.   Next, there are two configurations with $M = 1$, and two with $M = -1$; some linear combinations of these will provide the substates of our D state, with $L = 2$ and $M = \pm 1$.   However we had initially *four* distinct configurations of this type; we are therefore left with two further independent functions, with $M = +1$ and $M = -1$, which are now unique and must therefore also be eigenfunctions of $\mathbf{L}^2$.   These must be two of

TABLE 4.1   Possible values of M for various values of m of the two $2p$ electrons in carbon

Magnetic quantum number of electron 2	Magnetic quantum number electron 1		
	1	0	-1
1	2	1	0
0	1	0	-1
-1	0	-1	-2

the substates of a level with $L = 1$, that is a P state.   And finally we have three configurations with $M = 0$; linear combinations of these provide the missing substates ($M = 0$) in our D and P levels, while the third must represent an independent state with $L = 0$, that is an S state.

Let us now consider the spins of our electrons.   The two $2p$ electrons must occupy different spin-orbitals, to satisfy the Pauli principle; the configurations with $M = \pm 2$ must therefore correspond to states in which the electrons have antiparallel spins, because otherwise they could not both occupy the same $2p$ AO (with $m = 1$ or $m = -1$).   Since the five substates of the D state differ only in the way the atom orients itself in a magnetic field, the same must be true of all of the other substates also; this then is a ^1D state with all the electrons paired.

Consider now the other state with $M = 1$.   In order to distinguish this from the corresponding component of the ^1D state, it must differ in total spin momentum; the P state must therefore be one in which the electrons have parallel spins, occupying different AOs.   It must therefore be a ^3P state.

Now there are only three ways we can place a pair of electrons with the *same* spin into a given set of $2p$ AOs; any other states must correspond to situations where the electron spins are paired.   Our final state must therefore be a ^1S state.

This way of constructing possible configurations for a set of orbitals of equal orbital energy is called the *vector model;* its extension to systems with three or more such electrons is obvious.   The arguments given earlier imply that the lowest of the three possible states of carbon (namely ^3P, ^1D, and ^1S) should be ^3P; this is in agreement with experiment.

Can we deduce the relative energies of the other two levels?   Not too easily in intuitive terms, but here we can use another generalization, known as *Hund's second rule*.   This says that if two states have identical total orbital energies and identical multiplicities (i.e. equal numbers of unpaired electrons with parallel spins), then the state with the higher value of L has the lower energy.   The second lowest state of carbon is therefore ^1D, rather than ^1S.

The reader may very reasonably feel dubious about these arguments, on the grounds that they are based on an admittedly very approximate treatment of atomic structure; how do we know that any of these conclusions will survive the introduction of electron correlation, with loss of the simplifying assumptions on which the orbital picture is based?   This difficulty can be met quite easily.   Suppose we start with an orbital picture of an atom, and then introduce the mutual interelectronic repulsions by using perturbation theory.   Consider the mutual repulsion of two electrons i and j.   Since the force between them acts along the line joining them, the interaction will have no effect on the *sum* of their angular momenta; for any change in the angular momentum of electron i will be offset by an exactly equal and opposite change in the angular momentum of electron j.   The real states of the atom will therefore correlate exactly with our orbital approximations, each real state having the same values of M and L as one of our orbital states.   Moreover comparison of the energies calculated for various states of atoms by the Hartree-Fock method with those observed suggests that the correlation energy due to the interaction of a given pair of electrons depends remarkably little on the orbitals they occupy; even conclusions concerning the relative energies of different states should therefore carry over quite well from the orbital approximation to the real atom.

4.3   THE HYDROGEN MOLECULE

The molecule H_2 contains two atoms; in the LCAO approximation, its MOs will therefore be written as combinations of two AOs ϕ_1, ϕ_2 of the two atoms.   We shall assume that these are $1s$ AOs, an assumption which will be justified later.

First, let us treat H_2 in terms of the Hückel method.   In the Hückel method, the diagonal F-matrix elements H_{ii} ($\equiv \alpha_i$) are parameters which are supposed to be equal to the ionization potentials of electrons in the corresponding AOs of isolated atoms; their values are therefore characteristic of the AOs in question, a conclusion which carries over to the more sophisticated interpretation of Sec. 3.7.   Here then

$$\alpha_1 = \alpha_2 \equiv \alpha \tag{4.10}$$

The diagonal F-matrix elements F_{ij} and F_{ji} are necessarily equal in any treatment, since they are matrix elements of real hermitian operators between two real functions ϕ_i, ϕ_j.   In the Hückel treatment, where these matrix elements are treated as parameters, the two elements F_{12}, F_{21} are set equal to the same parameter β;

$$F_{12} = F_{21} = \beta \tag{4.11}$$

The secular equation (3.72) then becomes:

$$\begin{vmatrix} \alpha - E & \beta \\ \beta & \alpha - E \end{vmatrix} = 0 \tag{4.12}$$

Expanding the determinant,

$$(\alpha - E)^2 - \beta^2 = 0 \tag{4.13}$$

or
$$E = \alpha \pm \beta \tag{4.14}$$

As we shall see presently, β is a negative quantity; the MO with lowest energy is therefore the one with energy $\alpha + \beta$.   Both electrons in H_2 occupy this MO; according to the Hückel method, the total energy E_{tot} of H_2 should then be:

$$E_{tot} = 2\alpha + 2\beta \tag{4.15}$$

Since by assumption the energy of an electron in an isolated hydrogen atom is α, the molecule has a lower energy than a pair of isolated hydrogen atoms.   The difference, 2β, can then be equated to the heat of formation of H_2, or *minus* the bond energy of the bond in H_2.

Substituting the value E_1 of the energy of this MO (ψ_1) in the equation (3.72) for the coefficients a_{11}, a_{12} of the two AOs contributing to ψ_1, we find:

$$a_{11}[\alpha - (\alpha + \beta)] + a_{12}\beta = 0 \qquad (4.16)$$

Hence:

$$a_{11} = a_{12} = A \qquad (4.17)$$

The MO ψ_1 therefore has the form:

$$\psi_1 = A(\phi_1 + \phi_2) \qquad (4.18)$$

The factor A is chosen to normalize ψ_1; hence:

$$\int \psi^2 \, d\tau = A^2 \int (\phi_1 + \phi_2)^2 \, d\tau = 2A^2 = 1 \qquad (4.19)$$

The normalized MO ψ_1 is therefore given by:

$$\psi_1 = \frac{1}{\sqrt{2}} (\phi_1 + \phi_2) \qquad (4.20)$$

Electrons in ψ_1 have a lower energy than they would if they occupied AOs of isolated hydrogen atoms; this difference is responsible for the existence of a stable molecule H_2. The orbital H_1 is therefore called a *bonding MO* (BMO). A similar analysis shows that the second MO ψ_2 is given by:

$$\psi_2 = \frac{1}{\sqrt{2}} (\phi_1 - \phi_2) \qquad \text{energy } \alpha - \beta \qquad (4.21)$$

The energy of ψ_2 is therefore greater than that (α) of an isolated hydrogen atom. If an electron in H_2 were to occupy this MO, the effect would be to increase the energy above that of an isolated hydrogen atom; such an orbital is therefore termed an *antibonding MO* (AMO).

Next let us try a somewhat more sophisticated approach to H_2, viz. the Pople method. Here the matrix elements are given [see Eqs. (3.23) and (3.62)] by:

$$F_{11} = W_1 + \tfrac{1}{2}q_1(11,11) + (q_2 - 1)(11,22) \qquad (4.22)$$
$$F_{22} = W_2 + \tfrac{1}{2}q_2(22,22) + (q_1 - 1)(22,11) \qquad (4.23)$$
$$F_{12} = F_{21} = \beta_{12}{}^c - \tfrac{1}{2}p_{12}(11,22) \qquad (4.24)$$

From the definitions of electron repulsion integrals [Eq. (2.223)],

$$(11,22) = (22,11) \qquad (4.25)$$

Since moreover hydrogen atoms are identical,

$$W_1 = W_2 = W_h \qquad (4.26)$$
$$(11,11) = (22,22) \qquad (4.27)$$

where W_h is the ionization potential of a hydrogen atom in its ground state. The Pople equations have of course to be solved by an iterative procedure; to start this, we need to assume initial values of the q_i and p_{ij}. Let us here assume values corresponding to the Hückel MO ψ_1 [Eq. (4.20)];

$$q_1 = 2a_{11}{}^2 = 2\left(\frac{1}{\sqrt{2}}\right)^2 = 1 \tag{4.28}$$

$$q_2 = 2a_{12}{}^2 = 2\left(\frac{1}{\sqrt{2}}\right)^2 = 1 \tag{4.29}$$

$$p_{12} = 2a_{11}a_{12} = 2\left(\frac{1}{\sqrt{2}}\right)\frac{1}{\sqrt{2}} = 1 \tag{4.30}$$

Combining Eqs. (4.22) to (4.30):

$$F_{11} = F_{22} = W_h + \tfrac{1}{2}(11,11) \tag{4.31}$$
$$F_{12} = F_{21} = \beta_{12}{}^c - \tfrac{1}{2}(11,22) \tag{4.32}$$

The secular equation thus becomes

$$\begin{vmatrix} W_h + \tfrac{1}{2}(11,11) - E & \beta_{12}{}^c - \tfrac{1}{2}(11,22) \\ \beta_{12}{}^c - \tfrac{1}{2}(11,22) & W_h + \tfrac{1}{2}(11,11) - E \end{vmatrix} = 0 \tag{4.33}$$

with the solutions:

$$E_1 = W_h + \tfrac{1}{2}[(11,11) - (11,22)] + \beta_{12}{}^c \tag{4.34}$$
$$E_2 = W_h + \tfrac{1}{2}[(11,11) + (11,22)] - \beta_{12}{}^c \tag{4.35}$$

Here E_1 is clearly the lower root, since $\beta_{12}{}^c$ is necessarily negative, while all the electron repulsion integrals are positive. Substituting for E_1 in the equations for the orbital coefficients, we find:

$$a_{11}[W_h + \tfrac{1}{2}(11,11) - \{W_h + \tfrac{1}{2}[(11,11) - (11,22)] + \beta_{12}{}^c\}]$$
$$+ a_{12}[\beta_{12}{}^c - \tfrac{1}{2}(11,22)] = 0$$

with the solution:

$$a_{11} = a_{12} \tag{4.36}$$

We therefore end up with an orbital identical with the one we assumed in setting up our F matrix; thanks to this fortunate choice of the initial values, our solution is therefore already self-consistent. The total energy of H_2 in the Pople method is given by a sum of the total orbital energy *less* the average electron repulsion. In this case the repulsion energy is equal to the energy of mutual repulsion of two electrons occupying the MO ψ_1, that is to J_{11} [Eq. (2.221)];

$$J_{11} = \iint \psi_1{}^2(1) \frac{e^2}{r_{12}} \psi_1{}^2(2) \, d\tau_1 \, d\tau_2 \tag{4.37}$$

Substituting from Eq. (4.20), we find:

$$J_{11} = \tfrac{1}{2}[(11,11) + (11,22)] \tag{4.38}$$

The total electronic energy E_{el} of H_2 is therefore given by:

$$E_{el} = 2E_1 - J_{11} = 2W_h + 2\beta_{12}{}^c + \tfrac{1}{2}(11,11) - \tfrac{3}{2}(11,22) \qquad (4.39)$$

The total energy E_{tot} of H_2 is found by adding to this the mutual repulsion between the two nuclei; this is assumed, in the Pople method, to be equal to the repulsion between a corresponding pair of electrons, in this case to the integral (11,22). Thus:

$$E_{tot} = E_{el} + (11,22) = 2W_h + 2\beta_{12}{}^c + \tfrac{1}{2}[(11,11) - (11,22)] \qquad (4.40)$$

Finally the heat of formation ΔH is found by subtracting from E_{tot} the energy $2W_h$ of two isolated hydrogen atoms; thus:

$$\Delta H = E_{tot} - 2W_h = 2\beta_{12}{}^c + \tfrac{1}{2}[(11,11) - (11,22)] \qquad (4.41)$$

The sum in square brackets is likely to be small; it represents the difference in repulsion between two electrons in the same AO and two electrons in AOs of different atoms which, however, are very close together (in H_2, at a distance of 0.8 Å). In this case all the integrals can be evaluated, and it is indeed found that the term $2\beta_{12}{}^c$ is much the larger. Hence ΔH is negative, corresponding to the existence of a stable molecule H_2.

The general conclusions are therefore very similar to those given by the Hückel method; however the Pople treatment gives a much closer insight into the physical situation responsible for the fact that hydrogen atoms combine to form a stable molecule H_2. The factor responsible for the binding is seen to be that embodied in the core resonance integral $\beta_{12}{}^c$; the binding is therefore a one-electron effect due to the fact that the electrons in H_2 occupy a MO which has a very high density between the nuclei. The resulting concentrated cloud of negative charge thus acts as a kind of electrostatic cement that holds the nuclei together. The repulsion between the electrons tends to weaken the bond, but it is overruled [compare the two terms in Eq. (4.41)]. This situation turns out to be quite general; chemical bonding is mainly an effect of the additional attractive forces between the nuclei of atoms in molecules due to the overlap clouds contributing to their MOs. The same argument provides a further justification for use of the Hückel method in a qualitative sense. If the two-electron terms in Eq. (4.41) are neglected, the heat of formation has exactly the same form as in the Hückel method, with the Hückel β now interpreted as a simple one-electron resonance integral. Integrals of this type can reasonably be expected to be characteristic of given types of bond, regardless of the molecules in which they appear; the Hückel method should therefore serve well as a qualitative description of bonding, even if it cannot safely be used in any quantitative sense.

The next step of course would be to carry out a Roothaan treatment of H_2, again using as our basis set just the two $1s$ hydrogen AOs. If we do this, and if we use the Mulliken approximation [Eq. (3.22)] for the repulsion integrals, we arrive at exactly the same conclusions as those given by the Pople method.

Since the treatment is straightforward and leads to no new principles, it will be left to the reader as an exercise.

We have been assuming that our MOs should be constructed from ground-state AOs of the individual atoms; our conclusion, that bonding is a function mainly of the one-electron resonance integrals, provides a justification for this. We know, both from the Mulliken approximation and from the intuitive interpretation given in Sec. 3.4, that the resonance integral β_{ij} is proportional to some kind of mean of the binding energies W_i, W_j of the two corresponding AOs ϕ_i, ϕ_j. If we replaced $1s$ AOs in our calculation for H_2 by AOs of higher energy W_h', the corresponding resonance integral β_{12}' would then be numerically smaller. Moreover our expression for the total energy would then be further increased by positive contributions $W_h' - W_h$. Consequently the use of AOs other than $1s$ would lead to much higher total energies for H_2. This conclusion can be generalized; in an LCAO MO treatment of ground states of molecules, we must use as our basis set the lowest-energy AOs possible of the individual atoms.

One last point may be mentioned, since much confusion has been caused by failure to recognize it. The arguments given here in support of the Hückel method apply *only* to its use in treating ground states of molecules. For example attempts are often made to treat excited states in terms of Hückel theory, it being assumed that such a state can be represented in terms of ground-state orbitals, with one electron moved up into an AMO. Thus the first absorption band of H_2 is commonly identified with a process in which an electron jumps from the BMO ψ_1 to the AMO ψ_2, and in the Hückel method the corresponding energy change is then naturally equated to the difference 2β in energy between the two orbitals [Eq. (4.14)], i.e. equal, in the Hückel treatment, to the bond energy of H_2. The observed excitation energy is about double this, and similar discrepancies occur in all analogous applications of the Hückel method to calculating molecular spectra. The reason for the discrepancy is easily seen, from Eqs. (4.34) and (4.35). In the Pople method, the difference in energy δE between the bonding and antibonding MOs is not even approximately equal to $2\beta_{12}{}^c$; it is given by:

$$\delta E = 2\beta_{12}{}^c - (11,22) \qquad (4.42)$$

The two-electron integral $(11,22)$ is of the same order of magnitude as the term $2\beta_{12}{}^c$; thus the approximate cancellation of two-electron integrals that makes the Hückel method viable as a treatment of ground states breaks down completely in calculations of excitation energy.

4.4 HHe+; POLAR AND DATIVE BONDS

The molecule H_2 serves as a simple prototype of a system containing a symmetrical covalent bond between two identical atoms. Likewise the ion HHe+, which is isoelectronic with H_2, will serve as a prototype of covalent bonds between dissimilar atoms.

The binding energy (54.1 ev) of the electron in the hydrogenlike ion He^+ is very much greater than that (13.6 ev) of the electron in a hydrogen atom; in a Hückel treatment of HHe^+, we must then use different values for the diagonal F-matrix elements F_{11}, F_{22}, corresponding to He and H respectively. Writing them as α_{He}, α_H, the secular equation [compare Eq. (4.12)] now becomes:

$$\begin{vmatrix} \alpha_{He} - E & \beta \\ \beta & \alpha_H - E \end{vmatrix} = 0 \qquad (4.43a)$$

with the solutions:

$$E = \tfrac{1}{2}\{(\alpha_{He} + \alpha_H) \pm [(\alpha_{He} - \alpha_H)^2 + 4\beta^2 - 4\alpha_{He}\alpha_H]^{1/2}\}$$
$$= \tfrac{1}{2}\{(\alpha_{He} + \alpha_H) \pm [(\alpha_{He} - \alpha_H)^2 + 4\beta^2]^{1/2}\} \qquad (4.43b)$$

The covalent-bond energy E_{HHe} of the bond in HHe^+ is given by *minus* the difference between the energy of HHe^+ and that of $H + He^+$; thus:

$$E_{HHe} = \alpha_{He} + \alpha_H - 2E = \pm[(\alpha_{He} - \alpha_H)^2 + 4\beta^2]^{1/2} \qquad (4.44)$$

the sign depending on the choice between the two roots of Eq. (4.43). Here again, one orbital corresponds to a lower, and one to a higher, total energy of the molecule than of the entities (H, He^+) from which it is formed; one orbital [that with the negative sign in Eq. (4.43b)] is therefore a BMO, the other [positive sign in Eq. (4.43b)] an AMO.

Substituting the lower value E_1 of E in the equation for the orbital coefficients, we find:

$$a_{11}(\alpha_{He} - \tfrac{1}{2}\{(\alpha_{He} + \alpha_H) + [(\alpha_{He} - \alpha_H) + 4\beta^2]^{1/2}\}) + a_{12}\beta = 0 \quad (4.45)$$

where a_{11} is the coefficient of the $1s$ AO of He, a_{12} that of the $1s$ AO of H. The solution of this equation can be written:

$$a_{12} = a_{11}\left(\sqrt{1 + \frac{\alpha_{He} - \alpha_H}{4\beta^2}} - \frac{\alpha_{He} - \alpha_H}{2\beta} \right) \qquad (4.46)$$

It is easy to show that the term in parentheses on the right of Eq. (4.46) is less than unity; hence:

$$a_{11} > a_{12} \qquad (4.47)$$

In this case therefore the charge densities q_1, q_2 are no longer equal; the BMO is polarized in such a way that a larger part of it lies near the helium nucleus. Thus we have a picture of an unsymmetrical or *polar* covalent bond linking our two dissimilar atoms, the bond electrons being clustered round the atom with the higher affinity for electrons, i.e. with the higher ionization potential.

This example also illustrates a further point. Since the ionization potential of a neutral helium atom (24.6 ev) is greater than that (13.6 ev) of hydrogen, the ion HHe^+ can dissociate more easily into $H^+ + He$ than into $H + He^+$. The two processes correspond in conventional nomenclature to heterolytic and homolytic bond cleavage respectively; the combination of a proton with a helium atom to form HHe^+ represents the most primitive possible case of the formation of a dative bond. However the structure of the molecule HHe^+ is not affected by the possibility of this alternative mode of fission; in other words, the electron distribution and other properties of HHe^+ will correspond to those expected for a covalent bond between H and He^+, regardless of the fact that H and He^+ can themselves react exothermically to form H^+ and He. In treating dative bonds, one must be careful to remember that their electronic properties may correspond to those of strong covalent bonds between neutral species, even if the energy required for their heterolytic fission is quite small.

The arguments above were based on the Hückel treatment; here, and in the following sections, we shall often omit the corresponding Pople and/or Roothaan treatments since they lead to similar conclusions at the expense only of a good deal of tedious algebra. Enthusiastic readers may care to check the truth of this statement; they will find the exercise useful if a bit laborious.

4.5   THE SYSTEM He_2; ROLE OF THE ELECTRON PAIR IN BONDING

The system He_2 can be treated in exactly the same way as H_2; the MOs and orbital energies will be given by similar expressions in which α and β now have values appropriate to helium rather than hydrogen. Here, however, there are four electrons to be accommodated; only two can occupy the BMO, so the other pair is forced to occupy the AMO. In the Hückel treatment, the total energy of the system is then given by:

$$E_{tot} = 2(\alpha + \beta) + 2(\alpha - \beta) = 4\alpha \qquad (4.48)$$

This is the same as the energy 4α of the electrons in two isolated helium atoms; the atoms therefore have no tendency to form a molecule. The antibonding effect of electrons in the AMO thus cancels out the bonding effect of the electrons in the BMO; since there is room for only two electrons in the latter, any number of electrons greater than two is an embarrassment. Since the same situation will arise in all cases where two-center MOs are formed by combination of pairs of AOs, we can see at once why chemists were led, in the pre-Schrödinger era, to interpret chemical bonds in terms of the sharing of pairs of electrons between atoms.

4.6   TWO-CENTER COVALENT BONDS; ELECTRONEGATIVITY AND PAULING'S RULE

The arguments used in the previous section can be generalized to any situation where two-center MOs are formed from pairs of AOs of adjacent atoms X, Y. Writing their coulomb integrals as α_X and α_Y, the covalent-bond energy E_{XY} is found to be given [compare Eq. (4.44)] by:

$$E_{XY} = \sqrt{4\beta_{XY}{}^2 + (\alpha_X - \alpha_Y)^2} \qquad (4.49)$$

while the resulting BMO is again concentrated round the nucleus of the atom with the greater ionization potential, i.e. the greater numerical value for its coulomb integral.

Let us now compare the bond energies E_{XX}, E_{YY} for the two symmetrical molecules XX, YY with that for the unsymmetrical combination XY. If the corresponding resonance integrals are β_{XX}, β_{YY}, then:

$$E_{XX} = -2\beta_{XX} \qquad E_{YY} = -2\beta_{YY} \qquad (4.50)$$

In the Hückel method, these integrals are supposed to be defined by:

$$\beta_{ij} = \int \phi_i \mathbf{H} \phi_j \, d\tau \qquad (4.51)$$

If we use the Mulliken approximation [Eq. (3.24)],

$$\beta_{ij} \approx CS_{ij}(\alpha_i + \alpha_j) \qquad (4.52)$$

Thus:

$$\beta_{XX} \approx 2CS_{XX}\alpha_X \qquad \beta_{YY} \approx 2CS_{YY}\alpha_Y \qquad (4.53)$$

where S_{XX} is the overlap integral between the two X AOs in X—X and S_{YY} the corresponding integral for Y—Y. If we can assume that C has the same value for all three similar molecules, and that the overlap integrals are either all the same or at least that:

$$S_{XY} \approx \tfrac{1}{2}(S_{XX} + S_{YY}) \qquad (4.54)$$

then it follows that:

$$\beta_{XY} \approx \tfrac{1}{2}(\beta_{XX} + \beta_{YY}) \qquad (4.55)$$

We can write Eq. (4.49) in the form:

$$E_{XY} = -2\beta_{XY}\left[1 + \frac{(\alpha_X - \alpha_Y)^2}{4\beta_{XY}^2}\right]^{1/2}$$
$$= -2\beta_{XY}\left[1 + \frac{(\alpha_X - \alpha_Y)^2}{8\beta_{XY}^2} + \cdots\right] \qquad (4.56)$$

Neglecting higher terms in the expansion of the square root, and using Eqs. (4.50) and (4.55), we find:

$$E_{XY} \approx \tfrac{1}{2}(E_{XX} + E_{YY}) + \frac{(\alpha_X - \alpha_Y)^2}{E_{XX} + E_{YY}} \qquad (4.57)$$

Some time ago Pauling pointed out that the bond energy of an unsymmetrical bond X—Y was usually greater than the mean of the bond energies of two symmetrical bonds X—X and Y—Y, being given approximately by:

$$E_{XY} = \tfrac{1}{2}(E_{XX} + E_{YY}) + A(a_X - a_Y)^2 \qquad (4.58)$$

where A is a constant and a_i is a quantity characteristic of atom i and termed its *electronegativity*.   These electronegatives of atoms correlated well with chemical evidence concerning their relative avidity for electrons; thus measurements of dipole moments indicated that the bond between two elements is polar in the sense that the electrons forming it tend to cluster round the more electronegative atom.   Comparison of Eqs. (4.57) and (4.58) shows that we now have a theoretical basis for Pauling's equation; however the quantity A is now seen not to be a constant, but to depend on the bond energies of the atoms in question. Since bond energies do not vary over a wide range, Pauling's equation works quite well, and the relative electronegativities calculated from Eq. (4.57) agree correspondingly well with those given by Pauling.   However Eq. (4.57) fits the experimental data somewhat better, and it has moreover the advantage of being theoretically derived rather than based on open empiricism.

4.7 ORBITAL SYMMETRY

In Sec. 2.11 it was shown that the total electronic wave function Ψ of a molecule must conform to the symmetry of the nuclear core in whose field the electrons move.   We shall now show that the same is true of the individual MOs in the orbital treatment of a molecule.

Consider a molecule whose nuclear core has some element of symmetry represented by the operator $\mathbf{S}$.   The operator $\mathbf{S}$ thus leaves the nuclear field in which the electrons move unchanged.   We have seen that if $\mathbf{S}$ is an n-fold symmetry, then the wave function Ψ must be such that:

$$\mathbf{S}\Psi = S\Psi \qquad (4.59)$$

when S is an nth root of unity; i.e.

$$S = e^{2ik\pi/n} \qquad (4.60)$$

where k is a positive integer not greater than n.   The distribution of the electrons in space is given initially by the density function ρ:

$$\rho = \Psi\overline{\Psi} \qquad (4.61)$$

where $\overline{\Psi}$ is the complex conjugate of Ψ.   After carrying out the symmetry operation, the new density function ρ' is then given by:

$$\rho' = (\mathbf{S}\Psi)(\overline{\mathbf{S}\Psi}) = (e^{2ik\pi/n}\Psi)(e^{-2ik\pi/n}\overline{\Psi}) = \Psi\overline{\Psi} \equiv \rho \qquad (4.62)$$

The symmetry operation thus leaves the overall electron density distribution unchanged.   Now in the Hartree-Fock picture, each electron moves in a field representing the attraction of the nuclei and the mean repulsion of *all* the electrons in the system.   Equation (4.62) shows that the mean field of the whole electron cloud has the same symmetry as the field due to the nuclei.   The Hartree-Fock hamiltonian is consequently invariant to the symmetry operation $\mathbf{S}$; its eigenfunctions, i.e. the individual Hartree-Fock orbitals ψ_μ, must therefore obey the same symmetry relations as the total electronic wave function Ψ does; i.e.

$$\mathbf{S}\psi_\mu = e^{2ik\pi/n}\psi_\mu \tag{4.63}$$

In the particular case of a twofold symmetry:

$$\mathbf{S}\psi_\mu = \pm\psi_\mu \tag{4.64}$$

4.8 Li₂; THE CORE APPROXIMATION

Let us next extend our treatment to the system Li_2. Since two lithium atoms contain six electrons, we need MOs constructed from at least two AOs of each atom to accommodate them; the argument of Sec. 4.3 shows that these must be the two lowest-energy AOs available, i.e. the $1s$ and $2s$ AOs. Denote the $1s$ orbitals of atoms 1 and 2 by ϕ_1 and ϕ_2 respectively, and the corresponding $2s$ orbitals by ϕ_3 and ϕ_4 respectively. In the Hückel treatment, we shall then have five distinct parameters:

$$
\begin{aligned}
F_{11} = F_{22} = \alpha_1 \qquad F_{33} = F_{44} = \alpha_2 \\
F_{12} = \beta_1 \qquad F_{34} = \beta_2 \qquad F_{14} = F_{23} = \beta_3
\end{aligned}
\tag{4.65}
$$

(The resonance integrals between orbitals in the same atom, i.e. F_{13} or F_{24}, can be neglected since such orbitals are mutually orthogonal.) The Hückel secular equation becomes:

$$
\begin{vmatrix}
\alpha_1 - E & \beta_1 & 0 & \beta_3 \\
\beta_1 & \alpha_1 - E & \beta_3 & 0 \\
0 & \beta_3 & \alpha_2 - E & \beta_2 \\
\beta_3 & 0 & \beta_2 & \alpha_2 - E
\end{vmatrix} = 0
\tag{4.66}
$$

Now the $1s$ orbitals of lithium are very small, since they correspond to motion of two electrons in the field of an almost unscreened charge $+3e$; the third electron, moving in a $2s$ orbital, is nearly always further from the nucleus than either $1s$ electron, so its screening effect on the $1s$ electrons is virtually nil. At the normal bond distance in Li_2 the overlap between the $1s$ orbitals is therefore very small indeed, and the overlap between the $1s$ orbital of one atom and the $2s$ orbital of the other is also small. Let us therefore first carry out our calculation assuming that β_3 is zero; later we can check this assumption by reintroducing β_3, using perturbation theory, to see how much effect it is likely to have.

If β_2 is neglected, the determinant in Eq. (4.66) at once factorizes:

$$
\begin{vmatrix}
\alpha_1 - E & \beta_1 \\
\beta_1 & \alpha_1 - E
\end{vmatrix}
\begin{vmatrix}
\alpha_2 - E & \beta_2 \\
\beta_2 & \alpha_2 - E
\end{vmatrix} = 0
\tag{4.67}
$$

with the solutions:

$$
\begin{aligned}
E_1 = \alpha_1 + \beta_1 \qquad E_2 = \alpha_1 - \beta_1 \\
E_3 = \alpha_2 + \beta_2 \qquad E_4 = \alpha_2 - \beta_2
\end{aligned}
\tag{4.68}
$$

Now α_1 must be numerically very large since it corresponds to the ionization potential of very tightly bound electrons; the two orbitals of lowest energy will be the first two in Eq. (4.68). Four electrons occupying these orbitals will have the same total energy $4\alpha_1$ as the four $1s$ electrons in two isolated lithium atoms; the net bonding effect of these electrons is therefore zero, the situation being the same as in He_2. The remaining pair of electrons occupies the third orbital, of energy $\alpha_2 + \beta_2$; as in H_2, these contribute an amount $2\beta_2$ to the bonding.

The corresponding MOs can be found at once; they are:

$$\psi_1 = \frac{1}{\sqrt{2}}(\phi_1 + \phi_2) \qquad \psi_2 = \frac{1}{\sqrt{2}}(\phi_1 - \phi_2)$$

$$\psi_3 = \frac{1}{\sqrt{2}}(\phi_3 + \phi_4) \qquad \psi_4 = \frac{1}{\sqrt{2}}(\phi_3 - \phi_4)$$

(4.69)

Let us now try introducing the integral β_3, using perturbation theory. Since this integral is defined by:

$$\beta_3 = \int \phi_1 H \phi_3 \, d\tau = \int \phi_2 H \phi_4 \, d\tau \qquad (4.70)$$

the perturbation consists in a change in the values of these integrals from zero to β_3. The other resonance integrals, and the coulomb integrals, remain of course unchanged. We can therefore define the operator P describing the perturbation as follows, in terms of its effect on the basis set AOs ϕ_i;

$$\int \phi_i P \phi_i \, d\tau = 0 \qquad i = 1, 2, 3, 4$$

$$\int \phi_1 P \phi_j \, d\tau = 0 \qquad \text{unless } j = 4$$

$$\int \phi_2 P \phi_k \, d\tau = 0 \qquad \text{unless } k = 3$$

$$\int \phi_1 P \phi_4 \, d\tau = \int \phi_2 P \phi_3 \, d\tau = \beta_3$$

(4.71)

It follows that the first-order perturbations vanish; for if we expand the corresponding integrals $\int \psi_m P \psi_m \, d\tau$ in terms of AOs, the resulting integrals are all equal to zero.

The second-order perturbations are given by:

$$\delta E_1 = \sum_i \frac{P_{1i}^2}{E_1 - E_i} = \frac{\beta_3^2}{\alpha_1 - \alpha_2} \qquad (4.72)$$

$$\delta E_2 = \sum_i \frac{P_{2i}^2}{E_2 - E_i} = \frac{\beta_3^2}{\alpha_1 - \alpha_2} \qquad (4.73)$$

$$\delta E_3 = \sum_i \frac{P_{3i}^2}{E_1 - E_i} = \frac{\beta_3^2}{\alpha_1 - \alpha_2} \qquad (4.74)$$

$$\delta E_4 = \sum_i \frac{P_{4i}^2}{E_4 - E_i} = \frac{\beta_3^2}{\alpha_2 - \alpha_1} \qquad (4.75)$$

If we sum these contributions over the six electrons occupying the MOs ψ_1, ψ_2, ψ_3, the total contribution δE_{tot} to the binding energy is seen to be:

$$\delta E_{\text{tot}} = \frac{2\beta_3^2}{\alpha_1 - E_2} \tag{4.76}$$

Now as we have seen, β_3 is likely to be numerically quite small, while α_1 is numerically very large. The contribution of Eq. (4.76) is likely to be small compared with β_2, and so small compared with the total binding energy in Li_2. This conclusion is confirmed by detailed calculations; the mutual interaction between the "inner-shell" electrons occupying the MOs ψ_1, ψ_2 and the "valence-shell" electrons occupying ψ_3 is thus small. On this basis we can ignore the inner-shell electrons altogether, since their total energy is almost the same in the molecule Li_2 as it would be in two isolated lithium atoms. This situation turns out to be quite general; it explains why molecules can be represented in terms of interactions between the electrons in the valence shells of atoms, i.e. in the outer layer of orbitals which, in the atom, are incompletely filled. In the present case we can treat our lithium atoms as hydrogenlike systems, in which the valence-shell $2s$ electron moves in the field of a "core" composed of the nucleus and two $1s$ electrons. The corresponding secular equation for Li_2 becomes:

$$\begin{vmatrix} \alpha_2 - E & \beta_2 \\ \beta_2 & \alpha_2 - E \end{vmatrix} = 0 \tag{4.77}$$

in precise analogy to that for H_2. The corresponding orbitals ψ_3 and ψ_4 of Eq. (4.69) can then be described as bonding and antibonding respectively, their energies being respectively lower and higher than that (α_2) of the valence-shell electron in a lithium atom.

From now on we shall always make this approximation, treating atoms in terms of a *core* composed of the nucleus and tightly bound inner electrons, together with a *valence shell* of electrons that are less tightly bound. This of course greatly reduces the number of electrons that must be considered in treating molecules.

4.9 OTHER DIATOMIC MOLECULES FORMED BY FIRST-ROW ELEMENTS; σ AND π ORBITALS AND HYBRIDIZATION

When we proceed to diatomic molecules formed by atoms of higher atomic number, the increasing number of electrons forces us to introduce more AOs of the component atoms into our basis set. The set of orbitals next in energy are the $2s$ AO and the three $2p$ AOs; these do not differ greatly in energy—indeed, the three $2p$ AOs are degenerate—so we are no longer justified in selecting individual members of the set to use in our LCAO MO treatment. Our next problem then is to consider the types of MO that can be constructed from the $2s$ and $2p$ AOs of a pair of adjacent atoms, i.e. a basis set containing eight AOs.

The problem can be simplified by using the fact that molecules of this type have axial symmetry; the nuclear field in which the electrons move is unaffected by a rotation about the line joining the two nuclei. The angular momentum of the electrons about this axis (i.e. the line joining the nuclei) must therefore be a

constant of the motion in classical mechanics, since the forces between the electrons and the nuclei cannot alter this component of their total angular momentum.   If we call this axis the Z axis, then the wave function Ψ of the molecule
must be an eigenfunction of the operator $\mathbf{M}_Z$.   The arguments of Sec. 4.5 then
show that the same must be true of the individual orbitals in an orbital representation; if we use spherical polar coordinates with the Z axis as polar axis, each
MO ψ_p must be of the form:

$$\psi_p = F_p(r_1\theta)e^{im\phi} \tag{4.78}$$

where m is a quantum number indicating the angular momentum ($= m\hbar$) about
the Z axis.   The total angular momentum $M\hbar$ about the Z axis is given by summing these contributions for the individual electrons.   Each state of the molecule can therefore be distinguished by a quantum number M, defining this total
angular momentum; from analogy with atoms, these states are described by
capital Greek letters, corresponding to the capital Roman letters used to describe
atomic states.   Thus any state of a diatomic molecule with $M = 0$ is called a
Σ state, one with $M = \pm 1$ a Π state, $M = \pm 2$ a Δ state, and so forth.   Likewise individual MOs are designated by small Greek letters, to distinguish their
individual angular momenta $m\hbar$.   Thus orbitals with $m = 0$ are termed σ MOs,
ones with $m = \pm 1$ π MOs, with $m = \pm 2$ δ MOs, and so forth.

Equation (4.78) shows that all these orbitals, other than σ MOs, have complex
wave functions; it follows from the argument of Sec. 2.2 that they must occur in
degenerate pairs, the energies of the two orbitals with quantum numbers m and
$-m$ being equal.   As in the case of atoms (Sec. 2.2), we can replace these pairs
of degenerate MOs by equivalent pairs of real combinations ψ_p^+, ψ_p^-, given by:

$$\psi_p^+ = \frac{1}{2}(F_p e^{im\phi} + F_p e^{-im\phi}) = F_p \cos m\phi \tag{4.79}$$

$$\psi_p^- = -\frac{i}{2}(F_p e^{im\phi} - F_p e^{-im\phi}) = F_p \sin m\phi \tag{4.80}$$

The cross sections of these orbitals in a plane perpendicular to the nuclear axis
then resemble the cross sections of real p AOs that are now familiar from textbooks; thus the cross sections of the real π MOs look just like cross sections of
p AOs (Fig. 4.2).   If we choose cartesian coordinates such that the x and y axes
lie along the directions of maximum orbital density of the two real π MOs, we can
distinguish them as π_x and π_y, just as we distinguish the real p AOs of a given
set as p_x, p_y, p_z to indicate the directions along which their axes lie.   Let us now
return to the problem of constructing MOs of a diatomic molecule from our basis
set of valence orbitals, which now includes the $2s$, $2p_x$, $2p_y$, and $2p_z$ AOs of each
atom.   The corresponding MOs must be of σ or π type; the σ MOs have axial
symmetry about the z axis, while the π MOs, in real form, have symmetries
analogous to those of p_x and p_y AOs.   Thus a π_x MO is symmetric for reflection
in the xz plane and antisymmetric for reflection in the yz plane, while a π_y MO is

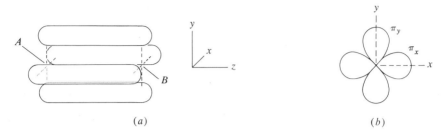

FIG. 4.2 Diagrammatic representation of the π MOs of a diatomic molecule AB in real form. (*a*) Plan; (*b*) section.

antisymmetric for reflection in xz but symmetric for reflection in yz. Since our MOs are written as linear combinations of the AOs s_1, x_1, y_1, z_1 of atom 1 and s_2, x_2, y_2, z_2 of atom 2, it is clear that they can have these symmetry properties only if each MO is constructed solely from AOs of corresponding symmetry. The MOs are therefore of three types:

σ MOs of type:	$as_1 + bs_2 + cz_1 + dz_2$	(4.81)
π_x MOs of type:	$ex_1 + fx_2$	(4.82)
π_y MOs of type:	$gy_1 + hy_2$	(4.83)

Each set of orbitals can be treated independently, by solving a secular equation involving only the appropriate AOs as the basis set.

Since this is an important point which will arise again later, we should perhaps consider it in a rather more rigorous manner. Consider the F-matrix element F_{ij} between two AOs ϕ_i, ϕ_j in a molecule; this is defined by:

$$F_{ij} = \int \phi_i \mathbf{H} \phi_j \, d\tau \qquad (4.84)$$

where $\mathbf{H}$ is a SCF one-electron hamiltonian. Since F_{ij} is a measure of the interaction between the AOs ϕ_i, ϕ_j, its value must obviously be independent of the coordinate system used to calculate it. Suppose now that a molecule has a two-fold symmetry, represented by the operator $\mathbf{S}$, and suppose that our basis-set functions ϕ_i are chosen to conform to this symmetry, so that:

$$\mathbf{S}\phi_i = \pm\phi_i \qquad (4.85)$$

Consider the effect of $\mathbf{S}$ on Eq. (4.84). Remembering that both F_{ij} and $\mathbf{H}$ must be invariant to any symmetry operation,

$$\mathbf{S}F_{ij} = F_{ij} = \int (\mathbf{S}\phi_i)(\mathbf{S}\mathbf{H})(\mathbf{S}\phi_j) \, d\tau = \pm\int \phi_i \mathbf{H} \phi_j \, d\tau = \pm F_{ij} \qquad (4.86)$$

the sign depending on whether ϕ_i and ϕ_j have similar or opposite symmetries; if opposite, then $F_{ij} = -F_{ij}$, so that F_{ij} vanishes. It follows that matrix elements F_{ij} between AOs of different symmetry type vanish. If then we set up our MOs as linear combinations of the AOs, the resulting secular equation will be of the form:

$$
\begin{vmatrix}
F_{11} - E & F_{i2} & \cdots & F_{1k} & & & \\
F_{22} & F_{22} - E & \cdots & F_{2k} & & 0 & \\
\vdots & \vdots & & \vdots & & & \\
F_{k1} & F_{k2} & \cdots & F_{kk} - E & & & \\
& & & & F_{k+1,k+1} - E & \cdots & F_{k+1,n} \\
& 0 & & & \vdots & & \vdots \\
& & & & F_{n,k+1} & \cdots & F_{nn} - E
\end{vmatrix} = 0 \quad (4.87)
$$

where the orbitals ϕ_i to ϕ_k are of one symmetry class and those from ϕ_{k+1} to ϕ_n of the other. This determinant immediately factorizes into two subdeterminants, each of which contains matrix elements corresponding to orbitals only of one type. The MOs therefore divide into two groups, according to their symmetry; each MO is a combination only of AOs with symmetry similar to itself, and the two sets of MOs are found by two independent LCAO MO treatments, each using as a basis set the set of AOs of one or the other symmetry type.

Returning to our diatomic molecule, it will be seen that the π MOs π_x, π_y will then be given in terms of the $2p$ AOs x_1, x_2, y_1, y_2 by a simple treatment exactly analogous to that used for H_2 or HHe^+. In the case of a homonuclear diatomic molecule, the orbitals will be given by:

$$
\pi_x^+ = \frac{1}{\sqrt{2}}(x_1 + x_2) \qquad \pi_y^+ = \frac{1}{\sqrt{2}}(y_1 + y_2)
$$

$$
\pi_x^- = \frac{1}{\sqrt{2}}(x_1 - x_2) \qquad \pi_y^- = \frac{1}{\sqrt{2}}(y_1 - y_2)
$$

$$(4.88)$$

In the Hückel approximation, the energies E_π^+ of the two bonding MOs π_x^+, π_y^+ will each be given by:

$$
E_\pi^+ = \alpha_p + \beta_{\pi\pi} \tag{4.89}
$$

where α_p is the coulomb integral for a $2p$ electron of one of the component atoms and $\beta_{\pi\pi}$ is the resonance integral for the π-type interaction of the two $2p$ AOs x_1, x_2 or y_1, y_2. Likewise the energies E_π^- of the antibonding MOs π_x^-, π_y^- will be given by:

$$
E_\pi^- = \alpha_p - \beta_{\pi\pi} \tag{4.90}
$$

In the case of a heteronuclear molecule such as CO, the π orbitals will of course no longer be symmetrical; their density will be concentrated round the more electronegative atom, here oxygen. The treatment of these unsymmetrical π MOs will be formally identical with the treatment of HHe^+ (Sec. 4.4).

We next have to consider the σ MOs, which will be written [Eq. (4.83)] as linear combinations of the $2s$ and $2p$ AOs of each atom. Since our basis set contains four AOs, the corresponding secular equation will contain a determinant with four rows and four columns.   In the case of Li_2, we had a similar secular equation (4.66); however we were able to simplify it by using the fact that certain of the off-diagonal matrix elements were small.   Here we cannot do this; for the orbitals are all of similar size and energy, so that the matrix element between the $2s$ and $2p_z$ AOs of one atom and the corresponding AOs of the other must all be of comparable magnitude.

However we can get an idea of the prevailing situation by the following trick. Suppose we replace our basis-set functions s_1, z_1, s_2, z_2 by four independent linear combinations χ_1, χ_2, χ_3, χ_4.   Since the χ's are linear functions of our AOs, any linear combination of the AOs can be expressed as a linear combination of the functions χ.   If then we use the χ's as our basis set in a Roothaan-type treatment, the resulting MOs will be *identical* with those that we would obtain from a conventional LCAO MO approach, using the four AOs s_1, z_1, s_2, z_2 as our basis set.

Let us then replace the AOs by the four following combinations, which are easily seen to be linearly independent:

$$\chi_1 = \frac{1}{\sqrt{2}}(s_1 + p_1) \qquad \chi_2 = \frac{1}{\sqrt{2}}(s_1 - p_1)$$

$$\chi_3 = \frac{1}{\sqrt{2}}(s_2 + p_2) \qquad \chi_4 = \frac{1}{\sqrt{2}}(s_2 - p_2)$$

(4.91)

Consider the combinations χ_1, χ_2.   As Fig. 4.3 shows, the resulting functions look like lopsided p AOs, with one large lobe and one small lobe; the large lobes of χ_1 and χ_2 point in opposite directions along the z axis.   We shall suppose that our molecule is homonuclear, so that in the Hückel approximation both $2s$ AOs have the same coulomb integral α_s, and both $2p_z$ AOs have the same coulomb integral α_p.   The diagonal element F_{11} of the F matrix, using the orbitals χ_1 to χ_4 in a Hückel treatment, is given by:

$$\begin{aligned}
F_{11} &= \int \chi_1 \mathbf{H} \chi_1 \, d\tau = \tfrac{1}{2}\int (s_1 + z_1)\mathbf{H}(s_1 + z_1)\, d\tau \\
&= \tfrac{1}{2}(\int s_1 \mathbf{H} s_1 \, d\tau + \int s_1 \mathbf{H} z_1 \, d\tau + \int z_1 \mathbf{H} s_1 \, d\tau + \int z_1 \mathbf{H} z_1 \, d\tau) \\
&= \tfrac{1}{2}(\alpha_s + \alpha_p)
\end{aligned}$$

(4.92)

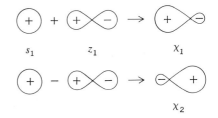

$$s_1 \qquad\qquad z_1 \qquad\qquad \chi_1$$

$$\chi_2$$

FIG. 4.3 Formation of two sp hybrid AOs χ_1, χ_2 by combination of a $2s$ AO (s_1) and a $2p$ AO (z_1).

since we are assuming that resonance integrals between two different AOs of the same atom vanish. Likewise we find for the other diagonal matrix elements:

$$F_{22} = F_{33} = F_{44} = \tfrac{1}{2}(\alpha_s + \alpha_p) \tag{4.93}$$

The transformation from the basis set of AOs to the basis set of χ's thus gives four functions of identical shape and energy, in place of the original $2s$ and $2p$ AOs. The functions χ are called *hybrid* AOs; since each is constructed from one s AO, and one p AO. They are described as sp hybrids.

Let us now consider the off-diagonal elements of the F matrix. If we examine the way in which the hybrid orbitals χ overlap (Fig. 4.3), it is evident that χ_1 and χ_3 will overlap very strongly with one another, while other pairs of χ's overlap very poorly. This is borne out by calculations of the F-matrix elements:

$$F_{13} = \tfrac{1}{2}\int(s_1 + z_1)\mathbf{H}(s_3 + z_3)\,d\tau = \tfrac{1}{2}(\beta_{ss} + \beta_{zz}) + \beta_{sz} \equiv \beta \tag{4.94}$$

where β_{ss}, β_{zz}, β_{sz} are the Hückel resonance integrals between corresponding pairs of AOs:

$$F_{12} = \tfrac{1}{2}\int(s_1 + z_1)\mathbf{H}(s_1 - z_1)\,d\tau = \tfrac{1}{2}(\alpha_s - \alpha_p) = F_{34} \equiv \beta' \tag{4.95}$$

$$F_{14} = \tfrac{1}{2}\int(s_1 + z_1)\mathbf{H}(s_2 - z_2)\,d\tau = \tfrac{1}{2}(\beta_{ss} - \beta_{zz}) = F_{23} \tag{4.96}$$

$$F_{24} = \tfrac{1}{2}\int(s_1 - z_1)\mathbf{H}(s_2 - z_2)\,d\tau = \tfrac{1}{2}(\beta_{ss} + \beta_{zz}) - \beta_{sz} \tag{4.97}$$

Since $2s$ and $2p$ AOs do not differ much in energy, the matrix elements F_{12} and F_{34} will be small. The same will be true of the matrix elements F_{14}, F_{23}, since the resonance integrals β_{ss}, β_{zz} are comparable. And finally, the element F_{24} will be very small indeed, since not only are the β's all comparable, but β_{sz} is also likely to be close to the mean of β_{ss} and β_{zz}. If we neglect these small matrix elements and use the abbreviations of Eqs. (4.93) and (4.94), the secular equation becomes:

$$\begin{vmatrix} \alpha - E & 0 & \beta & 0 \\ 0 & \alpha - E & 0 & 0 \\ \beta & 0 & \alpha - E & 0 \\ 0 & 0 & 0 & \alpha - E \end{vmatrix} = 0 \tag{4.98}$$

with the solutions:

$$E = \alpha \pm \beta = \tfrac{1}{2}(\alpha_s + \alpha_p) \pm \beta$$
$$E = \alpha = \tfrac{1}{2}(\alpha_s + \alpha_p) \quad \text{twice} \tag{4.99}$$

We can now reintroduce the small matrix elements F_{12}, F_{14}, F_{23}, F_{24} by using perturbation theory (compare Sec. 4.8); the effect of these is to remove the degeneracy of the two central levels and to increase the separation of the outer two. Combining these results with the ones arrived at earlier for the π MOs, we can now construct a schematic energy-level diagram for the molecule (Fig. 4.4). The relative location of the π MOs and σ MOs will of course depend on the mag-

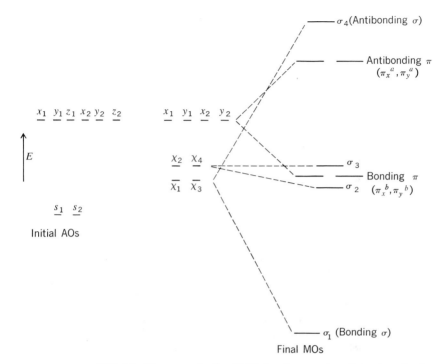

FIG. 4.4   The energy levels of MOs in a homonuclear diatomic molecule.

nitudes of the various parameters; the relationship shown in Fig. 4.4 is based on an argument given below.

The shapes of the eight MOs are indicated in Fig. 4.5.   Note that the σ MOs σ_2 and σ_3 are largely concentrated in lobes at the ends of the molecule; molecules in which these orbitals are occupied should therefore have a high electron density in these regions.   Only the π_x MOs are shown since the π_y MOs are exactly similar in shape; while the diagrams refer directly to homonuclear diatomic molecules, those for heteronuclear ones will be similar.   The order of energies of the MOs will remain the same, but each MO will be distorted in such a way as to be concentrated more around one nucleus than the other.

We can use these diagrams to interpret the general behavior of molecules of this kind in a simple way.   Consider for example a pair of beryllium atoms. Beryllium has two valence electrons, both $2s$.   In Be_2, only two of the four valence electrons can occupy a MO (σ_1) of lower energy than the $2s$ AOs.   The other two have to occupy a MO (σ_2) which is antibonding with respect to the $2s$ level.   Consequently beryllium vapor, like helium gas, is monatomic.   The same argument can be applied to other group II elements, all of which have ground states that can be written: (core)$(ns)^2$.   Mercury provides a very good example; the physical properties of its vapor resemble closely those of an inert gas.

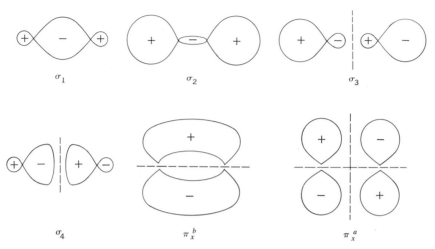

FIG. 4.5 Diagrammatic representation of the MOs of a first-row diatomic molecule; the dotted lines depict nodes.

In the heavier first-row atoms, $2p$ electrons are present.   If two such atoms come together, their $2s$ electrons occupy the two lowest MOs σ_1 and σ_2; as we have seen, this leads to no net decrease in energy, and so to no binding effect. The $2p$ AOs, however, are higher in energy than the $\pi_x{}^b$, $\pi_y{}^b$, and σ_z MOs; atoms with $2p$ electrons can therefore form diatomic molecules, and the strength of the binding increases with the number of p electrons up to a total of six, when all the three bonding MOs are filled. N_2 and CO fulfil this condition; the bonds in them are exceptionally strong, stronger than any other bonds known in chemistry.

In O_2 there are 12 valence electrons; 10 of these occupy the five lowest MOs, while the next 2 must be relegated to the antibonding π level.   Since this is degenerate, it follows from Hund's rule that the ground state of O_2 must be one in which the two extra electrons occupy different π MOs ($\pi_x{}^a$ and $\pi_y{}^a$) with parallel spins; O_2 thus has a triplet ground state.   The bond in it is weaker than that in N_2, since there are two electrons in antibonding MOs; removal of one of these electrons to give an ion $O_2{}^+$ therefore occurs readily, so the bond in $O_2{}^+$ is correspondingly stronger than that in neutral O_2.   Salts of $O_2{}^+$ are known, for example $(O_2{}^+)_2PtCl_6$.

In C_2 there are eight valence electrons.   Four of these occupy the MOs σ_1 and σ_2; the situation regarding the rest will depend on the relative energies of the third σ MO, σ_3, and the bonding π MOs $\pi_x{}^b$ and $\pi_y{}^b$.   If σ_3 lay lower, there would be just two electrons to be accommodated in the degenerate π level, and C_2 would then have a triplet ground state, like O_2.   Observation shows, however, that C_2 has a singlet ground state; the π levels therefore lie below σ_3, as indicated in Fig. 4.4, so that the valence electrons completely fill the orbitals σ_1, σ_2, $\pi_x{}^b$, and $\pi_y{}^b$.

We have seen that the MOs σ_2 and σ_3 are largely concentrated at the ends of the molecule (Fig. 4.4); when these are filled, the molecule has then a dense cloud of negative charge at each end.   The ability of CO to form complexes with metals depends on the interaction of this cloud of the carbon atom with electron-hungry atoms of metals.

One final point is illustrated by the properties of F_2, where all the MOs are filled except σ_4.   According to the simple Hückel treatment, the interaction of two similar AOs on two adjacent atoms of the same kind gives rise to a pair of MOs, one bonding, one antibonding, the energies of which are symmetrically related $(\alpha \pm \beta)$ to that (α) of either AO.   On this basis we deduced (Sec. 4.5) that He_2 should have the same energy as two isolated He atoms; this cannot be correct, for helium atoms in fact repel each other if we try to force them together.   The error lies once more in the unrealistic treatment of antibonding MOs in the Hückel method; more rigorous calculations show that the antibonding effect of electrons in a given AMO is greater than the bonding effect of electrons in the corresponding BMO.   Antibonding electrons are thus a very bad thing so far as bonding is concerned.   Consider for example the molecule HHe, where there are two bonding electrons and one antibonding electron, in the MOs formed from $1s$ AOs of the two atoms.   The bond in HHe is so very much weaker than that in H_2 that HHe immediately disproportionates into hydrogen and helium.   Here *one* antibonding electron very nearly succeeds in canceling the effect of *two* bonding electrons.   The same situation arises in F_2, where there are six bonding electrons (in the MOs σ_3, $\pi_x{}^b$, $\pi_y{}^b$) and four antibonding electrons (in $\pi_x{}^a$ and $\pi_y{}^a$).   The bond in F_2 is one of the weakest in chemistry, the bond energy being only 37 kcal/mole.

4.10   METHANE; PROMOTION, HYBRIDIZATION, AND LOCALIZED ORBITALS

Methane, CH_4, is known experimentally to have a symmetrical structure, the hydrogen atoms occupying the corners of a regular tetrahedron centered on the carbon atom.   We shall discuss the electronic structure of methane in terms of this geometry.

Alternate corners of a cube form a regular tetrahedron; CH_4 can be represented in the way indicated in Fig. 4.6, the four hydrogen atoms a, b, c, d lying on alternate corners of a cube with the carbon atom at its center.   Figure 4.6 also indicates the choice of coordinate axes we shall use, i.e. cartesian coordinates centered on carbon, the coordinate axes lying parallel to edges of the cube.

The MOs of methane are to be constructed from linear combinations of eight valence-shell AOs, the $1s$ AOs a, b, c, d of the four hydrogen atoms, and the $2s$ AO (s), and $2p_x$, $2p_y$, and AOs (x, y, z respectively) of the carbon atom.   In principle, each MO should be written as a linear combination of all eight AOs; since, however, methane is a very symmetrical molecule, we can simplify the problem by using the methods introduced in Sec. 4.9.

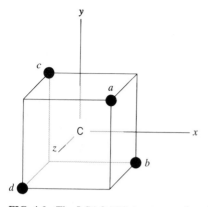

FIG. 4.6 The LCAO MO treatment of methane.

The methane molecule has three twofold axes of symmetry; in Fig. 4.6, these are the coordinate axes. Thus rotation through 180° about the x axis (operation $\mathbf{R}_x$) interchanges hydrogen atom a with atom b, and c with d; since hydrogen atoms are indistinguishable, this rotation leaves the molecule unchanged. Likewise rotation through 180° about the y axis (operation $\mathbf{R}_y$) interchanges a with c and b with d, and about the z axis (operation $\mathbf{R}_z$) interchanges a with d and b with c. Each MO of methane must therefore be symmetric, or antisymmetric, for each such rotation. Now the valence-shell AOs of the carbon atom themselves conform to this symmetry. Thus the spherical $2s$ AO (s) is unchanged by any rotation. The $2p_x$ AO (x), being axially symmetrical about the x axis, is unchanged by $\mathbf{R}_x$. The operations $\mathbf{R}_y$ and $\mathbf{R}_z$ interchange the two lobes of x; since the lobes of a p orbital have opposite signs, x is antisymmetric to $\mathbf{R}_y$ and $\mathbf{R}_z$. The symmetries of the four orbitals are indicated in Table 4.2.

It follows that at most *one* carbon AO can contribute to each MO; for no two of

TABLE 4.2 Behavior of orbitals used in the treatment of CH_4 to rotations about the coordinate axes ($+$ = symmetric; $-$ = antisymmetric)

Orbital	Operator		
	$\mathbf{R}_x$	$\mathbf{R}_y$	$\mathbf{R}_z$
s	$+$	$+$	$+$
x	$+$	$-$	$-$
y	$-$	$+$	$-$
z	$-$	$-$	$+$
sh	$+$	$+$	$+$
xh	$+$	$-$	$-$
yh	$-$	$+$	$-$
zh	$-$	$-$	$+$

the carbon AOs have the same symmetry. The MOs of methane must therefore fall into four categories, similar in symmetry to the four valence-shell AOs of carbon.

The hydrogen AOs do not themselves conform to the molecular symmetry; however we can again use a trick similar to that introduced in Sec. 4.9 [compare Eq. (4.91)]. We can replace the four hydrogen AOs by four linear combinations or *symmetry orbitals* (SO) sh, xh, yh, zh that do conform to the molecular symmetry. Equation (4.100) shows these combinations, and their symmetry properties are listed in Table 4.2.

$$sh = \tfrac{1}{2}(a + b + c + d) \qquad yh = \tfrac{1}{2}(a + b - c - d)$$
$$xh = \tfrac{1}{2}(a - b + c - d) \qquad zh = \tfrac{1}{2}(a - b - c + d) \tag{4.100}$$

The eight MOs of methane thus break down into eight pairs, each formed from one of the carbon AOs and a corresponding SO. Owing to the symmetry of the molecule, each pair of p-type MOs must be equivalent to the others; the MOs are therefore of the form:

$$S^+ = As + Bsh \qquad S^- = Bs - Ash$$
$$X^+ = A'x + B'xh \qquad X^- = B'x - A'xh$$
$$Y^+ = A'y + B'yh \qquad Y^- = B'y - A'yh \tag{4.101}$$
$$Z^+ = A'z + B'zh \qquad Z^- = B'z - A'zh$$

The coefficients A, B, A', B' will be found in the usual way by solving 2 two-row secular equations. In each pair of MOs, one (S^+, X^+, Y^+, or Z^+) will be bonding, the other antibonding, relative to the corresponding carbon AO (s, x, y, or z). The eight valence electrons in CH_4 can then occupy in pairs the four bonding MOs; consequently the total decrease in energy on forming CH_4 from atoms should be of the order of 4 times that involved in forming a simple diatomic molecule such as H_2, corresponding to the usual chemical picture of methane as a molecule containing four distinct bonds.

This MO description does not conform to the current chemical picture of methane, in which it is supposed that the eight valence electrons form localized electron-pair bonds between pairs of atoms, similar in all respects to the bond in H_2. We can, however, establish contact between the two pictures by using the following general theorem.

Suppose we have carried out a LCAO MO treatment of a closed-shell molecule, and obtained in this way a set of MOs ψ_μ. Suppose now we take the occupied MOs ($\mu = 1, 2, \ldots, n$) and construct from them a set of n linear combinations ξ_p that are mutually orthogonal. If we calculate the total energy of the molecule, assuming that the electrons occupy the orbitals ξ_p rather than the two MOs ψ_μ, we shall arrive at *exactly* the same result for the total energy of the molecule and its total electron distribution.

We can prove this result very simply in the case of a Hückel treatment. Suppose the energy of the MO ψ_μ is E_μ. The total energy E of the molecule is then given by:

$$E = 2 \sum_{\mu=1}^{n} E_\mu \tag{4.102}$$

Let us carry out a Hückel treatment of the molecule, using the functions ξ_p as our basis set. The corresponding matrix elements H_{pq} will be given by

$$H_{pq} = \int \xi_p \mathbf{H} \xi_q \, d\tau \tag{4.103}$$

The diagonal matrix elements ϵ_p will then be measures of the energies of electrons occupying the orbitals ξ_p. The secular equation thus becomes:

$$\begin{vmatrix} \epsilon_1 - E & H_{12} & H_{13} & \cdots & H_{14} \\ H_{21} & \epsilon_2 - E & H_{23} & \cdots & H_{24} \\ H_{31} & H_{32} & \epsilon_3 - E & \cdots & H_{34} \\ \vdots & \vdots & \vdots & & \vdots \\ H_{n1} & H_{n2} & H_{n3} & \cdots & \epsilon_n - E \end{vmatrix} = 0 \tag{4.104}$$

When we expand this determinant in descending powers of E, we find:

$$E^n - E^{n-1} \sum_p \epsilon_p + O(E^{n-2}) \tag{4.105}$$

The sum ΣE of the roots of this equation is given by *minus* the coefficient of E^{n-1}; that is

$$\Sigma E = \sum_{p=1}^{n} \epsilon_p \tag{4.106}$$

However we already know the solution of this problem; the roots of Eq. (4.104) must be equal to the "true" orbital energies E_μ. Hence:

$$\sum_{p=1}^{n} \epsilon_p = \sum_{\mu=1}^{n} E_\mu \tag{4.107}$$

From Eqs. (4.102) and (4.107),

$$E = 2 \sum_{p=1}^{n} \epsilon_p \tag{4.108}$$

If therefore we replace the "true" MOs ψ_μ by the set of linear combinations ξ_p, and if we calculate the total energy treating the ξ_p as if they were "true" MOs, we get exactly the same result as if we had used the "true" MOs ψ_μ. The same can be shown to be true of the total electron distribution.

Let us now apply this very important principle to the bonding MOs of Eq. (4.101). Let us replace S^+, X^+, Y^+, Z^+ by the four following combinations t_1 to t_4:

$$t_1 = \frac{BS^+}{B'} + X^+ + Y^+ + Z^+ = [A''S + A'(x + y + z)] + 4B'a$$

$$t_2 = \frac{BS^+}{B'} + X^+ - Y^- - Z^+ = [A''S + A'(x - y - z)] + 4B'b$$

$$t_3 = \frac{BS^+}{B'} - X^+ + Y^+ - Z^+ = [A''S - A'(x - y + z)] + 4B'c$$

(4.109)

$$t_4 = \frac{BS^+}{B'} - X^+ - Y^+ + Z^+ = [A''S - A'(x + y - z)] + 4B'd$$

where $A'' = \dfrac{AB}{B'}$ (4.110)

Owing to the symmetry of the carbon AOs, each of these four orbitals can be converted into any of the others by rotations about the coordinate axes; the energies and shapes of all four orbitals are identical. Each moreover is represented as a combination of the $1s$ AO of a single hydrogen atom and a hybrid AO t of carbon; the orbitals t thus correspond exactly to the chemical picture of CH_4, in terms of four localized bonds. Our arguments show that the total energy, and total electron distribution, of CH_4 will be reproduced satisfactorily if we suppose the electrons to occupy these four localized orbitals in place of the "true" MOs S^+, X^+, Y^+, Z^+. In other words CH_4 will behave in this respect *as if* the electrons in it were localized. Each localized orbital is formed by interaction of two AOs on two adjacent atoms, i.e. a hydrogen $1s$ AO and one of the hybrid AOs of carbon. According to this picture, the total energy of formation of CH_4 is partitioned equally between the four CH bonds, just as organic chemists had visualized.

This picture of methane is the one given in most textbooks; the hybrid carbon orbitals are termed sp^3 hybrids, being formed by mixing together all four valence-shell AOs of the carbon atom. One important error in the conventional picture should be noted. It is commonly assumed that the $2s$ and $2p$ AOs contribute equally to the hybrids, so that each hybrid AO is one-quarter s and three-quarters p. Comparison of Eqs. (4.101), (4.109), and (4.110) shows that this would be true only if $A = A'$; since A and A' are orbital coefficients given by two different eigenvalue problems, one involving a carbon $2s$ AO, the other a carbon $2p$ AO, there is no reason why this should be so. If it is so, it is so only through a pure coincidence, of no theoretical significance.

A second point which should be emphasized is that the use of the localized orbitals t_1 to t_4 is justifiable only for calculations of the *total* energy and *total* electron distribution, and so for predicting properties of the molecule that depend only on these quantities, e.g. its heat of formation or dipole moment. Such quantities may conveniently be termed *collective properties*, in contrast to *one-electron properties* that depend on the orbitals occupied by individual electrons. In calculating one-electron properties (e.g. light absorption or ionization potentials), it is essential to use the "true" MOs. The picture of methane in terms of localized bonds is thus completely artificial; we shall see in the next section that the same is true of the whole conventional picture of chemistry in which molecules are represented in terms of localized bonds.

One final point is concerned with the bond energies in methane. The localized-orbital approach represents each orbital as being formed by the localized overlap of a carbon sp^3 hybrid orbital and a hydrogen AO. It appears then that we must have the carbon atom initially in a state where its four valence electrons occupy separately the four hybrid AOs. Now the arguments given earlier in this section show that such a state, with the four electrons having parallel spins, is equivalent to one in which the four electrons occupy, again with parallel spins, the "normal" AOs $2s$, $2p_x$, $2p_y$, and $2p_z$. This, however, represents an excited ^5S state of the carbon atom, which is known to lie about 100 kcal/mole above the normal ^3P ground state (Sec. 4.2). The conventional textbook description of methane is therefore one in which we first "promote" the carbon atom into a ^5S state, and then form four localized bonds. The heat of formation ΔH is then equal to four times the "true" CH bond energy, *less* the promotion energy (100 kcal/mole).

This description is admittedly grossly oversimplified in that it implicitly assumes that the carbon hybrid AOs are one-quarter s and three-quarters p, so that they are together equivalent to the combination $2s + 2p_x + 2p_y + 2p_z$. This may very well be far from true. Although arguments of this kind contain a germ of truth, and are often useful, they should be used with caution and certainly not applied in the kind of quantitative sense indicated in the preceding paragraph.

4.11 THE PARAFFINS; THE LOCALIZED-BOND MODEL

In the case of methane, we were able to obtain a good overall description of the molecule in terms of localized two-center bonds formed by mutual interaction of the hydrogen AOs with sp^3 hybrid AOs of the central carbon atom. The success of this treatment suggests that we may also get a good description of other analogous compounds, in particular the paraffins, in terms of similar localized bonds. The geometry of such molecules is such that each carbon atom is surrounded tetrahedrally by the four atoms to which it is commonly supposed to be bonded; we can pick the four sp^3 hybrid orbitals of each carbon atom in such a way that they point toward its four partners. Our object in this section is to see how far such a description in terms of *localized orbitals* (LOs) may be expected to account for the properties of carbon compounds in general.

We are entirely at liberty to replace the carbon AOs in our basis set by linear combinations of hybrids; let us now take the further step of replacing the two orbitals invoked in a given localized bond by the two corresponding two-center MOs. Thus if ϕ_i is a given carbon hybrid AO, and ψ_i the AO of the adjacent atom to which it points (either a $1s$ hydrogen AO, or a hybrid orbital of another carbon atom), we can first carry out a simple LCAO MO treatment to get 2 two-center MOs ξ_i^+, ξ_i^-,

$$\xi_i^+ = a\phi_i + b\psi_i \qquad \xi_i^- = b\phi_i - a\psi_i \qquad (4.111)$$

We can then replace the orbitals ϕ_i, ψ_i in our basis set by the linear combinations ξ_i^+, ξ_i^-. The results of a rigorous treatment using these two-center MOs will of course be the same as those given by a conventional LCAO MO approach.

If, however, we are right in believing that our molecule should be represented reasonably well in terms of the LOs ξ_i, we should get a reasonable estimate of its collective properties by using the ξ_i directly, i.e. by neglecting any interactions between them. If so, the effect of such interactions must be small; perturbation theory should then provide an excellent tool for studying them.

The interactions can be divided into three classes, those between bonding LOs corresponding to bonds of similar types (CH or CC), those between bonding LOs of different types, and those between filled bonding LOs and empty antibonding LOs. Interactions between empty LOs can of course be ignored since the energies of empty orbitals have no bearing on the total energy of a molecule.

Interactions of the first type, between LOs of the same energy and so degenerate, will be first-order perturbations and large; however the arguments given in the previous section show that they will have no effect in the total energy of the molecule, since they involve only a scrambling of a set of occupied orbitals. Interactions of this kind will therefore have no effect on the collective properties of a molecule, although they will of course greatly affect its one-electron properties.

Interactions of the second type will be less important, being second-order perturbations; these again will influence only the one-electron properties since they also involve mutual interactions of a set of orbitals, all of which are filled with electrons.

We are therefore left only with interactions between filled bonding LOs and empty antibonding LOs. These are likely to be small, for two reasons. First, the individual sp^3 hybrid orbitals of a given carbon atom are, as we have seen, directed tetrahedrally; each such orbital therefore overlaps efficiently only with its partner in the corresponding pair of LOs. The second-order perturbation between a given bonding LO ξ_i^+ and some antibonding LO ξ_j^- is given by:

$$\delta E_i^+ = \frac{(\int \xi_i^+ \mathbf{P} \xi_j^- \, d\tau)^2}{E_i^+ - E_j^-} \qquad (4.112)$$

The term in the numerator will be small since the orbitals in question do not overlap well in space. Secondly, the denominator in Eq. (4.112) is very large; it represents the difference in energy between a bonding LO and an antibonding LO; in the case of CC or CH bonds, this difference is known to be of the order of 10 ev. The contributions of these second-order perturbations to the energies of the individual LOs, and so also to the total energy of the molecule, should be quite small.

These arguments suggest that one may again get a reasonable description of the collective properties of a molecule of this type in terms of localized orbitals, and that such properties, e.g. the heat of formation, should consequently be additive functions of the bonds in them.   Indeed, the situation is really even better than this.   In applying additivity relationships of this kind, we naturally treat the bond properties (e.g. bond energies) as parameters, to be determined empirically.   Now the interactions of the type indicated in Eq. (4.112) must be short-range effects, since LOs separated by at most one bond will be too far apart to overlap significantly with one another.   We can therefore include in our expression for the energy of a given LO an average correction for the second-order interactions, which will apply to a wide range of molecules and greatly increase the adherence to additivity.   It is of course true that the second-order corrections will not be wholly independent of environment; e.g. they will depend, in the case of a given CC bond, on the nature of the neighboring bonds (i.e. whether they are bonds to hydrogen or to other carbon atoms).   On this basis one would expect corresponding deviations from additivity in comparing heats of formation of isomeric paraffins that differ in the degree of branching.   Such deviations, although small, exist, and have been shown to conform to the pattern that would be expected from the perturbational approach outlined here.[1]

It has of course long been known by chemists that the collective properties of molecules such as paraffins can be expressed quite accurately in terms of additive bond properties.   Properties of this kind include the total energy (i.e. heat of formation), the dipole moment, and bond lengths and bond angles (collective properties, since they must be such as to minimize the total energy of the molecule).   Chemists of course interpreted these relationships in terms of localized bonds, the bond between two atoms having fixed properties independent of its environment.   The uncritical acceptance of this "fact" has led to a great deal of confused thinking and wasted effort.   Theoreticians have tried to explain why electrons in molecules should be thus localized, while experimentalists have tried to establish the extent to which such localization occurs, usually by studying one-electron properties such as the distribution of unpaired spin in radicals. The arguments given here show very clearly that both these endeavors are a waste of time.   The electrons in molecules are *not* localized.   They occupy extended MOs, even in the case of saturated molecules such as paraffins.   Any attempt to discuss one-electron properties in terms of a localized-bond picture is therefore unsound and likely to prove very misleading.   On the other hand the collective properties of many molecules behave, for reasons we have indicated, *almost as if* the valence electrons were localized in definite bonds.   The localized-bond model of molecules therefore acts as an analog, rather than a description, of reality.   Its virtue lies not in its truth, but in its usefulness in enabling us to predict simply and easily properties of molecules which we cannot at present calculate directly by using quantum theory.   A good parallel is provided by the use in engineering of analog computers.   We can simulate the stresses in a bridge by a set of electric circuits in such a computer; to ask if electrons in a molecule are "really" localized is as silly as asking if the bridge is "really" composed of electric circuits.

Reversing this argument, we see that the sole test of bond fixation is an empirical one. We describe the bonds in a molecule as localized if the molecule behaves *as if* the bonds in it were localized. The sole test of localization is then provided by the degree to which its collective properties can be approximated by sums of empirical contributions by the bonds in it.

4.12   THE LOCALIZED-BOND PRINCIPLE

One conclusion from the previous section is sufficiently important to deserve a separate heading. As we have seen, we are always at liberty in a LCAO MO calculation to replace the individual AOs of our basis set by an equivalent set of linear combinations; in particular, we can replace the s and p AOs of a given valence shell by a set of hybrid orbitals. Suppose we can find a set such that the orbitals of the atoms overlap in pairs, each orbital overlapping well with an orbital of one other atom, but not at all well with any other orbital in the molecule. In that case a description of the molecule in terms of a corresponding set of two-center localized orbitals should be a good one, so far as its collective properties are concerned. Although this *localized-bond principle*, as we may term it, is obvious, its usefulness does not seem to have been generally appreciated. In many cases, theoretical descriptions of molecules have been made unnecessarily complicated by an unsuitable choice of basis-set orbitals.

4.13   HYBRIDIZATION AND GEOMETRY

Two main factors are responsible for determining the geometry of molecules, the mutual repulsion of valence electrons, and effects of changes in hybridization due to the fact that s, p, and d orbitals in a given shell have very different energies.

The first factor dominates in compounds of elements of groups II, III, and IV, where the covalency is equal to the number of valence electrons. We can discuss such compounds in terms of structures where all the valence electrons occupy LOs; their mutual repulsion enforces a linear geometry in bivalent molecules of group II (e.g. $HgMe_2$), a trigonal geometry in trivalent compounds of group III (e.g. BMe_3), and a tetrahedral geometry in quadrivalent compounds of group IV (e.g. CH_4).

In the bivalent and trivalent compounds one needs to use only two, or three, of the valence-shell AOs of the central atom. One of these will of course be the corresponding s AO since this has a lower energy than the p AOs. Following the localized-bond principle, we therefore look for hybrids of these that will form the best LOs to the adjacent groups; the linear geometry of the bivalent compounds will clearly be met best by sp hybrids (see Fig. 4.3), while the trivalent geometry of the group III compounds is best met by sp^2 hybrids of the type indicated in Fig. 4.7. Note that here, as in carbon, the geometry is determined solely by the relative contributions of the p components; there is no need for sp hybrids to be exactly half s and half p, or for sp hybrids to be exactly one-third s and two-thirds p.

The situation in trivalent elements of group V, or bivalent compounds of group VI, is more complex. In the localized-orbital picture, all four valence-shell orbitals of the central atom are used either to form LOs or to house unshared pairs of electrons. The geometry of these compounds is therefore much more complicated than that of elements from the preceding groups.

The mutual repulsion of the four pairs of electrons would certainly be minimized by a tetrahedral geometry, i.e. one in which the groups attached to the central atom occupied three, or two, corners of a tetrahedron and in which the unshared pairs of electrons occupied orbitals directed to the remaining vertices of the tetrahedron. This is the geometry that we would expect if the four valence-shell orbitals were equivalent. In practice, however, the orbitals are *not* equivalent; the s AO of the set lies below the rest in energy. We can then consider a second extreme case, in which the heat of formation of the molecule is very small; this would imply that the resonance integrals of the LOs are small, so that in a complete LCAO MO treatment, the off-diagonal elements of the F matrix (i.e. the resonance integrals in a Hückel treatment) would be small compared with the difference in energy between the s AO, and the p AOs. In this case we can use the arguments of Sec. 4.8 to conclude that the s AO should behave as an inner-shell orbital, the bonds being formed exclusively by the p electrons. Since the strength of a bond depends mainly on the value of the corresponding resonance integral, and this in turn on the extent to which the relevant orbitals overlap in space, we would then expect the bond angles to be close to $90°$.

Now in a given group of the periodic table, bond energies in general decrease with increasing atomic weight. The reason for this can be seen easily from the Mulliken approximation for the corresponding integral [Eq. (3.24)]. As we proceed to heavier atoms, the ionization potentials, and so the corresponding coulomb integrals, decrease. Moreover the orbitals are now split up by nodes into

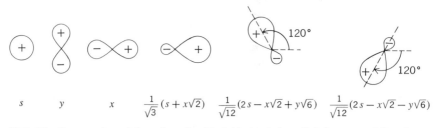

$\quad s \qquad\qquad y \qquad\qquad x \qquad \dfrac{1}{\sqrt{3}}(s+x\sqrt{2}) \quad \dfrac{1}{\sqrt{12}}(2s-x\sqrt{2}+y\sqrt{6}) \quad \dfrac{1}{\sqrt{12}}(2s-x\sqrt{2}-y\sqrt{6})$

FIG. 4.7   Construction of three "pure" sp^2 hybrids (each $\frac{1}{3}s + \frac{2}{3}p$) from an s AO and two p AOs; the hybrids lie in a plane, their axes being at angles of $120°$ apart.

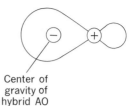

Center of
gravity of
hybrid AO

FIG. 4.8 Dipole moment due to an electron occupying a hybrid orbital.

regions where the phases alternate; the overlap integral between two such orbitals is decreased by negative contributions from regions where the orbitals overlap out of phase.

The same argument leads us to expect compounds formed by the earlier group V and VI atoms (N, S) to have approximately tetrahedral bond angles but those of the later atoms to have angles approaching 90°. This is the case; indeed, the critical division apparently comes between the first and second rows, phosphine and hydrogen sulfide having bond angles that are close to 90°.

According to the localized-orbital principle, the unshared pairs of electrons in compounds such as ammonia or water should occupy orbitals that are close to sp^3 in type; for the valence angles in each case are not far short of the tetrahedral angle (109°). Now an sp^3-hybrid orbital is very unsymmetrical; the center of orbital density does not coincide with the nucleus. An electron occupying such an orbital thus contributes largely to the dipole moment of the molecule (Fig. 4.8); indeed, refined MO calculations suggest that the greater part of the dipole moments of molecules such as NH_3 or H_2O is due to the unshared pairs. Dipoles of this type are particularly useful in forming complexes by dipole-dipole attraction, since an unshared pair presents less hindrance to the approach of another molecule than a polar bond would, and since dipole-dipole attractions vary rapidly with distance. For the same reason, the best types of dipole to be attracted by unshared pairs are polar bonds between hydrogen and some very electronegative atom X, such that the bond is polarized in the sense $H^{\delta+}\!-\!X^{\delta-}$. Interactions of this kind are of course responsible for the existence of hydrogen bonds. Our argument shows that bonds of this type between neutral molecules can be strong only when the "donor" has an unshared pair of electrons occupying a hybrid orbital, and when the "acceptor" has a very electronegative group attached to hydrogen. As a rule, bonds of this type are therefore formed only by first-row elements acting as donors, since in the heavier atoms the unshared electrons occupy s or p AOs, the center of gravities of which coincide with the nuclei.

4.14 DOUBLE AND TRIPLE BONDS
Ethylene, C_2H_4, is known from physical measurements to have a symmetrical planar structure (Fig. 4.9); it follows that the MOs of ethylene must be either

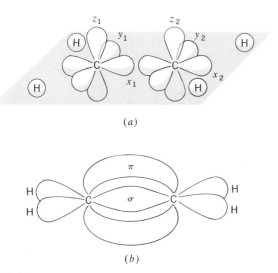

(a)

(b)

FIG. 4.9   The structure of ethylene. (a) Choice of AOs; (b) LOs.

symmetric or antisymmetric with respect to reflection in this plane (which we take to be the xy plane).   In a localized-bond treatment, we must then pick our carbon orbitals to conform to this symmetry; we can do this by aligning the $2p$ AOs along the coordinate axes, the $2p_z$ AO being antisymmetric, and the $2s$, $2p_x$, and $2p_y$ AOs symmetric, for reflection in the plane xy.   Overlap of the $2p_z$ AOs of the two carbon atoms will then give rise to π MOs similar to those encountered in our first-row diatomic molecules (Sec. 4.9); each of these will be a true MO since it represents the only possible combination of AOs that has the corresponding symmetry.

Each carbon atom then has three valence orbitals left over in the xy plane. From these we can construct three sp^2-hybrid orbitals, which we can use to form LOs linking the carbon atoms, and linking each carbon to two hydrogens.   The resulting picture (Fig. 4.9b) is of course very familiar nowadays from standard texts.   So too is the conventional picture of acetylene (Fig. 4.10).   Since acetylene is a linear molecule, the arguments of Sec. 4.9 can be applied directly; as in the first-row diatomic molecules, two p AOs of each carbon atom are used to

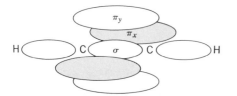

FIG. 4.10   Localized-orbital picture of acetylene.

form a pair of mutually perpendicular π MOs, while the remaining s and p orbitals combine to form sp hybrids (Fig. 4.3). One hybrid orbital of each carbon is used to form a σ LO linking them, while the other two are used to form LOs to the hydrogen atoms. Here again the π orbitals are "true" MOs, whereas the σ LOs represent an "as if" description of the electrons lying in the plane of the molecule.

The localized-bond picture explains certain other important properties of multiple bonds in a simple way. First, one can see from the shapes of hybrid orbitals that a pair of such hybrids, forming a σ LO between two adjacent carbon atoms, will overlap most efficiently when the atoms are at some finite distance apart. Since the resonance integral must be approximately proportional to the overlap, and since the bond energy is determined mainly by the value of the resonance integral, the bond energy has a maximum value at some finite internuclear separation. On the other hand the overlap between the p AOs forming a π LO increases uniformly with decreasing internuclear separation, reaching a maximum value (unity) when the nuclei coincide. The bond length of the double bond in ethylene (1.34 Å) is therefore less than that (1.53 Å) in ethane, this representing a compromise between the σ bond, which resists compression from its optimum length, and the π bond, which would really prefer the nuclei to be even closer together. In acetylene, with two π bonds and only one σ bond, the σ bond has to yield even more ground and the length is correspondingly less (1.20 Å).

This argument leads immediately to the surprising conclusion that the π bonds in acetylene must be *stronger* than the π bond in ethylene, the acetylenic π electrons being held correspondingly more tightly. The observed ionization potentials (acetylene, 11.4 ev; ethylene, 10.5 ev) support this conclusion. It follows that acetylene should be less reactive than ethylene in any connection where reactivity depends on the formation of donor bonds through the π electrons; this is indeed the case, e.g. for electrophilic addition (see Chap. 8) and the formation of π complexes with metals (see Chap. 7). For example acetylene does not react with bromine water, a phenomenon which has embarrassed generations of chemists who have tried the reaction, without previous test, as a lecture demonstration. Reactions which destroy the triple bond of acetylene are more exothermic than the corresponding reactions of ethylene, but the extra energy comes from relief of strain in the σ bond, not from any weakness in the π bonds. The textbook statement that acetylene is "more unsaturated" than ethylene is thus a misleading anachronism.

4.15   THE EFFECTS OF HYBRIDIZATION AND
ELECTRONEGATIVITY ON BOND PROPERTIES

The collective properties of many molecules can be expressed as additive sums of bond properties; this, as we have seen, is the purely empirical basis of the localized-bond model. In our attempts to explain why this additivity should hold, we have introduced a number of concepts such as hybridization and electronegativity; while these are purely artificial concepts, unrelated to physical reality, we have given them a clear-cut meaning within the framework of the localized-bond model. Our object in this section is to see how far we may expect our empirically determined bond properties (bond energies, bond lengths, bond dipole moments, etc.) to run parallel to these theoretical constructs.

In Sec. 4.6 we derived a relationship [Eq. (4.57)] between bond energies and electronegativity, equivalent to the Pauling relation [Eq. (4.58)] and serving to define the electronegativity of atoms. The difficulty here lies in the fact that the term "bond energy" carries two different connotations. The bond energies discussed in Sec. 4.6 are ideal bond energies of localized bonds formed by pairs of electrons occupying LOs. Empirical bond energies are derived by dissecting the observed heat of formation of a molecule from atoms in their ground state into contributions by the individual bonds. Two difficulties arise in comparing the two quantities. First, the localized-bond model represents the molecule as being formed from atoms in some ill-defined "valence states," rather than in their ground states; the bond energies of Sec. 4.6 refer to the heat of formation of molecules from these excited atoms. Since the states are not simple spectroscopic states of the atoms in question, the corresponding promotion energies cannot be estimated empirically. Secondly, empirical bond energies from their nature include contributions from all the electrons involved in bonding between the atoms in question, including possible contributions from electrons in AMOs. Thus the experimental bond energy of the bond in F_2 represents a sum of the bonding and antibonding effects of electrons in seven distinct MOs; it cannot reasonably be equated to the bond energy of a pair of electrons in a single LO constructed from hybrid AOs of the two fluorine atoms. Indeed, the bonding contributions of the electrons in this LO are probably very great; the low overall energy of the bond in F_2 is due to the strong overall antibonding effect of the eight electrons occupying the π MOs. The definitions of electronegativity and hybridization are also of course rather arbitrary for reasons we have already indicated. Since, however, the localized-bond model is in any case a purely artificial construct, being but an analog description of reality, it seems rather pointless to press our analysis of these fictitious quantities further. In particular, attempts to derive "better" definitions of bond energies or electronegativity, or to determine the "true" hybridization of atoms in molecules, seem misguided.

In view of these difficulties, it is surprising that the empirically determined bond energies of single bonds should conform to Eq. (4.57) as well as they do. Table 4.3 lists the electronegativities of a number of elements calculated in this way, energies being expressed in electron volts. Since Eq. (4.57) gives only the

TABLE 4.3   Electronegativities deduced from Eq. (4.57)

ELEMENT	H	C	N	O	F	S:	P	S	Cl	Br	I
ELECTRONEGATIVITY, ev	3.9	2.5	4.2	4.8	6.0	1.5	2.5	2.5	4.2	3.4	2.5

TABLE 4.4   Bond energies of bonds between first-row elements and hydrogen

BOND	BH	CH	NH	OH	FH
BOND ENERGY, kcal/mole	93	98.6	101.7	117.2	147.5

relative electronegativities and different elements, it is necessary to assume that of one element to fix the scale.   We have chosen the value for carbon to be the same as that given by Pauling.

The arguments of Sec. 4.3 imply that the bond energy of a given localized bond should in general run parallel to its one-electron resonance integral; this in turn [Eq. (3.24)] should run parallel to the mean of the coulomb integrals of the two atoms, which are identified in Eq. (4.57) with their electronegativities.   Thus since electronegativity increases in the order $B < C < N < O < F$, one might expect the bond energies of the corresponding bonds to hydrogen to rise in that order; this indeed is the case (Table 4.4).   The bonds formed by saturated carbon, e.g. in compounds of the type $(CH_3)_nX$, also show the same pattern.   Here again bond energy rises in the order $CB < CC < CN < CO < CF$.   The arguments on which this conclusion was based assume of course that the bond energy of a given bond can be identified with the bond energy due to a single LO. In cases where the atoms have lone pairs of electrons, so that antibonding MOs are involved (compare F_2), one could not expect the correlation to hold.   Indeed, the bond energies of single bonds *fall* in the series CC, NN, OO, FF; no doubt the "true" bond energies of the σ LOs rise along this series, but this is completely outweighed by the increasing number of antibonding interactions between the lone pairs of electrons.

One important corollary of this principle is that bond energies should vary with the hybridization of the atoms involved.   Consider carbon.   The $2s$ AO lies well below the $2p$ AOs in energy; the energy of a sp^n hybrid will therefore be lower, the greater the contribution of the $2s$ AO.   In bonds formed by such orbitals, the effective electronegativity of carbon will therefore vary with its hybridization, in the order $sp > sp^2 > sp^3$.   One should not therefore expect the empirically determined bond energies to be the same.   This is a very important point; for until recently it was usual to assume a common value for the CC bond energy, regardless of the state of hybridization of carbon; as we shall see in the next chapter, this has led to a great deal of confusion in the literature.

The $2s$ AO of carbon has a smaller mean radius than do the $2p$ AOs, corresponding to the fact that its binding energy is greater.   The mean size of hybrid orbitals therefore also varies with the state of hybridization, in the order $sp < sp^2 < sp^3$.   The arguments of Sec. 4.14 then suggest that bond lengths should vary in the same order—and they do.   Indeed, there is a good linear relation between the bond lengths of single CX bonds formed by atom X with carbon in

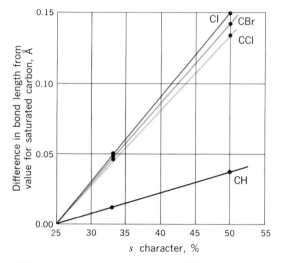

FIG. 4.11   Correlation of lengths of CX bonds with the hybridization of carbon.

different states of hybridization and the s character of the corresponding carbon orbitals (Fig. 4.11).   We are assuming here that the orbitals of saturated, olefinic, and acetylenic carbon are respectively $\frac{1}{4}$, $\frac{1}{3}$, and $\frac{1}{2}$ s; Fig. 4.11 suggests that this simple picture is good enough to be useful.

The arguments of Sec. 4.4 indicate that the polarity of a given bond XY should be greater, the greater the difference between the coulomb integrals (i.e. electronegativities) of the two atoms.   An increase in electronegativity of X polarizes the bond electrons in such a way that their center of gravity moves toward X.   Here again one would expect corresponding changes in the polarity of bonds formed by carbon as the state of hybridization of the atom changes. Changes of this kind are observed, although, as we shall see in the next chapter, they have often been misinterpreted.[2]

Changes in the effective electronegativity of atoms can also be brought about by the so-called inductive effect.   Consider for example a compound in which one carbon atom is linked to one or more very electronegative atoms, e.g. O or F. The bonds $C^{\delta+}$—$O^{\delta-}$ and $C^{\delta+}$—$F^{\delta-}$ are strongly polar in the sense indicated; the carbon atom in such a situation is therefore positively charged.   This charge must clearly increase the attraction for electrons in its other orbitals; i.e., its electronegativity, relative to other bonds, must correspondingly increase.   This in turn should lead to a shortening of the bonds and an increase in their bond energies, and the effect should obviously increase with the number of electro-negative atoms bonded to the carbon atom in question.   This effect is indeed observed in the series of compounds R_3CF, R_2CF_2, RCF_3, CF_4; the CF bonds be-come shorter and stronger, the greater the number of fluorine atoms attached to a given carbon.   A similar effect is also observed in acetals, $R_2C(OR)_2$, and orthoesters, $RC(OR)_3$, the heats of formation of which are much greater than one would predict from additivity of bond energies; the discrepancies in the case of acetals are 10 to 15 kcal/mole, and in orthoesters as much as 20 kcal/mole.[3] Both these effects can be attributed to changes in the effective electronegativity of carbon, as Burawoy[4] first suggested some time ago.

4.16 BOND-DISSOCIATION ENERGIES

The empirical bond energies of bonds are rather ill-defined quantities.   They are chosen in such a way as to make the heats of formation of a certain class of molecules additive functions of the bond energies of the bonds in them.   How is this class of molecules defined?   It is defined as the class of molecules whose heats of formation are additive functions of the bond energies of their bonds! This is clearly a circular definition, and it suffers further from the fact that bond energies would not be expected in theory to be accurately additive in *any* class of molecules.   The amount of latitude that is allowed between the calculated and observed heats of formation is therefore rather arbitrary.

Many authors have therefore discussed the strength of bonds in terms of their bond-dissociation energies, the bond-dissociation energy of a given bond being defined as the energy required to rupture that bond with corresponding cleavage of the molecule in which it occurs.   Bond-dissociation energies have the advantage of being clearly defined and directly measurable.   They are also more directly related to chemical reactivity, since we may expect the ease of a reaction involving the rupture of a given bond to run parallel to the corresponding bond-dissociation energy.

It is, however, important to realize that bond energies and bond-dissociation energies are entirely different quantities and that we cannot substitute one for the other.   When a given bond $X-Y$ breaks, the two atoms X, Y will in general undergo a reorganization; their geometry, and so the hybridization of the orbitals used in forming other surviving bonds, will change, and their electronegativities will also alter with disappearance of the bond between them if this was polar. In a localized-bond model, the bond energies of the surviving bonds in the fragments formed by rupture of the $X-Y$ bond will differ from the corresponding values for bonds in the original molecule.   The bond-dissociation energy of the $X-Y$ bond will therefore not only be different from its bond energy, but it will also vary from one molecule to another; for the reorganization energy will depend on the nature of the other bonds formed by X and Y.

Bond-dissociation energies in short are chemical properties of molecules that we can measure, and that we may hope to calculate theoretically.   Bond energies are artificial constructs, introduced as part of the localized-bond model, the purpose of which is to help in calculating the chemical properties of molecules. Obviously neither quantity can act as a substitute for the other.

PROBLEMS

4.1 Write down expressions for the total energy of H_2 and triangular H_3 (compare Prob. 3.2) using the Pople method. *Note:* The charge densities and bond orders in these molecules are determined by symmetry; in H_2, $q = p = 1$; in H_3, $q = 1$, $p = \frac{1}{3}$. Should H_3 be stable?

4.2 Using the vector model, deduce the possible states of the nitrogen atom that can be represented by configurations of the type $(1s)^2(2s)^2(2p)^3$. Arrange the states in predicted order of stability.

4.3 Are the hybrid orbitals of Eqs. (4.109) and (4.110) mutually orthogonal? Under what conditions are sp^3 hybrid orbitals truly combinations of $\frac{1}{4}s + \frac{3}{4}p$?

4.4 Does inclusion of overlap affect the conclusions of Sec. 4.3? (Compare Probs. 3.3 and 3.4.)

4.5 In groups II to IV, the tendency to form compounds with a valency two units less than the group number increases with increasing atomic weight. Thus in group IV, the tendency to form divalent compounds becomes more pronounced in the order $C < Si < Ge < Sn < Pb$. Explain this.

REFERENCES

1 Dewar, M. J. S., and R. Pettit: *J. Chem. Soc.* **1954**, 1625.

2 Dewar, M. J. S.: "Hyperconjugation," The Ronald Press Company, New York, 1962.

3 Dewar, M. J. S.: *Trans. Faraday Soc.* **42**, 767 (1946).

4 Burawoy, A.: Contribution à l'étude de la structure moléculaire, in "Victor Henri Memorial Volume," p. 73, Desoer, Liège, 1948.

CONJUGATED AND AROMATIC HYDROCARBONS

5.1 INTRODUCTION; THE HÜCKEL APPROXIMATION

It has long been recognized that the additivity of bond properties breaks down in the case of aromatic compounds; thus the CC bonds in benzene all have the same length (1.40 Å), intermediate between the lengths of normal double and single bonds, while the heat of formation is greater than one would predict for cyclohexatriene. This apparent anomaly was first resolved by Hückel.[1] If the carbon atoms in benzene have the same geometry as those in ethylene, one would expect the molecule to be planar. In the localized-bond model, each carbon atom should then form σ bonds to its three neighbors by using sp^2 hybrid orbitals; the third $2p$ orbital then has its axis perpendicular to the plane and can be used to form π bonds to the two adjacent carbon atoms (Fig. 5.1).

In cyclohexatriene, the π system would be represented in terms of three π LOs, each formed by mutual overlap of a pair of AOs of two adjacent carbon atoms. In this case there would be an alternation of bond lengths round the ring; one could account for the localization of the π LOs on the grounds that the overlap, and so also the resonance integrals, between the p AOs participating in a given π LO would be less than those between p AOs participating in different π LOs. On the other hand the favored geometry of benzene might be one in which all the bonds have equal lengths; in this case one could not use the localized-bond model to describe the π orbitals, since the interactions between a given carbon $2p_z$ AO (the z axis being taken to be perpendicular to the ring; Fig. 5.1) and the $2p_z$ AOs of the two adjacent atoms would be equal. The choice

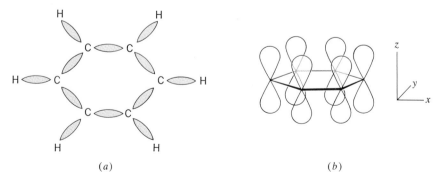

(a)   (b)

FIG. 5.1   (a) Localized σ bonds and (b) p AOs in benzene.

between these alternatives is by no means self-evident; the observed behavior of benzene of course suggests that it has the symmetrical structure.

A similar situation can arise in any of the class of compounds that organic chemists term *conjugated;* a conjugated molecule is one with a chain of "unsaturated" atoms, linked by both σ and π bonds. In this chapter we consider the structures of conjugated hydrocarbons; conjugated compounds containing heteroatoms will be discussed in Chap. 7.

Nearly all existing treatments of conjugated systems have been based on the general kind of approach introduced by Hückel, i.e. one in which the in-plane or σ bonds are treated by the localized-bond model while the π orbitals are calculated independently for each molecule by some kind of LCAO MO procedure. This general approximation, of treating σ and π electrons separately, is called the *Hückel approximation* (not to be confused with the Hückel method; Sec. 3.7).

5.2 HÜCKEL TREATMENT OF CONJUGATED HYDROCARBONS

In his pioneer investigations, Hückel used the method that now bears his name to study the π electrons of conjugated hydrocarbons. Here each π MO ψ_μ is written as a linear combination of $2p_z$ AOs ϕ_i of the individual carbon atoms;

$$\psi_\mu = \sum_i a_{\mu i}\phi_i \tag{5.1}$$

These orbitals represent the motion of the π electrons in the field of a core that now includes not only the nuclei and inner-shell electrons, but also the valence electrons that are represented, in localized-bond terminology, as taking part in σ bonds or unshared pairs. Each carbon atom uses three of its valence electrons, and three of its valence orbitals, in this way; the π electrons therefore move in the field of a positively charged framework to which each carbon atom contributes a charge $+e$. If we neglect any small differences between the carbon atoms due to polarity of the bonds in the σ framework, the Hückel coulomb integrals for the various p AOs ϕ_i will then be the same ($= \alpha$). The Hückel resonance integrals β_{ij} are assumed to vanish unless ϕ_i, ϕ_j are AOs of adjacent atoms; in conjugated hydrocarbons, we therefore set $\beta_{ij} = 0$ unless atoms i and j are linked by a σ bond. If the atoms i, j are linked by a σ bond, the value of β_{ij} will depend on the type of structure that the conjugated molecule has. If it has a "localized" structure, i.e. one in which the π electrons can be regarded as occupying two-center π LOs, then β_{ij} will vanish unless atoms i, j are linked by such a localized π bond; if they are so linked, β will have the same value that it has for the π MO of ethylene. If on the other hand the molecule has a "nonlocalized" structure in which the bonds are intermediate in type between "pure single" and "pure double," then β_{ij} will have a finite value for all pairs of linked carbon atoms.

In his pioneering studies Hückel made the simplifying assumption that the nonvanishing β_{ij} always have a common value ($= \beta$); in this case one can calculate immediately the total energies of the localized and nonlocalized structures and so deduce which of the two is the more stable.   Thus in a nonlocalized benzene, we would set $\beta_{ij} = \beta$ for each pair of bonded atoms, while in localized cyclohexatriene we would set $\beta_{12} = \beta_{34} = \beta_{56} = \beta$, while all the other β_{ij} vanish. The corresponding secular equations, and their roots, are as follows:

Nonlocalized benzene:

$$\begin{vmatrix} \alpha - E & \beta & 0 & 0 & 0 & \beta \\ \beta & \alpha - E & \beta & 0 & 0 & 0 \\ 0 & \beta & \alpha - E & \beta & 0 & 0 \\ 0 & 0 & \beta & \alpha - E & \beta & 0 \\ 0 & 0 & 0 & \beta & \alpha - E & \beta \\ \beta & 0 & 0 & 0 & \beta & \alpha - E \end{vmatrix} = 0 \qquad E = \begin{cases} \alpha + 2\beta \\ \alpha + \beta \text{ (twice)} \\ \alpha - \beta \text{ (twice)} \\ \alpha - 2\beta \end{cases}$$

$$(5.2)$$

Localized cyclohexatriene:

$$\begin{vmatrix} \alpha - E & \beta & 0 & 0 & 0 & 0 \\ \beta & \alpha - E & 0 & 0 & 0 & 0 \\ 0 & 0 & \alpha - E & \beta & 0 & 0 \\ 0 & 0 & \beta & \alpha - E & 0 & 0 \\ 0 & 0 & 0 & 0 & \alpha - E & \beta \\ 0 & 0 & 0 & 0 & \beta & \alpha - E \end{vmatrix} = 0 \qquad E = \begin{cases} \alpha + \beta \text{ (three times)} \\ \alpha - \beta \text{ (three times)} \end{cases}$$

$$(5.3)$$

Since each carbon atom contributes one $2p_z$ electron, there are six π electrons all together, to be accommodated in each case in the three lowest MOs.   The total energy E_{tot} of each of the two structures is then:

Delocalized benzene: $E_{\text{tot}} = 6\alpha + 8\beta$

Localized cyclohexatriene: $E_{\text{tot}} = 6\alpha + 6\beta$

$$(5.4)$$

The delocalized structure is thus predicted to have the lower energy, in agreement with experiment.

If we calculate the bond orders of bonds in the two structures, we find:

Delocalized benzene: $p_{12} = p_{23} = p_{34} = p_{45} = p_{56} = p_{16} = \frac{2}{3}$

Localized cyclohexatriene: $p_{12} = p_{34} = p_{16} = 1; p_{23} = p_{45} = p_{16} = 0$

$$(5.5)$$

The arguments in Sec. 3.9 showed that the bond order of a given bond is a measure of its strength, while the arguments in Sec. 4.14 imply that a multiple bond between two given atoms should be shorter, the stronger the π bonds taking part in it; we would therefore expect the length of a bond between two conjugated carbon atoms to be shorter, the greater its bond order.   Since the bond orders of the bonds in delocalized benzene ($\frac{2}{3}$) are intermediate between the orders in ethylene (1) or a pure σ bond (0), the bond lengths in delocalized benzene would be expected to be intermediate between the lengths of pure double or pure single bonds.   This is the case; the observed bond length in benzene is 1.397 Å, that of the double bond in ethylene 1.338 Å, and that of a pure σ bond between sp^2 hybridized carbon atoms in the range 1.51 to 1.52 Å (for details see Sec. 5.3).

This approach can of course be extended to other conjugated hydrocarbons; until recently it enjoyed a virtual monopoly in this field. Calculations of this kind lead to the conclusion that all conjugated hydrocarbons should be delocalized to a greater or less degree, all the bonds in them having orders between 0 and 1, and usually in the range 0.4 to 0.8. The calculated difference in energy between the localized and delocalized structures of a given hydrocarbon is commonly described as the *resonance energy;* it is usually taken as a measure of the extra stabilization to be expected in comparison with a localized structure, the heat of formation of the latter being found by assuming all the CC bonds to be pure single or pure double bonds, and assuming additivity of bond energies for localized molecules.

The assumptions and approximations underlying the Hückel method are, however, much too drastic and it has become increasingly apparent in recent years that it cannot safely be used for any kind of quantitative work. The widespread acceptance of the method, in the face of obvious theoretical shortcomings, was due to an unfortunate coincidence. As we shall see presently, there is just *one* class of compound where the method might be expected to be successful, i.e. the benzenoid hydrocarbons, and early applications of the Hückel method were mostly in this uniquely favorable area.

5.3 SEMIEMPIRICAL SCF MO TREATMENTS OF CONJUGATED HYDROCARBONS, USING THE POPLE METHOD

As we have seen in Chap. 3, the best approach to molecular problems currently available is one based on a semiempirical SCF LCAO MO method using the Pople approximation, i.e. neglect of differential overlap. In this section we shall examine the application of such an approach to conjugated hydrocarbons, using the Hückel approximation; our SCF treatment will therefore be limited to the π electrons. We shall also assume that our hydrocarbons are both neutral and *even*, i.e. that they have even numbers n of conjugated carbon atoms; the extension to *odd* conjugated hydrocarbons, i.e. ions or radicals such as allyl or benzyl, will be considered later. In this preliminary treatment we shall also ignore any effects of polarity in the σ bonds of the core; the n π electrons therefore move in the field of a core carrying n units of positive charge, each associated with one carbon atom. The bonding energies of electrons occupying the $2p_z$ orbitals of such carbon atoms will therefore have a common value ($= W_c$), and the only other core-electron interactions we need consider are those between the π electrons and the n positively charged carbon atoms in the core.

The Pople equations for the π electrons are then of the form:

$$|F_{ij} - E\delta_{ij}| = 0 \tag{5.6}$$

$$\sum_j a_{\mu j}(F_{ij} - E_\mu \delta_{ij}) = 0 \qquad i = 1, 2, \ldots, n \tag{5.7}$$

where E_μ is one root of the secular equation (5.6). The matrix elements F_{ij} are given [compare Eqs. (3.64) and (3.65)] by:

$$F_{ii} = W_c + \tfrac{1}{2}q_i(ii,ii) + \sum_{j \neq i}(q_j - 1)(ii,jj) \tag{5.8}$$

$$F_{ij} = \beta_{ij}{}^c - \tfrac{1}{2}p_{ij}(ii,jj) \qquad i \neq j \tag{5.9}$$

Here q_i is the π-charge density at atom i, and p_{ij} is the π-bond order between atoms i and j (see Sec. 3.6). With our assumptions, atom j will be neutral if $q_j = 1$; the quantity $q_j - 1$ in Eq. (5.8) is therefore the net formal charge on atom j, in units of e, the electronic charge.

The next problem is to estimate the values of the various integrals appearing in Eqs. (5.8) and (5.9). Consider first the integral W_c. W_c is the energy required to remove an electron from the $2p_z$ AO of a carbon atom which is linked to three other atoms by bonds but which is not π-bonded to them. This is rather a tricky quantity to calculate, but fortunately its value does not concern us here. Our object is to calculate the heats of formation of molecules from atoms, i.e. the relative energies of a molecule and the atoms of which it is composed. In an isolated atom, a "π" electron has energy W_c. The total energy of the n "π" electrons is thus nW_c. We shall find that the total π energy of the molecule is of the form $nW_c + X$, where X does not involve W_c. If we are interested only in the difference in energy between the two systems, the terms in W_c cancel. This simplification is of course due to the fact that all the conjugated atoms in our molecule are the same; if heteroatoms are present, the W terms must be retained (see Chap. 9).

Consider now the electron repulsion integrals (ii,jj). These could in principle be calculated, using appropriate expressions for the AOs ϕ_i, ϕ_j, together with Eq. (2.223); such a procedure would, however, be contrary to the whole philosophy of our approach. We know that the results of even an exact Hartree-Fock treatment would be too inaccurate to be of chemical value; our only chance of achieving useful results is to introduce parameters in the hope that these may help to take up some of the slack. The integrals in Eqs. (5.8) and (5.9) must therefore be determined as far as possible by empirical means.

The one-center integrals (ii,ii) are usually estimated by the following procedure, first introduced by Pariser and Parr.[2] Consider a carbon atom C· in an appropriate sp^2 valence state, i.e. attached by neutral σ bonds to three adjacent atoms, and with a single electron occupying its $2p_z$ AO. Assuming that π bonds are absent, the energy of this electron will be W_c. Consider now the two ions C⁻, C⁺ formed by adding one electron to, or removing one electron from, this $2p_z$ AO. The energy required to remove an electron from C· to form C⁺ is the corresponding valence-state ionization potential I; by definition

$$I = -W_c \tag{5.10}$$

The energy liberated when an electron combines with C to form C^- is likewise the valence-state electron affinity A. Consider now the process:

$$2C\cdot \rightarrow C^+ + C\colon^- \tag{5.11}$$

where the dots represent two p electrons. The total energy change in this process is equal to the energy required to remove an electron from one $C\cdot$ (that is I) *less* the energy liberated when the electron combines with the other $C\cdot$ (that is A). The core energy of the two electrons is the same in two isolated carbon atoms of this type as it is in the ion C^-, assuming as a first approximation that the $2p_z$ AO is the same in both cases; however in C^- there is an additional energy term representing the mutual repulsion of the two electrons, this being by definition equal to the corresponding one-center integral $(ii,ii)_c$. Thus while the total energy of the two p electrons on two isolated carbon atoms is $2W_c$, in C^- it is $2W_c + (ii,ii)_c$, $(ii,ii)_c$ being the one-center integral for a carbon $2p$ AO. Equating these two estimates for the change in energy involved in Eq. (5.11),

$$A - I = 2W_c - [2W_c + (ii,ii)_c] \tag{5.12}$$

or
$$(ii,ii) = I - A \tag{5.13}$$

The value estimated in this way by Pariser[3] was:

$$(ii,ii)_c = 10.96 \text{ ev} \tag{5.14}$$

Other authors have recently revised this calculation, making allowance for changes in size of $2p_z$ AO with changes in the number of electrons in it, and for polarization of the core. The revised values are somewhat smaller than that given by Pariser. (See for example Ref. 4, which recommends a value of 9.8 ev.)

The quantities I and A cannot of course be measured experimentally since they do not refer to a real physical system; they can, however, be calculated from spectroscopic data once we accept the localized-bond model and assume that the σ bonds formed by carbon are neutral. The value for $(ii,ii)_c$ given by the Pariser-Parr procedure is chosen to make these semiempirical values for I and A consistent with the assumed model.

Unfortunately this procedure cannot be used for the remaining repulsion integrals; we are therefore forced to relate these in some way to the "theoretical" values found by direct quadrature using Eq. (2.223). Now the theoretical value for the one-center integral $(ii,ii)_c$, using SZOs, is very much higher (16.9 ev) than the empirical one of Eq. (5.14); if we could find some explanation of this discrepancy, it might guide us to a method for deducing the "best" values of the two-center integrals from the theoretical ones found by using SZOs.

Two possible factors of this kind have been proposed. First, the repulsion integrals should strictly be calculated using Hartree-Fock AOs rather than the simpler Slater-Zener orbitals.   As we have seen (Sec. 2.17), Hartree-Fock SCF AOs are more diffuse than SZOs; two electrons occupying a Hartree-Fock AO will therefore on an average be further apart, and so their mean mutual repulsion will be less than if they occupied a corresponding SZO.   The few calculations that have been reported support this conclusion (e.g. Ref. 5); certainly a large part of the discrepancy between the "empirical" and theoretical values of $(ii,ii)_c$ can be attributed to it.

Until recently, the use of SCF AOs would not have been practicable in this connection since they were not available in analytical form; however good approximations are now available in terms of SZOs (see Sec. 2.17), and these could be used to calculate the repulsion integrals (ii,jj).   So far little work of this kind has been reported, partly because analytical SCF AOs have only recently become available, but partly also because the use of such AOs would not in itself solve our integral problem; for our object is to do better than we could with even a full Hartree-Fock treatment, and we cannot hope to achieve this if we use the same values for our basic parameters.

The second factor responsible for the discrepancy between the empirical and theoretical values for $(ii,ii)_c$ is the neglect of electron correlation inherent in any orbital approximation.   The repulsion between two electrons occupying a given AO is less than the corresponding one-center repulsion integral, because the electrons do not move independently of one another.   This difference, the so-called *correlation energy*, amounts to 1 to 2 ev for a pair of electrons occupying a $2p$ AO.[6]   About one-third of the discrepancy (5.9 ev) between the empirical and theoretical values for $(ii,ii)_c$ is therefore due to electron correlation.   By using appropriately modified values for the other repulsion integrals also, we may then hope to introduce an empirical correction for electron correlation into our treatment.

The values of the two-center integrals (ii,jj) depend of course only on the internuclear separation r_{ij}; we wish to find some function $F(r_{ij})$ which will express this dependence.   Such a function must satisfy two boundary conditions; first, when $r_{ij} = 0$, $F(r_{ij})$ must be equal to the one-center integral (ii,ii); secondly, since the mutual repulsion of two widely separated clouds of charge is independent of their shape and equal to e^2/r, r being the separation at their centers of gravity, $F(r_{ij})$ must approximate to e^2/r_{ij} for large internuclear separations.

Two procedures have been used to deduce suitable functions of this type. The first is purely empirical.   It is assumed that the factors responsible for the reduced value of the one-center integral will apply equally to the two-center integrals, so that all the two-center integrals can be written as a single function $F(r_{ij})$, obeying the required boundary conditions.   The second procedure is based on a more detailed analysis of the reasons for the reduced value of the one-center integral; this leads to the conclusion that the integral (ii,jj) can have two distinct values, depending on the term of the F matrix in which it appears.

Most of the work in this field has made use of the first type of procedure, using an expression for $F(r_{ij})$ suggested by Pariser and Parr.[2] This approach has been widely described in the literature as the Pariser-Parr-Pople (PPP) approximation. Here we shall describe an alternative expression for $F(r_{ij})$ which gives results almost identical with the Pariser-Parr values, and which will form the basis for our discussion of the alternative procedure for determining integrals.

The starting point is a method developed by Pariser and Parr[2] for approximating the "theoretical" value, $(ii, jj)^{th}$, that would be found by direct quadrature using SZOs. This integral represents the mutual repulsion of two dumbbell-shaped clouds of charge: one representing an electron in the p AO ϕ_i, the other an electron in ϕ_j. Pariser and Parr suggested the approximation of replacing each such cloud of charge by two charged spheres, each of charge $-e/2$ and radius R, lying along the Z axis and touching at the corresponding nucleus (Fig. 5.2); the repulsion between these clouds can be calculated very simply, since the electrostatic field produced by a spherical cloud of charge q is equivalent to that of a point charge q placed at the center of the sphere. In the case of two identical atoms, e.g. carbon, R will be the same for each AO, so that:

$$(ii, jj) = 2\left[\frac{(-\tfrac{1}{2}e)(-\tfrac{1}{2}e)}{r_{ij}} + \frac{(-\tfrac{1}{2}e)(-\tfrac{1}{2}e)}{\sqrt{r_{ij}^2 + 4R^2}}\right] = \frac{e^2}{2r_{ij}}(1 + \rho) \tag{5.15}$$

where
$$\rho = \left(1 + \frac{4R^2}{r_{ij}^2}\right)^{-1/2} \tag{5.16}$$

This method of estimating theoretical repulsion integrals is called the *uniformly-charged-sphere* approximation; the value of R is of course chosen to give the best agreement with integrals found by direct quadrature.

Dewar and Wulfman[7] pointed out some time ago that the empirical one-center

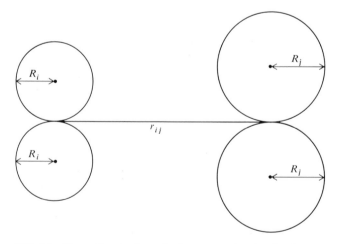

FIG. 5.2   The uniformly-charged-sphere approximation for electron repulsion integrals.

integral $(ii,ii)_c$ is very close to the value (10.3 ev) that would be calculated by the uniformly-charged-sphere approximation if it were assumed that the two electrons occupy different lobes of the pAO, their mutual repulsion being then given by $e^2/4R^2$. This suggests that one might replace the expression of Eq. (5.15) by one representing the repulsion between the electrons occupying p lobes on opposite sides of the mutual nodal plane of the two p AOs, the resulting *upper-lower* integral (ii,jj) being given by:

$$(\bar{\bar{ii}},jj) = \frac{e^2}{\sqrt{r_{ij}^2 + 4R^2}} \equiv \frac{\rho e^2}{r_{ij}} \qquad (5.17)$$

Values calculated in this way are very close to those given by the empirical relation proposed by Pariser and Parr and can be used interchangeably with them in Pople-type calculations.

Now the correlation of two electrons in a given p AO will tend to make them synchronize their motions in such a way as to reduce the chance of their being found at the same time in the same lobe of the AO. If this effect were complete, the repulsion between them would then be given by an integral of upper-lower type. Dewar and Hojvat[8] suggested that the whole discrepancy between the empirical and theoretical values for the one-center integral might be due to this type of correlation; following this model, they suggested that one might take account of correlation in π systems by writing the wave function in terms of lobes of p AOs, rather than whole p AOs. This is the basis of the so-called *split-p-orbital* (SPO) method.

In its original form, the SPO method was open to serious objections; moreover it ascribed too high a value (5.9 ev) to the correlation energy of two electrons occupying a given $2p$ AO. Later studies, however, have shown[9] that a modified version can be used to establish values for the repulsion integrals in a Pople treatment that should take into account the effect of *vertical correlation*, i.e. the tendency of the pair of electrons occupying a given p AO or π MO to synchronize their motions in such a way as to keep in opposite lobes of the orbital.

Consider the expression for the total energy E of a closed-shell molecule [Eq. (2.204), repeated here for convenience]:

$$E = 2\sum_{\mu}^{occ} E_\mu + \sum_{\mu}^{occ}\sum_{\nu}^{occ} (2J_{\mu\nu} - K_{\mu\nu}) \qquad (5.18)$$

The synchronization of motions responsible for vertical correlation should not to a first approximation alter the distributions of the individual electrons; the term E_μ, representing the core energy of an electron occupying the MO ψ_μ, should therefore remain unchanged. Consider next the term $J_{\mu\nu}$, which occurs four times in Eq. (5.18), representing the mutual repulsion between the pair of electrons in the MO ψ_μ and the pair in ψ_ν. These terms together represent the mutual repulsion of two clouds of charge, one representing the pair of electrons in ψ_μ, the other the pair in ψ_ν. The shapes of these clouds will not be affected by vertical correlation; for vertical correlation between the electrons in ψ_ν will merely affect the way this overall two-electron cloud is partitioned at any instant between the two electrons, not its overall shape. Therefore although the four individual terms $J_{\mu\nu}$ in Eq. (5.18) may be affected by vertical correlation, their sum should remain unchanged.

The main effect of vertical correlation must then be through the two-electron exchange terms $K_{\mu\nu}$. The term $K_{\mu\nu}$ occurs twice, representing the mutual repulsions between the α-spin electron in ψ_μ and the α-spin electron in ψ_ν, and the corresponding repulsion between electrons of β spin. These terms *can* be affected by vertical correlation. Thus if the α-spin electrons each tend to occupy lobes on the same side of the π-nodal plane more often than they occupy lobes on the opposite side, the corresponding integral $K_{\mu\nu}$ will clearly be greater than if their motions are not correlated.

This increase in the $K_{\mu\nu}$ can be included in our treatment by using increased values for the electron repulsion integrals $(ii,jj)^K$ that arise from expansion of the $K_{\mu\nu}$. We shall then have two distinct values for a given integral (ii,jj), i.e. a "normal" value $(ii,jj)^J$ to be used in terms arising from expansion of the molecular coulomb integrals $J_{\mu\nu}$, and a somewhat larger value $(ii,jj)^K$ for terms arising from the molecular exchange integrals $K_{\mu\nu}$. Each set of integrals will be a function of the internuclear distance r_{ij}, the functions being chosen to give the correct values for the two corresponding one-center integrals $(ii,ii)^J$ and $(ii,ii)^K$, and to converge to the common value e^2/r_{ij} at large internuclear separations.

The value for the one-center integrals can be deduced from an argument similar to that used by Pariser and Parr, from a consideration of the system $C:^-$ of Eq. (5.11). The total energy E of the two p electrons is given [compare Eq. (5.18)] by:

$$E = 2E_c + 2(ii,ii)_c^J - (ii,ii)_c^K \tag{5.19}$$

where E_c is the core energy of a $2p$ electron. Comparison with (5.12) and (5.13) shows that the empirical one-center integral $(ii,ii)_c$ of Eq. (5.13) is given by:

$$(ii,ii)_c^{\mathrm{emp}} = 2(ii,ii)_c^J - (ii,ii)_c^K \tag{5.20}$$

As we have seen, this is also equal to the upper-lower integral $(\bar{i}i,ii)$ calculated by the uniformly-charged-sphere approximation. Now $(ii,ii)_c^J$ represents the repulsion that would exist between two electrons occupying the AO ϕ_i if there were no correlation; the correlation energy (CE) is given by:

$$\mathrm{CE} = (ii,ii)_c^J - (ii,ii)_c^{\mathrm{emp}} = (ii,ii)_c^K - (\bar{i}i,ii)_c^J \tag{5.21}$$

Substituting the empirical values (11.0 and 2 ev) for $(\bar{i}i,ii)_c^{\mathrm{emp}}$ and CE, we find:

$$(ii,ii)^J = 13.0 \text{ ev} \qquad (ii,ii)^K = 15.0 \text{ ev} \tag{5.22}$$

The theoretical value $(ii,ii)_c{}^{\text{th}}$ calculated using SZOs is 16.9 ev; consequently:

$$(ii,ii)^J = (\bar{i}\bar{i},ii)_c + \tfrac{1}{3}[(ii,ii)_c{}^{\text{th}} - (\bar{i}\bar{i},ii)_c]$$
$$(ii,ii)^K = (\bar{i}\bar{i},ii)_c + \tfrac{2}{3}[(ii,ii)_c{}^{\text{th}} - (\bar{i}\bar{i},ii)_c]$$

(5.23)

A reasonable representation of the other repulsion integrals $(ii,jj)^J$ and $(ii,jj)^K$ can be obtained by assuming that a similar relation will apply to these also, using the uniformly-charged-sphere approximation [Eq. (5.15)] to estimate the theoretical integrals $(ii,jj)^{\text{th}}$. Thus:

$$(ii,jj)^{\text{th}} = \tfrac{1}{2}[(\bar{i}\bar{i},jj) + (\bar{i}\bar{i},\bar{j}\bar{j})]$$

(5.24)

$$(ii,jj)^J = (\bar{i}\bar{i},jj) + \tfrac{1}{3}[(ii,jj)^{\text{th}} - (\bar{i}\bar{i},jj)]$$
$$= \tfrac{5}{6}(\bar{i}\bar{i},jj) + \tfrac{1}{6}(\bar{i}\bar{i},\bar{j}\bar{j})$$

(5.25)

$$(ii,jj)^K = (\bar{i}\bar{i},jj) + \tfrac{2}{3}[(ii,jj)^{\text{th}} - (\bar{i}\bar{i},jj)]$$
$$= \tfrac{2}{3}(\bar{i}\bar{i},jj) + \tfrac{1}{3}(\bar{i}\bar{i},\bar{j}\bar{j})$$

(5.26)

Since we now have two different sets of values for the repulsion integrals, we need to know which of them to use in the various terms of the F matrix. This is simply a matter of tracking down each of the various repulsion integrals and seeing whether it came from expansion of a molecular coulomb integral $J_{\mu\nu}$ or a molecular exchange integral $K_{\mu\nu}$ in the original expression for the orbital energy [Eq. (2.205)]. In this way it is easily shown that:

$$F_{ii} = W_c + q_i[(ii,ii)^J - \tfrac{1}{2}(ii,ii)^K] + \sum_{j\neq i} (q_j - 1)(ii,jj)^J$$

(5.27)

$$F_{ij} = \beta_{ij}{}^c - \tfrac{1}{2}(ii,jj)^K$$

(5.28)

In this treatment, we distinguish between the two factors mentioned earlier as being responsible for the decreased value of the empirical integral (ii,ii) in comparison with the theoretical value $(ii,ii)^{\text{th}}$. The J integrals are less than the theoretical ones; this should correspond to the error due to using SZOs in calculating the latter. The difference between the J and K integrals represents an empirical correction for correlation. Note that the one-center integral (ii,ii) in Eq. (5.8) has a smaller value than any of the integrals used here; Eq. (5.27) shows that this represents the difference between two terms, each involving a one-center integral (ii,ii)—but one-center integrals of different types. This kind of approach, based on the use of different sets of integrals to allow for electron correlation, is now termed the SPO approximation.

The last quantities whose values need to be determined are the core resonance integrals $\beta_{ij}{}^c$. These are found by calculating a measurable property of some standard reference compound or compounds, and adjusting the β's to make the calculated values agree with experiment. Most of the work in this field has made use of β's found by fitting observed spectroscopic data to the calculated differences in energy between ground states and excited states; such a procedure is logical if we are interested in calculating the light absorption of molecules, but not if we are concerned with the chemical and physical properties of molecules in their ground states.   A proper SCF description of an excited state of a molecule would involve a set of MOs different from those appropriate to the ground state (compare Sec. 3.10).   If we try to describe the excited states in terms of ground-state orbitals, using parameters appropriate to the ground state, the results are bound to be unsatisfactory.   We may nevertheless be able to use a treatment of this kind if the parameters are chosen to give the best fit to the calculated spectra; however the parameters appropriate to this purpose will now be equally unsuitable for describing the ground state.

Since our concern is primarily with ground states, we must fix the values of our β's by calculating some measured ground-state property of a suitable reference compound.   In the case of π systems, the most successful approach of this kind has been one introduced by Dewar and Schmeising[10] for use in Hückel calculations, and later adapted to Pople-type treatments (both PPP and SPO) by Chung and Dewar.[11, 12]   This depends on a comparison of the energies of a C=C bond and a C—C bond, stretched or compressed to a common length r at which we wish to estimate β^c.   The difference in energy is equal to the bond energy of the π component of the double bond, a quantity we call the *π-binding energy $E_{\pi b}$*.   The calculated value of $E_{\pi b}$ is given [compare Eq. (4.41)] by:

$$E_{\pi b} = 2\beta^c + \tfrac{1}{2}[(11,11)^J - (11,22)^K] \tag{5.29}$$

The experimental value is estimated from the following thermocycle:

$$C \overset{r'}{-} C \xrightarrow{c'} C \overset{r}{-} C \xrightarrow{E_{\pi b}} C \overset{r}{=} C \xrightarrow{-c''} C \overset{r''}{=} C \tag{5.30}$$

$$\underset{E_{C=C} - E_{C-C}}{\underbrace{\hspace{5cm}}}$$

Here c' is the energy required to compress a C—C bond from its equilibrium length r' to r, and c'' is the corresponding energy required to stretch the double bond from its equilibrium length r''. $E_{C=C}$ and E_{C-C} are the bond energies of a C=C bond and a C—C single bond (i.e. one with no π component whatsoever) at their equilibrium bond lengths.   The compression energies c', c'' are found by using the Morse function; thus:

$$c' = E_{C-C}(1 - e^{-a'(r'-r)}) \tag{5.31}$$

$$c'' = E_{C=C}(1 - e^{-a''(r''-r)}) \tag{5.32}$$

The Morse constants a', a'' are given by:

$$a' = \left(\frac{k'}{2E_{C-C}}\right)^{1/2} \qquad a'' = \left(\frac{k''}{2E_{C=C}}\right)^{1/2} \tag{5.33}$$

where k', k'' are the force constants at the two bonds.   From Eqs. (5.29) and (5.30),

$$\beta^c = \frac{1}{2}E_{\pi b} - \frac{1}{4}[(11,11)^J - (11,22)^K]$$
$$= \frac{1}{2}[(E_{C-C} - E_{C=C}) + (c'' - c')] - \frac{1}{4}[(11,11)^J - (11,22)^K] \qquad (5.34)$$

In order to use this expression, it is necessary to know the quantities $E_{C=C}$, c'', k'', E_{C-C}, c', k'. The first three present no difficulties, since they refer to a normal carbon-carbon double bond; appropriate values are listed in Ref. 15. The remaining quantities are more troublesome, since it is difficult to devise any suitable method for measuring experimentally the properties of a "pure" σ bond between sp^2-hybridized (i.e. olefinic) carbon atoms, i.e. a bond which has *no* π component whatsoever so that its π-bond order is zero. The best estimate seems to be provided by the following argument.

In certain molecules, the coefficients of the AOs in their MOs are determined by symmetry; this was true for H_2 (Sec. 4.3), and it is also true for the same reason for ethylene. The bonding π MO ψ_0 in ethylene is given by:

$$\psi_0 = \frac{1}{\sqrt{2}}(\phi_1 + \phi_2) \qquad (5.35)$$

when ϕ_1, ϕ_2 are the two p AOs; the corresponding π-bond order p_{12} is then:

$$p_{12} = 2\left(\frac{1}{\sqrt{2}}\right)^2 = 1 \qquad (5.36)$$

It can be shown by similar but more elaborate arguments that the π-bond orders in benzene and graphite are also determined by symmetry, assuming in each case that all the CC bonds have the same lengths. Now we have seen (Sec. 4.14) that a π bond between two atoms tends to reduce their separation, and we have also seen (Sec. 3.6) that the bond order of a given bond is a measure of its strength. We might therefore expect there to be a $1:1$ relation between π-bond order and bond length for carbon-carbon bonds. Figure 5.3 shows a plot of bond order vs. measured bond length for ethylene, benzene, and graphite; the three points lie accurately on a straight line. Combined with our previous argument, this suggests that we may reasonably assume the relation between bond order and bond length to be linear; extrapolation of the line then gives us an estimate of the length of a "pure" σ bond between sp^2 carbon atoms, i.e. a bond whose π-bond order is zero. Given the length of the "pure" C—C σ bond, we can estimate its bond energy and force constant from known empirical relationships between the lengths, bond energies, and force constants for carbon-carbon bonds.[10,13,15] We now have all the quantities needed to calculate β [Eq. (5.34)].

Given values for all the integrals involved in the F matrix, we can now solve the Pople equations without difficulty. They must of course be solved by an iterative procedure, and we must in some way provide an initial set of π-charge densities and π-bond orders to allow the first F matrix to be calculated; this, however, is all straightforward and the construction of suitable computer programs presents no difficulties. In this way we find the coefficients $a_{\mu i}$ and

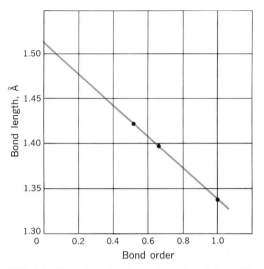

FIG. 5.3 Plot of bond order vs. bond length for CC bonds.

orbital energies E_μ of the various MOs, and also the π-charge densities q_i and π-bond orders p_{ij}. The total electronic energy E_π is then given [compare Eq. (2.204)] by:

$$E_\pi = 2 \sum_\mu^{occ} E_\mu - \sum_\mu^{occ} \sum_\nu^{occ} (2J_{\mu\nu} - K_{\mu\nu}) \tag{5.37}$$

Expanding the $J_{\mu\nu}$ and $K_{\mu\nu}$ in terms of integrals over the AOs, and using the definitions of π-charge density and π-bond order, we find:

$$E_\pi = 2 \sum_\mu^{occ} E_\mu - \frac{1}{2} \sum_i q_i[(ii,ii)^J - \tfrac{1}{2}(ii,ii)^K]$$
$$- \sum_{i<j}\sum q_i q_j (ii,jj)^J + \frac{1}{2} \sum_{i<j}\sum p_{ij}(ii,jj)^K \tag{5.38}$$

The total π-bond energy $E_{\pi b}$ is the energy liberated when n isolated carbon atoms, each with a p electron of energy W_c, combine to form π bonds; we can dissect this process as follows:

$$nC\cdot \xrightarrow{-nW_c} nC^+ \xrightarrow{CR} (C^+)_n \xrightarrow{E_\pi} \text{molecule} \tag{5.39}$$

First we remove the n p electrons; to do this we have to supply energy nW_c. Next we allow the resulting ions to come together. During this process there will be changes in energy due to the formation of σ bonds; these are irrelevant to our present purpose, which is concerned solely with the binding effect of the π electrons. There is also, however, a relevant term CR (the core repulsion) representing the energy that must be supplied to overcome the mutual coulomb repulsions of the charged carbon atoms. Finally we replace the n electrons to form the molecule; the energy change here is equal to the total π-electron energy E_π. The overall energy change in this process is by definition $E_{\pi b}$; hence:

$$E_{\pi b} = E_\pi + \text{CR} - nW_c \tag{5.40}$$

In the case of a hydrocarbon, the diagonal F-matrix element [Eq. (5.8) or (5.27)] can be written in the form:

$$F_{ii} = W_c + F'_{ii} \tag{5.41}$$

where F'_{ii} does not involve W_c. The secular equation (5.6) then becomes:

$$|F'_{ij} - (E - W_c)\delta_{ij}| = 0 \tag{5.42}$$

where $F'_{ij} = F_{ij}$ if $i \neq j$. The roots E_μ of this equation can then be written in the form:

$$E_\mu = E'_\mu + W_c \tag{5.43}$$

where E'_μ is independent of W_c. Thus Eq. (5.40) can be written in the form:

$$E_\pi = nW_c + 2\sum_\mu^{\text{occ}} E'_\mu - \sum_\mu^{\text{occ}}\sum_\nu^{\text{occ}} (2J_{\mu\nu} - K_{\mu\nu}) = nW_c + E'_\pi \tag{5.44}$$

where E_π does not involve W_c. Substituting this expression in Eq. (5.40), we see that W_c cancels; this is why we do not need to know W_c in order to estimate $E_{\pi b}$ for hydrocarbons.

Let us now consider the core repulsion CR. Consider the term $(\text{CR})_{ij}$, representing the repulsion between the cores of atoms i, j. We have written the attraction between an electron in the AO ϕ_i and the core of atom j as $-(ii,jj)$ (compare Sec. 3.5); this is the attraction that would exist between two clouds of electron charge, one negative and one positive, representing an electron occupying the AO ϕ_i and a positron occupying the AO ϕ_j. We have therefore implicitly assumed that the field due to the core of atom j is equivalent to that which would be produced by a positive electron occupying the AO ϕ_j; to be consistent, we must then assume that the repulsion between the cores of atoms i, j is equal to the mutual repulsion of such a pair of p positrons, i.e. to the integral (ii,jj). Summing over the whole core,

$$\text{CR} = \sum_{i<j}\sum (ii,jj) \tag{5.45}$$

Collecting together Eqs. (5.38), (5.40), (5.44), and (5.45), we have

$$E_{\pi b} = 2\sum_\mu^{\text{occ}} E'_\mu - \frac{1}{2}\sum_i q_i[(ii,ii)^J - \tfrac{1}{2}(ii,ii)^K]$$

$$+ \sum_{i<j}\sum [(1 - q_iq_j)(ii,jj)^J + \tfrac{1}{2}p_{ij}(ii,jj)^K] \tag{5.46}$$

One last point needs to be considered, the calculation of bond lengths. In principle, we should determine them by finding the geometry that minimizes the

total bond energy E_b of the molecule, this being given by summing the σ-bond energy $E_{\sigma b}$ and the π-bond energy $-E_{\pi b}$. The σ-bond energy is found by adding together the bond energies of the σ bonds; the bond energy of a given σ bond of given length can be found in terms of its equilibrium length by using a Morse function [compare Eq. (5.31)]. An approach of this kind would, however, be far too difficult for any but the simplest molecules. A more feasible approach is to assume the relation between π-bond order and bond length shown in Fig. 5.3, and to use this to calculate bond lengths from the π-bond orders. A further refinement in studies of this kind is to recalculate the bond lengths at each cycle of the iterative procedure used to solve the Pople equations, and then to recalculate the various integrals involved in the treatment, using the new bond lengths. The final result is then self-consistent for variations in the values of the integrals with bond length. In order to do this rigorously, it would of course be necessary to recalculate the whole geometry of the molecule at each iteration; for varying the lengths of the bonds will also alter the distances between atoms that are not directly linked. However such calculations are again very difficult, since the geometry of a molecule depends on the bond angles as well as the bond lengths; the bond angles have to be chosen to minimize the total energy, and in doing this one would have also to take nonbonded interactions into account. Fortunately, however, the effect of changes in the long-range terms is quite small; it is therefore usually sufficient to recalculate only those integrals that refer to pairs of atoms i, j that are directly linked, and to do this, we need only know bond lengths, not bond angles.

The rest of this chapter will be concerned with applications of the procedure outlined above to various classes of conjugated hydrocarbons. Since the methods used are frankly semiempirical, it is of course very important at each step to relate the results to experiment, both to test the validity of the method, and to check the values of the parameters used in it. Since the chemical behavior of molecules is determined primarily by energies, and differences in energy, the main criterion of our treatment must be its success in predicting the total energies of molecules, i.e. their heats of formation from atoms. Calculations of this kind can therefore be justified only if it can be shown that they predict heats of formation of molecules with an accuracy sufficient to be chemically useful. One of the great dangers in work of this kind is an insidious malady that might be termed *computeritis*, i.e. the fatal temptation, once one has a computer program, to use it indiscriminately, regardless of whether the results mean anything or not.

5.4 CONJUGATED HYDROCARBONS

By summing the appropriate bond energies for the σ bonds in a hydrocarbon, and the calculated π-binding energy $E_{\pi b}$, we arrive at an estimate of its heat of atomization, which can be compared directly with that derived experimentally by standard thermochemical methods.

The first studies of this kind[11,12,14] were confined to aromatic hydrocarbons, where the C—C bond lengths are all very similar; it was assumed that the corresponding σ-bond energies would likewise be similar, so that a common value could be used for the σ-bond energy of the "aromatic" σ bond. This quantity was treated as a parameter, chosen to give the best fit to the experimental data; the value found in this way was close to, but not identical with, that used in the thermocycle of Eq. (5.30). Heats of atomization were so calculated by both the Pople and SPO methods, with results in very good agreement with experiment in each case.

This approach suffered from three obvious defects. First, it could not be extended satisfactorily to compounds such as polyenes, in which the C—C bond lengths vary greatly. Secondly, it suffered from an internal inconsistency in that the assumed value for the C—C σ-bond energy differed from the value calculated for a bond of that length by the procedure of Eq. (5.30). Thirdly, the treatment of the σ-bond energy as a parameter involved an unjustifiable increase in the total number of parameters.

Recently we[15] have found that both these difficulties can be avoided by a careful reexamination of the parameters used in Eq. (5.30). The treatment is now entirely self-consistent, in that the σ-bond energies are calculated directly as a function of bond length, from the assumed value for a "pure" σ bond and the corresponding force constant. As an unexpected and gratifying bonus, the accuracy of the calculations has proved greater than that of the earlier treatment, in spite of the fact that the latter contained an additional parameter. A further interesting point was that self-consistency of this kind could be obtained *only* in the Pople treatment. Apparently the extra allowance for correlation in the SPO approach is unnecessary, the Pople treatment containing sufficient parameters to take all forms of correlation adequately into account. This is also a satisfactory conclusion, given that the SPO method again involves additional parameters.

Table 5.1 lists the parameters used in this treatment; the bond energy for CH bonds was chosen to give the correct heat of formation for ethylene, using the

TABLE 5.1   Parameters in the Pople treatment of conjugated hydrocarbons

Bond	Bond energy, ev	Bond length, Å	Force constant, dynes/nm
C—C	3.9409	1.512	53.3
C=C	5.5600	1.338	109
C—H	4.4375		

assumed value $E_{C=C}$ for the bond energy of the "pure double" bond in this molecule.

Table 5.2 compares calculated and observed heats of formation for a number of conjugated hydrocarbons for which heats of atomization can be estimated from heats of combustion.

The agreement between the calculated and observed values is extraordinarily good. With six exceptions, the differences are within the limits of error of the experimental measurements, most of which were made more than 30 years ago,

TABLE 5.2   Comparison of calculated[15] and observed heats of formation of conjugated hydrocarbons from atoms

Compound	Formula	ΔH, ev		Error	
		Calc	Obs	ev	%
BENZENE		57.16	57.16	0	0
NAPHTHALENE		90.61	90.61	0	0
ANTHRACENE		123.89	123.93	−0.04	0.03
PHENANTHRENE		124.22	124.20	0.02	0.02
AZULENE		89.47	89.19	0.28	0.31
PYRENE		138.62	138.88	−0.26	0.19
PERYLENE		172.15	172.04	0.11	0.07
TRIPHENYLENE		157.94	157.76	0.18	0.11

TABLE 5.2   (Cont.)

Compound	Formula	ΔH, ev		Error	
		Calc	Obs	ev	%
BENZO[c]PHENANTHRENE		157.77	157.48	0.29	0.18
CHRYSENE		157.77	157.73	0.04	0.03
1,2-BENZANTHRACENE		157.58	157.49	0.09	0.06
NAPHTHACENE		157.11	157.56	−0.45	0.29
1,3-BUTADIENE		57.16	57.16	0	0
BIPHENYL		109.75	109.76	−0.01	0
STYRENE		75.91	75.83	0.08	0.11
STILBENE		128.54	128.48	0.06	0.05
BIPHENYLENE		104.87	102.00	2.87	
ACENAPHTHYLENE		104.86	104.32	0.54	
FLUORANTHENE		138.67	138.11	0.56	

when techniques for measuring heats of combustion were less highly developed than they are today.   One of the six exceptions (naphthacene) can also probably be attributed to experimental error; naphthacene was a difficult compound to purify 30 years ago, and it may also have undergone partial oxidation while being equilibrated with oxygen in the bomb prior to combustion.   This would have made its observed heats of combustion too low and the calculated heat of atomization correspondingly too high.

The remaining five exceptions all refer to compounds that are subject to steric strain, either through geometrical interference (3,4-benzophenanthrene), or because they contain strained rings (azulene, biphenylene, acenaphthylene, and fluoranthene).   Since effects of this kind are not taken into account in our calculations, the calculated heats of atomization should be too great, by an amount equal to the strain energy.   The calculated values are indeed greater than those observed thermochemically, and in four cases the differences (azulene, 6.5; benzo[c]phenanthrene, 6.7; acenaphthylene, 12.4; fluoranthene, 12.9 kcal/mole) are close to those that have been estimated classically, from force constants for the bending of bonds.   The difference in the case of biphenylene is again in the right direction, but in this case it seems to be rather large (66 kcal/mole), given that the strain energies in cyclobutane and cyclobutene are both less than 30 kcal/mole.

The Pople method therefore seems to give extraordinarily good estimates for

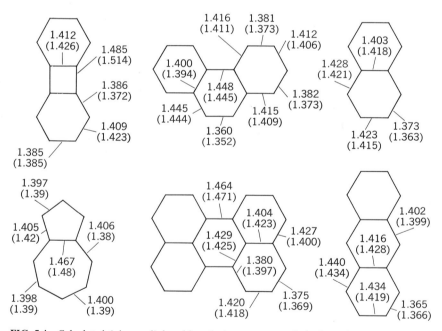

FIG. 5.4   Calculated (observed) bond lengths in some aromatic hydrocarbons.

the heats of formation of a wide range of conjugated hydrocarbons, both aromatic and nonaromatic, strained and unstrained. Only in one case is there any suggestion that the calculated value differs from experiment by an amount greater than the possible experimental error.

The agreement between theory and experiment is of course very gratifying; for it implies that the semiempirical SCF LCAO MO method can give results of "chemical" accuracy. It is perhaps worth emphasizing once more the inadequacy of a priori treatments for this purpose; it is still not possible to calculate the heats of formation of systems with but three electrons (e.g. HHe, or He_2^+) to this degree of accuracy by a priori methods. It should also be emphasized that no experimental data were used in determining the parameters in this treatment, other than those referring to isolated carbon atoms, to isolated C—C and C=C bonds, and to ethylene; the fact that the method gives the absolute heats of formation with such accuracy is therefore a striking test.

The procedure outlined in Sec. 5.3 also provides estimates of bond lengths; these agree well with experiment, given that hardly any of the bond lengths are known with certainty to 0.01 Å. Some examples are listed in Fig. 5.4.

5.5 CLASSICAL POLYENES

There has been a good deal of controversy in recent years concerning the bonding in classical polyenes,‡ following a suggestion that the bonds in compounds of this type are localized.[10,16] As we have seen (Sec. 4.11), the question of bond localization is a purely empirical one; a compound is said to have localized bonds if its collective properties can be represented as additive functions of bond properties. Unfortunately there are insufficient experimental data for compounds of this type to establish whether or not the bonds in them are localized; it is therefore interesting to see if the SCF MO treatment outlined above can throw light on this problem, in other words to see if the heats of formation and bond lengths calculated for classical polyenes do in fact conform to a localized-bond model.

Consider first a linear conjugated polyene, with n single bonds and $n + 1$ double bonds; i.e.

$$H_2C=CH-(CH=CH)_{n-1}-CH=CH_2$$

If the bonds in this are localized, its heat of formation ΔH should be given by:

$$\Delta H = nE'_{C-C} + (n + 1)E'_{C=C} + (2n + 4)E_{CH}$$
$$= n(E'_{C-C} + E'_{C=C} + 2E_{CH}) + (E'_{C=C} + 4E_{CH}) \qquad (5.47)$$

where E'_{C-C}, $E'_{C=C}$, E_{CH} are bond energies for C—C, C=C, and CH bonds respectively. Thus a plot of ΔH vs. n should be a straight line, of slope $E'_{C-C} +$

---

‡ A classical polyene is a polyene for which only a single classical structure ("unexcited resonance structure") can be written.

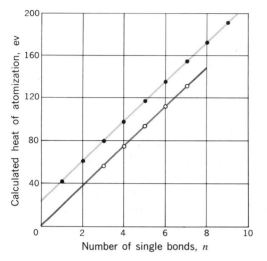

FIG. 5.5 Plot[15] of n vs. ΔH [Eq. (5.47)], for linear polyenes (●), and for radialenes (○).

$E'_{C=C} + 2E_{CH}$ and intercept $E'_{C=C} + 4E_{CH}$. Figure 5.5 shows this plot for the values of ΔH calculated in the manner indicated above; evidently the calculated values of ΔH do conform very closely indeed to Eq. (5.47), implying that they can be represented accurately in terms of additive bond energies.

As a further check, we may compare calculated and observed heats of formation for a second, and apparently very dissimilar, series of conjugated polyenes, i.e. the radialenes; these are compounds containing a ring of carbon atoms, each doubly bound to a methylene group. The first few members are as follows:

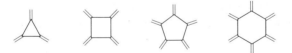

Here the number of single and double bonds should be the same ($= n$); if the bonds in them are localized, the heats of formation (corrected for ring strain, which is ignored in our calculation of ΔH) should be given by:

$$\Delta H = n(E'_{C-C} + E'_{C=C} + 2E_{CH}) \tag{5.48}$$

A plot of ΔH vs. n should now be a straight line parallel to the plot for linear polyenes, but this time passing through the origin. Figure 5.5 shows that this relationship holds accurately for the heats of formation calculated by our SCF MO procedure.

From these plots one can of course estimate the bond energies of single and double bonds in a polyene; these are shown in Table 5.3. Note that the value (100.3 kcal/mole) for the single bond is very high, much higher than that (89.0 kcal/mole) assumed for a pure σ bond between sp^2 carbon atoms. This of

TABLE 5.3   Bond energies of localized bonds in conjugated polyenes

Bond	Bond energy	
	ev	kcal/mole
C—C	4.4399	100.31
C=C	5.5378	127.70

course is because the single bond in a polyene has significant π character.   The bond orders and bond lengths for some typical polyenes are shown in Fig. 5.6; the "single" bonds are seen to have significant π character and to be shorter than the value (1.512 Å) assumed for a pure σ bond.   However the existence of π bonding in the "single" bonds of polyenes in no way affects our conclusion that the bonds in compounds of this type are localized; for as we have emphasized, the test of localization is a purely empirical one, quite unrelated to the nature of bonding involved.   If our calculations are correct, they imply that the amount of π bonding in such "single" bonds is essentially constant, a single bond in a polyene varying as little from one molecule to another as does the C—C bond in a paraffin.   Note also that the "double" bonds in polyenes are predicted to differ little from a "pure" double bond (length, 1.338 Å; bond energy, 128.2 kcal/mole).

Calculations of this kind have been carried out[15] for a variety of classical open-chain polyenes; the calculated heats of formation in all cases agree closely with those estimated assuming additivity of bond energies, using the values listed in Table 5.3, and the bond lengths in all cases conform closely to the values shown in Fig. 5.6.

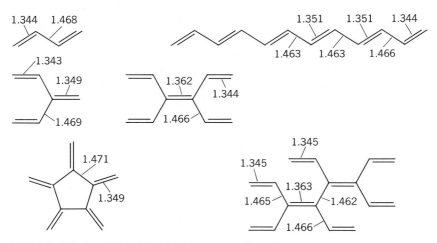

FIG. 5.6   Calculated[15] bond lengths, in angstroms, in various conjugated polyenes.

5.6   RESONANCE ENERGIES; BENZENOID AND NONBENZENOID HYDROCARBONS AND AROMATICITY

While the calculated heats of formation of classical polyenes conform closely to those expected for localized bonds, the calculated (and observed) values for benzenoid hydrocarbons are uniformly larger.   This extra stability is of course responsible for the special chemical behavior of such compounds; the extra stabilization, over and above that expected for a localized structure, may be termed the *resonance energy*.

This term requires some comment; for an extraordinary amount of confusion exists in the literature concerning its meaning.   It was originally introduced by Pauling[17] to describe the extra stability of certain molecules, over and above that predicted by the localized-bond model; unfortunately other authors have used the term in a number of other connections, e.g. to describe the differences between the heats of hydrogenation of molecules and those of arbitrarily chosen reference compounds.   Further confusion has been caused by failure to allow for changes in bond properties with the state of hybridization of the atoms involved.[13]   The "resonance energies" quoted in the literature are therefore mostly meaningless, as also have been the attempts of various theoreticians to "explain" these "experimental" values, which they have accepted uncritically.   The definition given here of course suffers from the use of theoretical values for the "bond energies" E'_{C-C} and $E'_{C=C}$ (see Table 5.3).   Unfortunately there are hardly any good experimental data for compounds of this type which could be used to determine bond energies.   In the few cases where such data are available (e.g. 1,3-butadiene), the calculated heats of formation do conform closely to those predicted, using Eq. (5.47) and Table 5.3.

Table 5.4 shows resonance energies calculated in this way for a number of benzenoid and nonbenzenoid hydrocarbons, together with values calculated by the Hückel method and from heats of combustion.   For reasons indicated in the previous paragraph, the values are much smaller than those commonly quoted in the literature; the ones in Table 5.4 should be direct measures of stability in comparison with an analogous classical polyene, rather than with some idealized structure with "pure single" and "pure double" bonds.   The Hückel parameter β was chosen by fitting the resonance energy for benzene; the corresponding value (10 kcal/mole) is of course also much smaller than that commonly quoted.

The results given by the Pople treatment are in excellent agreement with the known behavior of these compounds; only the benzenoid hydrocarbons and azulene are predicted to have significant resonance energies, and they alone are aromatic in a chemical sense.   The Hückel method gives quite reasonable results for the aromatic compounds, but it completely fails to differentiate between the aromatic and nonaromatic types.   As we shall see later, the Hückel method would be expected to be much more successful in the case of benzenoid hydrocarbons.

The calculated bond lengths also indicate a sharp division between the two

TABLE 5.4   Resonance energies for conjugated hydrocarbons

Compound	Resonance energy, kcal/mole		
	Pople[15]	Hückel	Exp.
BENZENE	20.0	20.0	20.0
NAPHTHALENE	30.5	36.8	30.5
ANTHRACENE	36.9	53.1	37.8
PHENANTHRENE	44.6	54.5	44.0
CHRYSENE	57.3	71.9	56.3
TRIPHENYLENE	61.2	72.7	57.0
PERYLENE	60.4	82.5	60.2
PYRENE	48.4	62.5	54.2
AZULENE	4.2	33.6	0
BUTALENE	−6.2	16.6	
PENTALENE	−6.5	24.6	
HEPTALENE	−2.1	36.2	
FULVENE	1.0	14.7	
HEPTAFULVENE	0.5	19.9	
FULVALENE	2.5	28.0	
HEPTAFULVALENE	2.3	40.0	
SESQUIFULVALENE	4.1		

groups of compounds.   In the aromatic hydrocarbons, the calculated bond lengths vary little from a mean "aromatic" value of 1.40 Å (see Fig. 5.4).   On the other hand the bond lengths in the nonaromatic hydrocarbons are predicted to alternate strongly, corresponding closely to those that would be expected for corresponding classical polyenes with "localized" double and single bonds. Some examples are given in Fig. 5.7.

5.7 HÜCKEL'S RULE

In his pioneering work, Hückel extended his calculations to the polymethines, i.e. compounds containing a single ring compound entirely of CH units.   The ones with an even number $2n$ of such units, termed annulenes, can be represented as neutral cyclic polyenes ($-CH=CH-)_n$, while those with an odd number of CH units must occur as radicals or positive or negative ions.   The secular equations for compounds of this type can be solved in closed analytical form, the solution being:

$$E = 2\beta \cos \frac{2k\pi}{l} \quad k = 1, 2, \ldots, l \qquad (5.49)$$

when l is the number of CH units.   Now it can be shown at once that

$$\cos \frac{2k\pi}{l} = \cos \frac{2(l-k)\pi}{l} \qquad (5.50)$$

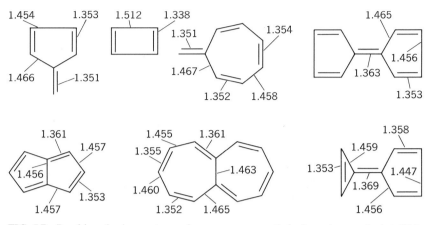

FIG. 5.7   Bond lengths, in angstroms, in some nonaromatic hydrocarbons, calculated[15] by the Pople method.

If l is odd, there is then one unique orbital (with $k = l$) of energy 2β, while all the remaining orbitals have higher energies and occur in degenerate pairs.   If l is even, there is also a second unique orbital with $k = l/2$, of energy -2β, the remaining levels again being degenerate.

Two of the π electrons occupy the MO of energy 2β; the rest must then occupy twofold-degenerate levels.   Each such level can hold four electrons; in order to get a closed-shell structure, we must then have a total of $(4n + 2)$ π electrons, n being an integer.   Hückel suggested that the special stability of aromatic compounds might be due to their having closed-shell structures, from analogy with the inert gases; in this case cyclic polymethanes should be aromatic if, and only if, they contain $(4n + 2)$ π electrons.   This is the generalization known as *Hückel's rule*.   At the time it was formulated, only two examples were known, i.e. benzene, and the ion $C_5H_5^-$, each with six π electrons; since then it has been shown that rings with 2, 6, 10, or 14 electrons are aromatic, while those with 3, 4, 5, 7, 8, 12, 16, 20, 24, 26, and 30 definitely are not.   [18]Annulene is probably also aromatic, judging by its proton nmr spectrum; the π electrons in aromatic compounds produce characteristic shielding effects due to the presence of "ring currents," and [18]annulene shows similar magnetic shielding.[18]   The evidence thus seems to suggest that only the compounds with $(4n + 2)$ π electrons are aromatic, but that they too cease to be above a certain critical ring size.

Calculations by the Pople method support these conclusions for the cyclic polyenes; calculations for the ions are more difficult to interpret since one cannot easily establish the energy to be expected for a "classical" compound of this type.   Complications also arise in the case of the cyclic polyenes of moderate ring size, because of the fact that compounds of this type cannot exist in an unstrained planar form.   However, as we shall see in the next chapter, moderate distortions from planarity should not greatly affect the resonance energies of conjugated systems; the calculations were therefore carried out for symmetrical planar arrangements of the carbon atoms with bond angles of 120°.   The results are shown in Table 5.5.   All the compounds with $4n$ atoms, and the larger ones with $4n + 2$ atoms, are predicted to be nonaromatic, having negligible or negative resonance energies and bond lengths which alternate between values close to those expected for localized single and double bonds.   On the other hand the small ring compounds with $4n + 2$ atoms have positive resonance energies and bond lengths which are all equal, or almost equal.   The general picture is clearly very satisfactory; the only discrepancy lies in the prediction that aromaticity should disappear too rapidly in the $4n + 2$ series with increasing n.   However the evidence for aromaticity in compounds with 18 and 22 π electrons comes solely from magnetic measurements; chemically they show no aromatic behavior, being very reactive and polymerizing easily.   Any resonance stabilization must here be very small indeed; the error in predicting the crossing point thus probably corresponds to a very small error in predicting energies.

Here again the Hückel method fails badly, predicting large positive resonance energies for *all* the polymethines with more than four π electrons.   While it is true that the compounds with $(4n + 2)$ π electrons are predicted to be more stable than their neighbors, the differences rapidly decrease with increasing ring size and soon become negligible.

The two smallest [$4n$]annulenes, cyclobutadiene and cyclooctatetraene, deserve special mention in view of their historical and chemical interest.   Since it was thought from an early stage that the special aromatic properties of benzene must be associated with the fact that two equivalent classical structures can be written for it, and since similar pairs of structures can also be written for cyclobutadiene and cyclooctatetraene, it was clearly of vital importance to chem-

TABLE 5.5   Resonance energies and bond lengths in annulenes

[n]Annulene, n	Resonance energy, kcal/mole	Bond length, Å	
		Min.	Max.
4	−18	1.34	1.51
6	20	1.40	1.40
8	−2.5	1.35	1.47
10	7.8	1.37	1.44
12	1.8	1.35	1.46
14	3.5	1.35	1.46
16	2.8	1.35	1.46
18	3.0	1.35	1.46
20	2.8	1.35	1.46
22	2.8	1.35	1.46

ical theory to see if the latter compounds would also prove to be aromatic. Interest in this field became intensified by the development of resonance theory, which of course predicted unambiguously that all three compounds should be aromatic.

Willstätter had in fact prepared cyclooctatetraene in 1917 and had shown it not to be aromatic; this work was, however, doubted for many years because of the failure of less skilled chemists to repeat Willstätter's long and difficult synthesis. In recent years cyclooctatetraene has been prepared both by Willstätter's method, and by alternative routes,‡ and Willstätter's conclusions have been completely confirmed. Cyclobutadiene on the other hand long resisted many determined attempts at synthesis, and it has only recently been prepared by Pettit and his collaborators;[19] not only is it not aromatic, but its reactivity is such as to suggest that it must be *less* stable than a normal diene, i.e. antiaromatic. The properties of both compounds are therefore in total disagreement with the predictions of resonance theory or HMO theory.

The SCF MO calculations outlined in Sec. 5.7 of course account for this behavior very well. Both cyclobutadiene and planar cyclooctatetraene are predicted to have *negative* resonance energies and so to be antiaromatic. Cyclooctatetraene can escape this fate by abandoning a planar geometry; the molecule does in fact have a tub-shaped structure, in which each double bond is almost perpendicular to its neighbors, the π overlap between them being consequently very small. However there is no such loophole for cyclobutadiene; it can escape only by undergoing some chemical reaction, and for this reason it is probably the most reactive diene known.

Cyclooctatetraene cannot of course exist in an unstrained planar form; any gain in resonance energy due to π interactions in planar cyclooctatetraene would be offset by the energy required to flatten out the ring. On this basis one cannot exclude the possibility that cyclooctatetraene might be aromatic, were it possible to avoid the complicating factor of ring strain. The SCF MO calculations of course reject this possibility; they imply that planar cyclooctatetraene should be antiaromatic, with a negative resonance energy and alternating bond lengths. This prediction has been vindicated by Anet,[20] who has shown by an ingenious experiment that the bonds in planar cyclooctatetraene must alternate in length.

5.8 VALIDITY OF THE BOND-ORDER–BOND-LENGTH RELATION
In our treatment, we estimate the lengths of bonds in conjugated hydrocarbons from an assumed linear relation between bond order and bond length (Fig. 5.3); it is interesting to see if the values estimated in this way are the same as those

---

‡ One of these, the tetramerization of acetylene over nickel carbonyl in tetrahydrofuran could indeed be used to manufacture cyclooctatetraene cheaply on a large scale! This process was discovered by Reppe, at I. G. Farbenindustrie, during the Second World War.

that would be given by a more rigorous procedure in which the bond lengths are chosen to minimize the total energy of the molecule.   In cases where calculations of the latter type have been carried out, the two sets of values do in fact agree very closely.   For example, the bond length which minimizes the calculated energy of benzene (1.3975 Å) agrees to within 0.0015 Å with the value (1.396 Å) given by the assumed linear relation between bond order and bond length.[15]

An interesting further check is provided by calculations of the energy of benzene as a function of bond length in the vicinity of equilibrium.   From these one can estimate the stretching force constant for the "breathing" vibration, in which the ring expands and contracts without changing its shape.   The value[15] found in this way (7.4 $\times$ 10^5 dynes/cm) is in remarkably good agreement with that estimated from the observed frequency[21] of this vibration (7.6 $\times$ 10^5 dynes/cm).

5.9   DIPOLE MOMENTS

It can be shown that the contributions of the σ bonds to the dipole moment of a conjugated hydrocarbon should vanish, if the bond angles are all close to 120°; any overall polarity in such a molecule must then be due to polarization of the π electrons.   The contribution of these is very easily calculated, accepting our model in which differential overlap is neglected.   As we have seen, the net formal charge on atom i due to polarization of the π electrons is given by $q_i - 1$.   The net π dipole moment can be calculated immediately, knowing the positions of the atoms in a molecule and the charges on them.

When we apply this treatment to even conjugated hydrocarbons, they are seen to fall into two distinct categories.   Compounds containing no odd-numbered rings are predicted to be completely nonpolar, the π-charge density being exactly unity at each position; this is true both of the Hückel method and of the Pople method.   Later we shall prove that the result is quite general for such compounds; it is also supported by the available experimental evidence, the measured dipole moments being zero within the limits of experimental error.

Compounds containing odd-numbered rings, e.g. fulvene or azulene, are, however, predicted to be polar, and they do in fact possess significant dipole moments.   Here again the Hückel method fails badly in that it predicts moments which are several times too large.   The SCF MO treatments give quite reasonable results, especially in view of the unrealistic approximations made in them concerning the cancellation of polarity due to the σ bonds.   This cancellation should be exact in benzenoid hydrocarbons, where the bond angles can all be equal to 120°, but not in systems with odd-numbered rings.   Some examples are given in Table 5.6.

The case of calicene is particularly interesting.   Some authors have suggested that this should represent a new aromatic system, partly on the basis of the large resonance energy calculated for it by the Hückel method (Table 5.4), and partly

TABLE 5.6 Comparison of calculated and observed dipole moments[a]

Compound	μ, Debyes		
	Obs.	Pople[15]	Hückel
FULVENE	1.2	0.86	4.7
AZULENE	1.0	2.15	6.9
CALICENE		3.82	13.4

[a] The direction of the dipole is in each case along the axis of the molecule, with the negative end toward the five-membered ring.

because derivatives of it have large dipole moments. The SCF MO treatment predicts that calicene should have a dipole moment of the right order of magnitude, but at the same time that its resonance energy should be small (Table 5.4) and the bond lengths in it close to those for pure double and single bonds (Fig. 5.7). A relatively large dipole moment need not therefore imply any significant degree of aromaticity.

5.10 BOND LOCALIZATION IN CONJUGATED SYSTEMS

The calculations outlined above suggest that conjugated hydrocarbons fall into two distinct classes; those with small or negative resonance energies and bonds with alternating lengths approximating closely to two widely separated values, and those with appreciable positive resonance energies and bonds of approximately equal length, intermediate between the values for the first class. In terms of our empirical definition, the first class of hydrocarbons can be regarded as having localized bonds; the second class, which correspond to the hydrocarbons termed *aromatic* by organic chemists, clearly do not.

The calculations outlined above suggest that classical conjugated hydrocarbons, both cyclic and acyclic, fall into the first class. All the cases that have been studied have negligible resonance energies and bonds that are localized in accordance with their classical valence structures. Classical valence structures therefore seem to be closely associated with the structures of such molecules; indeed their significance seems to extend beyond the category of classical compounds.

In certain nonclassical hydrocarbons, with two or more distinct valence structures, it may happen that certain bonds are either single or double in every one of the possible structures. Calculation suggests that such *essential single* or *essential double* bonds, as we may term them following a suggestion by Longuet-Higgins, can also be regarded as localized. Their calculated lengths approximate closely to those of "single" or "double" bonds, and the resonance energy of the molecule as a whole is the same as that of the residue left if we excise all the essential single and double bonds.

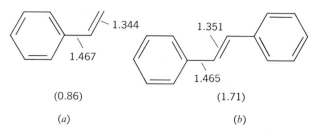

(0.86)   (1.71)

(a)   (b)

FIG. 5.8   Resonance energies, in electron volts, and lengths, in angstroms of essential single and double bonds in (a) styrene and (b) stilbene.

Several examples have appeared above.   For example the central bond in azulene is an essential single bond; the calculated and observed values (Fig. 5.7) are close to the length expected for a localized single bond (compare Fig. 5.6). Again, the calculated resonance energy of perylene (60 kcal/mole, Table 5.4) is just twice that of naphthalene (30 kcal/mole, Table 5.4); perylene consists of two naphthalene units linked by essential single bonds.   Moreover the lengths of these bonds (Fig. 5.4) are again if anything greater than the values expected for single bonds in a classical polyene.   Styrene and stilbene provide two final examples; the calculated and observed resonance energies are close to those for one (0.87 ev), and two (1.74 ev) molecules of benzene respectively, while the lengths of the essential single and double bonds correspond closely to the "polyene" values (Fig. 5.8).

It seems from these results that bonds in conjugated hydrocarbons can be delocalized only if they occur both as single and double in at least one possible classical structure for the molecule.   While, however, this may be a necessary condition for delocalization, it is not a sufficient one.   Thus the bonds in the [4n]annulenes, and in various antiaromatic structures such as pentalene and heptalene, are predicted to show strong alternation, even though they occur both as single bonds and as double bonds in possible classical structures.   A general discussion of this problem will be given in the following chapter.

5.11   ODD CONJUGATED SYSTEMS

Our discussion so far has been concerned only with even conjugated systems, containing an even number of conjugated atoms; however numerous conjugated systems are known in which the number of conjugated atoms is odd, and which therefore must exist as radicals, or positive or negative ions.   The allyl anion (I) and tropylium (II) are typical examples.

$$[CH_2 {=\!\!=} CH {=\!\!=} CH_2]^-$$

I   II

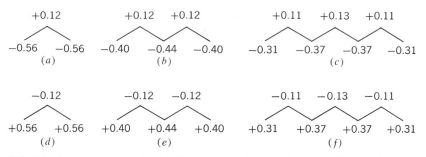

FIG. 5.9 Formal charges calculated[23] by the Pople method for odd linear polyene ions. (a) to (c) Anions; (d) to (f) cations.

Radicals contain unpaired electrons and cannot therefore be treated by the Pople method in the form used in this chapter; we shall consider systems of this type later (Chap. 7). However the odd ions have closed-shell structures and can be treated in the same way as the neutral even systems.

First, let us consider odd open-chain ions such as allyl; Fig. 5.9 shows formal charges calculated for several of these by the Pople method.

One striking feature is immediately apparent from Fig. 5.9, viz. the presence of positive formal charges at certain positions in the odd anions and negative formal charges at the corresponding positions in cations. This is in direct contradiction of common sense, resonance theory, or the results of HMO calculations, all of which predict that the formal charges in these ions should be confined to alternate atoms, the formal charges at the intervening positions being zero. This is illustrated in Fig. 5.10 by the results of HMO calculations for the same set of polyene anions as in Fig. 5.9.

The reason for this difference is, however, very easily seen. In the HMO method, all carbon atoms are assumed to have a common value for the coulomb integral α, regardless of the molecule or ion in which the atom appears. In the Pople method, the corresponding diagonal matrix element F_{ii} is given by:

$$F_{ii} = W_c + \tfrac{1}{2}q_i(cc,cc) + \sum_{j \neq i}(q_j - 1)(ii,jj) \tag{5.51}$$

where W_c, (cc,cc) are respectively the valence-state ionization potential and one-center repulsion integral for a carbon $2p$ AO. This is the quantity corresponding to α_i in the HMO method; in the Pople method, F_{ii} is not a constant, but depends both on the charge density at atom i and also on the charge densities

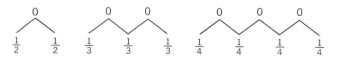

FIG. 5.10 Formal charges calculated for odd polyene ions by the HMO method.

at other atoms j. Suppose we start our iterative SCF calculation for the allyl anion with HMO orbitals as our starting set. Here (Fig. 5.10),

$$q_1 = q_3 = 1.5 \qquad q_2 = 1 \tag{5.52}$$

In the next iteration,

$$F_{11} = F_{33} = W_c + 0.75(cc,cc) + 0.5(11,33) \tag{5.53}$$
$$F_{22} = W_c + 0.5(cc,cc) + (11,22)$$

Hence:

$$F_{22} - F_{11} = F_{22} - F_{33} = (11,22) - \tfrac{1}{4}(cc,cc) - \tfrac{1}{2}(11,33) \tag{5.54}$$

Now the one-center integral (cc,cc) is greater than the other integrals, but not much greater; if we assume the bond lengths in allyl to be 1.4 Å and the CC bond angle 120°,

$$(cc,cc) = 11.0 \text{ ev} \qquad (11,22) = 7.55 \text{ ev} \qquad (11,33) = 5.2 \text{ ev} \tag{5.55}$$

Consequently $F_{22} - F_{11} > 0$, implying that the quantity corresponding to the Hückel α is greater (i.e. less negative) for the central atom in the allyl anion than for the terminal atoms. In other words, the negative charges on the terminal atoms of the allyl anion have a greater effect on the electronegativity of the central atom than on that of a terminal atom! The reason for this unexpected result is that an electron on the central atom is repelled by *all* the electrons on the terminal atoms, while an electron on a terminal atom is repelled by only half the electrons there; for the Pauli principle allows at most two electrons, of opposite spin, to occupy a given AO at a given time, so that an electron in a terminal AO can be repelled only by electrons of opposite spin, the net density of which is half the total density at that position.

Now the HMO charge densities (Fig. 5.10) are calculated on the assumption that all the atoms in allyl have equal electronegativities; we have shown that the central atom is in fact effectively less electronegative than the terminal ones. Consequently we might expect the total π-electron density at the central atom to be less than that calculated by the HMO method, i.e. less than unity, so that the net formal charge at that atom is positive.

Similar differences between charge densities calculated by the HMO and Pople methods appear for all molecules and ions where the charge densities differ from unity. There is a general tendency for atoms adjacent to negatively charged centers to be unexpectedly positive, and those adjacent to positively charged centers to be unexpectedly negative. No definite evidence is as yet available concerning the correctness of this prediction for odd-hydrocarbon ions, but recent nmr studies seem to support it in the case of conjugated systems containing heteroatoms, where the same effect should be observed (see Chap. 9).

The calculated bond orders in ions of this type normally show no alternation, as one might expect since they contain no essential single or double bonds. It is also difficult to attach much meaning to their heats of formation; for the heats of formation of ions in solution contain large contributions from solvation which cannot be estimated in any convincing way.   Heats of formation have been estimated for certain of these ions by mass spectroscopy; however the values are again uncertain since they relied on measurements of appearance potentials, a technique that is known to be liable to errors of at least 0.5 ev, or 12 kcal/mole. With this proviso, we may compare the calculated[22] and observed heats of formation of the allyl cation:

$$3C + 4H + H^+ \rightarrow C_3H_5^+ \qquad \Delta H = \begin{cases} 23.72 \text{ ev (calc)} \\ 23.76 \text{ ev (obs)} \end{cases} \qquad (5.56)$$

The agreement is excellent.

The definition of resonance energy given above cannot of course be applied to odd ions; for there are no classical compounds of this type to serve as standards.   All odd ions are nonclassical, since it is always possible to write two or more equally satisfactory classical structures for them; the bonds in ions of this type are therefore generally delocalized.

We can, however, produce an extended definition of aromaticity which corresponds to the use of the term as applied by organic chemists to odd ions.   We can define a cyclic ion as aromatic if it has a greater effective π-binding energy than a corresponding open-chain system.   The term effective π-binding energy implies that allowance must be made for the compression energy of the σ bonds in the two ions; in particular, we must allow for the fact that the cyclic ion contains more σ bonds that have been compressed.   Thus in comparing the ions

we must allow for the fact that the cyclic ion contains five σ bonds that have been compressed to less than their usual length, while the acyclic ion contains only four.   The relative effective π-binding energy E_{ar}, which we may term the *aromatic energy* of the cyclic ion, is thus given by:

$$E_{ar} = (E_{\pi b})_{acyclic} - (E_{\pi b})_{cyclic} + (c')_{acyclic} - (c')_{cyclic} \qquad (5.57)$$

where $E_{\pi b}$ is the π-binding energy, and c' the total σ-bond compression energy, of one or the other ion.   The signs are chosen to make E_{ar} positive for systems where the cyclic ion is more stable, to conform to the usual convention for bond and resonance energies.

Table 5.7 shows aromatic energies calculated in this way for various cyclic ions; the second column of the table shows the reference compound used to calculate E_{ar} from Eq. (5.56).   In polycyclic systems, the reference ion differs from the cyclic one by one ring only; the values of E_{ar} are therefore measures of the extra stabilization due to closure of this one odd-numbered ring.

In the monocyclic ions, the aromatic energy is positive for positive ions with

TABLE 5.7   Aromatic energies for cyclic ions[23]

Cyclic ion	Reference ion	Aromatic energy, ev	
		Cation	Anion
△	⁓⁓	1.84	−1.56
⬠	⁓⁓⁓	−0.73	1.31
⬡	⁓⁓⁓⁓	0.93	−0.25
⬡–	⁓⁓⁓⁓	0.61	0.60

$(4n + 3)$-membered rings, and for negative ions with $(4n + 1)$-membered rings, but negative otherwise; this suggests that ions of this type with $(4n + 2)$ π electrons are aromatic, those with $4n$ π electrons antiaromatic. The calculations are therefore consistent with the predictions of Hückel's rule. Moreover similar conclusions seem to hold in polycyclic systems with one odd-numbered ring; if the ring has $4n + 1$ members, the anion is aromatic and the cation antiaromatic, by reference to an analogous ion in which the odd-numbered ring is opened; likewise if the ring has $4n + 3$ members, the cation is aromatic and the anion antiaromatic. These conclusions are of course in complete agreement with the available experimental evidence; the C_5 cyclic polymethine, like its benzo derivative, forms stable anions but unstable cations, whereas the reverse is true for the C_7 analogs.

The values for benzyl are also interesting; they imply that the C_7 cation (tropylium) should be more stable than the benzyl cation, while the reverse should be true for the anions. Some years ago Meyerson and his collaborators[24] showed that toluene and various benzyl derivatives give in the mass spectrometer a strong peak corresponding to an ion $C_7H_7^+$, which they showed almost unequivocally to be tropylium, rather than the benzyl cation. If so, this would suggest very strongly that a free benzyl cation in the gas phase rearranges spontaneously to tropylium, and that the latter ion is consequently much the more stable.

5.12   SCOPE AND LIMITATIONS OF THE SEMIEMPIRICAL SCF MO TREATMENT OF CONJUGATED HYDROCARBONS

The calculations outlined above suggest that we can obtain very good estimates of the heats of formation and geometries of conjugated hydrocarbons of all kinds, using an approach based on the Hückel approximation and the Pople

SCF MO method. Unfortunately a treatment of this kind, even if it were 100 percent successful, would be no panacea. Organic chemists need some general picture of chemistry that will help in their day-by-day thoughts on chemical problems, some pattern which will provide immediate previews of the expected behavior of organic molecules. General principles of this kind are essential in every branch of organic chemistry, whether it be synthesis, or the study of reaction mechanisms, or structural analysis of natural products. A procedure which gives accurate results for individual molecules, but no general principles, would be a substitute only if the calculations could be carried out in a matter of seconds with a portable computer the size of a small typewriter; this will certainly be achieved in due course, but not in the immediately foreseeable future. At present, calculations are far too slow and clumsy to serve as an adequate basis for chemical thought.

This of course is why the localized-bond model is so useful; it serves, as we have seen, as an analog of reality that does enable us to deduce many properties of molecules in a flash, without intricate calculations. What we need is some similar procedure that can be applied to molecules where the bonds are not localized.

The need for this has of course been recognized for many years and various solutions have been proposed from time to time, notably the classical electronic theory, introduced by Lapworth, Robinson, and Ingold around 1925, and the resonance theory, introduced by Pauling in 1930. However these treatments have been too crude and unreliable, and they have moreover suffered from a subjective element which makes their predictions a matter of chance.

A much better solution of this problem has in fact been available for a good many years, based on a simplified MO treatment which will be described in the next chapter. This certainly provides a good basis for chemical thinking; it has unfortunately been largely overlooked because it has not previously been available in book form. However a treatment of this kind is not in itself sufficient, for two reasons. First, it naturally cannot be relied on to give results of uniformly high accuracy; secondly, as we shall see, the method is not applicable to compounds of all types. There is therefore also a need for some much more exact treatment; the SCF MO procedure outlined in this chapter seems to fit the bill.

This procedure is not of course by any means a final answer to chemical problems; it is a hybrid between the purely empirical localized-bond approach and a complete theoretical approach in which all the valence electrons in a molecule are included in the SCF calculations. It is very likely that a complete approach of this kind will soon be available; nevertheless the hybrid treatment of conjugated systems may continue to prove useful for some time, for two reasons. First, it is only in conjugated systems that the localized-bond model fails badly; secondly, the inclusion of σ electrons enormously increases the problems of computation, requiring digital computers of types which are not yet generally available.

The Hückel method, on the other hand, no longer has a place in organic chemistry, except in the simplified version described in the next chapter. It filled a gap in the precomputer era, when calculations had to be carried out by hand, using desk calculating machines; now that such calculations are in any case carried out with digital computers, there seems little point in using a primitive and unreliable approximation when we can instead use a very much better one at the expense only of a little extra computer time.

PROBLEMS

5.1 Estimate the value of the penetration integral (ii, j) in the treatment of the π electrons of a conjugated system with the Hückel $(\sigma\text{-}\pi)$ approximation, using the uniformly-charged-sphere approximation and for an internuclear distance of 2 Å; assume that in Eqs. (5.15) and (5.16), $R = 0.647$ Å.

5.2 Derive Eqs. (5.27) and (5.28).

5.3 Calculate β^c for two carbon atoms at an internuclear separation of 1.4 Å, using Eqs. (5.29) to (5.34) and the following parameters:

$$E_{C-C} = 3.94 \text{ ev} \qquad E_{C=C} = 5.56 \text{ ev}$$
$$r' = 1.512 \text{ Å} \qquad r'' = 1.337 \text{ Å}$$
$$a' = 2.3177 \text{ Å}^{-1} \qquad a'' = 2.0022 \text{ Å}^{-1}$$

5.4 In benzene, the π MOs are determined by symmetry, the occupied MOs (in real form) being:

$$\psi_1 = \frac{1}{\sqrt{6}} (\phi_1 + \phi_2 + \phi_3 + \phi_4 + \phi_5 + \phi_6)$$

$$\psi_2 = \tfrac{1}{2}(\phi_2 + \phi_3 - \phi_5 - \phi_6)$$

$$\psi_3 = \frac{1}{\sqrt{12}} (2\phi_1 + \phi_2 - \phi_3 - 2\phi_4 - \phi_5 + \phi_6)$$

Calculate $E_{\pi b}$, assuming the ring to be a regular hexagon of side 1.40 Å, and using the uniformly-charged-sphere approximation to estimate electron repulsion integrals. Use the value of R from Prob. 5.1 and the value of β^c found in Prob. 5.3. Assume that the one-center repulsion integral $(11,11)$ for carbon has the value 10.98 ev.

5.5 If the reader has access to a computer, an obvious and very important exercise is to acquire, or write, a program for the Pople method and to repeat some of the calculations reported in this chapter as a check on the program's efficiency. Programs can be obtained from:
Quantum Chemistry Program Exchange
Chemistry Department, Room 204
Indiana University
Bloomington, Indiana 47401

REFERENCES

1 Hückel, E.: *Z. Physik* **70**, 204 (1931); **76**, 628 (1932); *Z. Elektrochem.* **43**, 752 (1937).

2 Pariser, R., and R. G. Parr: *J. Chem. Phys.* **21**, 466, 767 (1953).

3 Pariser, R.: *J. Chem. Phys.* **21**, 568 (1953); **24**, 250 (1956).

4 Julg, A.: *J. Chim. Phys.* **55**, 413 (1958).

5 Löwdin, P. O.: "Nikko Symposium on Molecular Physics," p. 113, Maruzen Co. Ltd., Tokyo, 1954.

6 Clementi, E.: *J. Chem. Phys.* **38**, 2248 (1963).

7 Dewar, M. J. S., and C. E. Wulfman: *J. Chem. Phys.* **29**, 158 (1958).

8 Dewar, M. J. S., and N. L. Hojvat: *J. Chem. Phys.* **34**, 1232 (1961); *Proc. Roy. Soc.* (*London*) **A264**, 431 (1961).

9 Dewar, M. J. S., and N. L. Sabelli: *J. Chem. Phys.* **66**, 2310 (1962).

10 Dewar, M. J. S., and H. N. Schmeising: *Tetrahedron* **5**, 166 (1959).

11 Chung, A. L.-H., and M. J. S. Dewar: *J. Chem. Phys.* **42**, 756 (1965).

12 Dewar, M. J. S., and G. J. Gleicher: *J. Am. Chem. Soc.* **87**, 685 (1965).

13 Dewar, M. J. S., and H. N. Schmeising: *Tetrahedron* **11**, 96 (1960).

14 Dewar, M. J. S., and G. J. Gleicher: *J. Am. Chem. Soc.* **87**, 692, 3255 (1965); *Tetrahedron* **21**, 1817, 3423 (1965); *Tetrahedron Letters* **50**, 4503 (1965); *J. Chem. Phys.* **44**, 759 (1966).

15 de Llano, C. R., and M. J. S. Dewar: in press; C. R. de Llano: *Ph.D. Thesis,* The University of Texas (1968).

16 Dewar, M. J. S., and H. N. Schmeising: *Tetrahedron* **11**, 96 (1960).

17 Pauling, L.: "The Nature of the Chemical Bond," 3d ed., Cornell University Press, Ithaca, N.Y., 1960.

18 Jackman, L. M., F. Sondheimer, Y. Amiel, D. A. Ben-Efraim, Y. Gaoni, R. Wolovsky, and A. A. Bothner-By: *J. Am. Chem. Soc.* **84**, 4307 (1962).

19 Watts, L., J. D. Fitzpatrick, and R. Pettit: *J. Am. Chem. Soc.* **87**, 3253 (1965).

20 Anet, F. A. L., A. J. R. Bourn, and Y. S. Lin: *J. Am. Chem. Soc.* **86**, 3576 (1964).

21 Crawford, B. L., Jr., and F. A. Miller: *J. Chem. Phys.* **17**, 249 (1949).

22 Dewar, M. J. S., J. A. Hashmall, and C. G. Venier: *J. Am. Chem. Soc.* **90**, 1953 (1968).

23 Dewar, M. J. S., and C. G. Venier: unpublished work.

24 Rylander, P. N., S. Meyerson, and H. M. Grubb: *J. Am. Chem. Soc.* **79**, 842 (1957); S. Meyerson and P. N. Rylander: *J. Chem. Phys.* **27**, 901 (1957); S. Meyerson, P. N. Rylander, E. L. Eliel, and J. D. McCollum: *J. Am. Chem. Soc.* **81**, 2606 (1959).

CHAPTER SIX

THE PMO
METHOD

6.1 CHEMISTRY AS AN EXERCISE IN PERTURBATION THEORY

So far we have considered the problem of calculating properties of individual molecules, in particular their heats of formation and molecular geometries; however from a purely practical point of view, chemical theory is rarely required to supply detailed information of this kind. The majority of chemical problems are concerned not so much with the absolute energies of individual molecules as with the relative energies of pairs of molecules that are closely related to one another. Thus the question of bond localization in a given molecule hinges on the relative energies of two very similar systems, the molecule itself and an analogous structure with "localized" bonds. Again, the equilibrium constant for a reversible reaction depends on the relative free energies of the reactants and products; since a simple chemical reaction rarely involves the formation and/or breaking of more than one bond, the reactants and products in a reaction are necessarily closely related in structure. A third example is provided by the rate of a chemical reaction; this is determined by the difference in free energy between the reactants and the corresponding transition state, which again are closely related to one another.

We can estimate these differences in a straightforward manner, calculating the properties of each of the two systems in question separately, and finding the difference in energy between them by subtraction; the trouble with this procedure is that the differences are small fractions of the whole, so that errors in calculating the energies of the two individual systems are greatly magnified in finding the difference. Thus the heat of formation of benzene from atoms is about 50 ev, while its resonance energy is about 1 ev; if we wish to estimate the resonance energy of benzene to ± 10 percent by comparing the calculated energies of benzene and cyclohexatriene, we shall need to know each of these energies to ± 0.1 percent.

Clearly it would be much better if we could calculate these differences directly; for then a much cruder calculation would suffice. In the example given above, we could tolerate a 10 percent error if this were an error in the difference in energy between benzene and cyclohexatriene, whereas we would need a hundredfold higher precision if the resonance energy were to be found by difference. Now if two systems are closely related, their hamiltonian operators must necessarily be very similar; in other words, if the hamiltonian operator for one system is $\mathbf{H}$, that for the other must be of the form $\mathbf{H} + \mathbf{P}$, where the term $\mathbf{P}$, representing the difference between the two operators, must be small. If then we know the solutions of the Schrödinger equation for the first system, we can find those for the second by using perturbation theory.   A calculation of this kind leads directly to estimates of the differences between the two systems; this is precisely what we need.

These arguments show very clearly that perturbation theory must provide the best approach to most chemical problems; indeed, one could legitimately regard chemistry in general as an exercise in perturbation theory on the part of nature. From a practical point of view this approach has obvious advantages. Since we can tolerate much greater errors in our calculations if they appear unmagnified in the final quantities we are estimating, much cruder methods can be used. Thus we do not need to have exact solutions of the Schrödinger equation for the unperturbed system; we can equally well carry out our perturbation calculation using approximate wave functions.   Indeed, in a calculation of this kind we can tolerate wave functions much inferior to those we could if the quantities we want were being estimated by difference; in particular, the HMO method may prove a sufficiently good basis, although, as we have seen, it is unsatisfactory for absolute estimates of molecular properties.

This kind of approach, which was first introduced by Coulson and Longuet-Higgins,[1] has proved extremely powerful; in this chapter we shall consider the basic principles involved in it, and then illustrate its potentialities by reference to the properties of conjugated hydrocarbons.   Later chapters will outline its application to systems and problems of other kinds; we shall find that it provides a complete and very simple theory of organic chemistry, covering the same ground as resonance theory equally simply and very much more effectively.

6.2 BASIC PRINCIPLES OF THE PMO METHOD

Our problem is to calculate the differences in properties between closely related systems, using perturbation theory; for reasons indicated in the last section, there is good reason to believe that this can be done within the framework of some very approximate method.   We shall therefore start by making the following assumptions:

1   We shall adopt the Hückel approximation (Sec. 5.1).

2   We shall adopt the localized-bond model (Sec. 4.11) for σ bonds and isolated π bonds.

3   Delocalized systems will be treated in terms of the simple HMO method.

4   In comparing closely related structures, we shall usually ignore changes in energy of localized bonds; e.g. in comparing two conjugated structures with slightly different π systems, we shall assume that the difference in energy can be equated to the difference in energy between the π electrons, contributions by stretching or compression of σ bonds being neglected.

This general approach[2] may be termed the *PMO* (perturbational MO) *method.*

In this chapter we shall consider molecules in which the only delocalized systems are π systems; the treatment can, however, be extended to delocalized systems of other types; examples of this will be found later (Chap. 9). With our assumptions, the difference δE_R in energy between two closely related systems, R and R', can be written in the form:

$$\delta E_R = (\delta E_R)_\sigma + (\delta E_R)_\pi \tag{6.1}$$

where $(\delta E_R)_\sigma$ is the difference in energy of "localized" electrons in R and R' and $(\delta E_R)_\pi$ is the corresponding difference in π energy. Since we are using the localized-bond model, $(\delta E_R)_\sigma$ can be found immediately from tables of bond energies; our problem therefore is to calculate $(\delta E_R)_\pi$.

Now $(\delta E_R)_\pi$ represents the difference in π energy between two closely related systems; in the HMO method, such differences can be of two kinds. First, the systems may differ in the electronegativities of one or more atoms; in the HMO method, this will correspond to changes in the coulomb integrals α_i. Secondly, the systems may differ in the strengths of one or more bonds; this will correspond to changes in the resonance integrals β_{ij}. Our problem therefore resolves itself into calculating the changes in properties of a π system, in particular its energy, when one or more of the basic parameters (α_i, β_{ij}) changes.

Such perturbations can conveniently be divided into two types: *intramolecular perturbations,* corresponding to changes of the parameters within a given molecule R, and *intermolecular perturbations,* corresponding to a situation where two or more different π systems R, S, . . . unite to form a single larger one. Thus a good example of an intramolecular perturbation would be provided by the problem of comparing the resonance energies of benzene and pyridine. Assuming that we know the difference δE in energy between benzene and cyclohexatriene (Fig. 6.1), our problem is to find the corresponding difference between pyridine

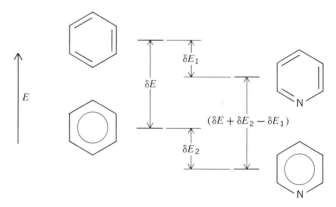

FIG. 6.1 Calculation of the resonance energy of pyridine by the PMO method, in terms of that (δE) of benzene.

and azacyclohexatriene (Fig. 6.1).   This can be done if we can estimate the difference in energy between benzene and pyridine δE_1, and between cyclohexatriene and azacyclohexatriene δE_2 (Fig. 6.1).   Now benzene and pyridine are *isoconjugate*, i.e. they have the same number of π electrons, occupying π MOs of similar size and shape formed by interaction of the same number of individual p AOs; the difference in energy between them can thus be written as a sum of a change in σ energy (found by assuming additivity of bond energies for σ bonds) and in π energy (this being a typical intramolecular perturbation energy, since the two π systems differ only in one coulomb integral α_N and two resonance integrals β_{CN}). The difference in energy δE_2 between cyclohexatriene and azacyclohexatriene can likewise be found in terms of an intramolecular perturbation.

A good example of an intermolecular perturbation is provided by the problem of estimating the resonance energy of biphenyl.   Biphenyl can be formed by *union* of two molecules of benzene, union being defined as a process in which two conjugated molecules combine in such a way that their two π systems unite into one larger one.   To do this, we have also to break and form σ bonds (in this case, break two CH bonds and form a CC bond); however since σ bonds are localized, the corresponding energy changes can be calculated in terms of bond energies.   We shall denote union by the symbol $\leftarrow\mathbf{u}\rightarrow$; e.g.

$$\langle\!\!\!\bigcirc\!\!\!\rangle\!\!-\!\mathrm{H} \;\leftarrow\mathbf{u}\rightarrow\; \mathrm{H}\!\!-\!\!\langle\!\!\!\bigcirc\!\!\!\rangle \;\rightarrow\; \langle\!\!\!\bigcirc\!\!\!\rangle\!\!\langle\!\!\!\bigcirc\!\!\!\rangle \qquad (6.2)$$

Our problem therefore resolves itself into one of calculating the relative π energies of biphenyl and of two molecules of benzene.   In the HMO method, the two systems differ only in that one resonance integral, that of the interannular bond, changes from β in biphenyl to zero in the two molecules of benzene.   The corresponding change in π energy can again be found by using perturbation theory.

6.3   INTRAMOLECULAR PERTURBATIONS

Consider a conjugated system R, whose π MOs Φ_μ, of energy E_μ, are expressed in terms of the component AOs ϕ_i by:

$$\Phi_\mu = \sum_i a_{\mu i}\phi_i \qquad \text{energy } E_\mu \qquad (6.3)$$

The total π energy E is given, in the HMO approximation, by:

$$E = \sum_\mu n_\mu E_\mu \qquad (6.4)$$

where n_μ is the number of electrons in the MO Φ_μ.   If R is a closed-shell system,

$$E = 2 \sum_\mu^{\text{occ}} E_\mu \qquad (6.5)$$

where the sum is over the occupied MOs.

Our first problem is to find how the π energy of R changes if we alter one of the component coulomb integrals α_i or resonance integrals β_{ij} by small amounts $\delta\alpha_i$ or $\delta\beta_{ij}$ respectively.

If the hamiltonian for R is $\mathbf{H}$, and that for the perturbed system R' is $\mathbf{H}'$, with

$$\mathbf{H}' = \mathbf{H} + \mathbf{P} \tag{6.6}$$

then from first-order perturbation theory, the energies E'_μ of the MOs Φ'_μ of R' are given by:

$$E'_\mu = E_\mu + \int \Phi_\mu \mathbf{P} \Phi_\mu \, d\tau \tag{6.7}$$

Now the coulomb integrals and resonance integrals of R are defined by:

$$\alpha_i = \int \phi_i \mathbf{H} \phi_i \, d\tau \qquad \beta_{ij} = \int \phi_i \mathbf{H} \phi_j \, d\tau \tag{6.8}$$

Likewise those of R' are defined by:

$$\alpha'_i = \int \phi_i \mathbf{H}' \phi_i \, d\tau \qquad \beta'_{ij} = \int \phi_i \mathbf{H}' \phi_j \, d\tau \tag{6.9}$$

From Eqs. (6.6), (6.8), and (6.9),

$$\int \phi_i \mathbf{P} \phi_i \, d\tau \equiv P_{ii} = \int \phi_i (\mathbf{H}' - \mathbf{H}) \phi_i \, d\tau = \delta\alpha_i \tag{6.10}$$

$$\int \phi_i \mathbf{P} \phi_j \, d\tau \equiv P_{ij} = \int \phi_i (\mathbf{H}' - \mathbf{H}) \phi_j \, d\tau = \delta\beta_{ij} \tag{6.11}$$

Thus the perturbation $\mathbf{P}$ is defined by its matrix elements for the AOs ϕ_i, by Eqs. (6.10) and (6.11). Substituting these values in Eq. (6.7), we find for the first-order perturbation δE_μ,

$$\delta E_\mu = E'_\mu - E_\mu = \int \left(\sum_i a_{\mu i} \phi_i \right) \mathbf{P} \left(\sum_j a_{\mu j} \phi_j \right) d\tau$$

$$= \sum_i a_{\mu i}{}^2 P_{ii} + \sum_{i \neq j} \sum a_{\mu i} a_{\mu j} P_{ij} \tag{6.12}$$

Since $\mathbf{H}'$ and $\mathbf{H}$ are both hermitian operators, so also is $\mathbf{P}$; hence:

$$P_{ij} = P_{ji} \tag{6.13}$$

Since each term in the last sum of Eq. (6.12) therefore appears twice over, we can write this equation equivalently as:

$$\delta E_\mu = \sum_i a_{\mu i}{}^2 P_{ii} + 2 \sum_{i<j} \sum a_{\mu i} a_{\mu j} P_{ij} \tag{6.14}$$

Using Eqs. (6.10) and (6.11),

$$\delta E_\mu = \sum_i a_{\mu i}{}^2 \, \delta\alpha_i + 2 \sum_{i<j} \sum a_{\mu i} a_{\mu j} \, \delta\beta_{ij} \tag{6.15}$$

Now we can find the corresponding change in the total energy E of R due to the changes in the α_i and β_{ij};

$$\delta E = E' - E = 2\sum_{\mu}^{\text{occ}} E'_{\mu} - 2\sum_{\mu}^{\text{occ}} E_{\mu}$$

$$= 2\sum_{\mu}^{\text{occ}} \delta E_{\mu} = 2\sum_{\mu}^{\text{occ}} \left(\sum_i a_{\mu i}^2\, \delta\alpha_i + 2\sum\sum_{i<j} a_{\mu i} a_{\mu j}\, \delta\beta_{ij} \right)$$

$$= \sum_i q_i\, \delta\alpha_i + 2\sum\sum_{i<j} p_{ij}\, \delta\beta_{ij} \tag{6.16}$$

The last line follows from the definitions of π-charge density and bond order [Eqs. (3.61) and (3.63)].

Equation (6.16) has a simple physical meaning. If we expand the expression for the total π energy of R [Eq. (6.5)], we find:

$$E = \sum_i q_i \alpha_i + 2\sum\sum_{i<j} p_{ij}\beta_{ij} \tag{6.17}$$

In the HMO method, α_i is supposed to be the binding energy of an electron in the AO ϕ_i. Since there are on average q_i electrons in this region of the molecule R, the corresponding contribution to the total energy is $q_i\alpha_i$. Likewise $2\beta_{ij}$ represents the contribution to the π energy of the two electrons occupying the overlap region between the AOs ϕ_i, ϕ_j in a simple diatomic molecule with $p = 1$ (see Sec. 3.1); in R, where the corresponding overlap charge is p_{ij} times that in a simple diatomic molecule, the contribution to the π energy is accordingly $2p_{ij}\beta_{ij}$. Of course p_{ij} may be negative; for the overlap of the AOs ϕ_i, ϕ_j can lead to a *decreased* π density in the overlap region. This will happen if a sufficient number of MOs have nodes there; the interaction of the two AOs then has a net antibonding effect. Thus in the case of a simple diatomic molecule, if both π electrons occupied the antibonding MO, the corresponding bond order would be -1. Suppose now that we alter the molecule R slightly; the corresponding changes in π energy will be found by recalculating the energies of the MOs, assuming that the MOs remain unchanged but using the new hamiltonian [see Eqs. (2.139) et seq.]. If the MOs remain unchanged, so also will the charge densities and bond orders; if then the coulomb and resonance integrals in the perturbed system are given by $\alpha_i + \delta\alpha_i$ and $\beta_{ij} + \delta\beta_{ij}$ respectively, the total perturbed energy is given by:

$$E' = \sum_i q_i(\alpha_i + \delta\alpha_i) + 2\sum\sum_{i<j} p_{ij}(\beta_{ij} + \delta\beta_{ij}) \tag{6.18}$$

Equations (6.17) and (6.18) lead to Eq. (6.16).

We could of course extend this treatment to include second-order perturbations, but these are rarely needed. The whole philosophy of our approach is to devise a simple treatment of chemical problems; including higher-order perturbations would spoil this simplicity. Besides we cannot expect any great accuracy from our treatment in view of the crude method (HMO) used to calculate our unperturbed wave functions; any apparent gain from introducing higher-order perturbations could therefore well prove an illusion. However a detailed study of second-order effects will be found in Ref. 2.

Let us next calculate the first-order changes in the MOs of R, and in the derived charge densities and bond orders, due to a change in one of the Hückel parameters. We shall carry out the calculation for a change $\delta\alpha_i$ in one of the coulomb integrals α_i. From Eq. (2.149), the perturbed MO Φ'_μ, corresponding to the unperturbed MO Φ_μ, will be given by:

$$\Phi'_\mu = \Phi_\mu + \sum_{\nu \neq \mu} \frac{\int \Phi_\mu \mathbf{P} \Phi_\nu \, d\tau}{E_\mu - E_\nu} \Phi_\nu \tag{6.19}$$

Using Eqs. (6.3) and (6.10),

$$\Phi'_\mu = \Phi_\mu + \sum_{\nu \neq \mu} \frac{a_{\mu i} a_{\nu i} \, \delta\alpha_i}{E_\mu - E_\nu} \Phi_\nu$$

$$= \left(a_{\mu i} + \sum_{\nu \neq \mu} \frac{a_{\mu i} a_{\nu i}^2 \, \delta\alpha_i}{E_\mu - E_\nu} \right) \phi_i + \sum_{j \neq i} \left(a_{\mu j} + \sum_{\nu \neq \mu} \frac{a_{\mu i} a_{\nu i} a_{\nu j} \, \delta\alpha_i}{E_\mu - E_\nu} \right) \phi_j \tag{6.20}$$

The corresponding charge densities and bond orders can now be found in the usual way. Since our calculation is a first-order one only, correct to first powers of the perturbation $\delta\alpha_i$, we can only get a first approximation to the perturbed charge densities q'_i and bond orders p'_{ij}. Thus:

$$q'_i = 2 \sum_\mu^{occ} (a'_{\mu i})^2 = 2 \sum_\mu^{occ} \left(a'_{\mu i} + \sum_{\nu \neq \mu} \frac{a_{\mu i} a_{\nu i}^2 \, \delta\alpha_i}{E_\mu - E_\nu} \right)^2$$

$$\approx 2 \sum_\mu^{occ} \left(a_{\mu i}^2 + 2 \sum_{\nu \neq \mu} \frac{a_{\mu i}^2 a_{\nu i}^2 \, \delta\alpha_i}{E_\mu - E_\nu} \right) \tag{6.21}$$

The terms in the sum where Φ_ν is an occupied MO cancel; for each appears twice in the double summation, with opposite signs. We therefore write:

$$q'_i = 2 \sum_\mu^{occ} a_{\mu i}^2 + 4 \sum_\mu^{occ} \sum_\nu^{unocc} \frac{a_{\mu i}^2 a_{\nu i}^2 \, \delta\alpha_i}{E_\mu - E_\nu} = q_i + \pi_{i,i} \, \delta\alpha_i \tag{6.22}$$

where $\qquad \pi_{i,i} = 4 \sum_\mu^{occ} \sum_\nu^{unocc} \frac{a_{\mu i}^2 a_{\nu i}^2}{E_\mu - E_\nu} \tag{6.23}$

and of course $\sum_\nu^{unocc}$ implies summation over MOs Φ_ν that are empty in R or R'.

Now from Taylor's theorem, the perturbed charge density q'_i can be written in the form:

$$q'_i = q_i + \frac{\partial q_i}{\partial \alpha_i} \delta\alpha_i + \frac{\partial^2 q_i}{\partial \alpha_i^2} (\delta\alpha_i)^2 + \cdots \tag{6.24}$$

Comparing Eqs. (6.22) and (6.23),

$$\frac{\partial q_i}{\partial \alpha_i} = \pi_{i,i} \tag{6.25}$$

This quantity, $\pi_{i,i}$, is called the *self-polarizability* of atom i; it is a measure of the way the π charge density of atom i changes with a change in the electronegativity of atom i. Since, by definition, $E_\nu > E_\mu$ in Eq. (6.21), Φ_ν being an empty MO and therefore higher in energy than the filled MO Φ_μ, $\pi_{i,i}$ is negative; this of course it must be, to make chemical sense. If atom i becomes more electronegative, q_i will increase; since this change in atom i corresponds to a decrease in α_i, so that $\delta\alpha_i$ is negative, $\pi_{i,i}$ must therefore also be negative.

A similar calculation leads to the following values for the perturbed charge densities of other atoms in R:

$$q_j' \approx q_j + 4 \sum_\mu^{\text{occ}} \sum_\nu^{\text{unocc}} \frac{a_{\mu i} a_{\mu j} a_{\nu i} a_{\nu j} \, \delta\alpha_i}{E_\mu - E_\nu} \equiv q_i + \pi_{j,i} \, \delta\alpha_i \tag{6.26}$$

where, as before,

$$\pi_{j,i} = \frac{\partial q_j}{\partial \alpha_i} = 4 \sum_\mu^{\text{occ}} \sum_\nu^{\text{unocc}} \frac{a_{\mu i} a_{\mu j} a_{\nu i} a_{\nu j}}{E_\mu - E_\nu} \tag{6.27}$$

This quantity, $\pi_{j,i}$, is called the *atom-atom polarizability* of atoms j and i. It is a measure of the way the charge density of atom j changes with a change in the electronegativity of atom i. In this case there are no restrictions on the sign; $\pi_{j,i}$ can be positive or negative. From the symmetrical form of $\pi_{j,i}$ [Eq. (6.27)], it is evident that:

$$\pi_{j,i} = \pi_{i,j} \tag{6.28}$$

Thus a change in the electronegativity of atom i has the same effect on the charge density of atom j as has a corresponding change in the electronegativity of atom j on the charge density of atom i.

The analogous change in bond order, due to a change in α_i, can be found likewise:

$$p_{kl}' = p_{kl} + 2 \sum_\mu^{\text{occ}} \sum_\nu^{\text{unocc}} \frac{a_{\mu i} a_{\nu i} (a_{\mu k} a_{\nu l} + a_{\mu l} a_{\nu k}) \, \delta\alpha_i}{E_\mu - E_\nu}$$

$$= p_{kl} + \pi_{kl,i} \, \delta\alpha_i \tag{6.29}$$

where the *bond-atom polarizability* $\pi_{kl,i}$ is defined by:

$$\pi_{kl,i} = \frac{\partial p_{kl}}{\partial \alpha_i} = 2 \sum_\mu^{\text{occ}} \sum_\nu^{\text{unocc}} \frac{a_{\mu i} a_{\nu i} (a_{\mu k} a_{\nu l} + a_{\mu l} a_{\nu k})}{E_\mu - E_\nu} \tag{6.30}$$

The effects of a change $\delta\beta_{kl}$ in one of the resonance integrals β_{kl} can be found in a similar manner; the calculation is left to the reader as an exercise. The corresponding perturbed charge densities and bond orders are given by:

$$q'_i = q_i + \pi_{i,kl}\,\delta\beta_{kl} \tag{6.31}$$

where the *atom-bond polarizability*, $\pi_{i,kl}$, is given by:

$$\pi_{i,kl} = \frac{\partial q_i}{\partial \beta_{kl}} = 2\sum_{\mu}^{occ}\sum_{\nu}^{unocc} \frac{a_{\mu i}a_{\nu i}(a_{\mu k}a_{\nu l} + a_{\mu l}a_{\nu k})}{E_{\mu} - E_{\nu}} \tag{6.32}$$

Again,

$$p'_{ij} = p_{ij} + \pi_{ij,kl}\,\delta\beta_{kl} \tag{6.33}$$

where the *bond-bond polarizability*, $\pi_{ij,kl}$, is given by:

$$\pi_{ij,kl} = \frac{\partial p_{ij}}{\partial \beta_{kl}} = \sum_{\mu}^{occ}\sum_{\nu}^{unocc} \frac{(a_{\mu i}a_{\nu j} + a_{\mu j}a_{\nu i})(a_{\mu k}a_{\nu l} + a_{\mu l}a_{\nu k})}{E_{\mu} - E_{\nu}} \tag{6.34}$$

From Eqs. (6.30) and (6.32),

$$\pi_{kl,i} = \pi_{i,kl} \tag{6.35}$$

6.4   ALTERNANT HYDROCARBONS; THE PAIRING THEOREM

The results derived in Sec. 6.3 allow us to calculate the properties of a π system in terms of those of any other π system that is isoconjugate with it; in particular, one can calculate the properties of a π system containing heteroatoms from that of the isoconjugate hydrocarbon. We have therefore at one stroke simplified our problem enormously, by reducing chemical problems in general to problems in hydrocarbon chemistry; for if we know the properties of a given hydrocarbon, we can calculate the properties of any heteroatomic system that is isoconjugate with it.

This in itself is good, but better is to come. As we shall now see, the properties of a certain class of hydrocarbons, comprising most of the systems that are of major chemical interest, follow a very simple pattern; this will enable us to solve most of our chemical problems without the need for any equipment other than pencil and paper.

The compounds in question are *alternant* hydrocarbons (AH). A conjugated system is termed alternant if the atoms in it can be divided into two groups, *starred* and *unstarred*, in such a way that no two atoms of *like parity* (i.e. belonging to the same group) are directly linked. It is easily seen that this definition comprises all conjugated systems that are free from odd-numbered rings; thus naphthalene (Fig. 6.2c) and benzyl (Fig. 6.2b) are alternant, whereas azulene and fulvene (Fig. 6.2c and d) are not. If the numbers of atoms in the two sets differ, we shall call the more numerous set the starred one (compare Fig. 6.2b). We may further distinguish between *odd* and *even* conjugated systems, containing respectively odd and even numbers of conjugated atoms. An odd AH (e.g. benzyl; Fig. 6.2b) must of course appear either as a radical, with one unpaired electron, or as a positive or negative ion.

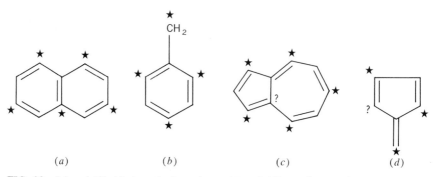

FIG. 6.2 (a) and (b) Alternant hydrocarbons; (c) and (d) nonalternant hydrocarbons.

We shall now prove the following statements which together comprise the so-called *pairing theorem:*

Theorem 6.1a   The MOs of an even AH occur in pairs, with energies $\alpha \pm E_\mu$, α being the coulomb integral for carbon.

Theorem 6.1b   If one of the MOs Φ_μ of a pair (energy $\alpha + E_\mu$) is given by:

$$\Phi_\mu{}^+ = \sum_i {}^* a_{\mu i}^* \phi_i^* + \sum_j {}^\circ a_{\mu j} \phi_j^\circ \qquad \text{energy } \alpha + E_\mu \qquad (6.36)$$

where ϕ_i^* is the p AO of a starred atom and ϕ_j° that of an unstarred atom, then the twin MO $\Phi_\mu{}^-$ (energy $\alpha - E_\mu$) is given by:

$$\Phi_\mu{}^- = \sum_i {}^* a_{\mu i}^* \phi_i^* - \sum_j {}^\circ a_{\mu j} \phi_j^\circ \qquad \text{energy } \alpha - E_\mu \qquad (6.37)$$

In other words, the coefficients of the AOs are numerically the same for both MOs, but the signs of one set of AOs are reversed in going from one MO to the other.   Which set of signs is reversed is of course irrelevant; for the wave functions ψ and $-\psi$ are equivalent.

Theorem 6.1c   In an odd AH, where the total number of MOs is correspondingly odd, all but one of the MOs are paired as in parts a and b.   The odd MO Φ_0 has energy α, and is confined to one set of atoms (starred or unstarred); e.g.

$$\Phi_0 = \sum_i {}^* a_{0i}^* \phi_i^* \qquad \text{energy } \alpha \qquad (6.38)$$

This MO is termed a *nonbonding MO* (NBMO) since electrons occupying it have the same energy α that they would have if they occupied the p AO of an isolated carbon atom.‡

---

‡ Of course this statement applies only because we are using the HMO approximation; a more detailed analysis is given later in this section.

We shall start by proving Theorems 6.1a and 6.1b, i.e. the results for an even AH.   The Hückel equations for the orbital coefficients in this case are as follows [see Eq. (3.69)]:

$$a_i^*(\alpha - E) + \sum_{j \neq i}^* a_j^* \beta_{ij} + \sum_k^\circ a_k^\circ \beta_{ik} = 0 \qquad (6.39)$$

$$a_r^\circ(\alpha - E) + \sum_s^* a_s \beta_{rs} + \sum_{t \neq r}^\circ a_t^\circ \beta_{rt} = 0 \qquad (6.40)$$

There is one equation of type (6.39) for each starred atom i, and one of type (6.40) for each unstarred atom r.   To solve these equations, we would substitute for E one of the roots E_μ of the corresponding secular equation,

$$|H_{ij} - E\delta_{ij}| = 0 \qquad (6.41)$$

In the HMO approximation, we assume that resonance integrals vanish except between pairs of atoms that are linked by a σ bond.   In an AH, such a bond must by definition link a starred atom to an unstarred one.   Consequently the integrals β_{ij} in Eq. (6.39), and β_{rt} in Eq. (6.40), vanish.   The equations thus become:

$$a_i^*(\alpha - E) + \sum_k^\circ a_k^\circ \beta_{ik} = 0 \qquad (6.42)$$

$$a_r^\circ(\alpha - E) + \sum_s^* a_s^* \beta_{rs} = 0 \qquad (6.43)$$

Suppose one solution of these equations is:

$$E = (\alpha + E_\mu) \qquad a_s^* = c_s \qquad a_k^\circ = d_k \qquad (6.44)$$

Thus:

$$c_i(-E_\mu) + \sum_k d_k \beta_{ik} = 0 \qquad (6.45)$$

$$d_r(-E_\mu) + \sum_s c_s \beta_{rs} = 0 \qquad (6.46)$$

Let us try substituting the following values in Eqs. (6.42) and (6.43):

$$E = (\alpha - E_\mu) \qquad a_s^* = c_s \qquad a_k^\circ = -d_k \qquad (6.47)$$

Equation (6.42) becomes:

$$c_i(+E_\mu) + \sum_k (-d_k)\beta_{ik} = -[c_i(-E_\mu) + \sum_k d_k\beta_{ik}] = 0 \qquad (6.48)$$

from Eq. (6.45); while Eq. (6.43) becomes:

$$-d_r(+E_\mu) + \sum_s c_s\beta_{rs} = d_r(-E_\mu) + \sum_s c_s\beta_{rs} = 0 \qquad (6.49)$$

from Eq. (6.46).   Thus the values listed in Eq. (6.47) also satisfy Eqs. (6.42) and (6.43); comparison of Eqs. (6.44) and (6.47) therefore shows that the MOs must occur in pairs, of energies $\alpha \pm E_\mu$, thus satisfying Theorem 6.1a, and with coefficients that satisfy Theorem 6.1b.

Next let us consider an odd AH.   The proof given above nowhere made use of the fact that our AH was even; it must therefore apply equally to an odd AH. The MOs in an odd AH must therefore be paired.   However the total number of MOs in an odd AH is odd, and so there must be one unpaired MO.   For these statements to be consistent, the energy of this MO must be α, and it must be confined to one set of atoms; for only in this case do we get an orbital that is identical with its twin.

This completes our proof of Theorem 6.1; later we shall show that the NBMO of an odd AH is in fact confined to the starred set of AOs (i.e. the more numerous set).

One immediate deduction from Theorem 6.1 is that half the MOs in an even AH are bonding, half antibonding, the energies of the two MOs of a pair being $\alpha \pm E_\mu$.   Since the choice of an energy scale involves an arbitrary definition of zero energy, we may for convenience adopt a scale on which zero energy for an electron corresponds to the energy it would have if it occupied a carbon $2p$ AO. This corresponds to setting $\alpha = 0$ in Eqs. (6.39) to (6.49).   On this scale, which we shall adopt henceforth, bonding MOs (BMO) have negative energies, antibonding MOs (AMO) positive energies, and NBMOs zero energy.

These conclusions are illustrated in Fig. 6.3a, which shows diagrammatically the energies of MOs in an even AH and the way in which they are occupied by the π electrons.   Figure 6.3b shows the corresponding situation for an odd-AH radical, e.g. allyl, $CH_2{=}CH{-}CH_2\cdot$; odd AHs can also exist as positive or negative ions, these differing from the radical in having one electron less (compare Fig. 6.3c) or one electron more (compare Fig. 6.3d) in the NBMO.

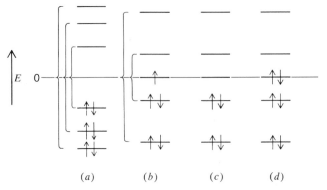

(a) (b) (c) (d)

FIG. 6.3   The pairing theorem. (a) An even AH; (b) an odd-AH radical; (c) an odd-AH cation; (d) an odd-AH anion.

6.5   CHARGE DENSITIES AND BOND ORDERS IN AHs

The symmetry relationships embodied in Theorem 6.1 lead to some very important and simple results for charge densities and bond orders in AHs. We shall
now prove the following theorems:

Theorem 6.2   The charge density at each position in an even AH, or odd-AH
radical, is unity.

Theorem 6.3   The bond order between two atoms of like parity in an even AH,
or odd-AH radical, is zero.

Consider first an even AH. The charge density at position i is given by:

$$q_i = 2 \sum_{\mu}^{\text{occ}} a_{\mu i}^2 \tag{6.50}$$

The number of π electrons in an even AH is equal to the number of atoms and
so to the total number of MOs; exactly half the π MOs are therefore filled by
electrons. Now from Theorem 6.1, half the MOs in an even AH are bonding,
half antibonding, since the MOs occur in pairs of equal and opposite energy relative to that of a carbon $2p$ AO; the π electrons in an even AH therefore exactly
fill the BMOs. From Theorem 6.1, $a_{\mu i}^2$ is the same for the two MOs (Φ_μ^+, Φ_μ^-)
of a pair; hence:

$$q_i = \sum_{\mu}^{\text{occ}} a_{\mu i}^2 + \sum_{\mu}^{\text{unocc}} a_{\mu i}^2 = \sum_{\mu}^{\text{all}} a_{\mu i}^2 \tag{6.51}$$

Now the MOs Φ_μ are given by the set of equations:

$$\Phi_\mu = \sum_i a_{\mu i} \phi_i \tag{6.52}$$

A well-known algebraic theorem tells us that there is a corresponding inverse
relation:

$$\phi_i = \sum_\mu a_{\mu i} \Phi_\mu \tag{6.53}$$

We assume that our AOs ϕ_i are normalized; hence:

$$\int \phi_i^2 \, d\tau = 1 = \int \left(\sum_\mu^{\text{all}} a_{\mu i} \Phi_\mu \right) \left(\sum_\nu^{\text{all}} a_{\nu i} \Phi_\nu \right) d\tau$$

$$= \sum_\mu^{\text{all}} \sum_\nu^{\text{all}} a_{\mu i} a_{\nu i} \int \Phi_\mu \Phi_\nu \, d\tau$$

$$= \sum_\mu^{\text{all}} a_{\mu i}^2 \int \Phi_\mu^2 \, d\tau = \sum_\mu^{\text{all}} a_{\mu i}^2 \tag{6.54}$$

The last line follows from the fact that the MOs of a given set are mutually orthogonal, and we assume here that they have been normalized. Comparing Eqs. (6.51) and (6.54),

$$q_i = 1 \tag{6.55}$$

Next consider an odd-AH radical. It is easily seen that the BMOs in this are filled, the odd electron occupying the NBMO. Hence:

$$q_i = 2 \sum_{\nu}^{\text{BMO}} a_{\mu i}^2 + a_{0i}^2 \tag{6.56}$$

where $\sum_{\mu}^{\text{BMO}}$ implies summation over the BMOs Φ_μ, and as before [Eq. (6.38)], Φ_0

denotes the NBMO. From Theorem 6.1,

$$q_i = \sum_{\mu}^{\text{BMO}} a_{\mu i}^2 + \sum_{\nu}^{\text{AMO}} a_{\nu i}^2 + a_{0i}^2 = \sum_{\mu}^{\text{all}} a_{\mu i}^2 = 1 \tag{6.57}$$

This completes our proof of Theorem 6.2.

Next let us consider the bond order p_{ij} in an even AH;

$$p_{ij} = 2 \sum_{\mu}^{\text{BMO}} a_{\mu i} a_{\mu j} \tag{6.58}$$

Note that atoms i and j need not be linked; bond orders are defined equally between pairs of unlinked atoms. Suppose that atoms i and j are not only not linked but also of like parity. Then in passing from the MO Φ_μ^+ to its twin Φ_μ^-, either both coefficients $a_{\mu i}$ and $a_{\mu j}$ remain unchanged or both change sign; in either case the product, $a_{\mu i} a_{\mu j}$, remains unchanged. Hence:

$$p_{ij} = \sum_{\mu}^{\text{BMO}} a_{\mu i} a_{\mu j} + \sum_{\nu}^{\text{AMO}} a_{\nu i} a_{\nu j} = \sum_{\mu}^{\text{all}} a_{\mu i} a_{\mu j} \tag{6.59}$$

In the HMO method, we assume our AOs to be orthogonal. Using Eq. (6.53) and the fact that our MOs form an orthonormal set,

$$\int \phi_i \phi_j \, d\tau = 0 = \int \left(\sum_{\mu}^{\text{all}} a_{\mu i} \Phi_\mu \right) \left(\sum_{\nu}^{\text{all}} a_{\nu j} \Phi_\nu \right) d\tau$$

$$= \sum_{\mu}^{\text{all}} \sum_{\nu}^{\text{all}} a_{\mu i} a_{\nu j} \int \Phi_\mu \Phi_\nu \, d\tau$$

$$= \sum_{\mu}^{\text{all}} a_{\mu i} a_{\mu j} \int \Phi_\mu^2 \, d\tau = \sum_{\mu}^{\text{all}} a_{\mu i} a_{\mu j} \tag{6.60}$$

Comparing Eqs. (6.59) and (6.60),

$$p_{ij} = 0 \qquad \text{atoms } i, j \text{ of like parity} \tag{6.61}$$

This demonstration can be extended as before to include odd-AH radicals, thus completing the proof of Theorem 6.3.

As we have seen, odd AHs can exist as positive or negative ions as well as radicals, the ions differing from the radicals only in the number of nonbonding electrons (Fig. 6.3). Using the definitions of bond order and charge density and Theorems 6.2 and 6.3, we arrive immediately at the following results for charge densities and bond orders in odd-AH ions:

Theorem 6.4 The charge density at atom i in an odd-AH anion is $1 + a_{0i}^2$, and in an odd-AH cation $1 - a_{0i}^2$, a_{0i} being the NBMO coefficient of atom i.

Theorem 6.5 The bond order between two atoms i and j of like parity in an odd-AH anion is $a_{0i}a_{0j}$, and in an odd-AH cation $-a_{0i}a_{0j}$, a_{0i} and a_{0j} being the NBMO coefficients at atoms i and j.

6.6 INTERMOLECULAR PERTURBATIONS

Our next problem is to consider the change in π-binding energy when two conjugated molecules, R and S, unite to form RS. We shall adopt the following notation for the AOs, MOs, and MO energies of the unperturbed systems, R, S:

$$\Phi_\mu = \mu\text{th MO of } R \qquad \Psi_\rho = \rho\text{th MO of } S$$

$$\phi_i = i\text{th AO of } R \qquad \psi_u = u\text{th AO of } S \qquad (6.62)$$

$$\Phi_\mu = \sum_i a_{\mu i}\phi_i \quad \text{energy } E_\mu \qquad \Psi_\rho = \sum_u b_{\rho u}\psi_u \quad \text{energy } F_\rho$$

We shall assume first that R is attached to S in RS by one bond only, between atom r in R and atom s in S (Fig. 6.4); the case of multiple union will be considered later. The perturbation can be represented, in HMO formalism, by an increase in the resonance integral between atoms r, s, from zero (in $R + S$) to some final value β_{rs}. The perturbation $\mathbf{P}$ is therefore defined by the matrix elements:

$$\int \phi_i \mathbf{P} \phi_j \, d\tau = \int \psi_u \mathbf{P} \psi_v \, d\tau = 0 \qquad (6.63)$$

$$\int \phi_i \mathbf{P} \psi_u \, d\tau = 0 \qquad \text{unless } i = r, u = s \qquad (6.64)$$

$$\int \phi_r \mathbf{P} \psi_s \, d\tau = \beta_{rs} \qquad (6.65)$$

Using these results, we can immediately calculate the matrix elements of $\mathbf{P}$ for the MOs of the system;

$$\int \Phi_\mu \mathbf{P} \Phi_\nu \, d\tau = \int \left(\sum_i a_{\mu i}\phi_i\right)\mathbf{P}\left(\sum_j a_{\nu j}\phi_j\right) d\tau \qquad (6.66)$$

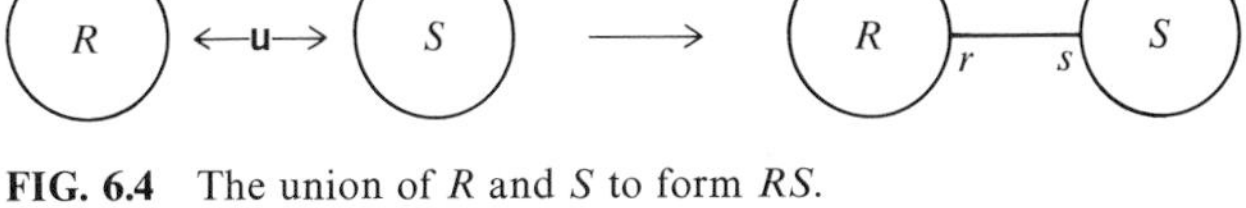

FIG. 6.4 The union of R and S to form RS.

Hence:

$$\int \Phi_\mu P \Phi_\nu \, d\tau = \sum_i \sum_j a_{\mu i} a_{\nu j} \int \phi_i P \phi_j \, d\tau = 0 \tag{6.67}$$

from Eq. (6.63).   Likewise:

$$\int \Psi_\rho P \Psi_\sigma \, d\tau = \int \left(\sum_u b_{\rho u} \psi_u \right) P \left(\sum_v b_{\sigma v} \psi_v \right) d\tau = 0 \tag{6.68}$$

Finally:

$$\int \Phi_\mu P \Psi_\rho \, d\tau = \int \left(\sum_i a_{\mu i} \phi_i \right) P \left(\sum_u b_{\rho u} \psi_u \right) d\tau = a_{\mu r} b_{\rho s} \beta_{rs} \tag{6.69}$$

from Eqs. (6.64) and (6.65).

First let us suppose that there is no degeneracy between the various MOs of R, S.   The first-order perturbations $\delta E_\mu{}^{I}$, $\delta F_\rho{}^{I}$ to the energies of the MOs Φ_μ, Ψ_ρ are then given by:

$$\delta E_\mu{}^{I} = \int \Phi_\mu P \Phi_\mu \, d\tau = 0 \qquad \delta F_\rho{}^{I} = \int \Psi_\rho P \Psi_\rho \, d\tau = 0 \tag{6.70}$$

from Eqs. (6.67) and (6.68).   Union of R with S to form RS therefore leads to no first-order change in π energy.

Next let us consider the corresponding second-order perturbations, $\delta E_\mu{}^{II}$, $\delta F_\rho{}^{II}$:

$$\begin{aligned}
\delta E_\mu{}^{II} &= \sum_{\nu \neq \mu} \frac{(\int \Phi_\mu P \Phi_\nu \, d\tau)^2}{E_\mu - E_\nu} + \sum_\rho \frac{(\int \Phi_\mu P \Psi_\rho \, d\tau)^2}{E_\mu - F_\rho} \\
&= \sum_\rho \frac{a_{\mu r}{}^2 b_{\rho s}{}^2 \beta_{rs}{}^2}{E_\mu - F_\rho}
\end{aligned} \tag{6.71}$$

from Eqs. (6.67) and (6.69).   Likewise:

$$\begin{aligned}
\delta F_\rho{}^{II} &= \sum_{\sigma \neq \rho} \frac{(\int \Psi_\rho P \Psi_\sigma \, d\tau)^2}{F_\rho - F_\sigma} + \sum_\mu \frac{(\int \Psi_\rho P \Phi_\mu \, d\tau)^2}{F_\rho - E_\mu} \\
&= \sum_\mu \frac{a_{\mu r}{}^2 b_{\rho s}{}^2 \beta_{rs}{}^2}{F_\rho - E_\mu}
\end{aligned} \tag{6.72}$$

Our next problem is to consider what will happen if there is degeneracy.   We can see immediately that degeneracy between the MOs of R, or between the MOs of S, will have no effect, since the matrix elements between pairs of MOs Φ_μ of R, or between pairs of MOs Ψ_ρ of S, vanish.   The secular equation for the first-order perturbed energies will then be of the form:

$$\begin{vmatrix} \epsilon - E & & 0 \\ & \epsilon - E & \\ 0 & & \epsilon - E \end{vmatrix} = (\epsilon - E)^k = 0 \tag{6.73}$$

where ϵ is the energy of one of the k-degenerate MOs; the solution is $E = \epsilon$, k times, so that the first-order perturbations vanish.   The second-order perturbations are still given by Eqs. (6.71) and (6.72).

A different situation arises, however, if one MO (Φ_λ) of R has the same energy ϵ as one MO (Ψ_σ) of S. In this case there is a first-order effect on union of R and S, the energies of the two perturbed MOs in RS being the roots of the secular equation:

$$\begin{vmatrix} \int\Phi_\lambda(\mathbf{H} + \mathbf{P})\Phi_\lambda \, d\tau - E & \int\Phi_\lambda\mathbf{P}\Psi_\sigma \, d\tau \\ \int\Phi_\lambda\mathbf{P}\Psi_\sigma \, d\tau & \int\Psi_\sigma(\mathbf{H} + \mathbf{P})\Psi_\sigma \, d\tau - E \end{vmatrix} = 0 \qquad (6.74)$$

when $\mathbf{H}$ is the hamiltonian for the unperturbed system (that is $R + S$). By assumption,

$$\int\Phi_\lambda\mathbf{H}\Phi_\lambda \, d\tau = \int\Psi_\sigma\mathbf{H}\Psi_\sigma \, d\tau = \epsilon \qquad (6.75)$$

since the integrals represent the energies of the two degenerate MOs in the unperturbed system $R + S$. Using Eqs. (6.67) to (6.69), Eq. (6.75) becomes:

$$\begin{vmatrix} \epsilon - E & a_{\lambda r}b_{\sigma s}\beta_{rs} \\ a_{\lambda r}b_{\sigma s}\beta_{rs} & \epsilon - E \end{vmatrix} = (\epsilon - E)^2 - a_{\lambda r}^2 b_{\sigma s}^2 \beta_{rs}^2 = 0 \qquad (6.76)$$

with the solutions:

$$E = \epsilon \pm a_{\lambda r}b_{\sigma s}\beta_{rs} \qquad (6.77)$$

The perturbation therefore has the effect of replacing the two degenerate MOs by one of higher energy and one of lower energy, the splitting being symmetrical (Fig. 6.5).

This argument can be extended[2] at once to cases of multiple degeneracy. Suppose that there are k MOs of R ($\Phi_{\lambda 1}$, $\Phi_{\lambda 2}, \ldots , \Phi_{\lambda k}$) that are simultaneously degenerate with t MOs ($\Psi_{\sigma 1}$, $\Psi_{\sigma 2}, \ldots , \Psi_{\sigma t}$) of S. Then it can be shown that all but one of the k-degenerate MOs of R, and all but one of the t-degenerate MOs of S, survive unchanged (to a first approximation) in RS; the remaining two MOs have energies $\epsilon \pm E$, with:

$$E = \left(\sum_{i=l}^{k} a_{\lambda i,r} \right)\left(\sum_{u=l}^{t} b_{\sigma u,s} \right)\beta_{rs} \qquad (6.78)$$

where $a_{\lambda i,r}$ is the coefficient of ϕ_r in $\Phi_{\lambda i}$ and $b_{\sigma u,s}$ that of ψ_s in $\Psi_{\sigma u}$. The surviving degenerate MOs of R and S are linear combinations of the original MOs $\Phi_{\lambda i}$, $\Psi_{\sigma u}$, such that the coefficients of ϕ_r and ψ_s in each of them is zero. The proof of this

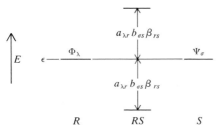

FIG. 6.5 The first-order perturbation to degenerate levels of R and S on union to RS.

theorem is left to the reader as an exercise; in practice we shall rarely be concerned with multiple degeneracies of this kind.

Next let us consider the effect of multiple union. Let us suppose that in RS, R is united to S through atom r in R to atom s in S, atom r' in R to atom s' in S, etc. It is very easily seen that the various matrix elements of P are now given by:

$$\int \phi_i P \phi_j \, d\tau = \int \psi_u P \psi_v \, d\tau = \int \Phi_\mu P \Phi_\nu \, d\tau = \int \Psi_\rho P \Psi_\sigma \, d\tau = 0 \tag{6.79}$$

$$\int \phi_i P \psi_u \, d\tau = 0 \qquad \text{unless atoms } i, u \text{ are linked in } RS \tag{6.80}$$

$$\int \phi_r P \psi_s \, d\tau = \beta_{rs} \qquad \int \phi_r' P \psi_s' \, d\tau = \beta_{rs}' \qquad \text{etc.} \tag{6.81}$$

$$\int \Phi_\mu P \Psi_\rho \, d\tau = \Sigma a_{\mu r} b_{\rho s} \beta_{rs} \tag{6.82}$$

where the sum in Eq. (6.80) is over pairs of atoms r, s through which R is united to S in RS. Thus Eqs. (6.71) and (6.72) become:

$$\delta E_\mu{}^{\mathrm{II}} = \sum_\rho \frac{(\Sigma a_{\mu r} b_{\rho s} \beta_{rs})^2}{E_\mu - F_\rho} \tag{6.83}$$

$$\delta F_\rho{}^{\mathrm{II}} = \sum_\mu \frac{(\Sigma a_{\mu r} b_{\rho s} \beta_{rs})^2}{F_\rho - E_\mu} \tag{6.84}$$

The expression for the case of degeneracy [Eq. (6.77)] is likewise replaced by:

$$E = \epsilon \pm (a_{\lambda r} b_{\sigma s} \beta_{rs} + a_{\lambda r}' b_{\sigma s}' \beta_{rs}' + \cdots) \tag{6.85}$$

In this case the perturbation is a sum of terms, each of which corresponds to the effects of one bond; this of course is because first-order perturbations are additive. The second-order perturbations [Eqs. (6.71), (6.72), (6.83), and (6.84)] do not show additivity of this kind, a point which will prove to be important in our perturbational treatment of conjugated systems.

6.7   UNION OF EVEN SYSTEMS

Consider the union of two even AHs R, S through a single bond rs (Fig. 6.4). The total π energy E of $R + S$ is given by:

$$E = 2 \sum_\mu^{\mathrm{occ}} E_\mu + 2 \sum_\rho^{\mathrm{occ}} F_\rho \tag{6.86}$$

where the sums are over the filled BMOs of each AH. Now consider the π energy E' of the united system RS. From Eqs. (6.72) to (6.74) and (6.86),

$$E' = 2 \sum_\mu^{\mathrm{occ}} E_\mu' + 2 \sum_\rho^{\mathrm{occ}} F_\rho'$$

$$\approx 2 \sum_\mu^{\mathrm{occ}} E_\mu + 2 \sum_\mu^{\mathrm{occ}} \delta E_\mu{}^{\mathrm{II}} + 2 \sum_\rho^{\mathrm{occ}} F_\rho + 2 \sum_\rho^{\mathrm{occ}} \delta F_\rho{}^{\mathrm{II}}$$

$$= E + 2 \sum_\mu^{\mathrm{occ}} \sum_\rho^{\mathrm{all}} \frac{a_{\mu r}{}^2 b_{\rho s}{}^2 \beta_{rs}{}^2}{E_\mu - F_\rho} + 2 \sum_\rho^{\mathrm{occ}} \sum_\mu^{\mathrm{all}} \frac{a_{\mu r}{}^2 b_{\rho s}{}^2 \beta_{rs}{}^2}{F_\rho - E_\mu} \tag{6.87}$$

Obviously the terms representing interactions between occupied MOs of R with occupied MOs of S cancel; hence:

$$E' = E + 2\left(\sum_{\mu}^{occ} \sum_{\rho}^{unocc\cdot} - \sum_{\mu}^{unocc} \sum_{\rho}^{occ}\right)\frac{a_{\mu r}{}^2 b_{\rho s}{}^2 \beta_{rs}{}^2}{E_\mu - F_\rho} \qquad (6.88)$$

From the pairing theorem (6.1), each unoccupied MO $\Phi_\mu{}^-$ of R, with energy $-E_\mu$, has a twin MO $\Phi_\mu{}^+$, with energy $+E_\mu$, such that the squares of corresponding AO coefficients $a_{\mu r}{}^2$ are the same. A similar relationship holds for S. Hence we can replace the sums over unoccupied MOs in Eq. (6.88) by sums over occupied MOs, if we invert the signs of the corresponding energies E_μ, F_ρ. Hence:

$$E' = E + 4\sum_{\mu}^{occ}\sum_{\rho}^{occ} \frac{a_{\mu r}{}^2 b_{\rho s}{}^2 \beta_{rs}{}^2}{E_\mu + F_\rho} \qquad (6.89)$$

Since the bonding MOs of an even AH all have negative energies, every term in the sum in Eq. (6.89) is negative; there is therefore a decrease in π energy when R unites with S, corresponding to an increase in stability.

Now the BMOs of AHs do not vary greatly in energy; we should get a fair approximation to the sum in Eq. (6.89) if we replace each of the orbital energies E_μ, F_ρ by some mean value, $\bar{E}$. In that case:

$$\begin{aligned} E' &= E + 4\sum_{\mu}^{occ}\sum_{\rho}^{occ} \frac{a_{\mu r}{}^2 b_{\rho s}{}^2 \beta_{rs}{}^2}{2\bar{E}} \\ &= E + \frac{\beta_{rs}{}^2}{2\bar{E}}\left(2\sum_{\mu}^{occ} a_{\mu r}{}^2\right)\left(2\sum_{\rho}^{occ} b_{\rho s}{}^2\right) \\ &= E + \frac{q_r q_s \beta_{rs}{}^2}{2\bar{E}} = E + \frac{\beta_{rs}{}^2}{2\bar{E}} \qquad (6.90)\end{aligned}$$

since the charge density at any position in an even AH is unity (Theorem 6.2). Thus the change in π energy on union of two even AHs has a value that is independent, to a first approximation, of the AHs that are uniting. It is immediately obvious that the bond between atoms r, s in such a system must be an essential single bond; for if R, S are even, and if we link one atom in R to one atom in S by a double bond, the remaining atoms in R and S are odd in number, so that we cannot write a structure in which they are all linked in pairs by double bonds. We can also see that any "single" bond in an open-chain system can be represented as a bond linking two even-AH fragments. The contribution of such bonds to the total energy of the system will therefore be constant, to this approximation, being given by:

$$E'_{CC} = E_{CC}{}^\sigma + \frac{\beta^2}{2\bar{E}} \qquad (6.91)$$

$E_{CC}{}^\sigma$ being the bond energy of the σ component. The heat of formation of an open-chain polyene should therefore be expressible as an additive function of single- and double-bond energies, if we use the value E_{CC} for the former. This of course corresponds very nicely to the conclusions reached in Sec. 5.5 on the basis of Pople calculations; the bonds in open-chain polyenes are localized. The same should also be true for essential single bonds linking even AHs, as in biphenyl, Ph—Ph; this again agrees with conclusions reached above on the basis of Pople calculations.

6.8   CYCLIC CLASSICAL POLYENES

A number of even cyclic polyenes are known which contain odd-numbered rings and for which only single classical structures can be written; fulvene is a good example.

$$(6.92)$$

Union of this type necessarily involves union through atoms of like parity in the original AH since it leads to the formation of an odd-numbered ring. In terms of perturbation theory, this union can be represented as a change in one resonance integral, i.e. that between the atoms r, s through which union is to take place [compare Eq. (6.92)], from zero to some value β_{rs}. The corresponding first-order change δE^{I} in π energy is given by Eq. (6.16);

$$\delta E^{\mathrm{I}} = 2p_{rs}\beta_{rs} \tag{6.93}$$

Now since union through atoms r, s leads to the production of an odd-numbered ring, and since the unperturbed system is an AH,

$$p_{rs} = 0 \tag{6.94}$$

from Theorem 6.3. Thus the first-order perturbation δE^{I} vanishes. Moreover the second-order change in π energy δE^{II}, due to union, can be shown to be given again approximately by

$$\delta E^{\mathrm{II}} = \frac{\bar{\beta}^2}{2\bar{E}} \tag{6.95}$$

(The proof of this result is left to the reader as an exercise; it follows the same lines as that used in Sec. 6.7.) Now it is again self-evident that the new bond formed on union must be an essential single bond; the heat of formation of the cyclic polyene can therefore again be written as an additive sum of bond energies of "single" and "double" bonds, the π component of the former being absorbed into the bond energy.

This argument can easily be extended to other types of essential single bonds, e.g. the bonds linking the naphthalene units in perylene or the central bond of azulene. Bonds of this type should therefore be localized, in our sense of the word. The same analysis can also be applied to essential double bonds. Consider an essential double bond in some hydrocarbon R. By definition, all the flanking CC bonds must necessarily be essential single bonds. We can therefore build up R by union of ethylene with a hydrocarbon R' having two carbon atoms less than R; the π energy change will be given approximately by Eq. (6.91). The heat of formation of R can therefore be written as a sum of the heat of formation of R', *plus* the bond energies of the single bonds linking it to the ethylene unit, *plus* the energy of the ethylene unit, i.e. the bond energy of a C=C double bond.

We conclude therefore that all essential single and double bonds in hydrocarbons must be localized, in agreement with deductions made on the basis of Pople calculations.

This parallel raises an important point. The PMO method is of course much more approximate than the Pople method; however it has the advantage of leading directly to general theorems concerning the relation between molecular properties and molecular structure. The Pople method only enables us to calculate properties of individual molecules; any attempts to draw general conclusions from the results of such calculations fall in the same category as attempts to draw empirical conclusions from experimental data. In short, the Pople method is at best a substitute for experiment; it cannot provide us with the kind of general principles that chemists need in their day-by-day thinking. It is of course true that the Pople method is not exact; however we would be no better off even if we could solve the Schrödinger equation exactly for large molecules. In order to plan syntheses, deduce reaction mechanisms, or determine molecular structures, we would still need some source of general principles to guide our thoughts.

6.9 NONCLASSICAL SYSTEMS

Next we come to cyclic polyenes for which more than one classical structure can be written, e.g. benzene. A compound of this type could be derived by union of two classical polyenes by multiple linkage, e.g.

$$(6.96)$$

In this case the corresponding change in π-binding energy would be given by an obvious extension of Eq. (6.88), the terms $a_{\mu r}{}^2 b_{\rho s}{}^2 \beta_{rs}{}^2$ in the numerator being replaced [see Eqs. (6.71) and (6.83)] by:

$$(a_{\mu r} b_{\rho s} \beta_{rs} + a'_{\mu r} b'_{\rho s} \beta'_{rs} + \cdots)^2 \qquad (6.97)$$

there being one term for each new bond.

However a complication arises. The expression in Eq. (6.97) is not equal to a sum of the simple square terms $a_{\mu r}^2 b_{\rho s}^2 \beta_{rs}^2$ that appear in the expressions for linkage by single bonds; since the individual terms in Eq. (6.97) can be positive or negative, the total π energy of union may be greater or less than that which would be expected from the π energies of similar unions in which only one of the new bonds was formed at a time. In other words, the energy of the resulting cyclic system may be either greater or less than that which would be expected on the basis of additivity of bond energies. Bonds in systems of this type need not therefore be localized. This of course does not conflict with the principle established in the previous section; for bonds of the type we are now considering are no longer essential single or double bonds.

Our object is to compare the π energy of our cyclic nonclassical hydrocarbon with the π energy to be expected for a corresponding localized polyene. The simplest way to do this is of course to compare its energy with that of an analogous hydrocarbon formed by breaking one bond in the ring; thus benzene can be derived by intramolecular union from hexatriene:

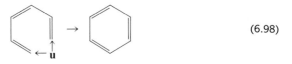

$$\text{(6.98)}$$

In this case union is through atoms of opposite parity; the corresponding bond order is no longer zero, so there is now a first-order change in π energy given by Eq. (6.93). Everything therefore depends on the sign of the bond order between the atoms through which union is to take place; if this is positive, the cyclic system has a lower energy than the polyene; if negative, a higher energy. In conventional terminology, the first case corresponds to a ring which is *aromatic*, i.e. more stable than one would expect from additivity of bond energies, the second case to one which is *antiaromatic*, i.e. less stable.

It is, however, difficult to estimate bond orders in systems of this kind other than by direct calculation, and the whole philosophy of the PMO method is to avoid such calculations like the plague. Fortunately we can make our comparison of related cyclic and acyclic structures by the following ingenious trick, without having to solve any secular equations.

6.10   UNION OF ODD AHs

The expression given above [Eq. (6.88)] for the energy of union of even AHs was derived on the assumption that there is no degeneracy between MOs of R and S; however the expression stands even if such degeneracy exists. In an even AH, all the BMOs are filled and all the AMOs are empty. If one MO of R is degenerate with one of S, it follows that the pair of MOs is either filled with electrons or empty. Since the first-order interaction between a pair of filled orbitals leads to

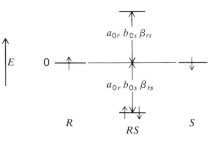

FIG. 6.6   First-order perturbation to the NBMOs of two odd AHs R, S on union to RS.

no change in total energy (see Fig. 6.5), degeneracy of this kind has no first-order effect on the total energy of union.

A different situation arises, however, in the union of two odd-AH radicals R and S.   In this case (Fig. 6.6) the unpaired electrons occupy NBMOs, which necessarily have the same energy; in RS, these combine to a pair of MOs, one bonding and one antibonding, and the two electrons in question can be accommodated in the lower of the two.   Here there is a first-order change in energy δE given [see Eq. (6.85)] by:

$$\delta E = \Sigma 2 a_{0r} b_{0s} \beta_{rs} \qquad (6.99)$$

where a_{0r} and b_{0s} are coefficients in the NBMOs Φ_0, Ψ_0 of R, S respectively, and where the sum is over pairs of atoms, r in R and s in S, through which R is linked to S in RS.

Consider benzene.   Benzene can be formed by union of two allyl radicals (Fig. 6.7a).   So can hexatriene (Fig. 6.7b).   The difference between the two π energies of union is clearly the difference in π energy between benzene and a classical structure for benzene in which the single and double bonds are localized, i.e. similar to those in a conjugated polyene.   Comparison of the two energies of union will therefore at once tell us if benzene is more stable, or less stable, then a corresponding classical structure would lead us to expect.

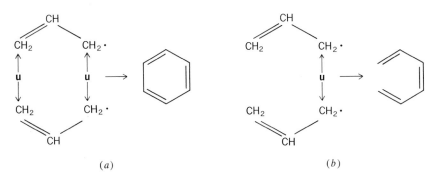

FIG. 6.7   Union of two allyl radicals to form (a) benzene and (b) hexatriene.

This approach can be put in an even simpler form if we remember that the energy of any NBMO is the same as that (α) of the $2p$ AO of an isolated carbon atom. Methyl can thus be regarded as the limiting case of an "odd AH," its "NBMO" being just a single AO. If we form an even AH by union of an odd AH R with methyl, the energy of union is then given by Eq. (6.99) with b_{0s} equal to unity; i.e.

$$\delta E = 2 \sum_r a_{0r} \beta_{rs} \qquad (6.100)$$

Thus benzene and hexatriene can both be formed by union of 2,4-pentadienyl with methyl, i.e.

$$\qquad (6.101)$$

methyl being represented by a large dot; writing β for the resonance integral between two adjacent carbon atoms, and taking the terminal atoms in pentadienyl to be r and s, we have:

Benzene: $\qquad \delta E = 2\beta(a_{0r} + a_{0s})$

Hexatriene: $\qquad \delta E = 2\beta a_{0r}$

$$\qquad (6.102)$$

From symmetry, $a_{0r} = \pm a_{0s}$; whether benzene is less stable, or more stable, than one would expect cyclohexatriene to be therefore depends on the relative signs of the two NBMO coefficients, a_{0r} and a_{0s}.

6.11 CALCULATION OF NBMO COEFFICIENTS

Normally one has to solve the HMO equations to find orbital coefficients, but NBMOs are an exception. Here one can find the coefficients by an extremely simple procedure, first pointed out by Longuet-Higgins.[1b] Consider the equations for the coefficients in an MO of an AH [Eqs. (6.42) and (6.43)]. In the case of an NBMO, $E = \alpha$; the equations thus become:

$$\sum_{k \neq i} a_{0k} \beta_{ik} = 0 \qquad (6.103)$$

Now in the HMO method, β_{ik} is assumed to vanish unless atoms i and k are directly linked; all the terms in Eq. (6.103) then vanish except those where k is an atom directly linked to atom i. If we make the usual simplifying assumption, that resonance integrals between adjacent carbon atoms have a common value β, Eq. (6.103) assumes a still simpler form:

$$\sum_{k}^{\substack{\text{linked} \\ \text{to } i}} a_{0k} = 0 \qquad (6.104)$$

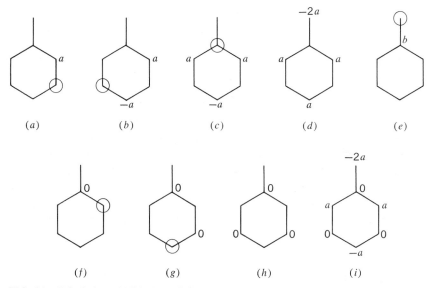

FIG. 6.8 Calculation of NBMO coefficients in benzyl.

This relation can be used to estimate NBMO coefficients in a matter of seconds, as the following examples show.

Consider benzyl. Suppose we denote the NBMO coefficient of atom 2 by a (Fig. 6.8a). Suppose we take atom 3 to be atom i in Eq. (6.104) (circled in Fig. 6.8a). Equation (6.104) tells us that the sum of NBMO coefficients of atoms adjacent to atom i vanish; the coefficient at position 4 must therefore be $-a$ (Fig. 6.8b). Repeating this process (Fig. 6.8b to d), we find that the coefficient of atom 6 must be a, and that of the methylene group $-2a$. Now we can go through the same procedure, starting with atom 1 (Fig. 6.8f). The sum of coefficients of atoms adjacent to atom 7 must vanish; since the only atom adjacent to atom 7 is atom 1, the coefficient of atom 1 must be zero. Following through the same argument as before (Fig. 6.8f to h), we find that the coefficients of atoms 3, 5 are also zero. The final coefficients are now known in terms of a single parameter a (Fig. 6.8i). To find a we normalize the orbital; the condition for normalization is that the sum of the squares of the NBMO coefficients must vanish; i.e.

$$a^2 + (-a)^2 + a^2 + (-2a)^2 = 7a^2 = 1 \qquad (6.105)$$

Thus $a = 1/\sqrt{7}$.

Note that the NBMO coefficients at all the unstarred positions in benzyl vanish; this is of course in agreement with the pairing theorem. Later we shall show that it is always the unstarred set in an odd AH that has vanishing NBMO coefficients.

Our next example is the perinaphthenyl radical (Fig. 6.9a).   The calculation of NBMO coefficients is illustrated in Fig. 6.9.   Note the situation indicated in Fig. 6.9c.   Here Eq. (6.104) contains two unknowns.   We deal with this by introducing a new parameter (Fig. 6.9d), the value of which is determined later in the calculation (Fig. 6.9h).   Equation (6.104) here becomes:

$$(a - 2b) + (2b - a) + b = b = 0 \qquad (6.106)$$

This general procedure can be used to determine NBMO coefficients in any AH. One can start anywhere one likes; the solutions of Eqs. (6.104) are unique.   Of course one may save oneself a little effort by choosing the first atom circumspectly.

Figure 6.9i illustrates another point.   The NBMO coefficient at the central atom vanishes, even though this is a starred atom.   Since NBMO coefficients play a basic role in our treatment, it is convenient to have some term to describe this situation; we shall term a position in an odd AH *inactive* if the NBMO coeffi-

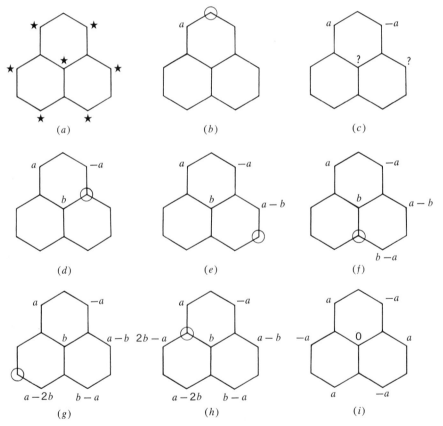

FIG. 6.9   Calculation of NBMO coefficients in perinaphthenyl.

cient there vanishes, *active* if the NBMO coefficient differs from zero.   Unstarred positions in an odd AH are necessarily inactive, but starred positions need not necessarily be active.

6.12   AROMATICITY IN EVEN AHs

We are now in a position to develop a general theory of aromaticity in even AHs, using the results reached in the two previous sections.

First, let us consider benzene [Eq. (6.101)].   The coefficients in pentadienyl are at once seen to be as follows:

$$\overset{a}{CH_2}=CH-\overset{-a}{CH}=CH-\overset{a}{CH_2} \qquad a = \frac{1}{\sqrt{3}} \qquad (6.107)$$

From Eq. (6.102), the π energies of union of pentadienyl with methyl to form benzene or hexatriene are:

Benzene: $\delta E = 4a\beta$

Hexatriene: $\delta E = 2a\beta$

(6.108)

Thus benzene is more stable than hexatriene.   Moreover this difference should be relatively large, being a first-order perturbation; it can of course be equated to the quantity we termed resonance energy in Sec. 5.6.

Next let us consider cyclobutadiene.   This can be formed by union of allyl with methyl, from which we can also derive the open-chain analog butadiene. The corresponding NBMO coefficients and energies of union are as follows:

$$\delta E = 2\beta(b - b) = 0 \qquad \delta E = 2b\beta \qquad (6.109)$$

Here the cyclic structure is *less* stable than the open-chain one; in other words cyclobutadiene should have a negative resonance energy, i.e. it should be antiaromatic.

This argument can be extended immediately to [2n]annulene.   We can form [2n]annulene by union of methyl with a linear conjugated radical having $2n - 1$ atoms.   The NBMO coefficients in this radical will be as follows:

$$\overset{d}{C}-\overset{-d}{C}-\overset{d}{C}-C-C\cdots\overset{d(-1)^{n-2}}{C}-\overset{d(-1)^{n-1}}{C}-C \qquad d = \frac{1}{\sqrt{n}} \qquad (6.110)$$

We can also form a linear polyene with $2n$ atoms by union of the same fragments. The corresponding energies of union are:

Annulene: $\delta E = 2\beta[d + (-d)^{n-1}]$

Polyene: $\delta E = 2d\beta$

(6.111)

The resonance energy of the annulene E_R is thus given by:

$$E_R = -2d\beta(-1)^{n-1} = \frac{2\beta(-1)^n}{\sqrt{n}} \qquad (6.112)$$

(The minus sign is due to the convention that a positive resonance energy implies greater stability. The resonance integral β is negative.) If n is odd, the annulene is therefore more stable than the polyene; if n is even, the reverse is true. Consequently the annulenes with $4k + 2$ atoms should be aromatic, those with $4k$ antiaromatic.

We can extend the argument still further. The calculations of NBMO coefficients indicated in Figs. 6.8 and 6.9 and Eqs. (6.107) to (6.110) are based on Eq. (6.104), i.e. on the assumption that all CC bonds are equivalent. If, however, the bonds in an AH alternate in length, this is no longer the case; β for the "double" bonds should be greater than β for the "single" bonds. If we write

$$\frac{\beta(\text{single})}{\beta(\text{double})} = \epsilon < 1 \qquad (6.113)$$

then the coefficients in a $2n - 1$ radical become:

$$\overset{d}{C}-\overset{-d\epsilon}{C}=\overset{d\epsilon^2}{C}-C=C-\cdots\cdots=\overset{d(-\epsilon)^{n-2}}{C}-\overset{d(-\epsilon)^{n-1}}{C}-C \qquad d = \left(\frac{1-\epsilon^2}{1-\epsilon^{2n}}\right)^{1/2} \qquad (6.114)$$

The resonance energy E_R' of the [2n]annulene is now given by:

$$E_R' = 2d\beta(-\epsilon)^n \qquad (6.115)$$

Since $\epsilon < 1$ by definition [Eq. (6.113)], E_R is numerically less than the value E_R estimated for equal bond lengths; consequently bond alternation should be energetically unfavorable for the aromatic [4k + 2]annulenes, but favorable for the antiaromatic [4k]annulenes.

This whole picture of course corresponds very closely to the one we deduced earlier, on the basis of PPP calculations for individual annulenes (Sec. 5.7). It is amusing to note that this simple treatment remained until recently the *only* theoretical basis for Hückel's rule! Admittedly it does not account for the fact that large [4k + 2]annulenes are not aromatic, although it does predict that the resonance energy should decrease with ring size; the effect is probably due to the tendency of the σ bonds to favor an alternating structure, a tendency which is ignored in our simple-minded PMO approach. As the number of bonds increases, and the resonance energy of the symmetrical structure decreases, a critical point is reached at which bond alternation sets in.

The argument given here can be extended to polycyclic AHs. Consider one ring in a polycyclic AH R. Removal of one atom from this ring leaves an odd AH S. We can regenerate R from S by union with methyl (Fig. 6.10a and b). We could also form two even AHs T, T' by union of the same fragments that differ

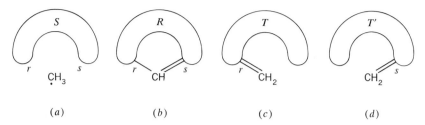

FIG. 6.10   The PMO treatment of aromaticity in one ring of a polycyclic AH R.

from R only in that the ring in question is now open (Fig. 6.10c and d).   The corresponding energies of union are:

R: $\qquad\qquad\qquad\qquad\qquad\delta E = 2\beta(a_{0r} + a_{0s})$

T: $\qquad\qquad\qquad\qquad\qquad\delta E = 2\beta a_{0r}$ $\qquad\qquad$ (6.116)

T': $\qquad\qquad\qquad\qquad\qquad\delta E = 2\beta a_{0s}$

where a_{0r}, a_{0s} are NBMO coefficients of the atoms r, s in S through which union takes place.   Evidently everything depends on the relative signs of a_{0r}, a_{0s}.   If they are the same, R is more stable than either T or T'; the relevant ring in R is thus aromatic.   Conversely if the signs are different, one of the open structures (T or T') will be more stable than R; the ring in question will then be antiaromatic.

The relative signs of the coefficients depend on the size of the new ring.   It can be shown[3] that if the new ring has $4n + 2$ members, the signs of the coefficients are the same; with $4n$ members, the signs are opposite.   This provides us with a general extension of Hückel's rule; in a polycyclic AH, $(4n + 2)$-membered rings are aromatic, $4n$-membered rings antiaromatic.‡

Biphenylene provides a good example of this rule.   Figure 6.11 shows in a self-explanatory manner that the terminal rings of biphenylene are aromatic, having six members, whereas the central four-membered ring is antiaromatic; for the π energy of biphenyl is predicted to be less than that of phenylhexatriene, and also less than that of biphenylene.

This result is particularly interesting, since it agrees with the SCF MO calculations outlined in the last chapter (see Table 5.1) but not with the HMO method (predicted resonance energy for biphenylene, 4.505β; for biphenyl, 4.383β).   As we have seen, this is one of the cases where the HMO method fails.

The argument outlined above for bond alternation in [$4k$]annulenes will of course apply equally to $4n$-membered rings in polycyclic systems.   The bonds linking the benzene units in biphenylene are indeed very long (Fig. 5.4).

‡ Earlier attempts to extend Hückel's rule had been based on the idea that aromaticity should always be associated with the presence of $4n + 2$ π electrons in the molecule as a whole; this is incorrect.   Thus pyrene behaves as though all the rings in it were aromatic, although it contains 16 ($= 4 \times 4$) π electrons.

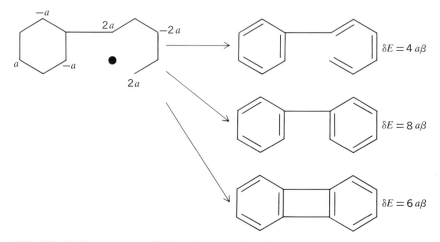

FIG. 6.11   PMO treatment of biphenylene, showing that the terminal rings are aromatic, while the central ring is antiaromatic.

6.13   AROMATICITY IN EVEN NONALTERNANT HYDROCARBONS

The PMO approach outlined above cannot normally be applied to nonalternant systems; however even hydrocarbons of this type with two odd-numbered rings fused together, e.g. azulene, can so be treated, since removal of one of the bridgehead atoms leaves an odd AH.   Thus azulene can be derived (Fig. 6.12) by union of methyl with a linear C_9 radical; Fig. 6.12 shows how the π energy of azulene can thus be compared with that of decapentaene, phenylbutadiene, [10]annulene, or azulene.   It will be noticed that the calculated π energy of azulene is the same as that for either of the monocyclic systems, and less than that for naphthalene, in agreement with experiment, and with the results of SCF MO calculations (Table 5.2).

According to this picture, azulene should be regarded as a slightly perturbed version of [10]annulene, the extra bond contributing nothing to the π energy; for in the union of methyl and the C_9 radical, an inactive position of the C_9 radical is involved.   The second-order perturbation due to formation of the extra bond in azulene compared with [10]annulene can be shown to be the same as that for essential single bonds in other molecules; we would therefore expect this bond in azulene to be a localized single bond, again in agreement with experiment and SCF MO theory (see Sec. 5.6 and Fig. 5.6).

An analogous argument (Fig. 6.13) shows that pentalene and heptalene should have π energies similar to cyclooctatetraene or [12]annulene and so be antiaromatic; the bonds in them should therefore alternate in length.   These conclusions again agree with the results of SCF MO calculations and with experiment (Sec. 5.6).

The same conclusions can also be reached by an alternative approach, which

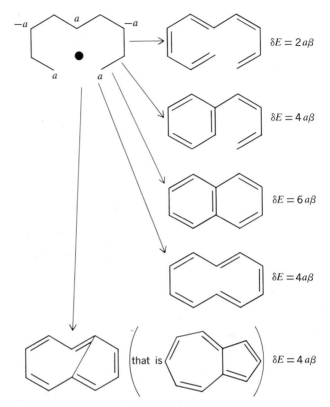

FIG. 6.12   Calculation of relative π energy of azulene.

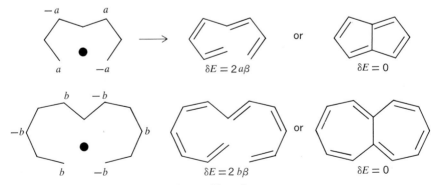

FIG. 6.13   PMO treatment of pentalene and heptalene.

has the further advantage of being applicable to a number of polycyclic systems containing two or more nonadjacent odd-numbered rings.   We could derive azulene, pentalene, or heptalene by intramolecular union from the monocyclic polyenes that form their perimeters; e.g.

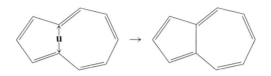

Since union here takes place between atoms of like parity in an AH, it leads to no first-order change in π-binding energy [see Eq. (6.93) and Theorem 6.3]; as we have seen, the second-order perturbation is automatically included in the bond energy of the new essential single bond.   This alternative derivation confirms our picture of these compounds as slightly perturbed monocyclic polyenes; it can also be applied to certain other types of nonalternant systems, e.g. the hydrocarbons I to IV below.   Each of them can be derived, as indicated, by intramolecular union from a cyclic polyene; the new bonds all link pairs of atoms of like parity, and should not therefore lead to any significant change in π energy. Compounds of this type with a $4n$-membered perimeter (e.g. I and III) should therefore be antiaromatic; since any type of addition will convert them to derivatives of benzene, one would expect them to be extraordinarily reactive.   Even the aromatic $(4n + 2)$-membered compounds should also show exceptional reactivity; for ionic addition reactions can convert them to normal aromatic systems containing two or more aromatic rings.   The gain in resonance energy in such a process should therefore be very great, particularly since the resonance energies of cyclic polyenes decrease with ring size, and here we are replacing one large aromatic ring by two or more smaller ones.   Of these compounds only indacene (I) has as yet been prepared; it is, as predicted, extremely reactive.[4]

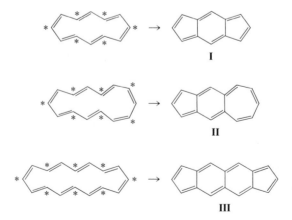

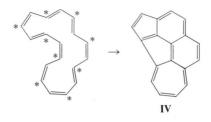

IV

6.14 ODD AHs

So far we have considered the resonance energies of only even systems; odd AHs were introduced as a device that would let us study their relative stabilities. Let us now consider odd conjugated systems, in particular odd AHs such as allyl or benzyl.

As we have seen, structures of this type can exist in three forms, as radicals or positive or negative ions. The three forms of a given AH differ only in the number of electrons occupying the NBMO; since these electrons are nonbonding, all three forms of a given odd AH must have similar π-binding energies and so have comparable chemical stabilities. Systems of this type are indeed stable in all three forms; thus triphenylmethyl, Ph_3C, forms stable salts, $Ph_3C^+BF_4$ and $Ph_3C^-Na^+$, and also exists in solution as a free radical, $Ph_3C\cdot$.

An odd AH can be formed by union of methyl with an even AH; since even AHs do not in general have NBMOs, there is no first-order change in energy on π union, since the even AH will have no MO of zero energy. If, however, we calculate the second-order π energy of union by Eq. (6.87), remembering in the notation of that equation that S (being methyl) has only a single orbital of zero energy (that is $F = 0$), we find:

$$E' = E + 2\sum_{\mu}^{occ} \frac{a_{\mu r}^2 \beta^2}{E_\mu} + n_0 \sum_{\mu}^{all} \frac{a_{\mu r}^2 \beta^2}{-E_\mu}$$

$$= E + 2\sum_{\mu}^{occ} \frac{a_{\mu r}^2 \beta^2}{E_\mu} \qquad (6.117)$$

where n_0 is the number of electrons occupying the NBMO of the final odd AH; the second sum vanishes in view of Theorem 6.1, since the value of $a_{\mu r}^2/E_\mu$ is equal and opposite for the two MOs Φ_μ^+, Φ_μ^- of a pair. If we make the approximation of replacing the E_μ by some mean value $\bar{E}$, then:

$$E' = E + \sum_{\mu}^{occ} \frac{2a_{\mu r}^2 \beta^2}{\bar{E}} = \frac{q_r \beta^2}{\bar{E}} = \frac{\beta^2}{\bar{E}} \qquad (6.118)$$

Thus the second-order perturbation is of the order of double that for linkage of two even AHs [Eq. (6.91)]; we can therefore immediately conclude that bonds in odd AHs are not localized. This of course agrees with chemical experience.

The approximation of setting the E_μ in Eq. (6.117) equal to some mean value is, however, too drastic; we shall now deduce the π energy of an odd AH by an alternative and more convincing route, which will have the further advantage of relating its π energy to that of an even AH with one more, or one less, conjugated carbon atom.

Consider an odd AH R.   If we unite this with methyl, through atom r in R, we shall obtain an even AH S with one carbon atom more than R (Fig. 6.14).   The new bond will moreover be an essential double bond; all bonds adjacent to it will therefore be essential single bonds.   Now consider the even AH T, derived from R by removing atom r.   This can be converted to S by union with ethylene (Fig. 6.14).   Since moreover the new bonds are all localized, it follows that the π-binding energies of S and T differ by that of ethylene, that is 2β in the HMO method. Finally, the difference in π energy δE_{RS} between R and S, being the π energy of union of an odd AH with methyl, will be given [compare Eq. (6.102)] by:

$$\delta E_{RS} = 2\beta a_{0r} \qquad (6.119)$$

Thus the difference in π-binding energy between R and T will be given by:

$$\delta E_{RT} = 2\beta a_{0r} - 2\beta = 2\beta(a_{0r} - 1) \qquad (6.120)$$

These results will be used extensively in Chap. 8, in a discussion of reactions involving odd AHs, or systems isoconjugate with them, as intermediates.   One simple example may, however, be given here by way of illustration.   Consider the dissociation of a substituted ethane to two methyl radicals,

$$R_3C-CR_3 \rightleftharpoons 2R_3C\cdot \qquad (6.121)$$

This reaction should be endothermic by the CC bond energy, less any gain of resonance energy due to conjugation in the resulting methyl radicals.   From Eq. (6.120), this gain in resonance energy will be given by:

$$2\delta E_{RT} = 4\beta(a_{0r} - 1) \qquad (6.122)$$

where a_{0r} is the NBMO coefficient at the methyl carbon in $R_3C\cdot$.   Consequently the smaller a_{0r}, the larger the gain in resonance energy and the smaller should

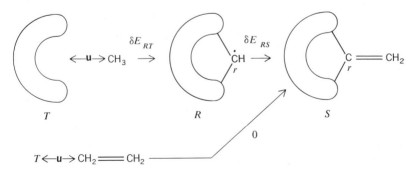

FIG. 6.14   PMO calculation of the π-binding energy of an odd AH.

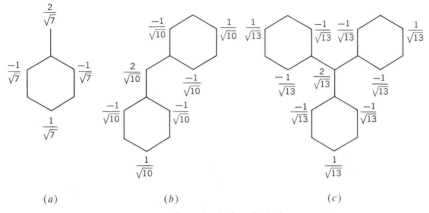

FIG. 6.15   NBMO coefficients.   (*a*) Benzyl; (*b*) benzhydryl; (*c*) trityl.

be the heat of dissociation of the ethane.   Figure 6.15 shows NBMO coefficients for benzyl, benzhydryl, and trityl; we would conclude that the ease of dissociation of the corresponding ethanes should increase in the order

$$PhCH_2CH_2Ph < Ph_2CHCHPh_2 < Ph_3CCPh_3$$

which of course is known to be the case.

6.15   ODD NONALTERNANT HYDROCARBONS

In Sec. 6.8 we considered even nonalternant systems that could be derived from even AHs by intramolecular union, forming an odd-numbered ring; we found that rings of this type have zero resonance energies, i.e. are nonaromatic, and that they contain localized bonds.   We shall next consider nonalternant systems derived in an analogous way by intramolecular union from odd AHs.

Here a question of definition arises.   Up till now we have implicitly defined aromatic compounds as ones in which the bonds are not localized and whose heats of formation are correspondingly greater than those calculated for a corresponding classical structure.   In the case of odd AHs, however, even the open-chain compounds have delocalized bonds (Sec. 6.14).   Moreover it would be impossible to give any satisfactory definition of resonance energy for systems of this kind since here there are no classical compounds that we could use for reference.   The only rational way of defining aromaticity for cyclic compounds of this type is therefore by reference to analogous open-chain compounds.   For example, we may define cyclopentadienyl as aromatic, or antiaromatic, accordingly as its heat of formation is greater, or less, than that of the analogous open-chain AH, i.e. pentadienyl, allowing of course for the extra CH bonds in the latter.

The relative energies of a given odd AH, and of a nonalternant system derived from it by intramolecular union, can be found at once by using Eq. (6.16) and Theorems 6.3 and 6.5. For intramolecular union between two atoms of like parity, r and s in an odd AH (Fig. 6.16), the corresponding changes in energy δE are:

Odd-AH radical: $\delta E = 2p_{rs}\beta_{rs} = 0$ (6.123)

Odd-AH anion: $\delta E = 2p_{rs}\beta_{rs} = 2a_{0r}a_{0s}\beta_{rs}$ (6.124)

Odd-AH cation: $\delta E = 2p_{rs}\beta_{rs} = -2a_{0r}a_{0s}\beta_{rs}$ (6.125)

The first result follows from Theorem 6.3, the second and third from Theorem 6.5.

From our definition, and Eq. (6.123), we see that cyclic radicals of this type are nonaromatic, as also are the corresponding ions if they are formed by union involving an inactive position in the odd AH. An example of this would be provided by the 1,2-bismethylene derivative of $C_5H_5^-$, formed by intramolecular union between the inactive (unstarred) 2,6 positions of heptatrienyl; for ions formed by union between active positions, the situation depends on the relative signs of the NBMO coefficients a_{0r}, a_{0s}. If their signs are the same, the anion will be aromatic and the cation antiaromatic; if the signs are opposite, the cation will be aromatic and the anion antiaromatic. From the rules for signs of coefficients in odd AHs (Sec. 6.12), we see at once that $(4n + 1)$-membered anions should be aromatic and the corresponding cations antiaromatic, while $(4n + 3)$-membered cations should be aromatic and the corresponding anions antiaromatic. In the case of cyclic polymethines, the aromatic systems will in each case contain $(4n + 2)$ π electrons; this completes our derivation of Hückel's rule.

Here again we can derive an extended version of Hückel's rule for polycyclic systems. If we form an odd-numbered ring by internal union in any odd AH, we conclude that the new ring is:

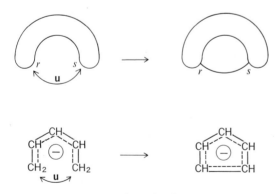

FIG. 6.16   Intramolecular union between two atoms r, s in an odd AH to form a corresponding nonalternant system.

Nonaromatic in the case of an odd radical, or of union between
positions one of which is inactive

Aromatic in the case of an anion if the new ring has $(4n + 1)$ members, antiaromatic in the case of the corresponding cation

Aromatic in the case of a cation if the new ring contains $(4n + 3)$
members, antiaromatic in the case of the corresponding anion

(6.126)

These predictions of course agree with the available chemical evidence.   Thus
the indenyl anion (V) is aromatic and should be formed more readily than the
corresponding AH anion 1-phenylallyl (VI); indene (VII) is therefore more acidic
than 1-phenylpropene (VIII), removal of a proton from VII to form V occurring
more easily than removal of a proton from VIII to form VI.   Likewise benzo-
tropylium (IX) is much more stable than the AH cation (X) would be.   Conversely, S_N1 solvolysis of 1-chloroindene (XI) occurs less readily than solvolysis
of cinnamyl chloride (XII), since the indenyl cation (XIII) is antiaromatic, while
the methylene protons in cycloheptatriene (XV) show no acidity, since their
removal would leave an antiaromatic anion XV.

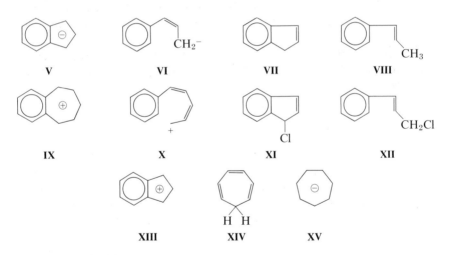

One important distinction may, however, be expected between the odd nonalternant cyclic systems and their even counterparts.   The aromaticity of an
even conjugated hydrocarbon is determined by its energy relative to that of a
classical polyene with localized bonds; bond alternation in the cyclic compound
will reduce the difference in energy between it and the classical structure.   Consequently we would expect bond alternation always to occur in any even antiaromatic hydrocarbon, alternant or nonalternant.   However in the case of an odd
cyclic radical or ion, aromaticity is determined by reference to an odd AH which
has delocalized bonds; bond alternation will reduce the difference in energy between the two structures, but it will also have the effect of destabilizing the AH.

Consequently there is no guarantee that bond alternation will stabilize an anti-aromatic odd system; the net effect of bond alternation is a sum of two conflicting contributions.

The results embodied in Eq. (6.126) have one obvious and important consequence. Whereas an odd AH occurs with almost equal facility as a radical or as a positive or negative ion, the same is no longer true for a nonalternant analog. Here one ion is aromatic, the other antiaromatic, and the radical nonaromatic; usually it is only the most stable of the three species, i.e. the aromatic ion, that is of chemical importance. Thus the cyclopentadienyl system is known mainly as the aromatic anion $C_5H_5^-$, and its derivatives, while the corresponding C_7H_7 system is known mainly as the positive ion (i.e. tropylium).

6.16   THE LCMO METHOD; NBMO COEFFICIENTS

Much of our perturbational approach has been based on the idea of treating a molecule RS in terms of the MOs Φ_μ, Φ_ν of its parts; this approach can also be used in a more conventional treatment. Since the MOs Φ_μ of R are linear combinations of the AOs ϕ_i, any linear combination of the AOs ϕ_i can be written equivalently as a linear combination of the MOs Φ_μ. Likewise any linear combination of the AOs ψ_j of S can be written equivalently as a linear combination of the MOs Ψ_ν. One can therefore write the MOs Ξ_M of RS either as linear combinations of the AOs ϕ_i and ϕ_j, or equivalently as linear combinations of the MOs Φ_μ and Ψ_ν;

$$\Xi_M = \sum_i a_{Mi}\phi_i + \sum_j b_{Mj}\phi_j \qquad (6.127)$$

or

$$\Xi_M = \sum_\mu a_{M\mu}\Phi_\mu + \sum_\nu b_{M\nu}\Psi_\nu \qquad (6.128)$$

If we use the first expression for Ξ_M in a variation treatment, we arrive at the usual LCAO MO formalism. However we should arrive at exactly the same final conclusions if we use a variation method based on the second expression for Ξ_M; this is the basis of the so-called *LCMO* (linear combination of molecular orbitals) *method.*[5]

Let us apply this formalism within the framework of HMO theory. The secular equation for RS will be of the form:

$$
\begin{vmatrix}
\int\Phi_1 H\Phi_1\,d\tau - E & \cdots & \int\Phi_1 H\Phi_m\,d\tau & \vdots & \int\Phi_1 H\Psi_1\,d\tau & \cdots & \int\Phi_1 H\Psi_n\,d\tau \\
\vdots & & \vdots & \vdots & \vdots & & \vdots \\
\int\Phi_m H\Phi_1\,d\tau & \cdots & \int\Phi_m H\Phi_m\,d\tau - E & \vdots & \int\Phi_m H\Psi_1\,d\tau & \cdots & \int\Phi_m H\Psi_n\,d\tau \\
\hline
\int\Psi_1 H\Phi_1\,d\tau & \cdots & \int\Psi_1 H\Phi_m\,d\tau & \vdots & \int\Psi_1 H\Psi_1\,d\tau - E & \cdots & \int\Psi_1 H\Psi_n\,d\tau \\
\vdots & & \vdots & \vdots & \vdots & & \vdots \\
\int\Psi_n H\Phi_1\,d\tau & \cdots & \int\Psi_n H\Phi_m\,d\tau & \vdots & \int\Psi_n H\Psi_1\,d\tau & \cdots & \int\Psi_n H\Psi_n\,d\tau - E
\end{vmatrix} = 0
$$

$$(6.129)$$

(The determinant falls into four parts, representing matrix elements between MOs of R, between MOs of S, and between MOs of R and of S; this is indicated in Eq. (6.129) by the horizontal and vertical dashed lines). The necessary matrix elements have already been found [Eqs. (6.66) to (6.69)]; using these, Eq. (6.129) becomes:

$$\begin{vmatrix} E_1 - E & \cdots & 0 & P_{11} & \cdots & P_{1n} \\ \vdots & & \vdots & \vdots & & \vdots \\ 0 & \cdots & E_m - E & P_{m1} & \cdots & P_{mn} \\ P_{11} & \cdots & P_{m1} & F_1 - E & \cdots & 0 \\ \vdots & & \vdots & \vdots & & \vdots \\ P_{1n} & \cdots & P_{mn} & 0 & \cdots & F_n - E \end{vmatrix} = 0 \qquad (6.130)$$

where

$$P_{\mu\nu} = \Sigma a_{\mu r} b_{\nu s} \beta_{rs} \qquad (6.131)$$

the sum being over pairs of atoms r, s through which R is united to S in RS.

The determinant in Eq. (6.130) is much simpler in form than the usual HMO secular equation; it can be expanded without difficulty to give the secular equation in closed algebraic form. While the expansion is not of interest here, certain other properties of Eq. (6.130) are very significant indeed. Suppose for example that the coefficients $a_{\mu i}$ of one MO Φ_μ vanish at all the points r of contact with S in RS. It follows at once that all the matrix elements $P_{\mu\nu}$ vanish. The only element left in the corresponding row and column of the determinant is then the diagonal element $E_\mu - E$; this element therefore factors out of the determinant. Consequently RS then possesses one MO of energy E_μ; it is easily shown that the corresponding MO is identical with the MO Φ_μ of R. This is a very reasonable result. When R is united with S, the MOs of R are perturbed through their interactions with the MOs of S. If one of the MOs of R vanishes at every point of contact with S, we would expect it to survive unchanged in RS. We have shown that this intuition is indeed correct.

Since this result will prove useful in a number of connections, we may list it as a formal theorem:

Theorem 6.6 If RS is formed by union of R with S in such a way that the coefficients of one MO Φ_μ of R vanish at all points of union with S, then Φ_μ survives unchanged in RS.

A very important example of Theorem 6.6 is the case when R is an odd AH to which S is united solely through inactive positions. In this case the NBMO of R survives unchanged in RS. A simple example is provided by 2-phenylallyl (Fig. 6.17b), which can be formed by union of phenyl with allyl through the inactive 2 position of the latter. As indicated in Fig. 6.17, the NBMO of 2-phenylallyl is confined entirely to the allyl group. Odd AHs of this type, where an *inactive seg-*

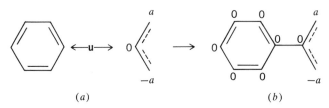

FIG. 6.17   (*a*) Union of phenyl with allyl, to form (*b*) 2-phenylallyl; the NBMO coefficients are as indicated ($a = 1/\sqrt{2}$).

ment of the molecule is composed entirely of inactive atoms, are termed *cross-conjugated,* since the classical phenomenon of cross conjugation is associated with this property.   While this point will be treated in detail later (Chap. 8), we may give one example here by way of illustration.   Let us estimate the heats of reactions in which a radical R adds to butadiene (XVI), 1-phenylbutadiene (XVIII), or 2-phenylbutadiene (XX) to form the radicals XVII, XIX, or XXI respectively.   It is easily seen that the change in σ energy is the same in each case; the relative heats of reaction should therefore be determined by the corresponding changes in π energy.   Now XVI, XVIII, and XX can be derived by union of methyl with XVII, XIX, and XXI respectively; the relative π energies of union will be the same as the relative π energies we are trying to find.   These π energies of union can be found at once, using Eq. (6.99) and the NBMO coefficients indicated below; we find:

$$\text{XVII} \rightarrow \text{XVI} \qquad \delta E_\pi = \frac{\beta}{\sqrt{2}} \equiv \frac{2\beta}{\sqrt{8}} \qquad\qquad (6.132)$$

$$\text{XIX} \rightarrow \text{XVIII} \qquad \delta E_\pi = \frac{2\beta}{\sqrt{11}} \qquad\qquad (6.133)$$

$$\text{XXI} \rightarrow \text{XX} \qquad \delta_\pi = \frac{\beta}{\sqrt{2}} \equiv \frac{2\beta}{\sqrt{8}} \qquad\qquad (6.134)$$

The reaction of XVIII should therefore be more exothermic than those of XVI and XX, which should both be the same.   In other words a phenyl substituent increases the ease of 4 addition of radicals to butadiene if it is in the 1 position, but not if it is in the 2 position.

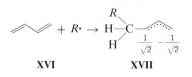

XVI   XVII

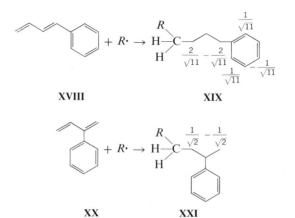

XVIII   **XIX**

XX   **XXI**

Another useful result can be derived from Eq. (6.130) in the case where R is an even AH, with equal numbers of starred and unstarred atoms, and RS is an odd AH derived from R by union with methyl (compare Fig. 6.14); the points of union r with R must of course be of like parity if RS is also to be alternant. In this case the secular determinant becomes:

$$
\begin{vmatrix}
E_1 - E & 0 & 0 & \cdots & 0 & P_1 \\
0 & E_2 - E & 0 & \cdots & 0 & P_2 \\
0 & 0 & E_3 - E & \cdots & 0 & P_3 \\
\vdots & \vdots & \vdots & & \vdots & \vdots \\
0 & 0 & 0 & \cdots & E_m - E & P_m \\
P_1 & P_2 & P_3 & \cdots & P_m & -E
\end{vmatrix} = 0 \qquad (6.135)
$$

where

$$
P_\mu = \Sigma a_{\mu r}\beta \qquad (6.136)
$$

the sum being over the atoms r (of like parity) in R through which R is united to methyl in forming RS. The determinant in Eq. (6.135) can be expanded immediately;

$$
\prod_{\mu}(E_\mu - E)\left(-E - \sum_{\mu}^{\text{all}} \frac{P_\mu{}^2}{E_\mu - E}\right) = 0 \qquad (6.137)
$$

where the sum is over all the m MOs of R. It can be shown very simply that the roots of this equation are all different from the orbital energies E_μ of R, except in cases where P_μ vanishes; the corresponding roots can then be factored out. The remaining roots are then given by:

$$
E + \sum_{\mu} \frac{P_\mu{}^2}{E_\mu - E} = 0 \qquad (6.138)
$$

Now from Theorem 6.1, the terms in this sum occur in pairs, with equal and opposite values from E_μ and identical values for $P_\mu{}^2$.‡ Equation (6.138) thus becomes:

$$E + \sum_{\mu}^{\text{BMO}} \left(\frac{P_\mu{}^2}{E_\mu - E} + \frac{P_\mu{}^2}{-E_\mu - E} \right) = E + \sum_{\mu}^{\text{BMO}} \frac{2P_\mu{}^2 E}{E_\mu{}^2 - E^2} = 0 \qquad (6.139)$$

One root of this equation is:

$$E = 0 \qquad (6.140)$$

Thus RS contains a NBMO. This of course is no news to us since RS is an odd AH; however the important point is that we can find this NBMO explicitly in terms of the p AO of S (i.e. the methyl group) and the MOs Φ_μ of R. The equations for the coefficients [see Eq. (6.125)] are:

$$a_\mu(E_\mu - E) + bP_\mu = 0 \qquad (6.141)$$

Substituting $E = 0$, we find:

$$a_\mu = -\frac{bP_\mu}{E_\mu} \qquad (6.142)$$

The NBMO Ξ_0 is thus given by:

$$\Xi_0 = b\left(\psi - \sum_{\mu} \frac{P_\mu \Phi_\mu}{E_\mu} \right) \qquad (6.143)$$

The NBMO therefore comprises the AO ψ. Now it is obvious that the starred set of AOs in RS includes ψ; for R by assumption contains equal numbers of starred and unstarred atoms, so the extra atom in RS must belong to the more numerous, or starred, set. We have therefore proved that in an odd AH with $m + 1$ starred atoms and m unstarred atoms, the NBMO covers only the more numerous, or starred, set, a result we quoted earlier, without proof.

6.17 NON-KEKULÉ HYDROCARBONS

So far we have tacitly assumed that at least one classical structure can be written for a conjugated hydrocarbon, our concern having been with the distinction between classical compounds, for which only single classical structures can be written, and nonclassical compounds, with two or more such structures. However it is easy to think of conjugated compounds which fall into neither of these categories. Consider for example the quinodimethanes (XXII to XXIV). Each of these isomeric hydrocarbons contains eight conjugated atoms, and a standard LCAO MO treatment shows that they can all be represented in terms of the usual

---

‡ Remember that the atoms r are all of like parity, so the values of P_μ for two paired MOs are either identical or equal and opposite.

σ-π model, with eight π electrons occupying MOs constructed from $2p$ AOs of the eight component carbon atoms.   However, whereas XXII and XXIII are normal classical polyenes, no classical structure can be written for XXIV.

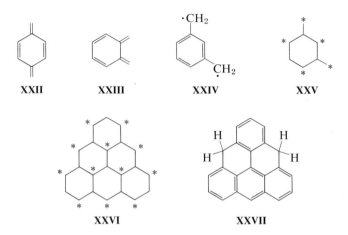

It is convenient to have a term for compounds such as XXIV; since the term nonclassical has been preempted, we shall describe them as *non-Kekulé* compounds, in contrast to normal or *Kekulé* compounds, for which at least one classical structure can be written.   This distinction is chemically a very important one; for all attempts to prepare stable non-Kekulé compounds have so far failed. Thus derivatives of XXII and XXIII are well known, but none of XXIV.   Again, Clar showed that the non-Kekulé benzenoid hydrocarbon triangulene (XXVI) is chemically unstable, dehydrogenation of its dihydro derivative (XXVII) giving only polymers.

The difference between compounds such as XXIV or XXVI and normal Kekulé compounds can be seen at once, if we star the atoms in them.   Both XXIV and XXVI are even AHs, but in each case there are two more starred atoms than unstarred ones (see XXV and XXVI).   Now a double bond in a classical structure for an AH necessarily links atoms of opposite parity; if the numbers of starred and unstarred atoms differ, it will then be impossible to write a structure in which they are all linked in pairs by double bonds.

We shall now prove the following theorems, which explain why non-Kekulé compounds are unimportant in organic chemistry:

Theorem 6.7   An AH with n starred atoms and m unstarred atoms has $n - m$ NBMOs, composed entirely of AOs of starred atoms.

Theorem 6.8   A neutral AH with n starred atoms and m unstarred atoms will exist as an $(n - m)$-fold radical, having $n - m$ unpaired π electrons occupying the $m - n$ NBMOs.

Theorem 6.9   An even non-Kekulé AH is much less stable than any isomeric Kekulé AH (i.e. there is a first-order difference in energy between them).

Theorem 6.8 is an immediate consequence of Theorem 6.7 and Hund's rule. A neutral AH with $n + m$ atoms has $(n + m)$ π electrons. Since there are $n - m$ NBMOs, Theorem 6.1 tells us that there must be m BMOs and m AMOs. The m BMOs can accommodate $2m$ π electrons; there are therefore $(n - m)$ π electrons to be placed in the degenerate set of $n - m$ NBMOs. The most favorable disposition of these will be that in which each NBMO is singly occupied, the $n - m$ unpaired electrons all having parallel spins.

An AH R with n starred atoms and m unstarred ones can be obtained by uniting $n - m$ methyl groups with an even Kekulé AH S containing m starred and m unstarred atoms. Let us regenerate S from R stepwise, by union with one methyl at a time; i.e.

$$ S \xrightarrow{\ \leftarrow u \rightarrow \text{CH}_3\ } S_1 \xrightarrow{\ \leftarrow u \rightarrow \text{CH}_3\ } S_{12} \rightarrow S_{123} \ldots \rightarrow R \qquad (6.144) $$

Here S_1 implies an odd AH derived by union of S with methyl 1, S_{12} an even AH derived by union of S with methyls 1 and 2, and so forth. S_1 is an odd AH; it will therefore contain an NBMO covering the starred atoms (Sec. 6.16). Such an odd AH of course represents a special case of Theorem 6.7, with $n = m + 1$. In the next step, methyl 2 must unite with S_1 through an inactive position in the latter; for by definition, atom 2 in S_{12} is a starred atom, being one of the starred atoms removed from R to form S. From Theorem 6.6, the NBMO of S_1 must therefore survive in S_{12}. But S_{12} is an even AH in which all the MOs are paired; if it contains one NBMO, it must therefore contain a second. One of these NBMOs can be written as the NBMO of S_1, spanning all the starred atoms in S_{12} other than atom 2. Now we could also generate S_{12} from S by union first with methyl 2 to form S_2, and then with methyl 1; we would then find that S_{12} contains a NBMO that can be written as the NBMO of S_2, that is a MO covering all the starred atoms in S_{12} other than atom 1. We have therefore identified two distinct NBMOs in S_{12}, both confined to starred atoms. This proves Theorem 6.7 for $n = m + 2$; stepwise extension of the argument shows it to hold equally well for any value of $n - m$.

The proof of Theorem 6.9 is also straightforward. Consider an even non-Kekulé AH R with n starred atoms and m unstarred atoms, where $n = m + 2$. This can be derived by union of methyl with an odd AH T containing $n - 1$ starred atoms and m unstarred ones. Since union takes place through an unstarred position of T, and since the NBMOs of T are confined entirely to starred atoms (Theorem 6.7), the π energy of union is zero [Eq. (6.99)]. Now let us unite T with methyl through one of the starred positions, forming an even AH R' isomeric with R. Since the added carbon atom is now unstarred, R' contains $n - 1$ starred atoms and $m + 1$ unstarred atoms; the difference between the numbers of starred and unstarred atoms is therefore two less than the corresponding difference for R.   However in this case union involves an active position of S; there is therefore a first-order difference in π energy between R' and S, and so also between R' and R.   Extending this argument, we see that there is a first-order change in energy each time we convert any non-Kekulé even AH to one with two fewer unpaired electrons, and the process will continue until we reach the limiting case of an even AH with equal numbers of starred and unstarred atoms, i.e. a Kekulé AH.

This argument is illustrated in Fig. 6.18, which compares the energy of XXIV, a typical non-Kekulé AH, with that of XXII or XXIII, two typical Kekulé isomers of XXIV.

One further point needs attention.   While it is true that no classical structure can be written for an even AH with different numbers of starred and unstarred atoms, the converse of this statement is not true.   Thus it is possible for an even AH RS with equal numbers of starred and unstarred atoms to be a non-Kekulé compound; this will happen if RS can be formed by union of two odd AHs R, S through inactive positions in each, such a compound being of non-Kekulé type because it is cross-conjugated.   The even AHs XXVIII to XXX illustrate this point; it is easily seen that each of them contains equal numbers of starred and unstarred atoms.

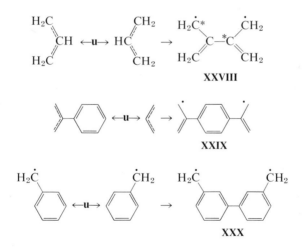

Here again we can convert the non-Kekulé RS into a Kekulé isomer $(RS)'$ with a first-order gain in energy by first disuniting RS into its components R, S, and then uniting these through a pair of active atoms.   Thus in the case of XXVIII:

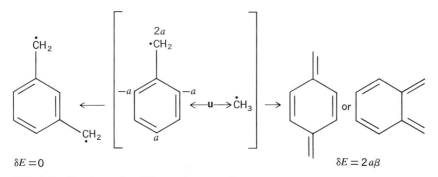

$\delta E = 0$ $\delta E = 2\,a\beta$

FIG. 6.18   The first-order difference in energy between a non-Kekulé AH (XIV) and that of a Kekulé isomer (XII or XIII); all three hydrocarbons are formed by union of methyl with benzyl, the NBMO coefficients in which are as indicated ($a = 1/\sqrt{7}$).

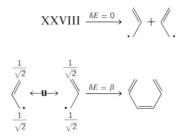

This completes the proof of Theorem 6.9.

Theorem 6.9 refers only to even AHs; the same approach can be used to prove the following obvious extension of it.

Theorem 6.10   A non-Kekulé odd AH is much less stable than a Kekulé odd AH, a Kekulé odd AH being defined as one for which a classical structure can be written in which all but one of the atoms are linked in pairs by double bonds.

**6.18   THE ROLE OF CLASSICAL STRUCTURES;
RESONANCE THEORY**
Although the localized-bond model does not correspond to physical reality, it provides a useful and satisfactory description of many molecules, in particular those where the AOs of the component atoms can be chosen in such a way that they overlap in pairs (see Sec. 4.11).   Here we shall consider possible extensions of this model to nonclassical conjugated hydrocarbons, compounds where this condition no longer holds.

In the previous sections of this chapter we have established the following results:

1 If only one classical structure can be written for a conjugated hydrocarbon, the hydrocarbon can be well represented in terms of that structure, the bonds in it all being localized single or double bonds.

2 In hydrocarbons with two or more possible classical structures, essential single and double bonds are still localized.

3 A hydrocarbon for which no classical structure can be written, i.e. a non-Kekulé hydrocarbon, is much less stable than any Kekulé isomer and should also exist as a polyradical; compounds of this type would be expected to polymerize immediately on formation, as apparently they do.

The localized-bond model can therefore be applied directly to classical conjugated systems; our next problem is to establish the possible usefulness of localized-bond structures in the description of nonclassical molecules.

Our analysis will rest on the following theorem:[3]

Theorem 6.11   In an odd AH R, the NBMO coefficient at atom r is numerically proportional to the number of classical structures that can be written for the even AH S formed by removing atom r, unless S contains a $4n$-membered ring.

The proof[3] of this theorem is not very relevant and need not be reproduced here; its significance is best illustrated by a couple of examples.

6.18.1   BENZYL   The NBMO coefficients of benzyl are shown below, together with the five possible classical structures that can be written for it.   It will be seen that the number of such structures that can be written with the odd atom at position r is proportional to $|a_{0r}|$, a_{0r} being the NBMO coefficient at atom r.

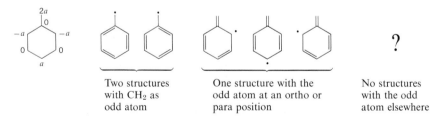

| Two structures with CH_2 as odd atom | One structure with the odd atom at an ortho or para position | No structures with the odd atom elsewhere |

6.18.2   PERINAPHTHENYL   The NBMO coefficients are shown in XXXI, and the numbers of classical structures with the odd atom in various positions in XXXII.   Here again the two sets of numbers are proportional, except for the central atom.   Removal of this atom leaves [12]annulene; removal of any other atom leaves a 12-atom system containing only 6- and 10-membered rings.

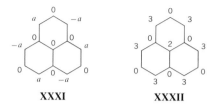

XXXI   XXXII

The breakdown of Theorem 6.11 in cases where $4n$-membered rings are present is a very important phenomenon, to which we shall refer later; for the moment we shall assume that our odd AHs are ones in which the parallel between NBMO coefficients and numbers of classical structures holds. We shall now show that if this is the case, then odd AHs of this type, and even AHs formed by their union, can be represented as averages or "hybrids" of their possible component classical structures.

First, we can see at once that the distribution of formal positive or negative charge in an odd-AH ion will run parallel to the numbers of classical structures with the charge localized at each position; for from Theorem 6.4, the formal charge at atom r is equal to $\pm a_{0r}^2$.

Next we shall show that the bond order of a given bond rs in an even AH R runs parallel to the fraction n_{rs}/N, where n_{rs} is the number of classical structures for R in which the bond rs is double, and N is the total number of classical structures. This result indicates that the bond orders in an even AH correspond to a picture in which the AH is represented as an average of the N possible classical structures, all having equal weights.

Consider the odd AH S, formed from R by removing atom r; we can as usual regenerate R by union of S with methyl. Suppose first that union takes place through a single atom s in S. The bond rs in R is then an essential double bond, since R is of the form:

The bond rs is double in any possible classical structure for R, so $n_{rs} = N$. Both pictures therefore agree in predicting that the bond rs will be a localized double bond.

Now consider the case where union takes place through more than one atom in S; we shall consider the most general case, where union takes place through atoms s, t, u. Since R is an even Kekulé AH, atoms s, t, u are starred atoms in S; denote their NBMO coefficients as usual by a_{0s}, a_{0t}, a_{0u} (Fig. 6.19).

The π energy of union δE can be calculated in two different ways.

Using Eq. (6.99), we find:

$$\delta E = 2a_{0s}\beta_{rs} + 2a_{0t}\beta_{rt} + 2a_{0u}\beta_{ru} \qquad (6.145)$$

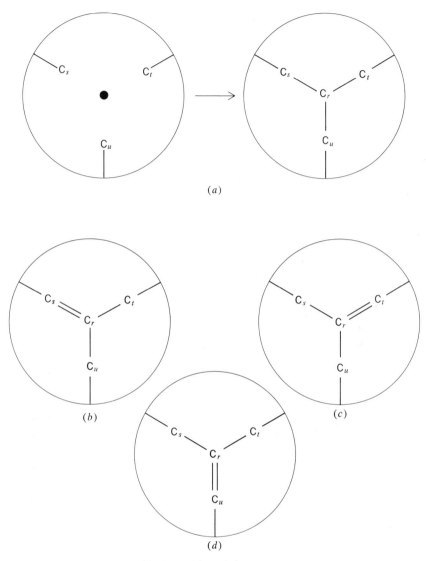

FIG. 6.19 (a) Union of an odd AH S with methyl to form an even AH R; (b) to (d) possible types of classical structures for R.

Using Eq. (6.16), we obtain an alternative first-order expression for δE:

$$\delta E = 2p_{rs}\beta_{rs} + 2p_{rt}\beta_{rt} + 2p_{ru}\beta_{ru} \qquad (6.146)$$

where p_{rs}, p_{rt}, p_{ru} are the bond orders of the bonds rs, rt, and ru respectively in the even AH R.   Since Eqs. (6.145) and (6.146) must hold irrespective of the values of the resonance integrals,

$$a_{0s} = p_{rs} \qquad a_{0t} = p_{rt} \qquad a_{0u} = p_{ru} \tag{6.147}$$

Now consider the possible classical structures for R. All these must have a double bond from atom r to one or other of its three neighbors s, t, u. Hence:

$$n_{rs} + n_{rt} + n_{ru} = N \tag{6.148}$$

Consider the structures with a double bond between atoms r and s. The total number of these is the same as the total number of structures of the even AH derived from R by removing both atom r and atom s. But this in turn is equal to the number n_s of structures of the odd AH S, with the odd atom localized at atom s. Applying the same argument to the other two sets of classical structures (Fig. 6.19b and c),

$$n_{rs} = n_s \qquad n_{rt} = n_t \qquad n_{ru} = n_u \tag{6.149}$$

But we know from Theorem 6.11 that:

$$n_s = A|a_{0s}| \qquad n_t = A|a_{0t}| \qquad n_u = A|a_{0u}| \tag{6.150}$$

where A is a proportionality factor. Provided therefore that a_{0r}, a_{0s}, and a_{0t} have the same signs,

$$p_{rs} : p_{rt} : p_{ru} = n_{rs} : n_{rt} : n_{ru} \tag{6.151}$$

The bond order of a bond is thus proportional to the number of classical structures in which it appears as double; the proportionality factor is chosen to make the bond order of an essential single bond unity.

Note that this result holds only if the NBMO coefficients a_{0r}, a_{0s}, a_{0t} have similar signs; this can be shown to be the case if, and only if, R contains no $4n$-membered rings. For compounds where this condition is met, the relation holds remarkably well; thus the lengths of bonds in benzenoid aromatic hydrocarbons can be predicted with surprising accuracy from the numbers of classical structures, simply by assuming a $1:1$ relation between the ratio n_{rs}/N and bond length.[6]

The general electron distribution in both odd and even AHs can therefore be represented quite well in terms of a model where the AH is pictured as a superposition, or average, of its possible classical structures. Similar parallels can be shown[3] to hold for other physical and chemical properties of AHs; e.g. the heats of formation of a set of isomeric even AHs should tend to run parallel to the numbers of classical structures that can be written for them. Of course this picture is no substitute for our PMO method; not only is it less accurate, but it also fails in cases where the parallel between NBMO coefficients and numbers of resonance structures (Theorem 6.11) breaks down. This happens in all AHs where there are $4n$-membered rings present; thus the simple picture of AHs in terms of superposed classical structures draws no distinction between aromatic and antiaromatic types.

Nearly 40 years ago Pauling proposed his resonance theory, in which nonclassical conjugated molecules were represented as superpositions or hybrids of contributing valence structures; this approach of course corresponds to the one outlined above, provided that only unexcited or classical structures are taken into account. The resonance theory was originally put forward as an intuitive extrapolation from the valence-bond method; later work, however, showed this argument to be invalid, the representation of molecules in terms of unexcited structures having no basis in the valence-bond approach.[7] The arguments outlined above explain why resonance theory has proved fairly successful in practice in spite of its apparent lack of any good theoretical basis; at the same time the PMO method is clearly much superior, being both more accurate, more generally applicable, and just as easy to use.

It might be added that the general acceptance of resonance theory by chemists was due more to good salesmanship than to any inherent virtues; for all the conclusions reached by it could have been achieved just as well with the earlier classical electronic theory that Lapworth, Robinson, and Ingold had devised some years previously. The two treatments are entirely equivalent in all respects, and can be regarded as expressions of the same general approach in different terminologies. Since neither had any direct basis in quantum mechanics, and since the terminology of resonance theory proved very misleading to chemists, it is difficult to see that its introduction represented any great gain to chemical theory. Certainly the continued use of resonance theory today must be regarded as an unfortunate anachronism.

6.19 THE PAIRING THEOREM IN SCF MO THEORY

The proof of Theorem 6.1 in Sec. 6.4 applied only to HMO wave functions for AHs; however many of the conclusions reached there can also be carried over into the Pople method.

Consider the Pople expressions for the elements of the F matrix of an even AH. Writing W_c for the valence-state ionization potential of carbon and (cc,cc) for the corresponding one-center repulsion integral, Eqs. (5.8) and (5.9) become:

$$F_{ii} = W_c + \tfrac{1}{2}q_i(cc,cc) + \sum_{j \neq i} (q_j - 1)(ii,jj) \tag{6.152}$$

$$F_{ij} = \beta_{ij}{}^c - \tfrac{1}{2}p_{ij}(ii,jj) \tag{6.153}$$

The Pople equations for the MO energies and orbital coefficients are:

$$|F_{ij} - E\delta_{ij}| = 0 \tag{6.154}$$

$$\sum_j a_{\mu j}(F_{ij} - E_\mu \delta_{ij}) = 0 \qquad i = 1, 2, \ldots, n \tag{6.155}$$

where as usual E_μ is one root of the secular equation (6.154), and n is the total number of carbon atoms. These equations have to be solved by an iterative method. Let us start the iterative process with a set of assumed MOs Φ_μ that obey Theorem 6.1; the charge densities and bond orders are thus given by:

$$q_i = 1 \qquad p_{ij} = 0 \qquad \text{if atoms } i, j \text{ are of like parity} \tag{6.156}$$

Equation (6.152) becomes:

$$F_{ii} = W_c + \tfrac{1}{2}(cc,cc) = \alpha_c \tag{6.157}$$

where α_c is the same for all values of i. Moreover since the core resonance integral $\beta_{ij}{}^c$ is assumed to vanish unless atoms i, j are directly linked (and so of opposite parity), and since p_{ij} vanishes unless atoms i, j are of opposite parity,

$$F_{ij} = 0 \qquad \text{if atoms } i, j \text{ are of like parity} \tag{6.158}$$

The arguments given in Sec. 6.4 can now be applied directly to the solutions of Eqs. (6.154) and (6.155); in view of Eqs. (6.157) and (6.158), the solutions must obey Theorem 6.1. Hence Eq. (6.156) holds for the q's and p's used in the next iteration; the same argument shows that the solutions of Eqs. (6.154) and (6.155) in the second iteration will again obey Theorem 6.1. Clearly therefore the solutions at each successive iteration will obey Theorem 6.1; consequently the same will be true for the final converged MOs and orbital energies. The Pople equations for an even AH must therefore have a self-consistent solution that obeys Theorem 6.1. It is of course possible that the equations may have more than one solution and that there is at least one solution that does not fulfil this condition; however the possibility of multiple solutions is a specter that we are always forced to ignore in SCF MO calculations, so we may with equal justification say that Theorem 6.1 holds for the Pople treatment of even AHs.

The same arguments also apply to neutral odd-AH radicals, provided that we assume all the electrons to occupy the same set of MOs. Unfortunately this is not strictly the case, as can best be seen from a very simple example. Consider allyl. Suppose we start our iterative cycle with the corresponding HMO orbitals, one bonding, one nonbonding, and one antibonding. Two electrons occupy the BMO Φ_1, one electron the NBMO Φ_2. Suppose that the odd electron has α spin. Let us calculate the orbital energies of the two electrons occupying the MO Φ_1. These are given [compare Eq. (2.200)] by:

α spin: $$\epsilon_\alpha = E_1 + J_{12} - K_{12} \tag{6.159}$$

β spin: $$\epsilon_\beta = E_1 + J_{12} \tag{6.160}$$

The two electrons occupying the MO Φ_1 therefore have different energies! The reason for this is very obvious; the repulsions between them and the unpaired electron differ because of the Pauli principle. The two electrons therefore move in different potential fields. This being so, the MOs they occupy must differ; we must therefore allow the two bonding electrons to occupy different MOs. The procedures for doing this will be considered later (Chap. 7); here we shall approach the problem in another way.

In the allyl radical, the MO Φ_2 is half filled. Suppose we constructed an artificial model of allyl in which Φ_2 was occupied not by one whole electron but by two half electrons of opposite spin. In this case the equations for the orbital energies of the two bonding electrons would become identical;

$$\epsilon_\alpha = \epsilon_\beta = E_1 + J_{12} - \tfrac{1}{2}K_{12} \tag{6.161}$$

The simple closed-shell picture of the radical would then be valid, and Theorem 6.1 would hold for its treatment by the Pople method. Moreover the total energies of the radical calculated for these two models would be the same, being given by:

$$E = 2E_1 + E_2 + J_{11} + 2J_{12} - K_{12} \tag{6.162}$$

The first two terms represent the core energies of the three electrons; the second and third terms their classical coulomb repulsions; while the final term is the exchange correction for the interaction between the two electrons in the MO Φ_1 and the two half electrons or one whole electron in Φ_2.

In passing from our half-electron model to the correct one, we introduce a perturbation into the electrons occupying Φ_1. The energy of one electron increases by $K_{12}/2$, that of the other decreases by the same amount. There will therefore be no first-order difference in energy between the two models; any differences will be small second-order effects. This suggests that our half-electron model may prove useful for estimating energies of odd-AH radicals, even though it will not correctly reproduce the distribution of the individual electrons; as we shall see later, the simple model does indeed fail to account for the distribution of unpaired spin in radicals, as estimated for esr spectra, but it gives good estimates of total energies (Chap. 7).

As we have pointed out at intervals throughout the last two chapters, there are numerous cases where the HMO method makes wrong predictions and where the Pople method makes correct ones. Good examples are provided by the various antiaromatic hydrocarbons for which the HMO method predicts large positive resonance energies. We have also pointed out that the PMO method succeeds admirably in these cases, a rather curious circumstance since it was based on an application of perturbation theory to the HMO method! The reason for this success is now apparent; we would have obtained precisely analogous equations if we had applied perturbation theory to the Pople method, at least in the form where radicals are treated in terms of our half-electron model.

Indeed, the situation is even better than this in the case of even AHs. Consider for example a typical PMO argument concerning the stability of such an AH RS. We determine its resonance energy by comparing the π energy of union of two odd AHs R, S to form either RS or an analogous classical structure RS'.

Now the odd AHs R, S enter this argument only as common building materials from which we can construct the two different even AHs, RS and RS'; there is no need for the fragments to correspond to real physical entities. We could therefore equally well use two pseudo radicals in which the unpaired electrons are replaced by half electrons; in this case Theorem 6.1 will apply rigorously to them in a Pople calculation as well as in a HMO one, and so the PMO treatment will be fully valid up to the approximation of the Pople method.

One place where the PMO method must fail is in its treatment of odd-AH ions. Here the HMO method is definitely incorrect, since it wrongly ignores the effect of formal charge on the diagonal elements of the F matrix. The charge distributions calculated by the HMO method (compare Theorem 6.4) are therefore erroneous (compare Sec. 5.11), and conclusions drawn from them by using the PMO method are consequently much less reliable than those for neutral systems.

6.20 VALIDITY OF THE HMO METHOD

The results of the preceding section throw an important new light on the HMO method. We have seen that the diagonal elements of the Pople F matrix for an even AH have a common value α_c [Eq. (6.157)], a value which is moreover the same for different AHs; the HMO assumption, that α is a constant characteristic of an atom and independent of the molecule in which it appears, is therefore justified.

Next let us consider the off-diagonal matrix elements F_{ij}. Here the integrals β_{ij} and (ii, jj) are functions only of the distances between atoms i and j. The bond orders between neighboring atoms are also a one-valued function of bond length. It follows that the same is true for the off-diagonal matrix element F_{ij}, if atoms i, j are adjacent. If the bond lengths in an AH are equal, all these matrix elements will then have a common value.

This condition is met closely in normal benzenoid aromatic hydrocarbons. The mean bond length varies very little from one such compound to another, while the overall spread of bond lengths is also small. The HMO approximation, of setting all such matrix elements equal to a constant (β), is therefore quite justifiable.

It is true that matrix elements between nonbonded atoms are neglected in the HMO method; however this seems unlikely to introduce large errors. Since the Pople functions for an even AH obey Theorem 6.1, matrix elements between atoms of like parity vanish; the off-diagonal elements for atoms 1,3 to one another (e.g. *meta* in benzene) therefore vanish. Only terms corresponding to 1,4 interactions, or interactions with still more distant atoms, survive. Now these terms will be relatively small; for the integral (ii, jj) decreases rapidly with increasing distance between atoms i, j, and the bond orders for pairs of non-bonded atoms are also mostly small. Moreover the bond orders can be either positive or negative; it is therefore quite likely that the net contribution of these long-range interactions may be negligible.

It is therefore not surprising to find the HMO method giving good results for compounds of this type. Unfortunately this success does not carry over to other kinds of compounds. In nonalternant hydrocarbons, in ions, or in systems containing heteroatoms, the assumption that α_i has a fixed value characteristic of atom i fails; while in antiaromatic systems, or molecules with essential single or double bonds, the assumed constancy of β proves grossly incorrect.

PROBLEMS

6.1 Estimate the relative heats of formation of the following isomeric hydrocarbons in terms of β, using the PMO method:

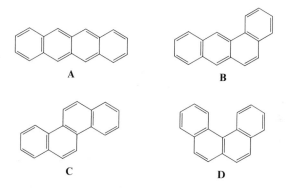

A

B

C

D

6.2 Which of the following hydrocarbons would you expect to be aromatic? In the case of aromatic hydrocarbons, how many aromatic rings are there effectively present?

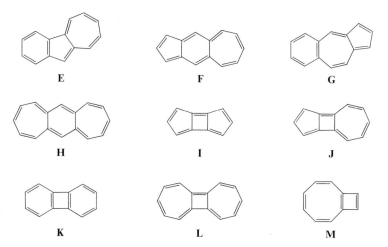

E

F

G

H

I

J

K

L

M

6.3 Calculate the atom-atom, atom-bond, and bond-bond polarizabilities in benzene, in the HMO approximation; here the MOs and MO energies are:

$$\psi_1 = \frac{1}{\sqrt{6}}(\phi_1 + \phi_2 + \phi_3 + \phi_4 + \phi_5 + \phi_6) \qquad E = \alpha + 2\beta$$

$$\psi_2 = \tfrac{1}{2}(\phi_2 + \phi_3 - \phi_5 - \phi_6) \qquad E = \alpha + \beta$$

$$\psi_3 = \frac{1}{\sqrt{12}}(2\phi_1 + \phi_2 - \phi_3 - 2\phi_4 - \phi_5 + \phi_6) \qquad E = \alpha + \beta$$

$$\psi_4 = \tfrac{1}{2}(\phi_2 - \phi_3 + \phi_5 - \phi_6) \qquad E = \alpha - \beta$$

$$\psi_5 = \frac{1}{\sqrt{12}}(2\phi_1 - \phi_2 - \phi_3 + 2\phi_4 - \phi_5 - \phi_6) \qquad E = \alpha - \beta$$

$$\psi_6 = \frac{1}{\sqrt{6}}(\phi_1 - \phi_2 + \phi_3 - \phi_4 - \phi_5 + \phi_6) \qquad E = \alpha - 2\beta$$

where α, β are respectively the coulomb and resonance integrals for carbon.

6.4 Calculate HMO charge densities in the cations of which the following are typical classical structures:

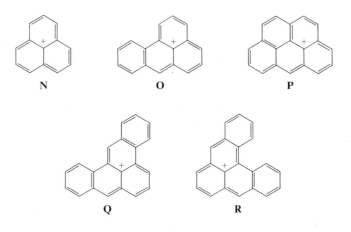

N   O   P

Q   R

6.5 Prove the result indicated in Eq. (6.95).

6.6 (a) Solve the HMO equations for 1,3-butadiene. (b) Compare the orbital energies with those given by second-order perturbation theory, treating 1,3-butadiene as being formed by the union of two molecules of ethylene. How does the energy of union compare with the approximation of Eq. (6.91)? (c) Using the MOs listed in Prob. 6.3, calculate the energy of union of benzene and ethylene to form styrene, and of two molecules of benzene to form biphenyl. How do the energies of union compare with Eq. (6.91)?

6.7 Derive an expression for the second-order perturbation energy for the union of two odd-AH radicals R and S, (a) using the unperturbed MOs of R and S, and (b) replacing the NBMOs by the combinations given by first-order perturbation theory.

6.8 Consider the union of two even AHs, R and S, through atom r in R to atom s in S, where R has an m-fold-degenerate level completely occupied by pairs of electrons, and where there is no other degeneracy. (a) Show that $m - 1$ of the degenerate levels survive unchanged in RS. (b) Calculate the second-order perturbation to the remaining level. (c) Show that in calculating the total energy of union of R and S to form RS, using second-order perturbation theory, the degeneracy of levels in R can be ignored (i.e. that one can use the original MOs of R unchanged in calculating the second-order perturbation).

6.9 Derive Eqs. (6.30), (6.32), and (6.34).

6.10 Various other problems have been left to the reader throughout this chapter; e.g. Eqs. (6.78) and (6.95).

REFERENCES

1 (a) Coulson, C. A., and H. C. Longuet-Higgins: *Proc. Roy. Soc.* (*London*) **A191**, 39 (1947); **A192**, 16 (1947); **A193**, 447, 456 (1948); **A195**, 188 (1948); (b) H. C. Longuet-Higgins: *J. Chem. Phys.* **18**, 265, 275, 283 (1950).

2 Dewar, M. J. S.: *J. Am. Chem. Soc.* **74**, 3341, 3345, 3350, 3353, 3357 (1952).

3 Dewar, M. J. S., and H. C. Longuet-Higgins: *Proc. Roy. Soc.* (*London*) **A214**, 482 (1952).

4 Hafner, K., K. H. Häfner, C. König, M. Kreuder, G. Ploss, G. Schulz, E. Sturm, and K. H. Vögel: *Angew. Chem.* **72**, 35 (1963); K. Hafner: *ibid.*, 1041.

5 Dewar, M. J. S.: *Proc. Cambridge Phil. Soc.* **45**, 639 (1949).

6 Robertson, J. M.: *Acta Cryst.* **1**, 101 (1948); "Organic Crystals and Molecules," Cornell University Press, Ithaca, N.Y., 1953.

7 Pullman, A., and B. Pullman: *Experientia* **2A**, 364 (1946).

CHAPTER SEVEN

OPEN-SHELL SYSTEMS:
CORRELATION AND
CONFIGURATION INTERACTION

7.1 INTRODUCTION

The compounds we have so far discussed have almost all had closed-shell structures; radicals were introduced in Chap. 6 only as an artifice in treating closed-shell molecules by perturbation methods. Here we shall consider the problem of conjugated hydrocarbon radicals, i.e. compounds such as allyl or benzyl that possess unpaired π electrons.

In the HMO treatment of such systems, it is assumed that the electrons occupy a single set of π MOs, analogous to those in the corresponding anion or cation. In the case of an AH radical, the bonding π MOs are doubly occupied, while the NBMO contains the odd electron. This, however, is not a satisfactory representation of radicals, for reasons which were outlined above (Sec. 6.19); thus in the allyl radical, the two bonding electrons have different energies because the repulsions between them and the unpaired electron differ. In a simple orbital model, we should allow the bonding electrons to occupy different MOs. The familiar pairing of electrons in MOs no longer holds in systems of this kind.

The way in which the two BMOs differ from that given by the HMO method is easily visualized. The allyl radical has a plane of symmetry passing through the central atom (Fig. 7.1a); all the MOs must then be either symmetric, or antisymmetric, for reflection in this plane of symmetry. This restriction holds in any MO treatment, however sophisticated; consequently the unpaired electron occupies an antisymmetric MO ψ_0, which must be given by:

$$\psi_0 = \frac{1}{\sqrt{2}}(\phi_1 - \phi_3) \tag{7.1}$$

where ϕ_1 and ϕ_3 are the $2p$ AOs of the terminal carbon atoms.

Suppose now that the unpaired electron has α spin. The repulsion between it and the bonding electron of α spin will then be less than that between it and the bonding electron of β spin, because in the former case the Pauli effect reduces the repulsion between the two electrons by preventing them from getting too close together (see Sec. 2.13). It will therefore be easier for the bonding electron of α spin to press on into one of the terminal AOs ϕ_1 or ϕ_3 than it will be for its partner with β spin. Now an orbital represents a volume of "orbital space" able to hold exactly two electrons: if one of the two electrons occupying such an orbital takes more than its share of one part of the orbital, the other

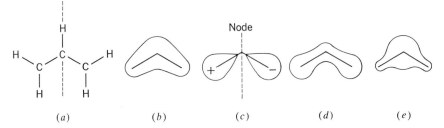

FIG. 7.1   The allyl radical.   (*a*) The radical has a plane of symmetry; (*b*) the BMO in HMO theory; (*c*) the NBMO ψ_0; (*d*) the SCF BMO for the bonding π electron of same spin as the unpaired π electron; (*e*) the corresponding SCF BMO for the electron of opposite spin.

electron will be squeezed out into some other part.   In the case of the BMO of allyl, the α-spin electron takes more than its share of the part of the BMO located on the end atoms (compare Fig. 7.1*b* with 7.1*d*); the β-spin electron therefore takes a correspondingly larger share of the center section (compare Fig. 7.1*b* with 7.1*e*).

In the HMO picture, we are equally likely to find either of the bonding electrons at any point in the BMO; since the unpaired electron is confined to the terminal AOs ϕ_1, ϕ_3, the probabilities of finding an α-spin electron, or a β-spin electron, in the central AO are equal, regardless of whether the unpaired electron has α spin or β spin.   The unpaired electron spends half its time on each terminal atom; at each of these we shall find the excess of α-spin electrons to be on average one-half.

In the SCF picture, the situation is different in two respects.   In the first place, the average densities of α-spin and β-spin electrons at the central atom are no longer equal; there is an excess of β-spin electrons at that point.   Secondly, there will be a corresponding greater excess of α-spin electrons at the terminal atoms, the excess at each of them being consequently greater than one-half.

The excess density of electrons of one spin or another at a given carbon atom can be estimated by esr spectroscopy, from the magnetic interactions between the unpaired electrons and the nuclei of adjacent hydrogen atoms.   If the HMO picture were correct, the amounts of unpaired spin of the three carbon atoms of allyl should be respectively $\frac{1}{2}$, 0, $\frac{1}{2}$.   The observed values are, however, 0.6, 0.2, 0.6, a result which can be explained only in terms of uncoupling of the two bonding electrons.   A similar phenomenon is observed in the case of other odd-AH radicals, where HMO theory would require the odd electrons to occupy a NBMO confined to the starred atoms.   The sum of the individual spin densities measured at the various positions is always greater than unity because uncoupling of the pairs of bonding electrons leads to negative spin density at the unstarred positions.

7.2 THE SCF MO TREATMENT OF OPEN-SHELL SYSTEMS

The SCF MO methods discussed in Chap. 5 were developed specifically for the treatment of closed-shell molecules; our next problem is to extend this approach to open-shell systems, where not all the electrons are paired. The arguments outlined above show that systems of this kind are radically different from closed-shell ones in that *none* of the electrons in them are paired; in a MO picture, the α-spin and β-spin electrons must occupy different sets of orbitals.

In the LCAO approximation, the coefficients of the AOs must be chosen so as to minimize the total electronic energy E given [see Eq. (2.191)] by:

$$E = \sum_\mu E_\mu + \sum_{\mu<\nu}\sum J_{\mu\nu} - \overset{\uparrow\ \uparrow}{\sum_{\mu<\nu}\sum} K_{\mu\nu} \tag{7.2}$$

where the sums are over occupied MOs, and where the final sum is over MOs of similar spin. As in the case of closed-shell molecules (Sec. 2.14), the orbitals that minimize E are the same as those that minimize the individual Hartree-Fock orbital energies ϵ_μ, subject to the condition that the MOs remain orthogonal; let us apply this result to an MO ψ_μ occupied by an electron of α spin. It is easily seen [compare Eq. (2.200)] that the corresponding orbital energy $\epsilon_\mu{}^\alpha$ is given by:

$$\epsilon_\mu{}^\alpha = E_\mu + \sum_\nu J_{\mu\nu} - \overset{\alpha}{\sum_\nu} K_{\mu\nu} \tag{7.3}$$

where the final sum is over MOs ψ_ν also occupied by electrons of α spin. If now we expand the various integrals in terms of integrals over the individual AOs ϕ_i [compare Eqs. (2.219) to (2.223)], Eq. (7.3) becomes:

$$\epsilon_\mu{}^\alpha = \sum_i\sum_j a_{\mu i}a_{\mu j}H_{ij}{}^c + \sum_i\sum_j\sum_k\sum_l a_{\mu i}a_{\mu j}\left[\overset{\alpha}{\sum_\nu} a_{\nu k}a_{\nu l}(ij,kl) - \sum_\nu a_{\nu k}a_{\nu l}(ik,jl)\right] \tag{7.4}$$

where the first sum in the final bracket is over all the occupied MOs ψ_ν, and the second over MOs ψ_ν that are occupied by electrons of α spin. We now introduce two quantities $p_{kl}{}^\alpha$ and $p_{kl}{}^\beta$, analogous to the generalized bond order p_{kl} of Eq. (2.226) and defined by:

$$p_{kl}{}^\alpha = \overset{\alpha}{\sum_\nu} a_{\nu k}a_{\nu l} \qquad p_{kl}{}^\beta = \overset{\beta}{\sum_\nu} a_{\nu k}a_{\nu l} \tag{7.5}$$

where the sums are over MOs occupied respectively by electrons of α spin and of β spin. Equation (7.4) then becomes:

$$\epsilon_\mu{}^\alpha = \sum_i\sum_j a_{\mu i}a_{\mu j}\left(H_{ij}{}^c + \sum_k\sum_l \{p_{kl}{}^\alpha[(ij,kl) - (ik,jl)] + p_{kl}{}^\beta(ij,kl)\}\right) \tag{7.6}$$

In a closed-shell molecule, the MOs occupied by electrons of α spin and of β spin are the same; in that case, from Eqs. (2.226) and (7.5),

$$p_{kl}{}^\alpha = p_{kl}{}^\beta = \tfrac{1}{2}p_{kl} \tag{7.7}$$

Substituting these values into Eq. (7.6), we recover Eq. (2.227).

The procedure of minimizing ϵ_μ^α now follows exactly the same course as that used in the corresponding closed-shell case. The coefficients and orbital energies are given by the following modified Roothaan equations:

$$\sum_j a_{\mu j}(F_{ij}^\alpha - \epsilon_\mu^\alpha S_{ij}) = 0 \qquad i = 1, 2, \ldots, n \tag{7.8}$$

where n is the number of basis-set functions (that is AOs) and ϵ_μ^α is one root of the secular equation

$$|F_{ij}^\alpha - \epsilon S_{ij}| = 0 \tag{7.9}$$

The matrix elements F_{ij}^α are given by

$$F_{ij}^\alpha = H_{ij}^c + \sum_k \sum_l \{ p_{kl}^\alpha[(ij,kl) - (ik,jl)] + p_{kl}^\beta(ij,kl) \} \tag{7.10}$$

As usual, the equations have to be solved by an iterative procedure; we first assume a set of p_{kl}^α and p_{kl}^β, construct the F^α matrix, solve the secular equation and equations for the coefficients $a_{\mu i}^\alpha$, use these to calculate a new set of p_{kl}^α and p_{kl}^β, calculate and solve the F^β matrix, and repeat the process until the results converge to a limit. In this way we find the coefficients $a_{\mu i}^\alpha$ in all the MOs ψ_μ^α that contain electrons of α spin. The β-spin MOs are found in a precisely analogous manner; the necessary equations are identical with Eqs. (7.8) to (7.10) with α replaced everywhere by β, and β by α. In the case of a closed-shell molecule, both sets of equations become identical with the normal Roothaan equations (2.213), (2.214), and (2.228).

We are concerned in this section with one specific application of the open-shell SCF treatment, i.e. to conjugated radicals containing unpaired π electrons, within the framework of the Hückel approximation. In this case the σ bonds are as usual treated as localized; the Roothaan equations are used only to calculate the π MOs, so the basis-set AOs are a set of p AOs of the conjugated atoms. As in the case of closed-shell systems of this kind, we are forced to adopt some kind of semiempirical procedure if our results are to be accurate enough for chemical purposes; in this case we may as well try the Pople approximation that proved so successful in the case of closed-shell conjugated hydrocarbons. The open-shell Pople equations can be derived from the Roothaan equations in exactly the same way that we followed in the closed-shell case. For MOs of α spin, they assume the following form:

$$\sum_j a_{\mu j}(F_{ij}^\alpha - \epsilon_\mu^\alpha \delta_{ij}) = 0 \qquad i = 1, 2, \ldots, n \tag{7.11}$$

where ϵ_μ^α is one root of the secular equation

$$|F_{ij}^\alpha - \epsilon \delta_{ij}| = 0 \tag{7.12}$$

and the matrix elements F_{ij}^α are given by

$$F_{ii}{}^\alpha = H_{ii}{}^c + q_i{}^\beta (ii,ii) + \sum_{j \neq i} (q_j{}^\alpha + q_j{}^\beta)(ii,jj) \tag{7.13}$$

$$F_{ij}{}^\alpha = \beta_{ij}{}^c - p_{ij}{}^\alpha (ii,jj) \qquad i \neq j \tag{7.14}$$

Here $q_j{}^\alpha$, $q_j{}^\beta$ are defined by:

$$q_j{}^\alpha = \sum_\nu^\alpha a_{\nu j}{}^2 \qquad q_j{}^\beta = \sum_\nu^\beta a_{\nu j}{}^2 \tag{7.15}$$

Just as q_j in the standard Pople treatment can be taken as a measure of the average number of electrons in the region defined by the AO ϕ_i, so the quantities $q_j{}^\alpha$, $q_j{}^\beta$ are corresponding measures of the average number of, respectively, α-spin and β-spin electrons in that region. It is easily seen that

$$q_j = q_j{}^\alpha + q_j{}^\beta \tag{7.16}$$

Likewise $p_{ij}{}^\alpha$ and $p_{ij}{}^\beta$, defined by

$$p_{ij}{}^\alpha = \sum_\nu^\alpha a_{\nu i} a_{\nu j} \qquad p_{ij}{}^\beta = \sum_\nu^\beta a_{\nu i} a_{\nu j} \tag{7.17}$$

are measures of the total contributions of α-spin electrons and of β-spin electrons to the total bond order p_{ij} between atoms i and j;

$$p_{ij} = p_{ij}{}^\alpha + p_{ij}{}^\beta \tag{7.18}$$

The Pople equations for the MOs of β spin are obtained by replacing α by β, and β by α, throughout Eqs. (7.11) to (7.14). In the case of a closed-shell molecule,

$$q_i{}^\alpha = q_j{}^\alpha = \tfrac{1}{2} q_j \qquad p_{ij}{}^\alpha = p_{ij}{}^\beta = \tfrac{1}{2} p_{ij} \tag{7.19}$$

Here the two sets of open-shell equations each become identical with the closed-shell equations derived earlier.

Counting α spin as positive, β spin as negative, the net spin density $\rho_j{}^\alpha$ at position j is clearly given by the difference between the individual densities of α-spin and β-spin electrons, i.e.

$$\rho_j{}^\alpha = q_j{}^\alpha - q_j{}^\beta \tag{7.20}$$

The result of our calculations can thus be compared directly with the spin densities deduced from esr measurements.

7.3 APPLICATION OF THE POPLE METHOD TO CONJUGATED HYDROCARBON RADICALS

In order to apply the Pople method to conjugated hydrocarbon radicals, we must be able to estimate the various quantities appearing in Eqs. (7.11) to (7.14). If such a treatment is to be convincing, the parameters in it should be the same as those in the corresponding treatment of closed-shell systems. On this basis the diagonal elements of the F matrices for α-spin and β-spin electrons assume the form:

$$F_{ii}{}^{\alpha} = W_i + q_i{}^{\beta}(ii,ii) + \sum_{j \neq i}(q_j{}^{\alpha} + q_j{}^{\beta} - 1)(ii,jj) \qquad (7.21)$$

$$F_{ii}{}^{\beta} = W_i + q_i{}^{\alpha}(ii,ii) + \sum_{j \neq i}(q_j{}^{\alpha} + q_j{}^{\beta} - 1)(ii,jj) \qquad (7.22)$$

Heats of formation have been estimated from thermochemical data for one or two radicals of this type, notably allyl and benzyl, while the distribution of unpaired spin has been measured by esr spectroscopy for a wider range of such materials. Tables 7.1 and 7.2 compare the observed values with those calculated by the Pople method, using the parameters adopted in the treatment of normal closed-shell conjugated hydrocarbons; the calculated spin densities are listed in the third column of Table 7.2 ("without projection").

Three points emerge clearly from this comparison. In the first place, the Pople treatment correctly predicts the presence of significant unpaired spin in the inactive positions of odd-AH radicals, in contrast to the HMO method. Secondly, the magnitude of these negative spin densities is uniformly much less than that calculated; the Pople method evidently overestimates the extent to which the bonding electrons are uncoupled by interaction with the unpaired electron. Thirdly, the calculated heats of atomization are too large, by about 0.5 ev.

7.4 THE S^2 PROBLEM

We assume in our treatment that our atoms follow Russell-Saunders coupling, so that the spin-orbital interactions in them are weak. In other words, we assume that any magnetic forces acting on the electrons in a molecule are small, so that the total energy of the molecule can be written as a sum of the kinetic energies of the nuclei and electrons and of the potential energy due to their mutual coulomb attractions and repulsions. In this case the total energy depends only on the positions and momenta of the particles, not on their spin; the hamiltonian operator **H** is a function only of the spatial coordinates of the electrons and nuclei, and does not contain spin coordinates. **H** therefore commutes

TABLE 7.1   Heats of atomization calculated[1] by the open-shell treatment

	ΔH_a, ev		Difference
	Calc.	Obs.	
ALLYL	32.42	$31.92 \pm .16$[a]	0.50
BENZYL	66.14	$65.78 \pm .29$[b]	0.36

[a] R. J. Akers and J. J. Throssell, *Trans. Faraday Soc.* **63**, 124 (1967).
[b] R. Walsh, D. M. Golden, and S. W. Benzon, *J. Am. Chem. Soc.* **88**, 650 (1966).

TABLE 7.2   Spin densities calculated by the open-shell method

Compound	Pos.	Coupling constant (J), gauss	Calculated spin density		Spin density[a] observed (ρ)
			Without projection	With projection	
ALLYL	1	14.38	0.7135	0.5869	0.5992[b]
	2	4.06	−0.4270	−0.1792	−0.1692[b]
PENTADIENYL[c]	1	8.99	0.5981	0.4101	0.3746[b]
	2	2.65	−0.4093	−0.1576	−0.1104[b]
	3	13.04	0.6223	0.4950	0.5433[b]
BENZYL	1	5.10	0.4250	0.2219	0.2125[d]
	2	1.60	−0.3504	−0.1210	−0.0667[d]
	3	6.30	0.4046	0.2024	0.2625[d]
	7	16.40	0.7994	0.7182	0.6833[d]
PERINAPHTHENYL	1	63.04	0.4809	0.2365	0.2627[e]
	2	1.82	−0.3850	−0.0840	−0.0758[e]

[a] Assuming $\rho = J/24$; the sign of ρ is taken to be the same as that calculated.
[b] R. W. Fessenden and R. H. Schuler, *J. Chem. Phys.* **39**, 2147 (1963).
[c] Actually for cyclohexadienyl.
[d] W. T. Dixon and R. O. C. Norman, *J. Chem. Soc.* **1964**, 4857.
[e] F. Gerson, E. Heilbronner, H. A. Reddock, D. H. Paskovich and N. C. Das, *Helv. Chim. Acta* **50**, 813 (1967).

with the spin functions of the electrons; indeed, we assumed this to be the case in our derivation of the total energy of a molecule whose wave function is written as a Slater determinant of one-electron functions or orbitals (see Sec. 2.13).   It follows that **H** must commute with the operators representing the total spin angular momentum S^2 and any one component of the total spin S_z; any eigenfunction of **H** must therefore be an eigenfunction both of S_z and S^2.

The component of the total spin momentum along the z axis is a sum of contributions by the individual electrons; in a many-electron system,

$$\mathbf{S}_z = \sum_j \mathbf{S}_{zj} \tag{7.23}$$

where $\mathbf{S}_{zj}$ is the operator corresponding to the z component of spin momentum of the jth electron.   Since moreover we are assuming that electrons do not interact with each other magnetically, the spin of any given electron must itself be quantized.   Thus the spin function of electron j must be either α_j or β_j, where α_j and β_j are the two eigenfunctions of $\mathbf{S}_{zj}$;

$$\mathbf{S}_{zj}\alpha_j = \tfrac{1}{2}\hbar\alpha_j \qquad \mathbf{S}_{zj}\beta_j = -\tfrac{1}{2}\hbar\beta_j \tag{7.24}$$

Furthermore, since the electrons do not interact, $\mathbf{S}_{zj}$ will commute with any other one-electron spin operator $\mathbf{S}_{zk}$ and with its eigenfunctions α_k and β_k.   Suppose now that we have a wave function ψ that is written as a product of spin-orbitals $\phi_j\sigma_j$.   It is obvious that ψ will be an eigenfunction of $\mathbf{S}_{zj}$; for everything in it commutes with S_{zj} except the spin function σ_j.   The eigenvalue will be $-\hbar/2$ if $\sigma_j = \beta_j$, and $+\hbar/2$ if $\sigma_j = \alpha_j$.   From this we can see that ψ is an eigenfunction of S_z:

$$S_z\psi = \sum_j S_{zj}\psi = \sum_j \sigma_j\psi = S_z\psi \qquad (7.25)$$

where
$$S_z = \tfrac{1}{2}(n_\alpha - n_\beta)\hbar \qquad (7.26)$$

and where n_α and n_β are respectively the numbers of α-spin and β-spin functions in ψ.   From this it follows that any linear combination Ψ of such product functions ψ_μ will be an eigenfunction of S_z if, and only if, the individual products contain equal numbers of α-spin and β-spin functions.   Since this condition is automatically satisfied by the set of terms obtained on expanding any Slater determinant, we see that such a determinant must automatically be an eigenfunction of S_z.

Next let us consider the effect of operating on a given Slater determinant Ψ with the operator S^2.   Using the notation indicated above,

$$S^2 = S_x{}^2 + S_y{}^2 + S_z{}^2 \qquad (7.27)$$

where
$$S_x = \sum_j S_{xj} \qquad S_y = \sum_j S_{yj} \qquad S_z = \sum_j S_{zj} \qquad (7.28)$$

The spin functions α_j, β_j of the jth electron are by definition eigenfunctions of S_{zj} [Eq. (7.24)]; however they cannot be eigenfunctions of S_{xj} or S_{yj}, in view of the uncertainty principle.‡

Our first problem is to establish the result of operating on the two spin functions, α_j and β_j, with S_{xj} or S_{yj}.

We assume that the spin operators obey the same commutation rules as the operators M_x, M_y, M_z that represent the three components of angular momenta of a rotating rigid body.   On this basis,

$$S_{xj}S_{yj} - S_{yj}S_{xj} = i\hbar S_{zj} \qquad S_{xj}S_{yk} - S_{yk}S_{xj} = 0 \qquad j \neq k \qquad (7.29)$$

Consider now the operator $S_j{}^2$, representing the square of the total spin momentum of electron j.   The spin functions α_j and β_j are eigenfunctions of $S_j{}^2$, with eigenvalues $\tfrac{1}{2}(\tfrac{1}{2} + 1)\hbar^2$; hence:

$$S_j{}^2\alpha_j = (S_{xj}{}^2 + S_{yj}{}^2 + S_{zj}{}^2)\alpha_j = \frac{3\hbar^2\alpha_j}{4} \qquad (7.30)$$

$$S_j{}^2\beta_j = (S_{xj}{}^2 + S_{yj}{}^2 + S_{zj}{}^2)\beta_j = \frac{3\hbar^2\beta_j}{4} \qquad (7.31)$$

‡ If α_j were an eigenfunction of S_{xj}, S_{yj}, and S_{zj}, this would imply that we could measure the three components of spin momentum of the electron simultaneously and exactly.   Such measurements would in turn determine the axis of spin exactly.   Consider now an axis at right angles to this.   We would know exactly the angular coordinate of the electron about this axis, and also the corresponding angular momentum ($= 0$).   Since these are a conjugate pair of position and momentum coordinates, such a result would violate the uncertainty principle.

Using Eqs. (7.24),

$$(\mathbf{S}_{xj}{}^2 + \mathbf{S}_{yj}{}^2)\alpha_j = \tfrac{1}{2}\hbar^2\alpha_j \qquad (\mathbf{S}_{xj}{}^2 + \mathbf{S}_{yj}{}^2)\beta_j = \tfrac{1}{2}\hbar^2\beta_j \qquad (7.32)$$

The functions α_j and β_j are thus eigenfunctions of $\mathbf{S}_{xj}{}^2 + \mathbf{S}_{yj}{}^2$, with eigenvalue $\tfrac{1}{2}\hbar^2$ in each case.

The argument from now on follows a pattern very similar to that used in Sec. 1.5 in our discussion of the simple harmonic oscillator; only an outline will be given since the analysis will serve as good exercise for the reader, and details of it can be found if desired in standard texts. First we introduce two operators $\sigma_j{}^+$ and $\sigma_j{}^-$, defined by:

$$\sigma_j{}^+ = \mathbf{S}_{xj} + i\mathbf{S}_{yj} \qquad \sigma_j{}^- = \mathbf{S}_{xj} - i\mathbf{S}_{yj} \qquad (7.33)$$

Using Eq. (3.29),

$$
\begin{aligned}
\sigma_j{}^+\sigma_j{}^- &= (\mathbf{S}_{xj} + i\mathbf{S}_{yj})(\mathbf{S}_{xj} - i\mathbf{S}_{yj}) \\
&= \mathbf{S}_{xj}{}^2 + \mathbf{S}_{yj}{}^2 - i(\mathbf{S}_{xj}\mathbf{S}_{yj} - \mathbf{S}_{yj}\mathbf{S}_{xj}) \\
&= (\mathbf{S}_{xj}{}^2 + \mathbf{S}_{yj}{}^2) + \hbar\mathbf{S}_{zj}
\end{aligned}
\qquad (7.34)
$$

Likewise:

$$\sigma_j{}^-\sigma_j{}^+ = (\mathbf{S}_{xj}{}^2 + \mathbf{S}_{yj}{}^2) - \hbar\mathbf{S}_{zj} \qquad (7.35)$$

Next we construct the operator $\sigma_j{}^+\sigma_j{}^-\sigma_j{}^+$ in two different ways, by multiplying Eq. (7.34) from the right, and Eq. (7.35) from the left, by $\sigma_j{}^+$. Equating these expressions, we find:

$$(\mathbf{S}_{xj}{}^2 + \mathbf{S}_{yj}{}^2 + \hbar\mathbf{S}_{zj})\sigma_j{}^+ = \sigma_j{}^+(\mathbf{S}_{xj}{}^2 + \mathbf{S}_{yj}{}^2 + \hbar\mathbf{S}_{zj}) \qquad (7.36)$$

Operating with both sides of this equation on the spin functions α_j and β_j, and using Eqs. (7.24) and (7.32), we find that

$$\sigma_j{}^+\alpha_j = 0 \qquad \sigma_j{}^+\beta_j = \hbar\alpha_j \qquad (7.37)$$

The operator $\sigma_j{}^+$ thus has the effect of converting a given eigenfunction of $\mathbf{S}_{zj}$ into another whose eigenvalue is greater by $\hbar$ than the first; since $\mathbf{S}_{zj}$ has only two eigenvalues, $+\tfrac{1}{2}\hbar$ and $-\tfrac{1}{2}\hbar$, operating with $\sigma_j{}^+$ on the eigenfunction with the higher eigenvalue $\tfrac{1}{2}\hbar$ must give zero. The operator $\sigma_j{}^+$ is therefore termed the *raising operator*, since it converts the spin function β, with eigenvalue $-\tfrac{1}{2}\hbar$, into the function α_j, with eigenvalue $+\tfrac{1}{2}\hbar$.

We can likewise construct the operator $\sigma_j{}^-\sigma_j{}^+\sigma_j{}^-$ in two different ways, by multiplying Eq. (7.34) from the left, or Eq. (7.35) from the right, by $\sigma_j{}^-$. Proceeding as above, we find that

$$\sigma_j{}^-\alpha_j = \hbar\beta_j \qquad \sigma_j{}^-\beta_j = 0 \qquad (7.38)$$

The *lowering operator* $\sigma_j{}^-$ thus converts a given eigenfunction of $\mathbf{S}_{zj}$ into one whose eigenvalue is less by $\hbar$; if this is not allowed, then operating with $\sigma_j{}^-$ on the eigenfunction of $\mathbf{S}_{zj}$ gives zero.

Next let us consider the operator S^2. Using the notation of the preceding paragraphs, and Eq. (7.29),

$$S^2 = S_x^2 + S_y^2 + S_z^2$$
$$= (S_x + iS_y)(S_x - iS_y) - i(S_xS_y - S_yS_x) + S_z^2 \tag{7.39}$$

Alternatively,

$$S^2 = (S_x - iS_y)(S_x + iS_y) + i(S_xS_y - S_yS_x) + S_z^2 \tag{7.40}$$

Combining these two equations, and using Eqs. (7.28),

$$S^2 = \tfrac{1}{2}[(S_x + iS_y)(S_x - iS_y) + (S_x - iS_y)(S_x + iS_y)] + S_z^2$$
$$= \frac{1}{2}\sum_j\sum_k[(S_{xj} + iS_{yk})(S_{xk} - iS_{yk}) + (S_{xj} - iS_{yi})(S_{xk} + iS_{yk})] + S_z^2$$
$$= \frac{1}{2}\sum_j\sum_k(\sigma_j^+\sigma_k^- + \sigma_j^-\sigma_k^+) + S_z^2 \tag{7.41}$$

Suppose now that we operate with S^2 on the same product ψ of spin-orbitals that we considered above [Eq. (7.25)]. The term S_z^2 in Eq. (7.39) will of course reduce to an eigenvalue [Eq. (7.26)] since ψ is an eigenfunction of S_z. This, however, is not true of the product $\sigma_j^+\sigma_k^-$. From Eqs. (7.36) and (7.37),

$$(\sigma_j^+\sigma_k^-)\psi = 0 \quad j \neq k \tag{7.42}$$

unless ψ is of the form

$$\psi = \phi\sigma_1\sigma_2\cdots\beta_j\cdots\alpha_k\cdots\sigma_n \tag{7.43}$$

where ϕ is a product of the space parts of the spin-orbitals of which ψ is composed. If ψ has this form, then

$$(\sigma_j^+\sigma_k^-)\psi = \hbar^2\phi\sigma_1\sigma_2\cdots\alpha_j\cdots\beta_k\cdots\sigma_n \tag{7.44}$$

Thus operating with $\sigma_j^+\sigma_k^-$ on ψ gives a different product of spin-orbitals, differing from ψ in that the spins of electron j (initially β) and of electron k (initially α) have been interchanged. Likewise:

$$(\sigma_j^-\sigma_k^+)\psi = 0 \quad j \neq k \tag{7.45}$$

unless ψ is of the form:

$$\psi = \phi\sigma_1\sigma_2\cdots\alpha_j\cdots\beta_k\cdots\sigma_n \tag{7.46}$$

in which case:

$$(\sigma_j^-\sigma_k^+)\psi = \hbar^2\phi\sigma_1\sigma_2\cdots\beta_j\cdots\alpha_k\cdots\sigma_n \tag{7.47}$$

It follows that:

$$\tfrac{1}{2}(\sigma_j^+\sigma_k^- + \sigma_j^-\sigma_k^+)\psi = 0 \quad j \neq k \tag{7.48}$$

unless the spin functions σ_j and σ_k are different; if they are different,

$$\tfrac{1}{2}(\sigma_j{}^+\sigma_k{}^- + \sigma_j{}^-\sigma_k{}^+)\psi = \tfrac{1}{2}\hbar^2\psi_{jk} \tag{7.49}$$

where ψ_{jk} is a product of spin-orbitals differing from ψ in that the spins of the orbitals j and k have been interchanged.

The case where $j = k$ can be dealt with likewise. It is easily seen that:

$$(\sigma_j{}^+\sigma_j{}^-)\psi = \begin{cases} \hbar^2\psi & \sigma_j \equiv \alpha_j \\ 0 & \sigma_j \equiv \beta_j \end{cases}$$

$$(\sigma_j{}^-\sigma_j{}^+)\psi = \begin{cases} 0 & \sigma_j \equiv \alpha_j \\ \hbar^2\psi & \sigma_j \equiv \beta_j \end{cases} \tag{7.50}$$

Suppose now that we have a Slater determinant Ψ, given by

$$\Psi = |(\phi_1\sigma_1)(\phi_2\sigma_2)\cdots(\phi_n\sigma_n)| \tag{7.51}$$

where ϕ_j and σ_j are respectively the space and spin parts of the jth spin-orbital. Since each term in the expansion of Ψ is a product of spin-orbitals, it is easily seen that if $j \neq k$,

$$\tfrac{1}{2}(\sigma_j{}^+\sigma_k{}^- + \sigma_j{}^-\sigma_k{}^+)\Psi = \hbar^2\Psi_{jk} \tag{7.52}$$

where Ψ_{jk} is a Slater determinant differing from Ψ in that the spin functions of the jth and kth spin-orbitals have been interchanged; i.e.

$$\Psi_{jk} = |(\phi_1\sigma_1)(\phi_2\sigma_2)\cdots(\phi_j\sigma_k)(\phi_k\sigma_j)\cdots(\phi_n\sigma_n)| \tag{7.53}$$

This of course assumes that the spin functions σ_j and σ_k are different; if they are the same, i.e. both α or both β, then:

$$\tfrac{1}{2}(\sigma_j{}^+\sigma_k{}^- + \sigma_j{}^-\sigma_k{}^+)\Psi = 0 \qquad \sigma_j, \sigma_k \text{ both } \alpha \text{ or both } \beta \tag{7.54}$$

Finally, from Eqs. (7.50),

$$\tfrac{1}{2}(\sigma_j{}^+\sigma_j{}^- + \sigma_j{}^-\sigma_j{}^+)\Psi = \tfrac{1}{2}\hbar^2\Psi \tag{7.55}$$

Let us now examine the effect of operating on Ψ with $\mathbf{S}^2$. From Eqs. (7.26), (7.48), (7.49), (7.52), and (7.55),

$$\mathbf{S}^2\Psi = \frac{1}{2}\sum_j\sum_k(\sigma_j{}^+\sigma_k{}^- + \sigma_j{}^-\sigma_k{}^+)\Psi + \left(\sum_j \mathbf{S}_{zj}\right)^2\Psi$$

$$= \tfrac{1}{2}n\hbar^2\Psi + \hbar^2\sum_{j\neq k}\sum\Psi_{jk} + \tfrac{1}{4}(n_\alpha - n_\beta)\hbar^2\Psi \tag{7.56}$$

Thus Ψ is not in general an eigenfunction of $\mathbf{S}^2$, and so functions of this form cannot be used satisfactorily for the description of atoms and molecules.

There are, however, two exceptions to this general rule. The first occurs in cases where all the spin functions σ_j are similar, i.e. all α or all β. In this case the determinants Ψ_{jk} vanish [Eq. (7.54)] and Ψ is then an eigenfunction of $\mathbf{S}^2$.

The second, and more important, exception arises when Ψ is the Slater determinant representing a closed-shell system, i.e.

$$\Psi = |\phi_1\bar\phi_1\phi_2\bar\phi_2\cdots\phi_m\bar\phi_m| \tag{7.57}$$

where the functions ϕ_j are the space parts of spin-orbitals and the usual bar notation is used to distinguish α and β spin. If j, k refer to spin functions associated with different spin-orbitals,

$$\Psi_{jk} = |\phi_1\bar\phi_1\phi_2\bar\phi_2\cdots\phi_j\phi_j\cdots\bar\phi_k\bar\phi_k\cdots\phi_m\bar\phi_m| = 0 \tag{7.58}$$

since this determinant has two pairs of identical columns. If on the other hand j, k refer to the two different spin-orbitals associated with a given space part ϕ_m, then:

$$\Psi_{jk} = |\phi\bar\phi\phi\bar\phi\cdots\bar\phi_m\phi_m\cdots\phi_m\bar\phi_m| = -\Psi \tag{7.59}$$

since this determinant differs from Ψ only by the transposition of two columns. Hence:

$$\sum_{j\neq k}\sum \Psi_{jk} = -m\Psi \tag{7.60}$$

Introducing this result into Eq. (7.56), and remembering that in a closed-shell system $n_\alpha = n_\beta$,

$$\mathbf{S}^2\Psi = m\hbar^2\Psi - m\hbar^2\Psi + (0)\Psi = 0 \tag{7.61}$$

Thus Ψ is an eigenfunction of $\mathbf{S}^2$ with eigenvalue zero.

It follows from this analysis that closed-shell atoms and molecules can be represented satisfactorily by single Slater determinants,‡ but open-shell atoms and molecules cannot be represented in this way.

Slater determinants for such systems are not eigenfunctions of $\mathbf{S}^2$. If we are to represent a system of this kind satisfactorily in terms of an orbital approximation, we must therefore use some function of the MOs other than a single Slater determinant.

The various problems that arise in treating open-shell systems can be best illustrated by an example; we shall now consider the LCAO MO treatment of the π electrons in the allyl radical, using first the simple closed-shell HMO picture where all the electrons occupy the same set of three π MOs, and secondly an open-shell picture where there are two sets of π MOs, three in each, one for the α-spin electrons and one for the β-spin electrons.

In the former case, there are 14 possible Slater determinants that can be constructed from the set of three MOs, corresponding to the orbital occupations indicated in Fig. 7.2. All these will of course be eigenfunctions of $\mathbf{S}_z$, and we have also shown that configurations q and r will be eigenfunctions of $\mathbf{S}^2$. It is also

---

‡ A fortunate conclusion since our whole treatment of such systems was based on this assumption!

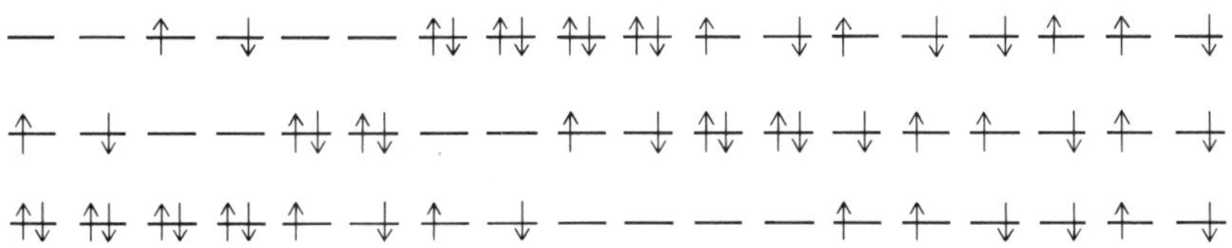

(a) (b) (c) (d) (e) (f) (g) (h) (i) (j) (k) (l) (m) (n) (o) (p) (q) (r)

FIG. 7.2   Schematic representation of the possible π configurations of the allyl radical, using a single set of π MOs.

easily seen that in the case of the other configurations, the functions Ψ_{jk} of Eq. (7.52) vanish, so these are also eigenfunctions of S^2.   So far as the spin operators are concerned, these determinants could therefore serve as satisfactory representations of states of the allyl radical.

This approach suffers of course from the disadvantage of being based on MOs that are not self-consistent; consequently the resulting wave functions give a poor representation of the distribution of unpaired spin in the ground state. However we can circumvent this difficulty by introducing configuration interaction (CI); we can write the wave function as a linear combination of the 16 Slater determinants representing the doublet configurations a to p, following the usual variation procedure.‡   In this way we can construct wave functions for allyl that are simultaneously eigenfunctions of the spin operators S_z and S^2 and also give reasonable values for the spin distribution.   The only trouble with this approach is that it is too complicated.   Even in the case of allyl, a system with but three electrons, there are no less than 16 doublet configurations.   Since the number of configurations increases very rapidly with the number of electrons, the CI treatment becomes impracticable for systems of quite moderate size. One could of course arbitrarily restrict the choice of configurations, e.g. to ones which are singly excited, or even to some fixed number of configurations of lowest energy, and approaches of this kind have been used to calculate spin distributions in radicals with some success.[2]   The objection to these simplified CI methods lies in their arbitrary nature.   One can never be sure that the neglect of higher configurations may not lead to serious errors.

The open-shell SCF MO approach circumvents the difficulties indicated in the last paragraph; however it does so at the expense of a different and serious complication, i.e. the fact that Slater determinants based on open-shell SCF MOs are not eigenfunctions of S^2.   One can see very easily where the difficulty lies, from the case of allyl.   One curious complication in the closed-shell treatment of Fig. 7.2 appears in the case of the quartet state of allyl.   This is a state with

---

‡ The quartet configurations, q and r, do not combine with the rest since matrix elements between configurations of different multiplicity vanish, because of the mutual orthogonality of the spin functions α and β.

total spin $\frac{3}{2}$; such a state gives rise to four substates, with values for S_z, the z component of total spin, of $3\hbar/2$, $\hbar/2$, $-\hbar/2$, and $-3\hbar/2$. The first and last of these correspond to configurations q and r in Fig. 7.2; however there is no way of representing the other two within the closed-shell framework. All the other configurations correspond to states with total spin $\frac{1}{2}\hbar$. It is easily seen that this situation holds quite generally; the closed-shell representation of open-shell systems can apply only to states in which the total spin vector is aligned along the z axis, so that the numerical value of S_z is as great as possible. This restriction no longer applies in the open-shell treatment, where the individual configurations are no longer eigenfunctions of $\mathbf{S}^2$. A configuration with $S_z = \pm\hbar/2$ need not therefore come from a doublet state; it may come from a state of higher multiplicity, i.e. quartet, sextet, etc. Now as we have seen, the open-shell SCF MO treatment of AH radicals such as allyl is not altogether satisfactory; while it does correctly predict the appearance of negative spin densities at the inactive positions, the predicted magnitude of these is too large. We can now attribute this to the fact that the corresponding Slater determinant does not represent a true doublet state. It is not an eigenfunction of $\mathbf{S}^2$. Presumably it represents a combination of the doublet state with a component of the quartet having the same value of S_z; such a combination would of course be an eigenfunction of $\mathbf{S}_z$, and it could well be a solution of the Hartree-Fock equations, but it would not be an eigenfunction of $\mathbf{S}^2$.

There are two ways in which we can circumvent this difficulty. The first is based on Eq. (7.56). When we operate on an open-shell Slater determinant Ψ with $\mathbf{S}^2$, the result is a combination of determinants Ψ_{jk} differing from Ψ only by an interchange of spin between two electrons. Since this interchange does not affect the numbers of α- and β-spin spin-orbitals, it is obvious that Ψ_{ik} will be an eigenfunction of $\mathbf{S}_z$ with the same eigenvalue as Ψ. Consider now the effect of operating with $\mathbf{S}^2$ on Ψ_{jk}. This will give rise to a set of determinants, each differing from Ψ_{jk} by an interchange of spins. Successive operations with $\mathbf{S}^2$ will therefore ultimately convert Ψ into a linear combination of all possible determinants derived from it by interchange of spins, i.e. to the set of determinants Ξ_μ derived from the same set of space orbitals, and with the same number of α- and β-spin functions associated with them as occur in Ψ, but with all possible combinations of space and spin-orbitals to form spin-orbitals. If now we construct a linear combination of these determinants,

$$\Omega = \sum_\mu A_\mu \Xi_\mu \qquad (7.62)$$

we should be able to choose the coefficients A_μ in such a way as to make Ω an eigenfunction of $\mathbf{S}^2$; we could then take Ω as a suitable wave function for our system. The coefficients can be chosen by a straightforward application of the variation method. What we are in effect trying to do is to solve the eigenvalue equation

$$S^2\Omega = S^2\Omega \tag{7.63}$$

when Ω is to be represented by a linear combination of the Slater determinants Ξ_μ. Since the Ξ_μ form an orthogonal set, being solutions of the Hartree-Fock equations, the equations for the coefficients A_μ are:

$$\sum_\nu A_{\nu k}(\int \Xi_\mu S^2 \Xi_\nu \, d\sigma - S_k^2 \delta_{\mu\nu}) = 0 \qquad \mu = 1, 2, \dots \tag{7.64}$$

The eigenvalues S_k^2 could of course be found by solving an appropriate secular equation, i.e.

$$|\int \Xi_\mu S^2 \Xi_\nu \, d\sigma - S^2 \delta_{\mu\nu}| = 0 \tag{7.65}$$

This, however, is unnecessary in practice since we know the eigenvalues of S^2, these being of the form $S(S + 1)\hbar^2$, where S is the spin quantum number. Thus for a doublet state,

$$S^2 = \tfrac{1}{2}(\tfrac{1}{2} + 1)\hbar^2 = \tfrac{3}{4}\hbar^2 \tag{7.66}$$

Figure 7.3 illustrates this procedure in the case of allyl. The orbitals for states with $S_z = \tfrac{1}{2}\hbar$ are as indicated, each α-spin MO lying below the corresponding β-spin MO. Figure 7.3a represents the normal open-shell SCF MO ground state, and Fig. 7.3b and c the configurations derived from this by permutation of spins. In our treatment, the true doublet ground state of allyl is represented by a linear combination of Fig. 7.3a, b, and c, the coefficients being calculated from Eq. (7.64) with S given by Eq. (7.66).

We can regard this approach as a kind of CI treatment, but one of rather unusual type. At first sight it seems wholly illogical to introduce the configurations b and c of Fig. 7.3, since these represent situations where the electrons occupy "wrong" MOs. Thus in both b and c, the electron occupying a β-type MO has α spin, while one of the α-type MOs is occupied by an electron of β spin. The fact of the matter is that none of these determinants represent possible states of allyl, since none is an eigenfunction of S^2. We introduce them simply as convenient basis-set functions for a variation treatment of allyl; the choice of functions in such a case is entirely optional, provided that they satisfy any necessary local conditions. In this case the only local condition is that the functions

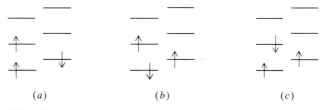

(a)   (b)   (c)

FIG. 7.3 Open-shell SCF MO configurations for the π electrons in allyl. (a) Normal ground-state configuration; (b) and (c) states derived from (a) by permutation of spins.

should all be eigenfunctions of S_z with a common eigenvalue, a condition satisfied by a, b, and c in Fig. 7.3.

In order to carry through this program, we need to evaluate the integrals in Eq. (7.64). Let us first calculate the quantities $S^2(a)$, $S^2(b)$, and $S^2(c)$. From Eq. (7.56),

$$S^2(a) = \tfrac{3}{2}\hbar^2(a) + \hbar^2(b) + \hbar^2(c) + \tfrac{1}{4}\hbar^2(a)$$
$$= \tfrac{7}{4}\hbar^2(a) + \hbar^2(b) + \hbar^2(c) \tag{7.67}$$

Likewise:

$$S^2(b) = \tfrac{7}{4}\hbar^2(b) + \hbar^2(a) + \hbar^2(c) \tag{7.68}$$
$$S^2(c) = \tfrac{7}{4}\hbar^2(c) + \hbar^2(a) + \hbar^2(b) \tag{7.69}$$

Since the three functions (a), (b), (c) form an orthonormal set, we can at once calculate the necessary matrix elements;

$$\int(a)S^2(a)\, d\sigma = \int(b)S^2(b)\, d\sigma = \int(c)S^2(c)\, d\sigma = \tfrac{7}{4}\hbar^2 \tag{7.70}$$
$$\int(a)S^2(b)\, d\sigma = \int(a)S^2(c)\, d\sigma = \int(b)S^2(c)\, d\sigma = \hbar^2 \tag{7.71}$$

The equations for the coefficients A, B, and C of (a), (b), and (c) respectively, thus become:

$$A(\tfrac{7}{4}\hbar^2 - \tfrac{3}{4}\hbar^2) + \hbar^2 B + \hbar^2 C = 0 \tag{7.72}$$
$$\hbar^2 A + B(\tfrac{7}{4}\hbar^2 - \tfrac{3}{4}\hbar^2) + \hbar^2 C = 0 \tag{7.73}$$
$$\hbar^2 A + \hbar^2 B + C(\tfrac{7}{4}\hbar^2 - \tfrac{3}{4}\hbar^2) = 0 \tag{7.74}$$

All three equations thus reduce to

$$A + B + C = 0 \tag{7.75}$$

The result is thus indeterminate! The trouble lies in the fact that states with a common value of S^2 are degenerate so far as the operator S^2 is concerned. In our variation treatment, we used three basis-set functions; our CI treatment should therefore lead to three distinct states, with $S_z = \tfrac{1}{2}\hbar$. One of these can be one component of a quartet (compare Fig. 7.2q and r); however the other two must correspond to doublet states. The solution of Eq. (7.35) is therefore indeterminate because it corresponds to a pair of degenerate states; we can choose any two sets of coefficients that satisfy this equation, provided that the resulting combinations

$$A_1(a) + B_1(b) + C_1(c) \quad \text{and} \quad A_2(a) + B_2(b) + C_2(c) \tag{7.76}$$

are orthogonal. However there is another restriction to consider. We require our wave function for allyl to minimize the total energy. The coefficients A, B, and C must therefore be chosen so as both to satisfy Eq. (7.75) and to make the integral

$$\int [A(a) + B(b) + C(c)] \mathbf{H}[A(a) + B(b) + C(c)]\, d\tau \tag{7.77}$$

a minimum.   This is an awkward condition to satisfy, and the problem becomes rapidly worse with increasing number of electrons; for the number of functions belonging to common eigenvalues of $\mathbf{S}^2$ and $\mathbf{S}_z$ increase rapidly.   Consequently the SCF CI approach outlined above does not provide a practicable treatment of open-shell systems.   A much better approach is fortunately available, due to Löwdin[3] and based on the use of *projection operators.*

   Consider an operator α, obeying the eigenvalue equation

$$\alpha|i\rangle = A_i|i \tag{7.78}$$

We assume that we know the eigenvalues A_i of α; our problem is to determine the corresponding eigenkets $|i\rangle$.   Suppose that we have some arbitrary ket $|\mu\rangle$. We know that $|\mu\rangle$ can be expressed exactly in terms of the kets of α:

$$|\mu\rangle = \sum_i A_{\mu i}|i\rangle \tag{7.79}$$

This expression for $|\mu\rangle$ describes it as a combination of contributions by the various eigenkets $|i\rangle$ of α, a procedure analogous to the expression of a vector in terms of components along the coordinate axes.   Following this analogy, if we could project $|\mu\rangle$ along the "direction" $|i\rangle$, the resulting component of $|\mu\rangle$ would be a multiple of the eigenket $|i\rangle$ of α.   To do this we need an operator $\mathbf{P}_i$ with the following properties:

$$\mathbf{P}_i|j\rangle = 0 \qquad j \neq i \qquad \mathbf{P}_i|i\rangle = 1 \tag{7.80}$$

If we operate with $\mathbf{P}_i$ on $|\mu\rangle$, the result will be:

$$\mathbf{P}_i|\mu\rangle = \mathbf{P}_i\left(\sum_j A_{\mu j}|j\rangle\right) = A_{\mu i}|i\rangle \tag{7.81}$$

Consider the operator $\mathbf{A}_j$, given by:

$$\mathbf{A}_j = \alpha - A_j \tag{7.82}$$

From Eq. (7.78),

$$\mathbf{A}_j|j\rangle = 0 \qquad \mathbf{A}_j|k\rangle = (A_k - A_j)|k\rangle \tag{7.83}$$

If $\mathbf{A}_j$ acts on some combination of the eigenkets of $|i\rangle$, say on $|\mu\rangle$, it will then delete the contribution by the ket $|j\rangle$.   Such an operator is termed an *annihilation operator* or *annihilator.*   Consider now the operator $\mathbf{P}'_i$, defined by:

$$\mathbf{P}'_i = \prod_{j \neq i} \frac{\mathbf{A}_j}{A_i - A_j} \tag{7.84}$$

Each term in the product is an annihilator which will annihilate contributions by one of the eigenkets of α; the whole operator therefore annihilates contributions by every single eigenket of α other than $|i\rangle$.   Furthermore, from Eq. (7.83),

$$\mathbf{A}_j|i\rangle = (A_i - A_j)|i\rangle \tag{7.85}$$

Hence:

$$\mathbf{P}'_i |i\rangle = |i\rangle \tag{7.86}$$

Comparing these results with Eq. (7.80), we see that:

$$\mathbf{P}'_i \equiv \mathbf{P}_i \tag{7.87}$$

Thus $\mathbf{P}'_i$ is our required projection operator.

Let us apply this technique to the allyl radical. Our purpose here is to project out of the open-shell SCF Slater determinant the part corresponding to a true doublet function. In this case the only possible contaminant is a quartet function, since it is impossible to construct systems of higher multiplicity with but three electrons; hence the doublet projection operator $\mathbf{P}^{II}$ takes the form:

$$\mathbf{P}^{II} = \frac{\mathbf{S}^2 - S^{IV}}{S^{II} - S^{IV}} \tag{7.88}$$

where S^{II} and S^{IV} are the eigenvalues of $\mathbf{S}^2$ for doublet and quartet states respectively; i.e.

$$S^{II} = \tfrac{1}{2}(\tfrac{1}{2} + 1)\hbar^2 = \tfrac{3}{4}\hbar^2 \qquad S^{IV} = \tfrac{3}{2}(\tfrac{3}{2} + 1)\hbar^2 = \tfrac{15}{4}\hbar^2 \tag{7.89}$$

Hence:

$$\mathbf{P}^{II} = \frac{\mathbf{S}^2 - \tfrac{15}{4}\hbar^2}{-3\hbar^2} \tag{7.90}$$

Let us then apply this operator to the open-shell SCF function of Fig. 7.3a. Using Eq. (7.67),

$$\begin{aligned}
\mathbf{P}^{II}(a) &= -\frac{1}{3\hbar^2}[\mathbf{S}^2(a) - \tfrac{15}{4}\hbar^2(a)] \\
&= -\frac{1}{3\hbar^2}[\tfrac{7}{4}\hbar^2(a) + \hbar^2(b) + \hbar^2(c) - \tfrac{15}{4}\hbar^2(a)] \\
&= \tfrac{2}{3}(a) - \tfrac{1}{3}(b) - \tfrac{1}{3}(c) \tag{7.91}
\end{aligned}$$

Note that the coefficients $\tfrac{2}{3}$, $-\tfrac{1}{3}$, and $-\tfrac{1}{3}$ satisfy Eq. (7.75), as of course they must if the resulting function is to be an eigenfunction of $\mathbf{S}^2$. Note also that projection gives the total component of $|\mu\rangle$ along the $|i\rangle$ direction, i.e. the quantity $A_{\mu i}|i\rangle$; in order to obtain the normalized eigenket $|i\rangle$, we must normalize the result. In this way we find for our normalized doublet ground-state function Φ,

$$\Phi = \frac{1}{\sqrt{6}}[2(a) - (b) - (c)] \tag{7.92}$$

Comparing Eqs. (7.91) and (7.92), we can see that the coefficient A_Φ of the doublet component Φ in (a) is given by:

$$A_\Phi = \frac{\tfrac{1}{3}}{1/\sqrt{6}} = 0.816 \tag{7.93}$$

The weight of the doublet configuration in (a) is given by $A_\phi{}^2$ $(= \frac{2}{3})$; only two-thirds of the SCF Slater function (a) corresponds to the true doublet ground state!

One point should be emphasized. The arguments given above might seem to imply that the projected function Φ is the true doublet ground-state function for allyl; this, however, is not the case. Consider the Schrödinger equation for the π electrons in allyl:

$$\mathbf{H}\phi_i = E_i\phi_i \tag{7.94}$$

Any well-behaved function ξ can be written as a linear combination of the eigenfunctions ϕ_i;

$$\xi = \sum_i a_i\phi_i \tag{7.95}$$

The functions ϕ_i will include all possible states of allyl, both doublet and quartet, including a whole spectrum of excited states of each type. If now we operate on ξ with the operator $\mathbf{P}^{II}$, we shall eliminate all contributions by states of multiplicity other than 2; however all the doublet states remain unaffected. Hence although the function Φ in Eq. (7.92) is free from contaminating higher multiplets, it may still contain contributions from excited doublet states.

The advantages of the projection-operator technique over CI are obvious. In this way we obtain an unambiguous approximation to the ground state of the system we are considering, and by a much simpler procedure. In the case of AH radicals, the results show a dramatic improvement over those given by the single-determinant approach; this is illustrated by the comparison of calculated and observed spin densities for allyl, shown in Table 7.3.

In the case of large radicals, however, the calculations can become quite protracted as the number of different multiplicities increases. Thus in benzyl, treated as a π system, one can have doublet, quartet, sextet, and octet states respectively; when the resulting operator is applied to the ground-state SCF Slater function, a plethora of different determinants is obtained. Most of the work on conjugated radicals has therefore made use of the following simpler approach.

In the case of a radical, the ground state is a doublet; any quartets represent excited states of high energy. The same argument shows that the energies of

TABLE 7.3   Spin densities on the allyl radical

Position	SCF function[1]		Exp.[a]
	Simple	Projected	
1	0.7135	0.5896	0.58
2	−0.4270	−0.1792	−0.16

[a] R. W. Fessenden and R. H. Schuler, *J. Chem. Phys.* **39**, 2147 (1963).

sextet states should be much higher again, since such a state involves a double excitation. If we can assume that the higher multiplets are unimportant, then it becomes unnecessary to eliminate them from our SCF function; we need retain in our projection operator only the term (Eq. 7.88) that annihilates the contributions of quartets. This treatment has been applied extensively by Amos and Snyder[4] to a study of spin distributions in conjugated radicals; the results agree quite well with experiment, and they certainly represent a very great improvement over those given by simple open-shell SCF treatment. Some examples are given in the penultimate column of Table 7.2 ("with projection").

7.5   OPEN-SHELL SCF TREATMENT OF EVEN SYSTEMS; HORIZONTAL CORRELATION AND THE ALTERNANT-ORBITAL METHOD

The Hartree-Fock method neglects electron correlation except in so far as it is automatically taken into account by using antisymmetrical wave functions. Here we shall consider certain aspects of the correlation problem in more detail for π systems.

In the orbital picture of a closed-shell atom or molecule, each occupied orbital represents a volume of orbital space capable of holding two electrons and so completely filled. The correlation effects involving such a pair of electrons are then of two kinds.

First, we have the tendency of the two electrons to keep apart inside their own orbital; this will increase the average distance between them, but will not alter the time average of their individual motions. In other words, the probabilities of finding one or other electron in a given small volume element will be the same. In an empirical treatment, we should be able to take correlation of this kind into account simply by reducing the J integral representing the mutual repulsion of the electrons occupying the orbital; this is one of the reasons why the empirical values for the one-center repulsion integrals (ii,ii) are less than those calculated by direct quadrature.

A second type of correlation involves synchronization of motions between two different pairs of electrons. The origin of this lies in the fact that two electrons occupying a given region of space repel each other less strongly if they have parallel spin than if they have antiparallel spin; for in the former case there is an exchange correction to the repulsion that would be calculated classically for point charges. The two pairs of electrons will therefore tend to correlate their motions in such a way that the electrons of like spin will on average be closer together than those of opposite spin.

Consider for example a diatomic molecule containing four electrons, where the electrons occupy in pairs two MOs ψ_1, ψ_2 constructed from AOs ϕ_1, ϕ_3 of one atom and ϕ_2, ϕ_4 of the other;

$$\psi_1 = \frac{1}{\sqrt{2}} (\phi_1 + \phi_2) \qquad \psi_2 = \frac{1}{\sqrt{2}} (\phi_3 + \phi_4) \qquad (7.96)$$

At any instant the two electrons in a given MO will tend to occupy different AOs, in order to reduce their mutual repulsion; this, an example of our first correlative effect, is responsible for bonds having more "covalent character" than the simple MO theory would predict, a point which has been covered in so many elementary texts that it need not be repeated here.   However in addition to this there will be a second correlation effect, due to mutual interaction of the two pairs of electrons.   When the α-spin occupant of ψ_1 is at the ϕ_1 end of the bond, there will be a tendency for the α-spin occupant of ψ_2 also to be in that region. The reason for this is that the repulsions between the α-spin electron in ψ_1 and the two electrons in ψ_1 are not the same; the repulsion between two α-spin electrons is less, other things being equal, than that between an α-spin electron and a β-spin electron.   The net effect of this second type of correlation is to produce at any instant a synchronized unpairing of the electrons; the effect is similar to that brought about in radicals, where interactions between the unpaired electron and the pairs of bonding electrons lead to uncoupling.   There is of course a very real difference between the two cases.   In a radical, the interactions produce a permanent polarization of each pair of bonding electrons.   In a closed-shell molecule, there will at any instant be an excess of α-spin electrons at some points, and of β-spin electrons at others; here, however, the interaction is symmetrical since there are equal numbers of electrons of each kind, so there can be no permanent polarization.   We may always tend to find an excess of electrons of one spin in certain places, but the excess may equally well be of α-spin electrons or of β-spin electrons.   Over a long period, the average number of electrons of each kind will be the same everywhere.

These arguments suggest that a special type of correlation might be important in the π MOs of AHs, where the conjugated atoms fall into two separated groups.   One could visualize a tendency for the electrons to segregate themselves between the two sets of AOs, so that at any instant there should be an excess of α-spin electrons in one and of β-spin electrons in the other.   Since moreover such a segregation should arise from our second type of correlation, it should extend to the pairs of electrons occupying given MOs.   This argument suggests that we might allow for such *horizontal correlation* of π electrons, i.e. correlation in a direction parallel to the nodal plane, by using different orbitals ψ_μ^α, ψ_μ^β for the electrons of α and β spin.   Since we assume that the net density is unaffected by correlation,

$$(\psi_\mu^\alpha)^2 + (\psi_\mu^\beta)^2 = 2\psi_\mu^2 \qquad (7.97)$$

where ψ_μ is the corresponding uncorrelated closed-shell orbital.

This is the idea underlying the *alternant-orbital method* introduced some years ago by Löwdin.[3,5]   Consider a given MO ψ_μ in an AH, written as a sum of starred and unstarred AOs ϕ_i,

$$\psi_\mu = \sum_i^* a_{\mu i}\phi_i^* + \sum_j^\circ a_{\mu j}\phi_j^\circ \tag{7.98}$$

We assume that the pair of orbitals $\psi_\mu{}^\alpha$ and $\psi_\mu{}^\beta$ have the following form:

$$\psi_\mu{}^\alpha = \left(\sum_i^* a_{\mu i}\phi_i^*\right)\sin\theta_\mu + \left(\sum_j^\circ a_{\mu j}\phi_j^\circ\right)\cos\theta_\mu \tag{7.99}$$

$$\psi_\mu{}^\beta = \left(\sum_i^* a_{\mu i}\phi_i^*\right)\cos\theta_\mu - \left(\sum_j^\circ a_{\mu j}\phi_j^\circ\right)\sin\theta_\mu \tag{7.100}$$

It is easily seen that these expressions satisfy Eq. (7.97), with ψ_μ given by Eq. (7.98).   Next we construct an open-shell Slater determinant Ψ from the spin-orbitals $\psi_\mu{}^\alpha\alpha$ and $\psi_\mu{}^\beta\beta$.   The final alternant-orbital wave function Ξ for the singlet ground state is derived from Ψ by the projection-operator technique, i.e.

$$\Xi = \rho_0\Psi = \left[\prod_{s>0}\frac{\mathbf{s}^2 - s(s+1)\hbar^2}{-s(s+1)\hbar^2}\right]\Psi \tag{7.101}$$

The energy E of the system is given by:

$$E = \frac{\int \Xi\mathbf{H}\Xi\,d\tau}{\int \Xi^2\,d\tau} \tag{7.102}$$

The orbital coefficients $a_{\mu i}$ and the parameters θ_μ are chosen to make E a minimum.

While the alternant-orbital method provides an elegant and ingenious solution to the problem of horizontal correlation, it is of limited chemical value.   In the first place, the minimization procedure involved in it is exceedingly complicated, so much so that the method has so far been applied almost entirely to molecules where the orbital coefficients are determined by symmetry (e.g. cyclic polyenes, with the geometry of regular polygons).   Secondly, the method is by its nature limited to alternant conjugated systems.   And thirdly, the underlying assumption, embodied in Eqs. (7.99) and (7.101), is by no means satisfactory, implying as it does that the correlation between starred and unstarred positions is the same in all parts of the π system.

An analogous, but much simpler, method for including horizontal correlation is to use the open-shell SCF treatment.   If there is any advantage in using different orbitals for electrons of different spin, the open-shell SCF method should lead to such a solution; moreover it will automatically give the best possible solution of this kind.   Equally, if the best solution is one in which the electrons are paired, i.e. that given by a closed-shell SCF treatment, we should still arrive at this if we use the open-shell approach.   Of course if the solution differs from the closed-shell one, the resulting Slater determinant Φ will not be an eigenfunction of $\mathbf{S}^2$; in this case we shall have to project out the singlet part Ω of Φ [compare Eq.

(7.101)] and calculate our final expression for the energy from this projected function.

The trouble with this approach lies in the procedure used to determine the MOs. What we want are the orbitals that minimize the total singlet energy E^{I},

$$E^{\mathrm{I}} = \frac{\int \Omega \mathbf{H} \Omega \, d\tau}{\int \Omega^2 \, d\tau} \tag{7.103}$$

However our orbitals have in fact been calculated in such a way as to minimize the expectation value E for the energy that corresponds to the single determinant Φ;

$$E = \frac{\int \Phi \mathbf{H} \Phi \, d\tau}{\int \Phi^2 \, d\tau} \tag{7.104}$$

Since Φ inevitably contains contributions both from excited singlet states and from states of higher multiplicity, minimizing E leads to a compromise in which a greater contribution of singlet excited states is accepted to keep down the contributions of triplets, quintets, etc. Although therefore the optimum projected open-shell function must give better results than a closed-shell one, the same need not necessarily be true for the function Ω derived in the manner indicated above. In practice, the open-shell treatment leads to paired orbitals in the case of small molecules such as butadiene or benzene, but to unpaired ones in larger systems.

While this approach to the problem of horizontal correlation is feasible, it is nevertheless much more complicated and time-consuming than the usual closed-shell treatment. Furthermore, if we are interested in accurate calculations of heats of formation, it suffers from a serious inconsistency. As we have seen, the simple closed-shell method gives extraordinarily good results for the heats of formation of conjugated hydrocarbons of all kinds. It does so because it contains parameters that are chosen to give the best possible agreement between calculated and observed heats of formation; in this way it makes implicit allowance for the effects of electron correlation that the SCF MO method explicitly ignores. Now the simple closed-shell SCF MO treatment ignores *all* types of electron correlation, except in so far as it uses antisymmetrical wave functions; in particular, it neglects horizontal correlation completely. Horizontal correlation is taken into account implicitly, through suitable adjustment of the parameters in our semiempirical treatment. In an open-shell treatment, on the other hand, horizontal correlation is explicitly taken into account. If therefore we try to use an open-shell treatment together with the closed-shell parameters, we shall in effect be allowing for horizontal correlation twice over; our calculated heats of atomization will consequently be too large. If we wish to use an open-shell treatment for closed-shell molecules, we must use an entirely different set of parameters appropriate to it. Since the closed-shell treatment is both extremely successful and very much simpler, such an endeavor would seem rather pointless.

7.6 HEATS OF FORMATION OF RADICALS

The arguments given at the end of the preceding section apply equally to radicals; if we try to calculate their heats of atomization by the open-shell SCF MO method using closed-shell parameters, our estimated values should be too large. This, as we have seen, is the case. In order to obtain good estimates of the heats of atomization or formation of radicals, we must either use the open-shell treatment with an appropriate set of parameters, or we must devise a "closed-shell" treatment of radicals in which horizontal correlation is neglected so that the closed-shell parameter can properly be used. The latter alternative is clearly the more attractive since it avoids the introduction of an entirely new set of parameters.

An appropriate treatment of this kind is provided by the trick outlined in Sec. 6.19, i.e. replacing the unpaired electron by two half electrons of opposite spin.‡ The calculations can be carried out using a standard closed-shell program, with just one minor modification. In such a closed-shell approach, we take into account the repulsions between all pairs of electrons; in the case of a radical, there will be a term representing the fictitious repulsion between the two halves of the unpaired electron, and this must obviously be removed. The total electronic energy E is thus given in terms of the closed-shell energy E' by

$$E = E' - \tfrac{1}{4} J_{00} \tag{7.105}$$

where J_{00} refers to the singly occupied MO. Table 7.4 shows values calculated in this way for several radicals; the agreement with experiment is excellent. Further examples will be found in Chap. 9.

‡ The use of half electrons may seem rather heretical; however it merely represents a convenient physical picture of an approximation that can be justified in more conventional ways (see Ref. 6).

TABLE 7.4   Heats of atomization of hydrocarbon radicals, calculated[1] by the closed-shell method

Radical	Heat of atomization, ev	
	Calc.	Obs.
ALLYL	32.08	31.92 ± 0.16[a]
BENZYL	65.64	65.78 ± 0.29[b]
α-PHENYLETHYL	77.89	78.19 ± 0.27[c]
CYCLOHEXENYL	63.71	63.54 ± 0.22[d]
CYCLOHEXDIENYL	58,30	58.14 ± 0.22[d]

[a] R. J. Akers and John J. Throssell, *Trans. Faraday Soc.* **63**, 124 (1967).
[b] R. Walsh, D. M. Golden, and S. W. Benson, *J. Am. Chem. Soc.* **88,** 650 (1966).
[c] J. A. Kerr, *Chem. Rev.* **66**, 465 (1966).
[d] S. W. Benson, *J. Chem. Educ.* **42**, 502 (1965).

7.7 IONIZATION POTENTIALS AND ELECTRON AFFINITIES; KOOPMAN'S THEOREM

Removal of an electron from a normal closed-shell molecule leaves a cation radical with one unpaired electron; likewise addition of an extra electron to a closed-shell molecule gives an anion radical, again with one unpaired electron. The energy required to bring about the former process is of course the ionization potential of the parent molecule in question, while the energy liberated in the latter process is its electron affinity.

Ion radicals of this kind can of course be treated by the method of Sec. 7.6; by comparing the energies of a given pair of ion radicals with that of the parent compound, we can arrive at estimates of the ionization potential and electron affinity.

In comparing these values with experiment, however, a complication arises. Ionization potentials of aromatic compounds have been measured by two basically different techniques. In the first, one estimates in effect the minimum energy that a photon must have to bring about ionization; this can be done either by studying Rydberg series in the far-ultraviolet spectrum or by photoionization or photoelectron spectroscopy. The values obtained by these different spectroscopic techniques agree closely, and the values obtained in this way undoubtedly correspond to "adiabatic" ionization, i.e. to a process in which the ion is produced in its most stable state. The second technique involves bombardment of the compound in question with electrons of variable and known energy; the minimum energy required to bring about ionization is taken to be a measure of the ionization potential. The values found in this way are consistently greater than those found spectroscopically, and it now seems fairly certain that the differences are real and not due to errors in technique. Various explanations have been suggested; the most plausible of these attributes the difference to a difference in time scale for ionization. The time involved in a collision with an incident electron is extremely short, so if ionization occurs during this period, it must leave the ion in the same geometrical configuration as that of the original molecule. Since removal of an electron from a molecule must lead to changes in the equilibrium bond lengths, the ion in this case is not produced in its state of lowest energy. The ionization in other words is "vertical," not adiabatic, and the difference between the spectroscopic and electron-impact values can then be taken as a measure of the gain in energy in the ion due to reorganization of its geometry.

The method of Sec. 7.6 can be used to calculate both these kinds of ionization potential. To find the adiabatic value, we calculate the energy of the ion by the usual procedure in which bond lengths are recalculated at each stage in the iterative cycle and the various two-center integrals are modified accordingly. Such a treatment gives us an estimate of the ground-state energy of the ion. To find the vertical ionization potential, on the other hand, we repeat the calculation with a fixed geometry identical with that of the parent molecule.

TABLE 7.5 Calculated[1] and observed ionization potentials

Compound	Ground state energy	Ionization potential					
		Adiabatic			Vertical		
		Calc.	Obs.	Source	Calc.	Obs.[a]	Source
BENZENE	−30.532	9.22	9.24[b]	18	9.35	9.38	17
			9.24[c]	1			
NAPHTHALENE	−55.111	8.30	8.12[b]	18	8.45	8.26	17
ANTHRACENE	−79.524	7.72	7.38[b]	14	7.83	7.55	17
			7.15[d]	2			
PHENANTHRENE	−79.850	8.10			8.28	8.03	17
TETRACENE	−103.865	7.31	6.88[b]	14	7.42		
STYRENE	−40.410	8.56	8.47[b]	19	8.71	8.86	9
			8.42[c]	15			
BIPHENYL	−65.378	8.31	8.27[b]	19	8.45	8.30	12
AZULENE	−53.973	7.54	7.43[d]	3	7.63	7.72	16
			7.41[b]	7			
ETHYLENE	−5.560	9.90	10.48[c]	1	10.14	10.56	5
			10.52[b]	18			
cis-BUTADIENE	−15.461	8.97	8.75[d]	13	9.14		
trans-BUTADIENE	−15.427	8.83	9.08[c]	1	9.02	9.18	4
			9.07[b]	18			
HEXATRIENE	−25.311	8.24	8.26[d]	10	8.43		
OCTATETRAENE	−35.197	7.89	7.80[d]	10	8.08		
ALLYL	−9.893	8.32			8.32	8.16	8
PENTADIENYL	−19.912	7.89			7.89	7.73	11
BENZYL	−34.576	7.47			7.48	7.73	8
BENZHYDRYL	−69.588	6.91			6.91	7.32	6
α-NAPHTHYLMETHYL	−59.175	7.02			7.03	7.35	6
β-NAPHTHYLMETHYL	−59.115	7.12			7.14	7.56	6

[a] All values are electron-impact data. [c] Photoelectron spectroscopy.
[b] Photoionization. [d] Spectroscopic.

1 M. I. Al-Joboury and D. W. Turner, *J. Chem. Soc.* **1964**, 4434.
2 J. G. Angus and G. C. Morris, *J. Mol. Spectry.* **21**, 310 (1966).
3 L. B. Clarke, *J. Chem. Phys.* **43**, 2566 (1965).
4 J. Collin and F. P. Lossing, *J. Am. Chem. Soc.* **79**, 5848 (1957).
5 F. H. Field and J. L. Franklin, "Electron Impact Phenomena," p. 253, Academic Press Inc., New York, 1957.
6 A. G. Harrison and F. P. Lossing, *J. Am. Chem. Soc.* **82**, 1052 (1960).
7 T. Kitigawa, H. Inokuchi, and K. Kodera, *J. Mol. Spectry.* **21**, 267 (1966).
8 F. P. Lossing, K. U. Ingold, and I. H. S. Henderson, *J. Chem. Phys.* **22**, 621 (1954).
9 J. D. Morrison and A. J. C. Nicholson, *J. Chem. Phys.* **20**, 1021 (1952).
10 W. C. Price and A. D. Walsh, *Proc. Roy. Soc.* (*London*) **A185**, 182 (1945).
11 A. Streitwieser, Jr., and P. M. Nair, *Tetrahedron* **5**, 149 (1959).
12 T. M. Sugden, A. D. Walsh, and W. C. Price, *Nature* **148**, 373 (1941).
13 T. M. Sugden and A. D. Walsh, *Trans. Faraday Soc.* **41**, 76 (1945).
14 A. Terenin and F. Vilessov, *Advan. Photochem.* **2**, 385 (1964).
15 D. W. Turner, *Advan. Phys. Org. Chem.* **4**, 31 (1966).
16 R. J. Van Brunt and M. E. Wacks, *J. Chem. Phys.* **41**, 3195 (1964).
17 M. E. Wacks and V. H. Dibeler, *J. Chem. Phys.* **31**, 1557 (1959).
18 K. Watanabe, *J. Chem. Phys.* **26**, 542 (1957).
19 K. Watanabe, T. Nakayama, and J. Mottl, *J. Quant. Spectry. Radiative Transfer* **2**, 369 (1962).

Table 7.5 shows calculations of ionization potentials for a number of conjugated hydrocarbons and hydrocarbon radicals, carried out by both these procedures, together with experimental values of both kinds where they are available.   The agreement is quite satisfactory, given that the calculated values are subject to errors both in the calculated heat of atomization of the parent hydrocarbon and in that of the parent ion.   The values for the ions are clearly comparable in accuracy with those for neutral hydrocarbons (compare Table 5.2).   The mean difference between the calculated adiabatic and vertical ionization potentials (0.15 ev) is also close to that observed experimentally between ionization potentials found spectroscopically and by electron impact; this supports the suggested explanation for the difference.   Table 7.6 shows a similar comparison of calculated and observed electron affinities; here again the agreement is good.

One point here needs comment.   In calculating heats of formation of hydrocarbons or hydrocarbon ions, the valence-state ionization potential of carbon need not be known since it cancels (see Sec. 5.3).   In calculating ionization potentials or electron affinities, however, this is no longer the case; for now we are comparing two systems with different numbers of electrons, so we need to know the absolute binding energies of electrons in them.   If, however, we assume W_c to have the value given by the Pariser-Parr method [Sec. 5.3 and Eq. (5.13)], we arrive at ionization potentials and electron affinities which are too large.   The values listed in Tables 7.5 and 7.6 were calculated with a considerably smaller value for W_c (9.59 ev).   There are two possible explanations for this apparent discrepancy.   First, it may be that the effective ionization potential for a $2p$ electron is less for a carbon atom in a molecule than it would be for an isolated carbon atom; the Pariser-Parr method refers of course to the values for an isolated

TABLE 7.6   Calculated[1] and observed electron affinities

Compound	A	
	Obs.[a]	Calc.
NAPHTHALENE	0.15	0.07
ANTHRACENE	0.55	0.65
PHENANTHRENE	0.31	0.27
BENZ[a]ANTHRACENE	0.70	0.64
BENZO[c]PHENANTHRENE	0.54	0.38
CHRYSENE	0.42	0.51
TETRACENE	1.15	1.06
TRIPHENYLENE	0.28	0.26
PYRENE	0.58	0.66
BENZO[a]PYRENE	0.83	0.93
BENZO[c]PYRENE	0.49	0.61
DIBENZ[a,h]ANTHRACENE	0.68	0.65
DIBENZ[a,j]ANTHRACENE	0.69	0.58

[a] R. S. Becker and E. Chen, *J. Chem. Phys.* **45**, 2403 (1966).

atom in the appropriate valence state.   This point of view has been put forward strongly by Julg.[7]   An alternative possibility is that W_c may vary with the formal charge on a molecule.   Certainly one would expect the orbitals in a positive ion to tend to contract, as a result of the excess of positive charge in the core.   If so, the energy of the ion must be less than that calculated by our procedure where it is assumed that the MOs of ions and neutral molecules alike are formed from AOs of identical size.   This in turn would make our calculated ionization potentials too high.   If the differences were much the same for different ions, as seems not unreasonable, then they could be compensated by an appropriate change in the value assumed for W_c.   Likewise the MOs of a negative ion should be more diffuse than those of the corresponding neutral molecule; our procedure would then overestimate the binding energy in the anion and so too the electron affinity of the parent hydrocarbon.   Here again, this could be compensated by assuming a smaller value for W_c.

In view of this uncertainty, and in view of the difficulty of estimating W_i for atoms other than carbon for states other than atomic valence states, it seems wiser to retain the Pariser-Parr values and to assume that the discrepancies in the case of ionization potentials and electron affinities are due to the second factor indicated above.

7.8 PMO TREATMENT OF RADICALS

Since the closed-shell approach can apparently account well for the heats of for-mation of radicals, the same model should serve in other connections.   In par-ticular, one should be able to use the simple PMO method to estimate energy changes in reactions where such radicals are involved.

The reactions of interest in this connection are ones where a closed-shell system is converted to a radical, or conversely, by breaking or forming one bond; e.g.

$$PhCH_3 \rightarrow PhCH_2 \cdot + \cdot H \qquad (7.106)$$

$$PhCH{=}CH_2 + R \cdot \rightarrow Ph\dot{C}HCH_2R \qquad (7.107)$$

In the case of an AH, the change in π energy in such a process is the difference in π energy between an odd-AH radical and an even AH derived from it by addi-tion or loss of one atom.   These π-energy changes can be found at once by the methods developed in Chap. 6.   The difference in π energy δE_π between an odd AH R and an even AH S formed by addition of one carbon atom is simply the energy of union of R with methyl.   This can be found at once in terms of the NBMO coefficients a_{0r} of the atom r in R through which union takes place, i.e.

$$\delta E_\pi = \sum_r 2\beta a_{0r} \qquad (7.108)$$

Likewise if R is converted to an even AH S' by loss of atom r, the change in π energy (see Sec. 6.14) is given by:

$$\delta E_\pi = 2\beta(1 - a_{0r}) \tag{7.109}$$

A simple example is provided by reactions in which radicals are formed by breaking bonds [compare Eq. (7.106)]. Let us for example compare the ease of formation of allyl and benzyl radicals in this way. For allyl,

$$\overset{-1/\sqrt{2}}{CH_2{=}CH{-}CH_2X} \rightarrow \overset{1/\sqrt{2}}{CH_2{=}CH{-}CH_2{\cdot}} + {\cdot}X$$

$$\Delta E_A = E_{CX} + \delta E_\pi = E_{CX} + 2\beta\left(1 - \frac{1}{\sqrt{2}}\right) \tag{7.110}$$

where E_{CX} is the bond energy of the CX bond and ΔE_A the energy of reaction. Likewise for benzyl,

$$PhCH_2X \rightarrow PhCH_2{\cdot} + {\cdot}X$$

$$\Delta E_B = E_{CX} + \delta E_\pi = E_{CX} + 2\beta\left(1 - \frac{2}{\sqrt{7}}\right) \tag{7.111}$$

Hence:

$$\Delta E_B - \Delta E_A = -2\beta\left(\frac{2}{\sqrt{7}} - \frac{1}{\sqrt{2}}\right) = -0.13\beta \tag{7.112}$$

Since β is negative, we would then expect the energy required to break the CX bond to be less for allyl than for benzyl; the available thermochemical data support this prediction. Since moreover $\beta \approx -1$ ev for PMO calculations, the difference should be about 3 kcal/mole; the average value for several series of compounds is close to this.[8]

PROBLEMS

7.1 Work out in detail the argument outlined in Eqs. (7.33) to (7.41).

7.2 Denoting the three α-spin π MOs of allyl by α_1, α_2, and α_3, and the three β-spin π MOs by β_1, β_2, and β_3, show (a) that the configuration $|\alpha_1\beta_1\alpha_2|$ is not an eigenfunction of S^2; (b) that the combination of configurations,

$$|\alpha_1\beta_1\alpha_2| + |\bar{\alpha}_1\beta_1\alpha_2| + |\alpha_1\beta_1\bar{\alpha}_2|$$

is an eigenfunction of S^2.

7.3 In the notation of Prob. 7.2, derive the doublet component of the configuration $|\alpha_1\bar{\beta}_1\alpha_2|$.

REFERENCES

1 Dewar, M. J. S., J. A. Hashmall, and C. G. Venier: *J. Am. Chem. Soc.* **90**, 1953 (1968).

2 Bloor, J. E., B. R. Gilson, and P. N. Daykin: *J. Phys. Chem.* **70**, 1457 (1966); J. E. Bloor, B. R. Gilson, and D. D. Shillady: *J. Phys. Chem.* **71**, 1238 (1967), and references therein.

3 Löwdin, P. O.: *Phys. Rev.* **97**, 1509 (1955).

4 Amos, T., and L. C. Snyder: *J. Chem. Phys.* **41**, 1773 (1964); L. C. Snyder and T. Amos: *ibid.* **42**, 3670 (1965).

5 Heer, J. de: *Rev. Mod. Phys.* **35**, 631 (1963); R. Paunz: *Tetrahedron Suppl.* **2**, 43 (1963).

6 Dewar, M. J. S., J. A. Hashmall, and C. G. Venier: *J. Am. Chem. Soc.* **90**, 1953 (1968).

7 Julg, A.: *Tetrahedron Suppl.* **2**, 25 (1963).

8 Cottrell, T. L.: "The Strengths of Chemical Bonds," 2d ed., Butterworth Scientific Publications, London, 1958.

CHAPTER EIGHT

THE CHEMICAL
PROPERTIES OF
CONJUGATED HYDROCARBONS

8.1 INTRODUCTION

In the three preceding chapters we have discussed in some detail the problem of calculating the properties of conjugated hydrocarbons in their ground states. Conjugated hydrocarbons were chosen in this preliminary analysis for three reasons: (1) the theoretical treatment is simpler for hydrocarbons than for compounds containing heteroatoms; (2) accurate thermochemical data are available for far more hydrocarbons than for organic compounds of other types; and (3) all the essential features of chemical theory can be illustrated by its application to conjugated hydrocarbons. Similar considerations apply to the theoretical analysis of chemical reactivity, and so before turning to compounds of other types, we shall first complete our analysis of conjugated hydrocarbons by discussing the rates and equilibria of reactions which they undergo.

8.2 BASIC PRINCIPLES

Our problem is to predict the equilibrium constants K_e of reversible reactions and the rate constants k_r of irreversible ones. According to the transition-state theory, both problems are equivalent; for the rate constant k_r of an irreversible reaction can be written as

$$k_r = \frac{kT\tau}{h} K^\dagger \tag{8.1}$$

where k is the Boltzmann constant, h is Planck's constant, T is the absolute temperature, τ is the transmission coefficient (usually assumed equal to unity), and $K^\dagger$ is the equilibrium constant between the reactants and the transition state. Using the usual thermodynamic expressions for equilibria, and assuming $\tau = 1$,

$$K_e = e^{-\Delta G/RT} = e^{\Delta S/R}e^{-\Delta H/RT} \tag{8.2}$$

$$k_r = \frac{kT}{h}e^{-\Delta G\dagger/RT} = \frac{kT}{h}e^{\Delta S\dagger/R}e^{-\Delta H\dagger/RT} \tag{8.3}$$

where ΔG, ΔS, and ΔH are respectively the free energy, entropy, and heat of reaction and $\Delta G^\dagger$, $\Delta S^\dagger$, and $\Delta H^\dagger$ the free energy, entropy, and heat of activation. In order to estimate equilibrium and/or rate constants, we must therefore be able to estimate differences in entropy and heat content between reactants and products or between reactants and transition states.

The entropy of a molecule depends only indirectly on its chemical structure, being determined by the frequencies of its modes of internal vibration and rotation. These can as yet be calculated only for the very simplest molecules; at present we are therefore quite unable to estimate the quantities ΔS or $\Delta S^{\dagger}$ in Eqs. (8.2) and (8.3), and so we cannot hope to predict absolute values for equilibrium or rate constants.

However the majority of practical chemical problems are concerned not so much with the absolute values of rate or equilibrium constants as with the way these quantities vary along a series of closely related reactions. In other words we are willing to accept the experimental fact that a given kind of reaction takes place; our problem is to predict how the equilibrium or rate will vary if we vary the structures of the molecules taking part in it. A typical example is provided by aromatic substitution. Our problem here is not to predict whether or not this type of reaction will take place, a prediction which would depend on estimates of the absolute value of the corresponding rate constants, but rather to predict the relative reactivities of different aromatic systems, and—even more important from a practical standpoint—the relative reactivities of different positions in a given system. This last piece of information is of course needed if we are to predict the orientation of the reaction products. Now the relative rates of two reactions with rate constants k_1 and k_2 is given [see Eq. (8.3)] by:

$$\frac{k_1}{k_2} = \frac{(kT/h)e^{-\Delta G_1^{\dagger}/RT}}{(kT/h)e^{-\Delta G_2^{\dagger}/RS}} = e^{(\Delta S_1^{\dagger}-\Delta S_2^{\dagger})/R}e^{(\Delta H_2^{\dagger}-\Delta H_1^{\dagger})/RT} \tag{8.4}$$

If the reactions are very similar, we may expect the corresponding entropies of activation to be similar too. If we can assume that they are identical, Eq. (8.4) becomes:

$$\frac{k_1}{k_2} = e^{(\Delta H_2^{\dagger}-\Delta H_1^{\dagger})/RT} = e^{(\Delta E_2^{\dagger}-\Delta E_1^{\dagger})/RT} \tag{8.5}$$

where ΔE_1, ΔE_2 are the corresponding activation energies, i.e. differences in internal energy between the reactants and transition states. [The final equality in Eq. (8.5) is a well-known thermodynamic consequence of the assumption that $\Delta S_1^{\dagger} = \Delta S_2^{\dagger}$.] A similar relation holds of course for the equilibrium constants (K_1 and K_2) of two related reactions if we can assume that the entropies of reaction are the same; i.e.

$$\frac{K_1}{K_2} = e^{(\Delta E_2-\Delta E_1)/RT} \tag{8.6}$$

or
$$-RT \log \frac{K_1}{K_2} = \Delta E_1 - \Delta E_2 \tag{8.7}$$

where ΔE_1, ΔE_2 are the differences in internal energy between the reactants and products of the two reactions.

Since we can calculate heats of formation of molecules, at least in certain cases, we have some hope of calculating the energy differences ΔE or $\Delta E^\dagger$ of Eqs. (8.5) and (8.7). If then our assumption concerning entropies of activation or reaction is correct, we have a good chance of being able to calculate relative rates and equilibria of series of related reactions, even though the absolute rate and equilibrium constants may be outside our reach.

However the assumption in question is not only dubious; it is contradicted by the available experimental evidence. If we examine a series of related reactions, we usually find large variations in the entropy of reaction or activation. This difficulty was pointed out some time ago by Hammett,[1] who concluded that attempts to interpret chemical reactivity in terms of chemical structure were consequently doomed to failure, except in the rare cases of series of reactions where the entropies of reaction or activation are all the same. From a purely experimental point of view this judgment is clearly much too pessimistic; for organic chemists have in practice been able to build up an impressively successful general theory of the relationship between chemical structure and reactivity. While this treatment has been largely qualitative, its existence indicates that there must be much closer relationships between structure and reactivity than the arguments outlined above would suggest. Since entropy is not a simple additive function of molecular structure, relationships of this kind might be anticipated only if reactivity is determined primarily by differences in energy between reactants and products, or reactants and transition states, differences in entropy playing only a minor part. The following argument reconciles these two apparently opposed points of view.[2]

Most of the reactions that concern us in organic chemistry take place in solution and involve ionic species; in such cases solvation plays a dominant role, as can be seen from the fact that organic ionic reactions are almost unknown in the gas phase. The formation of ions from neutral species involves the input of much energy to bring about the required charge separation; as a general rule, processes of this kind become feasible only if the resulting ions can be solvated, the solvation energies of ions in polar solvents being very high. Now solvation of an ion leads to a decrease in energy; however it also leads to a decrease in entropy since the solvent molecules bound to a given ion are no longer free to move about as they please. Since the free energy of solvation ΔG_s is given in terms of the heat ΔH_s and entropy ΔS_s of solvation by:

$$\Delta G_s = \Delta H_s - T \Delta S_s \qquad (8.8)$$

the changes in energy and entropy will tend to balance one another.

Let us now consider some reaction taking place in a polar solvent, and let us calculate the equilibrium constant K as a function of the degree of solvation. We can express K in the form:

$$-RT \log K = \Delta G = \Delta G_0 + \Delta G_s \qquad (8.9)$$

where ΔG_0 is the free energy of reaction in absence of solvent, and ΔG_s is the difference in free energy of solvation between reactants and products. Suppose now that we plot ΔG_s against ΔS_s for reactions involving various degrees of solvation. Since any change in solvation leads to changes in ΔH_s and ΔS_s whose contributions to ΔG_s tend to cancel [see Eq. (8.8)], we may expect ΔG_s to be a relatively insensitive function of ΔS_s and the plot to be consequently a rather flat curve (Fig. 8.1). The reaction will take place by the path that minimizes ΔG, where ΔS_s has the value a (Fig. 8.1). Consider now a second similar reaction; here again a plot of ΔG_s vs. ΔS_s should be a flat curve, and the reaction will again take place in such a way as to minimize ΔG_s, the corresponding value of ΔS_s being b (Fig. 8.1). The ratio of the two equilibrium constants is then given by

$$-RT \log \frac{K_1}{K_2} = (\Delta G_0)_1 - (\Delta G_0)_2 + (\Delta G_s)_1 - (\Delta G_s)_2 \qquad (8.10)$$

where $(\Delta G_s)_1$, $(\Delta G_s)_2$ are the minimum values of ΔG_s for the two reactions. Suppose now that we erroneously assume that both reactions will take place by paths corresponding to similar degrees of solvation, so that the entropy of solvation of the second reaction is a instead of b. The corresponding value of ΔG_s will then be $(\Delta G_s)'_2$ (Fig. 8.1). Our estimate of the ratio of the K's will then be:

$$-RT \log \left(\frac{K_1}{K_2}\right)' = (\Delta G_0)_1 - (\Delta G_0)_2 + (\Delta G_s)_1 - (\Delta G_s)'_2 \qquad (8.11)$$

Since, however, the curves in Fig. 8.1 are so flat,

$$(\Delta G_s)_2 \approx (\Delta G_s)'_2 \qquad (8.12)$$

It follows that

$$\frac{K_1}{K_2} \approx \frac{K_1}{K'_2} \qquad (8.13)$$

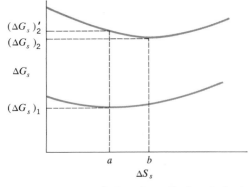

FIG. 8.1   The cancellation of contributions by heats and entropies of solvation to free energies of reaction.

Therefore even if the reactions differ appreciably in ΔS_s, we may still get good estimates of the relative equilibrium constants by neglecting this variation. Of course this result is due to the fact that changes in ΔS_s are balanced by corresponding changes in ΔH_s. We must not therefore try to equate experimentally determined heats of reaction to our calculated energies of reaction; for the experimental values will be directly affected by the variations in ΔH_s. In other words, we can hope to interpret free energies of reaction, and hence equilibrium constants, but not heats of reaction. From a chemical standpoint this is a matter of small consequence, since it is the equilibrium constants that are the major concern of chemistry.

Exactly similar arguments apply to reaction rates, the quantities ΔG_s, ΔH_s, and ΔS_s being replaced by corresponding differences in free energy, heat, and entropy of solvation between the reactants and the transition state. Here again it would be incorrect in principle to equate experimentally determined heats or energies of activation to the calculated differences in energy between the reactants and the transition state; for the experimental values contain uncertain contributions from heats of solvation. Our argument shows that so far as relative rates of reaction are concerned, we can without serious error assume that the contributions of solvation to reaction rates are the same along a series of related reactions.

A great deal of time has been wasted on attempts to interpret heats of reaction and activation energies theoretically. Here Hammett's arguments[1] apply with full force. Unless we are prepared—and able—to calculate entropies a priori, we are automatically restricted to predicting relative equilibria or reaction rates, and even there we can operate only on the assumption that they follow the pattern that would be predicted were all the entropy contributions the same. This point cannot be emphasized too strongly; for the measurement of activation energies, and heats of activation, has become a fetish among physical organic chemists. If the object is to interpret rates or mechanisms of reactions, it is usually much better to make measurements for a large number of reactions at one temperature than for a smaller number at several temperatures.

There are of course exceptions to this rule; however these are mostly a matter of common sense. For instance steric strain increases the energy of a molecule, and it also as a rule decreases the entropy by restricting degrees of freedom of vibration or internal rotation. Here the two corresponding contributions to the free energy act together instead of in opposition; an increase or decrease in steric strain in passing from reactants to products, or reactants to transition state, can therefore influence profoundly the equilibrium or rate constant for a reaction. Phenomena of this kind are of course well recognized in organic chemistry and various methods have been devised for estimating their importance (e.g. Ref. 3). As yet, however, they remain outside the scope of quantum chemistry, although it may before long be possible to include them in the kind of treatment described in the last chapter of this book.

8.3   REACTION RATES AND HEATS OF REACTION; THE BELL-EVANS-POLANYI (BEP) PRINCIPLE

The prediction of reaction rates presents even greater difficulties than the prediction of equilibria; for the rate of a chemical reaction depends on the difference in energy between the reactants and an intermediate (i.e. the transition state) whose structure cannot be established by direct experimental methods. Ideally of course we should be able to determine the structure of the transition state theoretically, by calculating a complete energy surface for the reacting system and so deducing the easiest path from reactants to products; the highest point on this path will represent the transition state.   While there is some hope that calculations of this kind may become possible in the not too distant future (see Chap. 10), at present they are still impracticable; we must therefore find some alternative procedure if we are to interpret rates of chemical reactions in terms of the structures of the reactants.

Often of course one can deduce the structure of the transition state of a given reaction in general terms, from a consideration of the bonds that are broken and formed during it.   For instance there can be little doubt that S_N2 reactions take place by the following path, through a transition state in which the central carbon atom has a trigonal bipyramidal configuration;

$$X^- + \underset{c}{\overset{a}{\underset{\displaystyle}{\overset{b}{\text{C}}}}}\!\!-Y \rightarrow \delta^-\ X\text{---}\underset{c}{\overset{b\ \ a}{\text{C}}}\text{---}Y\ \delta^- \rightarrow X\!-\!\underset{c}{\overset{b}{\text{C}}}\overset{a}{} + Y^- \tag{8.14}$$

However the rate of a reaction may depend critically on the detailed geometry of the transition state, information which we cannot obtain by this kind of intuitive approach.

An alternative procedure, which has proved extremely valuable in a variety of connections, depends on a general treatment of the problem of reactivity which was introduced by Evans and Polanyi[4] and Bell[5] some 30 years ago.   Polanyi‡ had observed that the activation energies of certain simple reactions in the gas phase ran parallel to the heats of reaction; the activation energy $\Delta E^\dagger$ for a given reaction could be written in the form:

$$\Delta E^\dagger = A + B\,\Delta H \tag{8.15}$$

where A and B are constant and ΔH is the heat of reaction.   This kind of relationship has since been observed in a number of cases, the proportionality factor B being of the order of one-third.   If this relation holds, then the ratio of the rate constants, k_1 and k_2, for two of the reactions will be given by:

$$-RT \log \frac{k_1}{k_2} = \Delta E^\dagger - \Delta E^\dagger = B(\Delta H_1 - \Delta H_2) \tag{8.16}$$

‡ For a review and references see Ref. 6.

In this case we can estimate relative values of the rate constants k from the corresponding heats of reaction; these of course are much easier to calculate than activation energies are since they represent differences between two sets of normal molecular species.

The existence of such relationships was explained by Evans and Polanyi,[4] and by Bell,[5] using an argument that has proved of general value in the study of reaction rates and mechanisms. Let us consider first a simple substitution reaction

$$A + B\!-\!C \to A\!-\!B + C \qquad (8.17)$$

in which just one bond (BC) is broken, and another (AB) is simultaneously formed. As the BC bond stretches, there will be just one position for A which makes the energy of the system a minimum; we can therefore represent the course of the reaction by a single *reaction coordinate*, each value of this corresponding to a definite BC bond length and a definite AB bond length. Let us now consider a two-stage alternative to the reaction (8.17) in which the BC bond is first broken completely, and then AB formed from the dissociated fragments $A + B$;

$$A + BC \to A + B + C \qquad (8.18)$$
$$A + B + C \to AB + C \qquad (8.19)$$

We can depict the course of each of these reactions by plotting the total energy E of the system against our reaction coordinate. In reaction (8.18), the BC bond length for each value of the reaction coordinate is the same as in Eq. (8.17), and the same is true of the AB bond length for reactions (8.19) and (8.17). Figure 8.2 shows the corresponding plots, the reaction coordinate varying from zero, for no reaction, to unity, for complete reaction.

Consider now the one-step reaction of Eq. (8.17). Initially the energy of the system will increase in much the same way as in Eq. (8.18), since the new bond AB cannot begin to form until the old bond BC is significantly weakened. Consequently the first part of the reaction path for Eq. (8.17) will be the same as that for Eq. (8.18) $(PQ$ in Fig. 8.2). At the point X, however, the systems $A + BC$ and $AB + C$ become energetically equivalent; instead of going further up the line PQ, we can then switch over to the reaction path of Eq. (8.19) $(RS$ in Fig. 8.2). In this way we can bring about the overall reaction with expenditure of far less energy than that required to break the BC bond completely. The corresponding reaction path $(PXS$ in Fig. 8.2) can be taken as an approximation to that for Eq. (8.17), the crossing point X representing the transition state, and the height of X above P the corresponding activation energy.

Suppose now that we have a series of analogous reactions in which a variety of reactants $A_1, A_2, \ldots, A_n$ combine with BC to form $A_1B, A_2B, \ldots, A_nB$ together with C. We can plot the course of these reactions in exactly the same

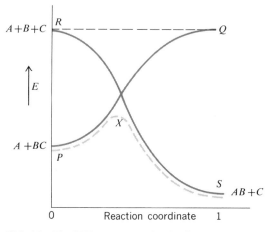

FIG. 8.2   The BEP treatment of a simple reaction, $A + BC \rightarrow AB + C$, indicating the reaction path (dashed line) and transition state X.

way as Fig. 8.2.   Figure 8.3 shows this plot for three of them, the plots being adjusted so that all three start at the same level P.   If the shapes of the curves RS_1, RS_2, and RS_3 are similar, as we may expect them to be in view of our assumption that the reactions are similar, and if the curves are reasonably straight near the crossing points X_1, X_2, and X_3, then it is obvious that the changes in the height of X above P (i.e. the activation energy) should be proportional to changes in the height of Q above P (i.e. the overall energy of reaction).   This of course is the relationship stated algebraically in Eq. (8.15).

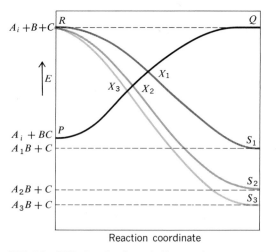

FIG. 8.3   BEP plots for three similar reactions, $A + BC \rightarrow AB + C$, illustrating the basis of Eq. (8.15).

Analogous plots can be devised for reactions of all kinds.   Some of the changes that occur during a reaction take place with absorption of energy, e.g. the breaking or distortion of bonds or the removal of solvent molecules; other changes release energy.   In the actual reaction, the endothermic processes are the more important initially, because considerable distortion of the reactants is necessary before the energy-releasing processes can come into play.   This is why reactions normally require activation.   Following Fig. 8.2, we can then plot the two types of process separately, obtaining curves analogous to PQ and RS in Fig. 8.2; the curve representing the course of the observed reaction is then a composite of these, analogous to PXS in Fig. 8.2.   Similar arguments then suggest that changes in activation energy with the structure of the reactants should run parallel to the corresponding changes in heats of reaction, i.e. that Eq. (8.15) should hold quite generally, at any rate as a first approximation.

Although this argument is relevant to us only in so far as it justifies our use of Eq. (8.15) for predicting relative reaction rates, some further remarks appear to be in order in view of widespread confusions that seem to exist in the literature concerning this treatment of reactions.

In the first place, it is evident from Fig. 8.3 that the proportionality factor B in Eq. (8.15) will be smaller, the smaller the slope of the curve PQ at the crossing point X.   It is also obvious that X will move to the left, and so to a point further down the curve PQ where the slope is less, the lower S, i.e. the more exothermic the reaction.   In this case three immediate consequences follow:

1   The activation energy decreases, so that the reactions become faster.

2   Bond-breaking processes have progressed to a much lesser extent in the transition state, so that the transition state resembles the reactants more closely.

3   The variations in rate with changes in ΔH become progressively smaller as B decreases, so that the variation in rate with the "reactivity" of the reagent becomes progressively less.

These conclusions not only are self-evident corollaries of this treatment, but they were also widely recognized as such and used to interpret numerous aspects of chemical reactivity.   A good example was the explanation given by the present author[7] for the fact that mesomeric anions often give different products with electrophiles, depending on the reactivity of the latter.   Thus enolate ions give enolic derivatives with very reactive electrophiles (e.g. H[+], $RCOCl$), but ketonic derivatives with less reactive ones (e.g. CH_3I).

During the last 10 years, however, various aspects of this treatment have apparently been rediscovered from time to time and published—and accepted— as original contributions to the chemical literature.   In view of the situation indicated above, it seems more proper, if these individual ideas are to be associated with specific names, to describe them collectively as the *Bell-Evans-Polanyi* (BEP) *principle.*

8.4 TYPES OF CHEMICAL REACTION

Our problem is to calculate differences in energy between the reactants and products of chemical reactions, or reactants and transition states; as was pointed out in Sec. 6.1, differences of this kind represent a very small percentage of the total binding energy, or even of the heats of formation from atoms, of the species involved.   Such quantities can be estimated either directly, by difference, or by the use of perturbation theory (i.e. by the PMO method).   In this chapter we shall follow both these paths.   The direct method can be made the more accurate by using the semiempirical SCF MO treatment of Chaps. 5 and 7; this, however, requires the use of a large digital computer.   The PMO approach has the advantage of extreme simplicity; it can be used as an effective replacement for earlier treatments (e.g. resonance theory) in one's day-by-day thinking, being equally easy to use and far more reliable and accurate.

The majority of simple chemical reactions involve the breaking and/or formation of one bond, and very few reactions involve the simultaneous breaking and/or formation of more than two bonds; the number of basic processes in chemistry is consequently quite limited.

Since we are concerned only with differences in energy between reactants and products, or reactants and transition states, we can ignore contributions by localized bonds that take no part in the reaction.

Consider for example a simple reversible bond-breaking process, viz. the conversion of a diarylethane to two diarylmethyl radicals:

$$\mathrm{ArCH_2CH_2Ar} \rightleftharpoons 2\mathrm{ArCH_2 \cdot} \qquad\qquad (8.20)$$

A classical example of this type of reaction is the reversible dissociation of hexaphenylethane into trityl radicals,

$$\mathrm{Ph_3CCPh} \rightleftharpoons 2\mathrm{Ph_3C \cdot} \qquad\qquad (8.21)$$

The energy of reaction ΔE can be divided up into contributions of three kinds:

1   A contribution E_{CC}, representing the bond energy of the bond that is broken during the reaction

2   Changes δE_{CH} in the bond energies of the CH bonds in the methylene groups due to the change in hybridization of the methylene carbons

3   A change ΔE_{deloc} in the energy of the delocalized electrons due to their conversion of two n-atom conjugated systems Ar into $(n + 1)$-atom ones, $\mathrm{ArCH_2 \cdot}$

Terms 1 and 2 will be the same, regardless of the nature of the aryl group. The energy of reaction ΔE can thus be written in the form:

$$\Delta E = E_{CC} + 4\delta E_{CH} + \Delta E_{deloc} = A + \Delta E_{deloc} \tag{8.22}$$

where A is the same for different diarylethanes. If we are concerned only with the way in which the equilibrium constant varies with aryl, not with its absolute magnitude, we need know only the ratios of the equilibrium constants K_i. From Eqs. (8.7) and (8.22), these are given by:

$$- RT \log \frac{K_i}{K_j} = \Delta E_i - \Delta E_j = (\Delta E_{deloc})_i - (\Delta E_{deloc})_j \tag{8.23}$$

The ratio of the two equilibrium constants is thus determined solely by variations in the quantity ΔE_{deloc} which we may term the *delocalization energy of reaction.* Exactly similar arguments will of course apply to rates of reaction, these being determined by differences in delocalization energy between the reactants and the transition state, a quantity which we may term the *delocalization energy of activation* $\Delta E^\dagger_{deloc}$.

If then we are interested only in the relative rates of a series of similar reactions, the determining factor is the way in which $\Delta E^\dagger_{deloc}$ varies along the series. The essential feature of the reaction from this point of view is the relationship between the two delocalized systems in question. The existing classifications of chemical reactions are therefore unsatisfactory for our purpose, emphasizing distinctions which are of no importance to us and obscuring resemblances which are vital. We need a new classification of reactions in terms of relationships between the delocalized systems of the reactants and products, or reactants and transition states.

Note that the term "delocalized system" is more general than "conjugated system"; it includes all situations which cannot be described in terms of localized bonds. Thus in the transition state for a classical S_N2 reaction,

$$X^- + b\!-\!\overset{a}{\underset{c}{C}}\!-\!Y \;\rightarrow\; X\overset{\overset{a}{|}}{\underset{\underset{b\;\;c}{}}{\cdots C\cdots}}Y^{\delta-} \;\rightarrow\; X\!-\!\overset{a}{\underset{c}{C}}\!-\!b + Y^- \tag{8.24}$$

we have four delocalized electrons occupying three-center MOs, constructed from AOs of the nucleophile X^- and the product Y^-, and from a $2p$ AO of the central carbon atom. In a MO description, these AOs enter only in the form of various integrals involving them (resonance integrals, electron repulsion integrals, etc.). The geometry of overlap can affect the magnitudes of these integrals, but not the qualitative way in which they appear in the treatment. We can therefore regard the transition state of Eq. (8.24) as topologically equivalent to, or isoconjugate with, any other system where AOs of two atoms A, C overlap with an AO of a third atom B, but not significantly with one another. An obvious example of such overlap is provided by the π system of allyl. Indeed, the transition state of Eq. (8.24) is isoconjugate with allyl. In this way we can correlate arbitrary three-dimensional delocalized systems with topologically equivalent, or isoconjugate, π systems. In our general description, such systems can be regarded as equivalent.

The two features that are important in our MO description are the relative numbers of atoms in the delocalized systems we are comparing and whether the numbers are odd or even. This second requirement follows from the fact that somewhat different treatments are needed for odd and even conjugated systems, particularly in the PMO approach. Our classification and symbolism is therefore as follows.

8.4.1 ISOCONJUGATE (I) REACTIONS These are reactions where the two conjugated systems in question are isoconjugate. A good example is provided by the conversion of pyridine bases to their salts; e.g.

$$\text{⟨N⟩} + H^+ \rightarrow \text{⟨NH}^+\text{⟩} \tag{8.25}$$

Here the base and its conjugate acid have the same number of conjugated atoms and the same numbers of π electrons.

8.4.2 EVEN-EVEN (EE) REACTIONS These are reactions in which both delocalized systems are even but differ in size. If that of the reactants is the smaller, the reaction is termed EE; if it is the larger, the reaction is then $\overline{\text{EE}}$. A typical example ($\overline{\text{EE}}$) is the internal Diels-Alder reaction of 1,3,5-hexatriene to form cyclohexadiene;

$$\text{⟨⟩} \rightarrow \text{⟨⟩} \tag{8.26}$$

Here the reactant has a six-atom conjugated system, the product a four-atom one.

8.4.3 ODD-ODD (OO) REACTIONS These likewise are reactions where both delocalized systems are odd, but differ in size. They are classed as OO if the delocalized system of the reactants is the smaller, $\overline{\text{OO}}$ if it is the bigger.

8.4.4 ODD-EVEN (OE) REACTIONS These involve interconversion of a smaller odd system and a larger even one; normally the two systems will differ by one atom. If the delocalized system of the reactants is odd, the reaction is termed OE; if it is even, then the reaction is of $\overline{\text{OE}}$ type. A good example ($\overline{\text{OE}}$) is provided by the protonation of benzene to the benzenonium ion;

$$\text{⟨⟩}-H + H^+ \rightarrow \text{⟨⊕⟩}\overset{H}{\underset{H}{\diagdown}} \tag{8.27}$$

8.4.5   EVEN-ODD (EO) REACTIONS   EO reactions likewise involve interconversion of an odd and an even system, the odd system in this case being the larger.
In EO reactions, the reactant is even, in $\overline{EO}$ odd.   A good example of an EO reaction is provided by the ionization of trityl chloride;

$$Ph_3CCl \rightarrow Ph_3C^+ + Cl^- \tag{8.28}$$

8.4.6   In certain cases, we may need to state explicitly the number of atoms by
which the two delocalized systems differ; this can be done by adding an appropriate number to the symbol.   Thus Eq. (8.26) depicts an $\overline{\overline{EE}}2$ reaction.   A
further distinction may be drawn in the case of odd systems, where the number
of delocalized electrons may be equal to, one less than, or one more than, the
number of atoms.   For example benzyl can exist as a radical, a cation, or an anion.
We may distinguish these three cases by adding a superscript R, $+$, $-$ to the
symbol O.   Thus equation (8.27) represents an $\overline{O}{}^+E$ reaction.   In the case of
compounds containing heteroatoms, the symbols do not necessarily correspond
to the formal charge on the π system.   For example aniline, $PhNH_2$, being isoelectronic with the benzyl anion, $PhCH_2{}^-$, would be classed as O^- even though it
is neutral.

8.5   ISOCONJUGATE REACTIONS
In an isoconjugate reaction, the conjugated systems of the reactants and products,
or reactants and transition state, are isoconjugate; any contribution to ΔE_{deloc}
can then arise only from changes in the nature of the constituent atoms or
changes in the nature of the binding between them.   In the example given above
[Eq. (8.25)], there is a change in the electronegativity of nitrogen due to its conversion from neutral N, with an unshared pair of σ electrons, to N^+, with no unshared electrons; there may also be corresponding smaller changes in the nature
of the π bonds between nitrogen and the two σ-carbon atoms.   In this chapter,
however, we are considering only reactions of hydrocarbons; here such processes
are rare.   About the only obvious example would be a reaction parallel to that of
Eq. (8.25) in which a base removes a proton from one carbon atom in a conjugated
system, e.g.

$$
\begin{array}{c}
\text{H} \quad \text{H} \qquad\qquad \text{H} \quad \text{H} \\
\text{H}-\!\!\!\!\bigcirc\!\!\!\!-\text{H} + Y^- \rightarrow \text{H}-\!\!\!\!\bigcirc\!\!\!\!- \ {}^- + HY \\
\text{H} \quad \text{H} \qquad\qquad \text{H} \quad \text{H}
\end{array}
\tag{8.29}
$$

Such reactions have been little studied.   There is, however, a class of reactions
which are almost isoconjugate and can be treated as such; these are reactions
which take place with such facility that the transition state is very similar in
structure to the reactants (compare Sec. 8.3).   A good example is provided by

the protonation of reactive carbanions R^-. Here the proton transfer is so facile that the transition state must resemble the reactants very closely, that is $R^- + HX$, HX being the proton source. Under these conditions the dominant factor in the transition state will be the electrostatic interactions between R^- and HX; in the case of a mesomeric carbanion, reaction should then take place preferentially at the atom carrying the greatest formal negative charge. A good example of this is provided by the Birch reduction of benzene derivatives by metals to cyclohexadienes. The first steps in this reaction are:

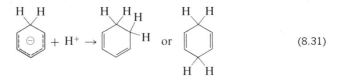

$$(8.30)$$

The product is formed by protonation of the final carbanion; this could give either 1,3- or 1,4-cyclohexadiene, i.e.

$$(8.31)$$

The distribution of formal charge in this carbanion can be calculated by the SCF MO method of Chap. 5; the results are shown in Fig. 8.4a.

The greatest negative formal charge appears at the central atom of the C_5 ion; we would therefore expect protonation to give 1,4-cyclohexadiene, as indeed it does.

This result incidentally shows the superiority of the SCF MO method for ions. The HMO method would predict equal charges at the 1, 3, 5 positions of the C_5 ion, with zero charges in between (Fig. 8.4b). On this basis one would expect a mixture of the two cyclohexadienes to be formed, in disagreement with experiment.

In this argument we have ignored differences in stability between the possible

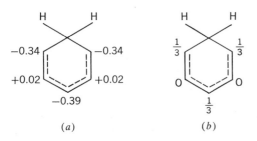

FIG. 8.4   Calculation of formal charges in the ion $C_6H_7^-$.   (a) SCF MO method; (b) HMO method.

isomeric products.   Ordinary intuition might have led one to expect the conjugated isomer to be much the more stable; this, however, is not the case.   The equilibrium between 1,3- and 1,4-cyclohexadiene is about $1:2$.[8]   Examination of models shows that 1,3-cyclohexadiene cannot exist in an unstrained planar configuration; in a configuration where the bond lengths and bond angles have normal values, the two double bonds are twisted through a large angle relative to each other.   Considerations based on the geometry of linear polyenes do not therefore apply here, and it is not surprising to find the unconjugated isomer almost as stable as the conjugated one.

8.6   OE REACTIONS; PROTONATION OF HYDROCARBONS

OE reactions are ones where the two conjugated systems differ by one atom, the even system being the bigger.   Let us first consider the example indicated above [Eq. (8.27)], i.e. the equilibrium

$$Ar + H^+ \rightleftharpoons ArH^+ \tag{8.32}$$

where Ar is an aromatic hydrocarbon.   Equilibrium constants for a number of reactions of this type have been measured[9] and the positions of protonation established in certain cases.

From Eq. (8.27), it can be seen that the difference ΔE in energy between the reactants and products can be written as a sum of several terms:

$$\Delta E = -E_{CH} + \Delta E_\sigma + \Delta E_s + \Delta E_{deloc} \tag{8.33}$$

Here E_{CH} is the bond energy of the new CH bond and ΔE_σ the change in total bond energy of the σ bonds adjacent to the reaction center due to the change in hybridization of the carbon atom at which protonation takes place; ΔE_s is the change in solvation energy during the reaction; and ΔE_{deloc} is the difference in energy between the delocalized systems of the hydrocarbon and the corresponding arenonium ion.   Making the assumption indicated above,

$$\Delta E = C + \Delta E_{deloc} \tag{8.34}$$

where C is the same for all hydrocarbons.   If so, and if Eq. (8.7) holds, a plot of $\log_{10} K$ against ΔE_{deloc} should give a straight line, of slope $(1/RT) \log_{10} e$.

The delocalization energies of reaction ΔE_{deloc} can be calculated either by the SCF MO treatment of Chap. 5 or by the simple PMO method of Chap. 6.   In the former case, the energies are calculated unambiguously, in electron volts or kilocalories per mole, and allowance is made for the changes in geometry on passing from the hydrocarbon to the corresponding arenonium ion.   In the case of the PMO treatment, the energies appear as multiples of a parameter β.

There is a complication that must be taken into account; aromatic hydrocarbons can protonate in more than one position, so that the observed equilibrium constants for the overall protonation are sums of equilibrium constants for protonation of the individual positions.   However theory and experiment both suggest that in the majority of cases the predominant contribution to K comes from the most reactive position in the hydrocarbon, so that corrections can easily be made for the smaller contributions from other positions.   One must also of course divide the observed equilibrium constant by an appropriate symmetry factor if there are two or more equivalent positions, to obtain the value corresponding to reaction at a single atom.

Figure 8.5 shows a plot of the experimental values for log K, against values of E_{deloc} calculated by the SCF MO method.   The points all lie close to a straight line, but the slope of the line is different from the theoretical value.   However better agreement could hardly be expected, since the arguments on which Eq. (8.7) were based would certainly not lead one to expect it to hold exactly. The effects of solvation cannot possibly be exactly the same in arenonium ions of greatly differing size and geometry.

Values for E_{deloc} can also be estimated for AHs by the PMO method of Sec. 6.10; they are simply energies of union of the odd AH arenonium systems with methyl.   If the NBMO coefficients at the atoms r, s adjacent to the point of protonation (atom t) are a_{0r} and a_{0s}, then from Eq. (6.100)

$$\Delta E_{\text{deloc}} = -2\beta(a_{0r} + a_{0s}) = -\beta N_t \qquad (8.35)$$

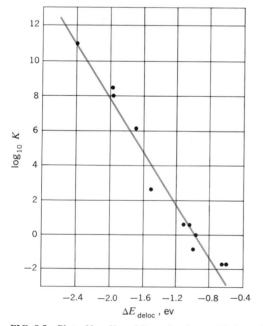

FIG. 8.5   Plot of log K vs. ΔE_{deloc} for the equilibrium of Eq. (8.34). Calculated values from Ref. 10; experimental values from Ref. 9.

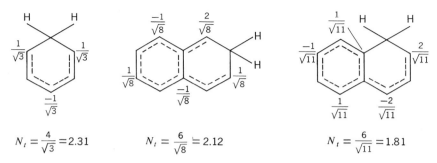

$$N_t = \frac{4}{\sqrt{3}} = 2.31 \qquad N_t = \frac{6}{\sqrt{8}} \doteq 2.12 \qquad N_t = \frac{6}{\sqrt{11}} = 1.81$$

FIG. 8.6 Calculation of reactivity numbers for benzene and for the α and β positions in naphthalene.

where the *reactivity number* N_t is defined by

$$N_t = 2(a_{0r} + a_{0s}) \qquad (8.36)$$

Figure 8.6 illustrates the calculation of reactivity numbers for benzene and for the α and β positions of naphthalene.   From Eq. (8.34), protonation should occur more easily, the smaller ΔE_{deloc}; the values for N_t in Fig. 8.6 thus indicate that naphthalene should be more basic than benzene, and should protonate preferentially in the α position.   Both these conclusions agree with experiment.

Figure 8.7 shows a plot of the experimentally determined values of log K for various AHs against reactivity numbers for the most reactive positions in each AH; in cases where there are two or more equally reactive positions, K has again been divided by an appropriate factor (e.g. 6 for benzene, 4 for naphthalene) to

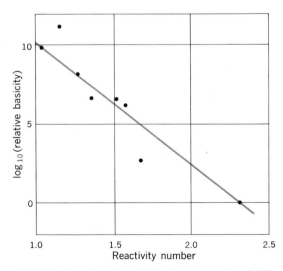

FIG. 8.7 Plot of log K vs. N_t for the protonation of AHs.

give the equilibrium constant for a single position.   The linearity of the plot compares remarkably well with that of Fig. 8.5, especially when one considers that the calculations of reactivity numbers took but a few minutes, a pencil, and a few cents' worth of paper, while the SCF MO calculations of Fig. 8.5 required the use of a large digital computer and cost several thousand dollars.

The quantities ΔE_{deloc} have been termed *localization energies* in the literature; the rationale behind this is an imaginary subdivision of the reaction into two stages, the first involving a polarization of the π electrons of the hydrocarbon to provide a localized pair of electrons at the reaction center, the second involving dative-bond formation to a proton using this localized pair of electrons; e.g.

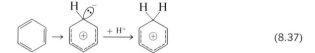

$$(8.37)$$

The energy required in the first (imaginary) step is easily seen to differ from our ΔE_{deloc} only by a constant additive contribution, this depending on the conventions used to describe the localized electron pair which is common to the localized states for all hydrocarbons.

8.7   OE REACTIONS; AROMATIC SUBSTITUTION

Aromatic substitution is now generally supposed to take place in two steps, via an intermediate arenonium structure, e.g.

$$\text{(8.38)}$$

In the majority of such reactions the first step is rate-determining; the reaction is then formally of $O\bar{E}$ type.

Substitution reactions can on this basis be subdivided into three groups, depending on the number of π electrons in the arenonium intermediate.   If the reagent X uses two π electrons to bind itself to the adjacent carbon, so that the π system of the intermediate has two electrons fewer than that of the parent aromatic, the reaction is termed *electrophilic*.   In the case of a hydrocarbon, the intermediate is then an arenonium cation; such a reaction would be classified as $\bar{O}^+\bar{E}$.   Likewise if the reagent X provides the two electrons that bind it to the adjacent carbon, so that the number of π electrons in the intermediate is the same as in the parent aromatic, the reaction is termed *nucleophilic*.   Here the intermediate is an arenonium anion and the reaction of type $\bar{O}^-\bar{E}$.   In the third case the reagent provides just one of the electrons; here the intermediate is a radical, and the reaction of type $\bar{O}^R\bar{E}$.

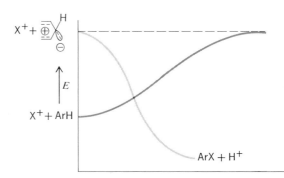

FIG. 8.8   BEP plot for electrophilic aromatic substitution.

Let us first consider the electrophilic $\overline{O}^{+}\overline{E}$ reactions, e.g. typical substitution processes such as nitration ($X = NO_2^+$), bromination ($X = Br^+$), or Friedel-Craft acetylation ($X = CH_3CO^+$).   We can apply the BEP treatment to this reaction, following the idea implied in the last paragraph of Sec. 8.6; Fig. 8.8 shows the corresponding potential-energy diagram.   The curve PQ represents a polarization of the parent hydrocarbon to a zwitterion in which two electrons are localized at the reaction center [Eq. (8.37)]; the curve RS represents combination of this localized carbanion with the electrophilic reagent X^+ to form the arenonium intermediate.   The energy ΔE liberated overall will be of the form [compare Eq. (8.34)]

$$\Delta E = A + \Delta E_{\text{deloc}} \tag{8.39}$$

where A is the same for all the reactions; using Eq. (8.15), the activation energy $\Delta E^\dagger$ for formation of the arenonium intermediate is then given by

$$\Delta E^\dagger = M + N\,\Delta E_{\text{deloc}} \tag{8.40}$$

where M and N are constants.   Consequently a plot of log k, where k is the rate constant for the substitution reaction against ΔE_{deloc}, should be linear, with a slope N times that for the protonation equilibrium [Eq. (8.32); see Fig. 8.5].

Extensive data are available for the relative rates of nitration of a variety of aromatic hydrocarbons; the data refer to rate constants for individual positions, having been derived from a combination of relative reactivities of different hydrocarbons with the orientation of substitution in the individual compounds.[11] Figure 8.9 shows a plot of the logarithms of the relative rate constants k for nitration against the values of ΔE_{deloc} calculated by the SCF MO method.   The points lie almost within experimental error of a straight line; the experimental data were collected under rather primitive conditions and the values of k cannot as a result be relied upon to much better than a factor of 2.   This is a remarkable vindication of our theoretical treatment, given that the predicted linear relation rests not only on the validity of the assumptions implicit in Eq. (8.7), but also on

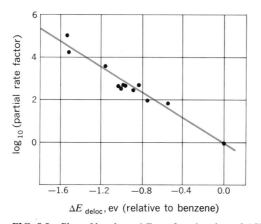

FIG. 8.9   Plot of log k vs. ΔE_{deloc} for nitration of AHs in acetic anhydride; the values for ΔE_{deloc} were calculated[9] by the SCF MO method of Chap. 5.

the validity of the BEP principle, that activation energies of related reactions should run parallel to their heats of reaction.

Here again we may calculate the values for ΔE_{deloc} by the PMO method; for AHs, they are given by Eq. (8.35).   A plot of log k against N_t should therefore give a straight line.   Figure 8.10 shows that this relation does hold reasonably well, although the linearity of the plot is much less convincing than that in Fig. 8.9.   Nevertheless the PMO method clearly provides a very practical method for calculating relative reactivities of AHs and, more important, the orientation of substitution in a given AH.   The PMO method invariably gives correct predictions for the orientation of the most abundant isomer.   This is a very satisfactory

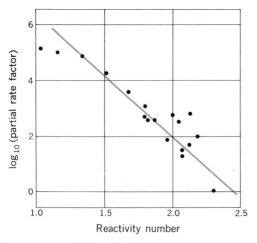

FIG. 8.10   Plot[11] of log k vs. N_t for nitration of AHs in acetic anhydride.

conclusion; for previous treatments at this level of simplicity had proved very unsatisfactory. Thus resonance theory could make no predictions concerning the relative reactivities of different hydrocarbons, and even its predictions of orientation were unreliable. A good example is provided by biphenylene (I). Since more unexcited structures (e.g. II) can be written for α substitution than for β substitution (e.g. III), resonance theory predicts that I, like naphthalene, should substitute predominantly α. However the reactivity number (see IV) is less at the β position than at the α position; the PMO method therefore predicts that I should substitute predominantly β rather than α, as indeed it does.[12]

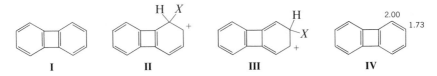

| I | II | III | IV |

Hydrocarbons also undergo substitution by free radicals, a reaction of $\overline{O}^R\overline{E}$ type proceeding via an intermediate arenonium radical. Extensive data are available for the relative rates of methylation[13] and trihalomethylation[14] of a variety of aromatic hydrocarbons by the radicals $CH_3\cdot$ and $CCl_3\cdot$; Fig. 8.11 shows a plot of log k for methylation against values of ΔE_{deloc} calculated by the closed-shell SCF MO method of Chap. 7. The points lie very close to a straight line, the agreement being better than for nitration (compare Fig. 8.9 with Fig. 8.11). This is not surprising; for solvation effects are far more important in the case of ions

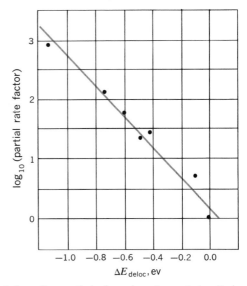

FIG. 8.11   Plot[13] of log k for the methylation of aromatic hydrocarbons by methyl radicals against ΔE_{deloc} calculated by the closed-shell SCF MO method of Chap. 6.

than neutral radicals, so the variations in solvation energy, which we neglect, must be likewise much greater in the case of ionic reactions such as electrophilic substitution.

Figure 8.12 shows a corresponding plot of log k against reactivity numbers; the linearity is excellent, very much better than for the electrophilic case. This again is not surprising; for as we have seen, the HMO treatment of odd-AH ions is defective in that it predicts that the inactive atoms in such an ion should be neutral (see Sec. 5.11). The SCF MO method predicts an alternation of charge in such ions, such that the net charges at inactive positions and active positions are opposite in sign. Any treatment based on HMO calculations for such ions must therefore be in error; this criticism of course also applies to any PMO treatment involving such ions. On the other hand both the closed-shell SCF MO treatment and the HMO treatment give similar results for odd-AH radicals; the PMO method therefore works better for radicals than for ions.

It might perhaps be argued that the relationship between the SCF MO description of ions, with alternating charge densities, and the corresponding HMO description should be regarded as analogous to the relationship between the open-shell SCF MO description of odd-AH radicals, with alternating spin densities, and the HMO or closed-shell SCF MO description; if so, the arguments used in Chap. 7 to justify the closed-shell treatment of radicals might be thought to support the HMO treatment of ions. However this is not a legitimate parallel; for the difference between the two descriptions of ions has nothing to do with electron correlation. It depends on changes in the electronegativity of atoms with the formal charges appearing at them, a factor neglected in the HMO treatment. Since, however, this effect is taken explicitly into account in the SCF MO approach, there is no question of its having been tacitly included in the parameters we use. The situation is therefore quite unlike that for radicals, where the difference is

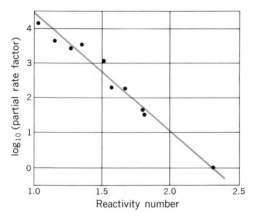

FIG. 8.12   Plot of log k vs. N_t for methylation of AHs.

due to horizontal correlation; correlation of this kind is not taken into account in the closed-shell SCF MO method, so allowance for it has to be made indirectly by suitable choice of parameters.

The third type of aromatic substitution, by nucleophiles, has not been studied quantitatively in the case of unsubstituted hydrocarbons; an example is the Chichibabin amination of naphthalene by sodamide. Reactions of this type are, however, important in the case of heteroaromatic compounds, such as pyridine, and in hydrocarbons carrying suitable substituents (e.g. NO_2); examples of both types will be given presently (Chap. 9).

8.8 SELECTIVITY EFFECTS IN AROMATIC SUBSTITUTION

The rates of substitution of a given hydrocarbon by different reagents can differ greatly; there are two obvious factors that must play a major role in this.

First, there is the problem of desolvation. In order that a reagent may approach our aromatic molecule sufficiently closely to react with it, we must first clear a space round the aromatic compound, and round the reagent, by removing molecules of solvent. The energy required to do this will of course contribute to the energy of activation for the reaction. Since the solvation energies of aromatic compounds are small, this contribution will be similar for substitution by a given reagent in different hydrocarbons and so will not affect the relative rates of reaction. The total solvation energy will of course depend on the reagent. In particular, since the solvation energies of ions are enormously greater than those of neutral species, ionic reactions, like electrophilic substitution, should take place with much greater difficulty than analogous processes involving neutral reagents such as radicals. This is why radical reactions tend to be much faster than analogous processes involving ions.

Secondly, there are the specific differences in rate due to differences in energy between the desolvated reagents and the transition state; these of course also contribute to the differences in reactivity shown along a series of related reactions.

Consider now a series of reactions in which desolvation might be expected to play a more or less constant role, e.g. a series of electrophilic substitutions of aromatic hydrocarbons by a given positively charged electrophilic species, or a corresponding series of radical substitutions by a neutral radical. Suppose now we examine the relative rates of substitution of a given hydrocarbon by one such series of reagents. Since the effects of desolvation are more or less constant, the differences in rate must reflect the differences between the ease of mutual reaction of the desolvated hydrocarbon and the desolvated reagent. Now we know that reactions of this kind follow the BEP relation [Eq. (8.15); compare Eq. (8.40)]; from the BEP principle, it follows that the corresponding proportionality factor between changes in activation energy and changes in energy of reaction [i.e. N in Eq. (8.40)] should be smaller, the faster the reaction. The relative rates of two such reactions are given [see Eqs. (8.5) and (8.40)] by:

$$-RT \log \frac{k_1}{k_2} = N[(\Delta E_{\text{deloc}})_1 - (\Delta E_{\text{deloc}})_2] \qquad (8.41)$$

where ΔE_{deloc} is the difference in delocalization energy between a hydrocarbon and the corresponding arenonium ion. The ratio k_1/k_2 therefore becomes less, the faster the overall reaction; consequently the more reactive the reagent, the less discrimination it will show between different hydrocarbons, or between different positions in a given hydrocarbon. If we wish to carry out reactions of this kind selectively, we should choose as unreactive a reagent as possible for the purpose. This of course is just a special case of part 3 of the BEP principle (Sec. 8.3); the more reactive a reagent, the less choosy it is about its partners in a reaction.

This selectivity effect can be seen very clearly from plots analogous to those of Figs. 8.9 and 8.10, for substitution by different reagents in a series of aromatic hydrocarbons.[15] Thus the rates of substitution by various electrophilic reagents fall in the order $NO_2^+ > (Cl_2$ in AcOH$) > (Cl_2$ in AcOH/CCl$_4$); the slopes of corresponding plots of log k vs. N_t increase in that order.

Brown and Nelson[16] have observed a similar correlation between absolute rates of substitution in toluene and the ratios of *meta* and *para* isomers formed; Brown has described this relation as the selectivity rule.

8.9 OE REACTIONS; MISCELLANEOUS EXAMPLES

Many other OE and $\overline{\text{OE}}$ reactions are known, but quantitative data for cases involving hydrocarbons are lacking. The rates and equilibria of such reactions can of course be calculated by the methods outlined above; however it seems rather pointless to quote such calculations in the absence of experimental data for comparison. Some examples of OE reactions of hydrocarbons are the following:

1 Addition of radicals or nucleophiles to vinyl derivatives; the propagation step in a vinyl polymerization is of this type, e.g.

$$R\cdot + CH_2{=}CHPh \rightarrow RCH_2{-}CHPh\cdot \xrightarrow{\ +\ CH_2{=}CHPh\ }$$

$$RCH_3{-}CHPh{-}CH_2{-}CHPh\cdot \quad \text{etc.} \qquad (8.42)$$

Electrophilic addition to olefines usually takes place by a different mechanism which will be discussed later (Sec. 8.23).

2 Deprotonation of alkylcarbonium ions, e.g.

$$R_2CH{-}CR_2^+ \rightarrow R_2C{=}CR_2 + H^+ \qquad (8.43)$$

The second step in E_N1 eliminations is of this type, e.g.

$$PhCHClCH_3 \rightarrow PhCHCH_3 \rightarrow PhCH{=}CH_2 + H^+ \qquad (8.44)$$

3 Disproportionation of radicals; this is one possible mode of termination in vinyl polymerizations, e.g.

$$\sim\!\!\sim\!\!\sim\!\!\sim CH_2{-}\overset{\cdot}{C}HR + S\!\cdot\ \rightarrow\ \sim\!\!\sim\!\!\sim\!\!\sim CH{=}CHR + SH \qquad (8.45)$$

where $S\!\cdot$ is another polymer radical.

8.10 EO REACTIONS; ACID-BASE EQUILIBRIA INVOLVING CARBONIUM IONS

A good example of an $\overline{E}\overline{O}^+$ reaction is provided by the reversible combination of carbonium ions with anions or Lewis bases; e.g.

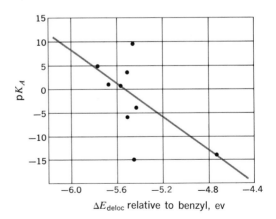

$$(8.46)$$

This reaction is formally analogous to a nucleophilic substitution, differing only in the relative sizes and roles of the odd and even systems. Equilibrium constants have been measured for the reaction of a number of such ions with water to form neutral unsaturated alcohols; the reaction generates a proton, so the net effect is the same as that produced by the dissociation of an acid. Ions of this type therefore behave as acids, and the value of the corresponding "dissociation constant" can be expressed on the usual pK scale. Figure 8.13 shows a plot of pK vs. ΔE_{deloc} for these reactions, the values being those calculated by the Pople method.

This time the points are badly scattered, unlike the plots for the $\overline{O}^+\overline{E}$ reactions

FIG. 8.13 Plot of pK_A vs. ΔE_{deloc} calculated by the SCF MO method, for various conjugated carbonium ions.

of hydrocarbons in Sec. 8.7.   This might of course be due to deficiencies in our whole theoretical approach, or possibly to some error in the (preliminary) calculations of ΔE_{deloc}; however it seems more likely that the trouble lies in differential effects of solvation, which of course we neglect.   The reactions discussed in this section were carried out under conditions where carbonium ions should be strongly solvated, unlike the reactions of hydrocarbons in Sec. 8.7.   Further evidence for this interpretation will be found in the following section.

In this case we are unable to use the PMO method, because most of the data refer to nonalternant systems.   Such systems represent the Achilles' heel of this approach.

8.11   EO REACTIONS; SOLVOLYSIS OF ALKYL HALIDES AND ESTERS

Solvolysis of an alkyl halide or ester by a limiting S_N1 mechanism involves ionization of the halide or ester as the rate-determining step; e.g.

$$Ph_2CHCl \xrightarrow[H_2O]{slow} Ph_2\overset{+}{C}H \ Cl^- \xrightarrow[fast]{H_2O} Ph_2CHOH + HCl \tag{8.47}$$

In our notation, this is an EO^+ process, being the inverse of the reactions discussed in Sec. 8.10.

Following the argument used in Sec. 8.7, and assuming that the BEP principle holds, we see at once that the rate constants for a series of such reactions should obey the following expression [compare Eq. (8.39)];

$$-RT \log k = A + B \, \Delta E_{\text{deloc}} \tag{8.48}$$

where ΔE_{deloc} is the difference in delocalization energy between the parent alkyl derivative and the corresponding carbonium ion.   A convenient series of reactions of this type are the solvolyses of arylmethyl chlorides $ArCH_2Cl$ in moist formic acid, ArH being an aromatic AH; reactions of this kind are known to be limiting S_N1 processes and rate data are available for a number of compounds.[17] Figure 8.14a shows a plot of the logarithms of rates of solvolysis against values for ΔE_{deloc} calculated by the SCF MO method; the points lie close to a straight line.

In the case of an AH, we can also calculate ΔE_{deloc} by the PMO method [see Eq. (6.120)].   If the NBMO coefficient in the cation at the atom originally attached to chlorine is a_{0r}, then

$$\Delta E_{\text{deloc}} = 2\beta(1 - a_{0r}) \tag{8.49}$$

A plot of $\log k$ against a_{0r} should therefore be linear.   Figure 8.14b shows this plot.   In this case the points seem to lie not on one straight line but on two parallel straight lines.   One of these includes all compounds analogous to β-naphthylmethyl chloride (V) in that both positions *ortho* to the chloromethyl

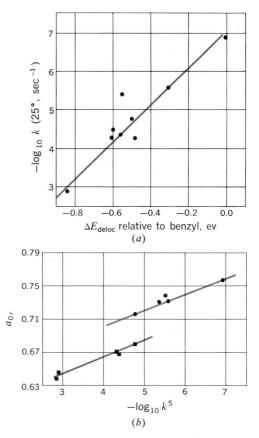

(a)

(b)

FIG. 8.14   (a) Plot[17] of log k vs. ΔE_{deloc} for the solvolysis of arylmethyl chlorides in moist formic acid at 25°; (b) similar plot[17] of log k vs. a_{0r}.

group are free; the second line includes compounds analogous to α-naphthylmethyl chloride (VI) in having one *ortho* position blocked by a second ring.

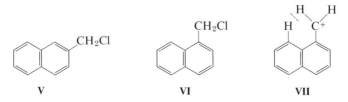

V   VI   VII

Dewar and Sampson[17] attributed this result to steric hindrance in the ions derived from chlorides such as VI.   Examination of models shows that the methylene group cannot be coplanar with the ring without one of its hydrogen atoms approaching the *peri* hydrogen too closely (see VII).   The resulting steric strain should introduce a constant extra contribution to the activation energy in the case of solvolysis of compounds such as VI; the plots for the two series of compounds should then be parallel, the difference between them being a measure of the strain energy. Dewar and Sampson estimated in this way a value for the strain energy of 2.3 kcal/mole, which is certainly not unreasonable.

On the other hand the SCF MO plot (Fig. 8.14a) shows no such distinction between the "α-naphthyl" and "β-naphthyl" types; points for chlorides of all types lie on a single line. It is of course possible that the PMO method here is right, and the SCF MO method in error; however it seems more likely that the difference is due to the known deficiencies of the HMO method in treating AH ions (compare Sec. 8.5), and that the strain energy in the α-naphthyl transition states is in fact small.

8.12 ALIPHATIC SUBSTITUTION; NUCLEOPHILICITY AND THE TRANSITION FROM THE S_N1 MECHANISM TO THE S_N2 MECHANISM

Figures 8.15 to 8.17 show plots similar to Fig. 8.14 for solvolysis reactions in more nucleophilic solvents. Four points emerge from a comparison of Figs. 8.14 to 8.16.

First, the slopes of the plots fall in the order Fig. 8.14 $>$ 8.15 $>$ 8.16 $>$ 8.17; on the other hand the rates of reaction also fall along the same series. This result is exactly the opposite of what one would expect on the basis of the BEP principle.

Secondly, the scatter of the points increases with increasing nucleophilicity of the solvent; this might be expected if our interpretation of the scatter in Fig. 8.13 as being due to differential solvation is correct.

Thirdly, the distinction between α-naphthyl and β-naphthyl types survives in the PMO plots, but becomes progressively less pronounced. In the SCF MO plots, all the points continue to lie on a single line.

Fourthly, the SCF MO plots tend to be curved, the slope increasing with the reactivity of the chloride. The effect is particularly pronounced for the reactions in aqueous ethanol (Fig. 8.16).

These results suggest very strongly that we are not dealing here with a simple type of reaction, a conclusion to be expected on the basis of the Hughes-Ingold theory of substitution; for the reactions in aqueous ethanol are no longer kinetically of pure S_N1 type. We are clearly confronted by a classical example of a controversial situation, the transition from the S_N1 mechanism to the S_N2. In formic acid, an excellent ionizing solvent of low nucleophilicity, the reactions are probably of true limiting type, involving the formation of an intermediate which can reasonably be regarded as a solvated, but otherwise free, carbonium ion. As the solvent becomes more and more nucleophilic, and its tendency to form covalent bonds to carbonium ions consequently greater, there is an increas-

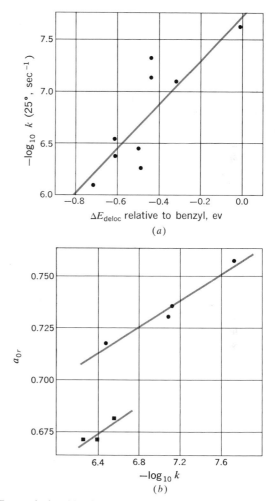

FIG. 8.15 (*a*) Plot of log k vs. ΔE_{deloc} calculated by the SCF MO method, for solvolysis of arylmethyl chlorides in a mixture of formic acid, water, and dioxan; (*b*) similar plot of log k vs. a_{0r}. The rate constants are taken from P. J. C. Fierens, H. Hannaert, J. V. Rysselberge, and R. H. Martin, *Helv. Chim. Acta* **38**, 2009 (1955).

ing amount of covalent binding of solvent in the intermediate, which therefore progressively loses the characteristics of a true carbonium ion.

In the classical Hughes-Ingold picture, aliphatic substitution reactions were divided into two distinct types: S_N1 reactions involve free carbonium ions as stable intermediates; S_N2 reactions take place in a single concerted step. This view has now been generally abandoned for one in which the classical S_N1 and

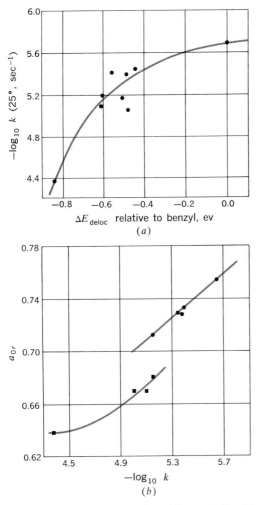

FIG. 8.16 (*a*) Plot[17] of log k vs. ΔE_{deloc} calculated by the SCF MO method, for solvolysis of arylmethyl chlorides in 80 percent ethanol; (*b*) similar plot of log k vs. a_{or}.

S_N2 processes represent the two ends of a graded series,[18] the intermediate reactions involving varying degrees of covalent binding. Thus in the intermediate region, Hughes and Ingold would envisage solvolysis as taking place simultaneously by two alternative routes, whereas in the other picture, one would envisage it as taking place by a single path of intermediate type.

Our problem is to infer the way in which our treatment will need to be changed if the reaction, instead of leading to a carbonium ion, leads to an analogous structure in which there is covalent bonding to the solvent. The transition states for the two processes will be as indicated in VIII and IX respectively, S denoting the solvent.

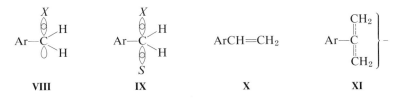

VIII	**IX**	**X**	**XI**

The transition state (VIII) for the limiting S_N1 process is isoconjugate with the arylethylene (X), while that (IX) for the S_N2 process is isoconjugate with the 2-arylallyl anion (XI). Let us try to get a rough estimate of the delocalization energies of activation $\Delta E^{\ddagger}_{\text{deloc}}$ for the two transition states, using the PMO method and neglecting differences in electronegativity between atoms of different types. The difference in delocalization energy δE between $ArCH_2^+$ and VIII is then given [see Eq. (6.120)] by

$$\delta E = 2\beta_{Cl}a_{0r} \qquad (8.50)$$

where a_{0r} is the NBMO coefficient of the methylene carbon in $ArCH_2^+$, and β_{Cl} is the resonance integral of the CCl bond in VIII. The formation of VIII from $ArCH_2Cl$ can be written as a sum of two steps:

$$ArCH_2Cl \rightarrow ArCH_2^+ + Cl^- \qquad (8.51)$$

$$ArCH_2^+ + Cl^- \rightarrow Ar\overset{\delta+}{C}H_2\text{---}\overset{\delta-}{Cl} \qquad (8.52)$$

The change in delocalization energy in the first step is the quantity ΔE_{deloc} that appeared in Eq. (8.49). Using this result, and Eq. (8.50), we find for $\Delta E^{\ddagger}_{\text{deloc}}$,

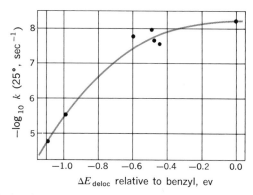

FIG. 8.17 Plot of log k vs. ΔE_{deloc} calculated by the SCF MO method, for solvolysis of arylmethyl chlorides in 79.5 percent aqueous dioxan; data from P. J. C. Fierens and J. Berkowitch, *Tetrahedron* **1**, 129 (1957), and M. Planchen, P. J. C. Fierens, and R. H. Martin, *Helv. Chim. Acta* **42**, 517 (1959).

$$\Delta E^{\dagger}_{\text{deloc}} = \Delta E_{\text{deloc}} + \delta E = 2\beta(1 - a_{0r}) + 2\beta_{\text{Cl}}a_{0r}$$
$$= 2\beta - 2a_{0r}(\beta - \beta_{\text{Cl}}) \tag{8.53}$$

The relative rates of two such reactions are then given by:

$$-RT \log \frac{k_1}{k_2} = (\Delta E^{\dagger}_{\text{deloc}})_1 - (\delta E^{\dagger}_{\text{deloc}})_2$$
$$= 2(\beta - \beta_{\text{Cl}})[(a_{0r})_2 - (a_{0r})_1] \tag{8.54}$$

Next let us consider the delocalization energy of activation, $(\Delta E^{\dagger}_{\text{deloc}})'$, for a reaction via the transition state IX. We can write this again as a sum of the change in energy in going from $ArCH_2Cl$ to $ArCH_2^+$ [Eq. (8.51)] and the change in energy $\delta E'$ in going from $ArCH_2^+$ to IX. In order to estimate $\delta E'$, we use the analogy between IX and XI. The difference in π energy between $ArCH_2^+$ and XI can be regarded as the energy of union of $ArCH_2^+$ with two methyl anions, i.e. groups, i.e.

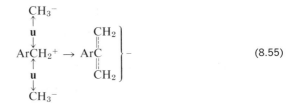

$$\tag{8.55}$$

To a first approximation, the change in π energy in this process can be equated to the first-order perturbation between the NBMO (ψ_0) of $ArCH_2$ and the $2p$ AOs (χ_1, χ_2) of the methyl groups. The perturbed energies are then given by the following secular equation, ϵ representing the common energy of a carbon $2p$ AO or an NBMO:

$$\begin{vmatrix} \epsilon - E & \int\psi_0 H\chi_1 \, d\tau & \int\psi_0 H\chi_2 \, d\tau \\ \int\psi_0 H\chi_1 \, d\tau & \epsilon - E & \int\chi_1 H\chi_2 \, d\tau \\ \int\psi_0 H\chi_2 \, d\tau & \int\chi_1 H\chi_2 \, d\tau & \epsilon - E \end{vmatrix} = 0 \tag{8.56}$$

Expanding the NBMO ψ_0 in terms of AOs ϕ_i, and writing β_{Cl} and β_S for the resonance integrals of the CCl and CS bonds in XI respectively, and using the convention that $\epsilon = 0$, being the energy of a carbon $2p$ AO, Eq. (8.56) becomes:

$$\begin{vmatrix} -E & a_{0r}\beta_{\text{Cl}} & a_{0r}\beta_S \\ a_{0r}\beta_{\text{Cl}} & -E & 0 \\ a_{0r}\beta_S & 0 & -E \end{vmatrix} = 0 \tag{8.57}$$

with the solutions:

$$E = 0 \text{ or } \pm a_{0r}(\beta_{\text{Cl}}^2 + \beta_S^2)^{1/2} \tag{8.58}$$

Since two electrons can occupy the BMO of energy $-a_{0r}(\beta_{Cl}^2 + \beta_S^2)^{1/2}$, the difference in delocalization energy between $ArCH_2^+$ and IX is given by:

$$\delta E' = -2a_{0r}(\beta_{Cl}^2 + \beta_S^2)^{1/2} \qquad (8.59)$$

Hence:

$$(\Delta E_{deloc}^{\ddagger})' = \Delta E_{deloc} + \delta E' = 2\beta(1 - a_{0r}) - 2a_{0r}(\beta_{Cl}^2 + \beta_S^2)^{1/2}$$
$$= 2\beta - 2a_{0r}[\beta + (\beta_{Cl}^2 + \beta_S^2)^{1/2}] \qquad (8.60)$$

The ratio of the rates of two reactions of the series [compare Eq. (8.59)] is then given by:

$$-RT \log \left(\frac{k_1}{k_2}\right)' = 2[\beta + (\beta_{Cl}^2 + \beta_S^2)^{1/2}][(a_{0r})_2 - (a_{0r})_1] \qquad (8.61)$$

Comparing Eqs. (8.59) and (8.61), we see that the ratio k_1/k_2 is numerically less in the latter case. The ratio R of the slopes of plots (compare Figs. 8.14 and 8.15) of $\log k$ vs. a_{0r} will be given by:

$$R = \frac{\beta - \beta_{Cl}}{\beta + (\beta_{Cl}^2 + \beta_S^2)^{1/2}} \qquad (8.62)$$

(remember that resonance integrals are negative!). Therefore as β_S increases, i.e. as covalent bonding to the solvent in the transition state increases, or in other words as the nucleophilic participation of the solvent increases, the slope of the plot of $\log k$ vs. a_{0r} should decrease. However the slope should still remain linear even if the amount of covalent bonding with the departing group (Cl in our case) and the entering group (i.e. the solvent, or nucleophile, S) is large, so long as it remains the same throughout the series of reactions we are considering.

On this basis we might expect the plot of $\log k$ against ΔE_{deloc} to be linear even for pure S_N2 reactions, although with a much diminished slope; Fig. 8.18 shows that this is the case for the pure S_N2 reactions of arylmethyl chlorides with iodide ion in dry acetone. The only deviation appears in the case of 9-chloro-methylanthracene, a compound which must be subject to severe steric effects, due to interference between chloromethyl and the two *peri* hydrogen atoms. Examination of models suggests that the strain should be relieved in forming an S_N2 transition state, and that reactions of this type should therefore take place more readily than would otherwise be expected. The observed deviation is in this direction.

Thus our correlation of $\log k$ with ΔE_{deloc} extends far beyond the reactions for which it was derived, viz. those of limiting S_N1 type. The decrease in slope of the plot of $\log k$ against ΔE_{deloc} with increasing nucleophilicity of the surrounding medium reflects the increasing importance of nucleophilic participation by the solvent, or by some added nucleophile. This is an important result for two

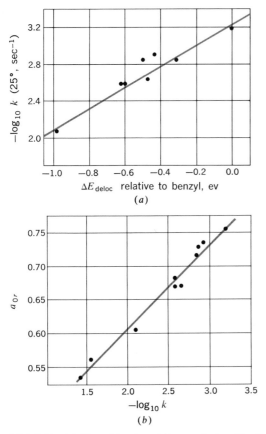

FIG. 8.18 (a) Plot of log k vs. ΔE_{deloc}, calculated by the SCF MO method for the S_N2 reaction of arylmethyl chlorides with iodide ion in dry acetone; (b) corresponding plot of log k vs. a_{0r}. See reference under Fig. 8.15.

reasons. First, the continuous gradation of the slopes of the plots of log k vs. ΔE_{deloc} indicates very strongly that there is a continuous change in reaction mechanism in passing from the extreme limiting S_N1 type to extreme S_N2. This indeed is the strongest argument as yet adduced for the idea that substitution reactions form such a continuous series, as opposed to a scheme where they fall into two distinct, qualitatively dissimilar, types. Secondly, the slope of the plot can be taken as a measure of the amount of covalent bonding to the nucleophile in the transition state; measurements of this kind should therefore provide a much better measure of "nucleophilicity" than the various alternatives that have been suggested on somewhat shaky intuitive grounds.

The argument has been given in some detail since it shows rather clearly the way in which this kind of approach can be used to assist in the analysis of reaction mechanisms.   By comparing the relative rates for a series of analogous compounds with the pattern predicted for various possible models of the transition state, one may be able to distinguish between otherwise intractable alternatives.

8.13 PMO TREATMENT OF TRANSITION STATES

In the final paragraphs of the previous section, we tacitly introduced a new approach to the problem of estimating activation energies.   Instead of invoking the BEP relation between activation energy and heat of reaction [Eq. (8.15)], we estimated the energy of the transition state directly by assuming some reasonable structure for it, and then using perturbation theory to estimate the difference in energy between it and the reactants.   Yet the results embodied in Eqs. (8.53) and (8.60) conform to the BEP relation; for using Eq. (8.49), we can write these equations in the form:

$$\Delta E^{\dagger}_{\text{deloc}} = 2\beta_{\text{Cl}} + \frac{\beta - \beta_{\text{Cl}}}{\beta} \Delta E_{\text{deloc}} \tag{8.63}$$

$$(\Delta E^{\dagger}_{\text{deloc}})' = -2(\beta_{\text{Cl}}{}^2 + \beta_S{}^2)^{1/2} + \frac{\beta + (\beta_{\text{Cl}}{}^2 + \beta_S{}^2)^{1/2}}{\beta} \Delta E_{\text{deloc}} \tag{8.64}$$

As long as the reactions take place through transition states which are similar, so that the resonance integrals β_{Cl} and β_S remain the same for reactions of different chlorides, Eqs. (8.63) and (8.64) are of the same form as Eq. (8.15).

Aromatic substitution provides another example.   Since the transition state must lie between the reactants and the arenonium intermediate, it must have the type of structure indicated below:

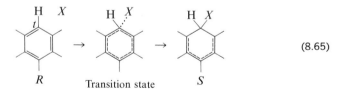

$$\tag{8.65}$$

$$R \qquad \text{Transition state} \qquad S$$

Here the carbon atom t at which attack takes place has a geometry intermediate between sp^2 and sp^3, and the bond to the approaching reagent X is still long and weak.   The π bonds between atom t and its neighbors are thus weaker than in the original hydrocarbon but still have extensive π character; in the PMO method we would represent this by attributing to the resonance integrals for these bonds a value β' which is numerically less than the "normal" value β.

Using the cycle indicated in Eq. (8.65), the delocalization energy of activation is given by:

$$\Delta E^{\dagger}_{\text{deloc}} = \Delta E_{\text{deloc}} - \delta E \tag{8.66}$$

where δE is the difference in delocalization energy between the transition state and the arenonium intermediate S. Now δE is just the energy of union of methyl with S to form the transition state; in the PMO approximation [compare Eq. (8.35)]:

$$\delta E = N_t \beta' \tag{8.67}$$

Hence from Eqs. (8.36), (8.66), and (8.67),

$$\Delta E^{\ddagger}_{\text{deloc}} = N_t \beta - N_t \beta' = N_t(\beta - \beta') \tag{8.68}$$

As long as the reactions take place by a common path, with comparable disturbances of the geometries of the carbon atoms at which reaction takes place, $\Delta E^{\ddagger}_{\text{deloc}}$ will be proportional to ΔE_{deloc}. The reactions will then obey the BEP relation of Eq. (8.15). Moreover the proportionality factor will be smaller, the greater β', i.e. the more closely the transition state resembles the parent AH R, or in other words the more reactive the reagent X; this provides us with an alternative derivation of the selectivity rule for this particular reaction.

8.14 EO⁻ REACTIONS; DEPROTONATION OF HYDROCARBONS

The hydrogen atoms in paraffins show virtually no acidic properties; however the situation is very different in analogous compounds containing double bonds. Cyclopentadiene, for example, is quite acidic and can be converted to salts containing the ion $C_5H_5^-$ by bases of moderate strength. The reason for this is of course familiar; the ion $C_5H_5^-$ is aromatic (see Sec. 6.15), unlike cyclopentadiene itself, so there is an increase in resonance energy during the reaction of cyclopentadiene with base. The energy of reaction is correspondingly reduced and deprotonation takes place correspondingly more easily.

Reactions of this kind involve the conversion of a neutral, even conjugated hydrocarbon to an odd anion with one extra conjugated atom; we would class them as of EO⁻ type. Streitwieser and his collaborators[19] have reported extensive studies of rates and equilibria of reactions of this kind, in particular the rates of deprotonation of methyl derivatives of aromatic hydrocarbons,

$$ArCH_3 + B^- \rightarrow ArCH_2^- + HB \tag{8.69}$$

The equilibrium constant K for this reaction is of course related to the pK_A of the hydrocarbon by:

$$\log K = (pK_A)_{HB} - (pK_A)_{ArCH_3} \tag{8.70}$$

where $(pK_A)_{HB}$ and $(pK_A)_{ArCH_3}$ are the pk_A of HB and $ArCH_3$ respectively. If the BEP relation holds for the forward reaction in Eq. (8.69), the corresponding rate constant k should then be given by:

$$\log k = A - B(pK_A)_{ArCH_3} \tag{8.71}$$

where A and B are the same for different hydrocarbons. Streitwieser et al.[19] showed that this relation held in a number of cases where the necessary equilibrium data were available, and then used it to estimate acidities of hydrocarbons where the rates of deprotonation could be measured, but not the equilibria.

We can treat these reactions in exactly the same way as the EO^+ analogs discussed in Secs. 8.11 and 8.12. A plot of log k against ΔE_{deloc} should be linear, ΔE_{deloc} being the difference in delocalization energy between the parent hydrocarbon and the anion derived from it. Figure 8.19a shows such a plot for values of ΔE_{deloc} calculated by the SCF MO method, and Fig. 8.19b for values calculated by the PMO method.

The parallel between Figs. 8.13 and 8.19 is obvious; in each case the points in the SCF MO plots lie on a single straight line, while those for the PMO plot lie

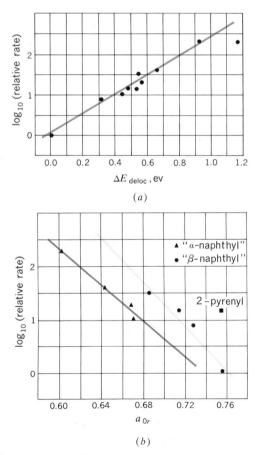

(a)

(b)

FIG. 8.19 Plots of log k vs. ΔE_{deloc} for Eq. (8.71), with values for ΔE_{deloc} calculated (a) by the SCF MO method; (b) by the PMO method.

on two approximately parallel straight lines; moreover the two lines in Fig. 8.19b again correspond to a distinction between α-naphthyl and β-naphthyl types. Streitwieser et al. attributed this distinction to steric hindrance in the α-naphthyl-methyl anions, by analogy with the corresponding explanation for the solvolytic reactions.   Here, however, there is an additional piece of evidence which sug-gests that the SCF MO treatment is correct, the segregation of α- and β-naphthyl types being an artifact of the PMO method.   Streitwieser et al.[19] correlated their rates with values of ΔE_{deloc} calculated by the HMO method; the results obtained in this way run closely parallel to those given by the PMO approach, points for α-naphthyl and β-naphthyl types falling on two different lines.   However the points for two of the compounds studied (2-methylpyrene and 3-methylfluoran-thene) lay on *neither* of these lines, the deviations being larger than the possible experimental error (which was somewhat greater than for the other compounds). In the case of the SCF MO plot of Fig. 8.19a, however, both these compounds behave quite normally; points corresponding to *all* the compounds, including these two, lie close to a single straight line.   Note that the point for 2-methyl-pyrene in Fig. 8.19b also shows a large deviation; one cannot of course apply the PMO method to fluoranthene since it is nonalternant.   This seems to argue strongly for the accuracy of the SCF MO results.

8.15   EE REACTIONS; THE DIELS-ALDER REACTION

The Diels-Alder reaction involves combination of a 1,3-diene with an olefine to form a cyclohexene;

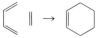

Reactions of this kind occur not only with a wide variety of dienes containing "localized" single and double bonds but also with many compounds where the diene moiety forms part of an aromatic system; a good example is the reaction of anthracene with maleic anhydride,

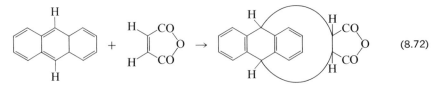

(8.72)

The Diels-Alder reaction is reversible, so reactions of this type can lead to equi-libria; moreover they are stereospecific, and lead exclusively to six-membered rings.   Analogous reactions are sometimes observed in which the products are derivatives of cyclobutane or cyclooctadiene; thus the dimerization of 1,3-buta-diene gives small amounts of 1,2-divinylcyclobutane (XII) and 1,5-cyclooctadiene

(XIII) as well as the "normal" Diels-Alder product, 4-vinylcyclohexene (XIV). As we shall see presently, however, these by-products are probably formed by an alternative reaction path.

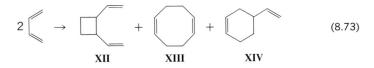

$$2 \quad \rightarrow \qquad + \qquad + \qquad \qquad (8.73)$$

XII   XIII   XIV

The overall effect of the Diels-Alder reaction is to replace the even conjugated system of the diene by a conjugated system with two fewer atoms; e.g. the reaction of Eq. (8.72) replaces the 14-atom conjugated system of anthracene with a 12-atom one, i.e. the two 6-atom conjugated systems of the isolated benzene rings in the product.   In our classification, such a reaction is of $\overline{\overline{EE}}$ type.

Following the principles outlined in the earlier sections of this chapter, we can write the equilibrium constant K for reaction of a diene with some given dienophile in the form:

$$-RT \log K = A + \Delta E_{\text{deloc}} \qquad (8.74)$$

where A is the same for reactions of different dienes with the given dienophile and ΔE_{deloc} is the differences in delocalization energy between the reactants and products, a quantity which can of course be calculated by the SCF MO method of Chap. 5.   Table 8.1 shows SCF MO values of ΔE_{deloc} for addition to various positions in various aromatic hydrocarbons.   Unfortunately few experimental values are available for comparison, but the qualitative information concerning the reaction of typical dienophiles such as maleic anhydride with aromatic hydrocarbons is consistent with these calculations.   Thus no stable adducts are formed by hydrocarbons with values for ΔE_{deloc} greater than -0.4 ev (e.g. benzene, naphthalene, or phenanthrene), while the products formed in other cases are the isomers predicted to be the most stable.

The values of equilibrium constants are of course independent of the reactions by which the reactants and products are interconverted; if, however, we wish to calculate the rates of Diels-Alder reactions, we must know the mechanism of the rate-determining step.

Two distinct mechanisms have been suggested for the reaction.   In one, the diene and dienophile first combine to form a stable intermediate biradical or zwitterion, which then cyclizes; e.g.

$$\qquad + \quad \rightarrow \qquad \rightarrow \qquad \qquad (8.75)$$

In the second, the reaction is supposed to take place in a single step, via a cyclic transition state; e.g.

TABLE 8.1   Values of ΔE_{deloc} for Diels-Alder reactions of various aromatic hydrocarbons, relative to benzene

Compound	ΔE_{deloc} for indicated positions	
	SCF, ev	PMO, β
	0	0
	-0.40	$--1.00$
	-0.96	-2.09
	-1.20	-2.57
	-0.73	-1.83
	-0.57	-1.61
	-0.68	-1.60
	-1.47	-3.02

$$\diagup\!\!\!\!\diagdown + \| \quad \rightarrow \quad \bigodot \quad \rightarrow \quad \bigcirc \qquad (8.76)$$

The available experimental evidence strongly supports the second alternative;[20] before considering this, however, let us first see if any predictions can be made on the basis of our general treatment of reaction rates by comparing the relative energies of the linear transition state leading to the intermediate in Eq. (8.75) and of the cyclic transition state in Eq. (8.76).[21]

The approximate geometries of the two transition states can be inferred from the structures of the reactants and products; they are shown in Fig. 8.20.   In the linear transition state, the $2p$ AO of one atom in the dienophile overlaps with the $2p$ AO of a terminal atom in the diene; in the cyclic transition state, the dienophile must be poised over the diene so that both its $2p$ AOs can overlap with the terminal $2p$ AOs of the diene.   In Fig. 8.20, the AOs have been written as normal $2p$ AOs; in practice the carbon atoms will have undergone partial changes in geometry and hybridization so that the AOs will have some s character.   However the topology of their overlap will be as represented in the figure.

In the linear transition state, the delocalized system is formed by overlapping of six AOs of the six participating carbon atoms, the AO of each atom overlapping with AOs of its two neighbors for internal atoms, and single neighbor for the terminal atoms.   Moreover the phases of the AOs can be chosen in such a way as to make all the AOs overlap in phase.   The delocalized system is therefore topologically equivalent to, or isoconjugate with, the π system in 1,3,5-hexatriene (XV).   Likewise the cyclic transition state of Fig. 8.20b is topologically equivalent to, or isoconjugate with, the π system in benzene (XVI).   Now we

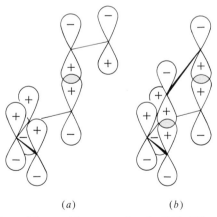

(a)   (b)

FIG. 8.20   Diagrammatic representations of possible transition states for the Diels-Alder reaction of butadiene with ethylene. (a) Linear transition state for the two-step mechanism; (b) cyclic transition state for the one-step mechanism.

know that the total π binding energy in XVI is much greater than that in XV; any overlap between the terminal AOs of the π system in XV should therefore decrease its energy.   We can therefore conclude at once that the cyclic transition state should be more stable than the linear one, so that other things being equal, the reaction should take place more readily by the one-step mechanism of Eq. (8.76) than by the two-step mechanism of Eq. (8.75).   The difference between the two transition states exactly parallels the difference between an aromatic compound (e.g. benzene) and an analogous nonaromatic one (e.g. hexatriene); we may therefore term the cyclic transition state an *aromatic transition state.*

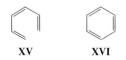

XV   XVI

This argument was first put forward nearly 30 years ago by Evans,[22] at a time when the majority of organic chemists favored the two-step mechanism for the Diels-Alder reaction.   Several immediate deductions can be made from it.

A number of reactions are known in which two olefines combine to form a cyclobutane, particularly in cases where one of the reactants is a polyfluorethylene derivative or tetracyanoethylene.   Such a reaction might again take place by alternative mechanisms, analogous to Eqs. (8.75) and (8.76); i.e.

$$\| + \| \;\rightarrow\; \ulcorner \urcorner \;\rightarrow\; \lfloor \,\cdot\,\cdot\, \rfloor \;\rightarrow\; \square \qquad (8.77)$$

$$\| + \| \;\rightarrow\; \lceil \rceil \;\rightarrow\; \square \qquad (8.78)$$

Here the transition states are isoconjugate with 1,3-butadiene and cyclobutadiene respectively, so the cyclic structure is now *antiaromatic* (Sec. 6.12); we would therefore expect reactions of this kind to take place by the two-step mechanism rather than via a cyclic transition state.   The available evidence suggests very strongly that this is the case.[23]

Given that the Diels-Alder reaction probably takes place by a one-step mechanism via a cyclic transition state, we are then left with the problem of deciding whether or not this transition state is symmetrical.   In other words, are the two partial bonds linking diene and dienophile of similar strength, or is one of them much stronger than the other?   In the latter case, the transition state would resemble that for the two-step reaction, the additional interaction between the ends of the six-atom conjugated system being relatively weak.

If the reaction were of two-step type, the intermediate would contain two distinct conjugated systems, one derived from the diene, one from the dienophile; for these are separated by saturated carbon atoms which will act as "insulators."

The energies of reaction of different dienes with a given dienophile would then be given by:

$$\Delta E = A + (\Delta E_{deloc})_{diene} \tag{8.79}$$

where A is a constant and $(\Delta E_{deloc})_{diene}$ is the difference in delocalization energy between the diene and the corresponding allyl system in the transition state [compare Eq. (8.75)].   The relative rates of two such reactions should then be given by:

$$-RT \log \frac{k_1}{k_2} = B[(\Delta E_{deloc})_{diene(1)} - (\Delta E_{deloc})_{diene(2)}] \tag{8.80}$$

where B is the BEP parameter of Eq. (8.15).   This is exactly the expression we would derive for the relative rates of a series of reactions when some arbitrary reagent R adds to one end of the diene; i.e.

$$R + \diagup\diagdown\diagup\diagup \rightarrow R\diagdown\diagup\diagdown\diagup \tag{8.81}$$

Such a reaction is of OE type, and the corresponding delocalization energy of activation can be calculated by the method of Sec. 8.

If on the other hand the reaction involves a synchronous addition, the energy of reaction will be of the form

$$\Delta E = A' + (\Delta E_{deloc})' \tag{8.82}$$

where $(\Delta E_{deloc})'_{diene}$ is now the difference in π energy between the diene and a system (i.e. the final adduct) with *two* fewer carbon atoms in the π system.   In this case Eq. (8.80) is replaced by:

$$-RT \log \frac{k_1}{k_2} = B'[(\Delta E_{deloc})'_{diene(1)} - (\Delta E_{deloc})'_{diene(2)}] \tag{8.83}$$

Finally if the transition state is cyclic, but not symmetrical, we may expect the relative rates of reaction to follow some relation intermediate between Eqs. (8.80) and (8.83), $(\Delta E_{deloc})_{diene}$ in Eq. (8.80) referring to reaction at the end of the diene which is more strongly bound to the dienophile in the transition state.

This approach therefore provides us with a way of estimating the symmetry of the cyclic transition state in a Diels-Alder reaction; it has been applied[24] to the reactions of various aromatic hydrocarbons with maleic anhydride.   Figure 8.21 shows plots of log k for these reactions against $(\Delta E_{deloc})_{diene}$ and $(\Delta E_{deloc})'_{diene}$, these being calculated for attack at the most reactive position or pair of positions. It is obvious that the rates conform closely to Eq. (8.83) but not at all to Eq. (8.80); the transition states in these reactions must therefore be nearly symmetrical.‡

If we examine the intermediate (XVII) for attack by maleic anhydride on anthracene by the two-step mechanism, we see that it is precisely analogous to

‡ Similar conclusions have been reached for other Diels-Alder reactions of maleic anhydride, using secondary isotope effects; see Ref. 20.

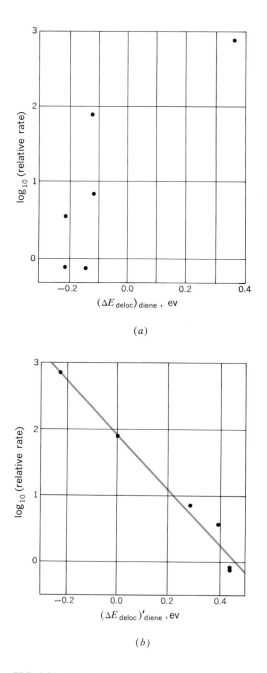

(a)

(b)

FIG. 8.21 Plot of log k against (a) (ΔE_{deloc})$_{\text{diene}}$, i.e. the localization energy for the most reactive position in the AH; (b) against (ΔE_{deloc})$'_{\text{diene}}$, i.e. the paralocalization energy for the most reactive pair of *para* positions.

the arenonium intermediate (XVIII) for substitution in anthracene at the 9 position.   Thus $(\Delta E_{deloc})_{diene}$ is simply the localization energy discussed in Sec. 8.7.
Likewise $(\Delta E_{deloc})'_{diene}$ is the difference in energy between the parent aromatic
compound and a system derived from it by removing two *para* carbon atoms
from the central ring (compare XIX); Brown[25] has suggested the term *paralocalization energy* for this.

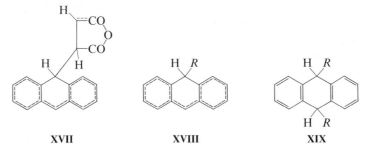

XVII   XVIII   XIX

The paralocalization energy can be estimated approximately for even AHs by the
PMO method.   Since the localization energy E_t^{loc} at position t in an AH represents the energy required to remove atom t from the π system, since this is a
first-order perturbation in the PMO treatment, and since first-order perturbations
are additive, the corresponding energy required to remove two para carbon
atoms t, u from the AH (i.e. the paralocalization energy E_{tu}^{para}) can be written as
a sum of the two corresponding localization energies, i.e.

$$E_{tu}^{para} = E_t^{loc} + E_u^{loc} = 2\beta(N_t + N_u) \tag{8.84}$$

from Eq. (8.35).
    The last column of Table 8.1 shows paralocalization energies calculated in this
way; it will be seen that they run closely parallel to the values calculated by the
SCF MO method.

8.16   EE REACTIONS; THE COPE REARRANGEMENT
When heated, derivatives of biallyl (XX) undergo rearrangements to isomeric
biallyls (XXIII) as indicated in Eq. (8.85), a type of reaction discovered by Cope
and known as the *Cope rearrangement*.[26]

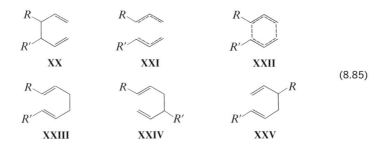

XX   XXI   XXII

(8.85)

XXIII   XXIV   XXV

Reactions of this type could in principle take place either by fission of XX to a pair of allyl radicals (XXI), which recombine, or in a one-step reaction via a cyclic transition state (XXII).   In the latter case only one product should be formed, since the atoms a, b in XX must necessarily be linked in the product; on the other hand recombination of the radicals (XXI) could equally well give two additional isomeric products, XXIV and XXV, by alternative pairing of radicals.   The latter possibility has been observed (e.g. Ref. 27), but in the majority of simple Cope rearrangements, just one product is formed.   Here we must be dealing with a synchronous process involving the cyclic transition state (XXII).

It can be seen at once that the delocalized system XXII is isoconjugate with benzene and consequently aromatic; the extra stabilization so acquired is no doubt responsible for the facility with which reactions of this type take place. However there is still one further aspect to be considered; a transition state such as XXII can exist in two geometrically isomeric forms, analogous to the boat and chair forms of cyclohexane.   In cases where XX carries suitable substituents, the products (XXIII) formed via these two transition states will differ in geometry.

The arrangements of orbitals in the two transition states is indicated in Fig. 8.22.   It will be seen that the orbitals in each case all overlap in phase, so the delocalized systems are both isoconjugate with benzene; however in the *cis* transition state (Fig. 8.22*b*) there is an additional interaction between two orbitals topologically equivalent to the $2p$ AOs of a pair of *para* carbon atoms in benzene.   The *cis* transition state is thus isoconjugate with butalene (XXVI).   Our problem is to decide whether or not this additional interaction is energetically favorable; we can determine this at once by comparing the π energies of benzene and butalene;

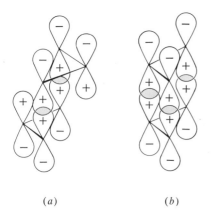

(*a*)   (*b*)

FIG. 8.22   Representation of transition states for the Cope rearrangement.   (*a*) *trans;* (*b*) *cis.*

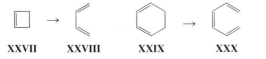

(8.86)

XXVI

This comparison can be made either by the SCF MO method (see Tables 5.2 and 5.4) or by the PMO treatment of Sec. 6.12. The answer in each case is clear; butalene is much less stable than benzene, as one might expect since it contains two antiaromatic cyclobutadiene rings.   The one-step Cope rearrangement should[21] therefore take place stereospecifically in the manner expected for the *trans* cyclic transition state of Fig. 8.22*a*; Doering and Roth[28] have shown this to be the case.

Since the transition state contains a six-atom delocalized system, and since both it and the reactant are even, the one-step Cope rearrangement is an EE reaction.

8.17   EE REACTIONS; THERMAL RING-OPENING REACTIONS IN CYCLIC OLEFINES; HÜCKEL AND ANTI-HÜCKEL SYSTEMS.

When cyclobutene (XXVII) is heated, it undergoes a ring-opening reaction to butadiene (XXVIII); similar reactions are shown by derivatives of cyclobutene, and also by derivatives of 1,3-cyclohexadiene (XXIX), which undergo conversion to 1,3,5-hexatrienes (XXX).   The latter reaction is reversible; the former is not, because the cyclobutene ring is highly strained and its resynthesis from butadiene would consequently be endothermic.

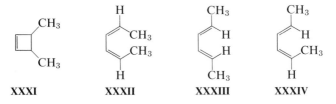

(8.87)

XXVII   XXVIII   XXIX   XXX

During these reactions, the methylene groups at the ends of the system have to rotate; e.g. in XXVII the methylene groups lie in a plane perpendicular to the ring, while in XXVIII, the whole molecule is—or can be—coplanar.   As the ring in XXVII opens, each methylene group must therefore rotate through 90° about the bond linking it to the adjacent unsaturated system.   Since two groups rotate in this way, and since either can rotate in either of two directions, the reaction can lead to various isomeric products in cases where the methylene hydrogen atoms are replaced by other groups.   Thus pyrolysis of 3,4-dimethylcyclobutene (XXXI) might give one of three distinct geometrical isomers (XXXII to XXXIV);

XXXI   XXXII   XXXIII   XXXIV

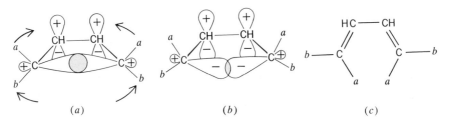

FIG. 8.23   The disrotatory ring opening of cyclobutene[21] (*a*) to butadiene (*c*) via the transition state (*b*).

Our problem is to predict the structure of the transition state for the reaction, and so to deduce which of these isomers should be the favored product.

Figure 8.23 indicates diagrammatically the course of the reaction when the methylene groups rotate in opposite directions; Woodward and Hoffmann[29] have suggested the term *disrotatory* for ring-opening processes of this type.   In the transition state, the relevant orbitals of the two methylene carbon atoms are still of hybrid type, but they can now overlap with the 2*p* AOs of the adjacent unsaturated atoms; such overlap should give rise to a cyclic delocalized system.

Consider the overlap between a hybrid AO ϕ of one of the central carbon atoms and the 2*p* AO ψ of the adjacent carbon atom in the conjugated system.   The hybrid AO ϕ can be written as a combination of a 2*s* AO and a 2*p* AO, and the latter can in turn be represented as a combination of "component" 2*p* AOs *x* and *y*, with axes respectively parallel and perpendicular to that of ψ (Fig. 8.24).   The overlap integral between the AOs ψ and ϕ thus becomes:

$$\int \psi \phi \, d\tau = \int \psi[as + b(x \cos \theta + y \sin \theta)] \, d\tau$$

$$= b \cos \theta \int \psi x \, d\tau \tag{8.88}$$

since the integrals $\int \psi s \, d\tau$ and $\int \psi y \, d\tau$ vanish through symmetry [compare Sec. 4.9, Eq. (4.87)].   The sign of the overlap integral between ψ and ϕ consequently depends on the relative phases of ψ and of the component *x* of ϕ; with the choice of phases indicated in Fig. 8.24, the integral is positive, i.e. the AOs overlap in phase.

Comparing Figs. 8.23 and 8.24, we see that the AOs in the transition state of

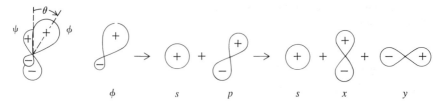

FIG. 8.24   Calculation of the overlap integral between a hybrid AO ϕ of one carbon atom and a 2*p* AO ψ of an adjacent one.

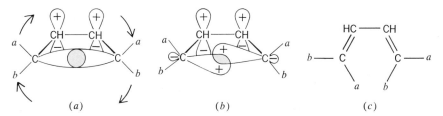

FIG. 8.25 Conrotatory ring opening of cyclobutene (a) to cyclobutadiene (c) via the transition state (b).

Fig. 8.23b all overlap in phase.   The transition state is therefore isoconjugate with cyclobutadiene, and so should be antiaromatic (Sec. 6.12).

Next let us consider the alternative mode of ring opening in cyclobutene, where both methylene groups rotate in the same direction (Fig. 8.25); Woodward and Hoffmann term processes of this kind *conrotatory*.   It is immediately obvious[21] from a comparison of Figs. 8.23 and 8.25 that the conrotatory transition state differs qualitatively from cyclobutadiene in one important respect; no matter how the phases of the AOs are chosen, one pair will invariably overlap out of phase (see Fig. 8.25b).   The sign of the corresponding resonance integral will then be opposite to the signs of the resonance integrals for the other bonds.   Let us consider the effect of this on the aromaticity of the delocalized system in question.

Figure 8.26 shows the NBMO coefficients in several odd-AH radicals, in the case where one of the bonds has an "abnormal" resonance integral ($-\beta$ instead of β).   It will be seen [compare Eq. (6.110)] that the relative signs of the coefficients at the terminal atoms are exactly opposite to those for "normal" odd AHs. We can construct our abnormal even AHs by union of an abnormal odd AH with methyl; the argument of Sec. 6.12 then shows that the rules for aromaticity in such abnormal even AHs should be just the opposite of those derived for normal conjugated hydrocarbons, i.e. rings with $4n$ atoms (and $4n$ π electrons) should be aromatic, rings with $4n + 2$ atoms [and $(4n + 2)\pi$ electrons] antiaromatic.   It is also easily seen from Fig. 8.26, and the argument of Sec. 6.14, that a similar inversion will apply to odd cyclic systems.   In the abnormal series, cyclic cations with $4n + 1$ atoms will be aromatic, and those with $4n + 3$ atoms

FIG. 8.26 NBMO coefficients in some anti-Hückel odd AHs.

antiaromatic, while cyclic anions will be aromatic with $4n + 3$ atoms and anti-aromatic with $4n + 1$. Here again aromaticity is associated with $4n$ π electrons, antiaromaticity with $4n + 2$. Systems of this kind therefore obey a rule for aromaticity which is exactly the converse of Hückel's rule; we may term conjugated systems of this kind *anti-Hückel* systems.

Using this result, we see at once that the transition state of Fig. 8.25b is aromatic, and we can therefore confidently predict[21] that cyclobutene should undergo ring opening by the conrotatory path of Fig. 8.25 rather than by the disrotatory path of Fig. 8.23. Conversely, the ring opening of 1,3-cyclohexadiene to 1,3,5-hexatriene should take place by the disrotatory path of Fig. 8.27b rather than by the conrotatory path of Fig. 8.27c; for here the transition states are isoconjugate with benzene and anti-Hückel benzene respectively, and of course it is normal Hückel benzene that is aromatic.

The experimental evidence shows that reactions of this kind are indeed stereospecific in the expected sense. Woodward and Hoffmann first pointed out that this striking phenomenon could be explained in theoretical terms; however the treatment given here is superior to theirs as we shall see in the next section.

Two final points deserve mention. First, the reader may have noticed that

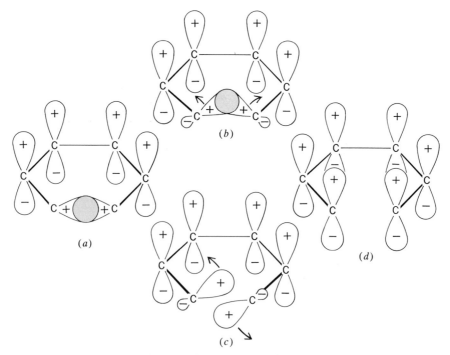

FIG. 8.27 Conversion of 1,3-cyclohexadiene (a) to 1,3,5-hexatriene (d) by (b) disrotatory or (c) conrotatory ring opening.

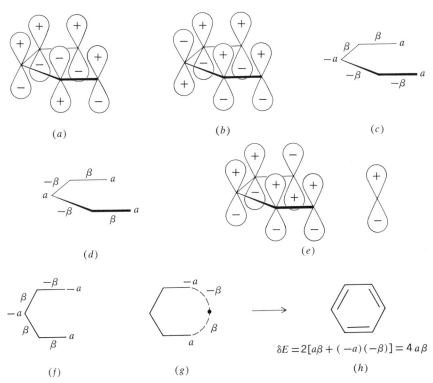

FIG. 8.28 Effect of alternative choices of phases of AOs on the PMO treatment of benzene. (a) and (b) effect of changing the phase of the 2p AO of an internal atom in the C_5 system; (c) and (d) signs of resonance integrals and NBMO coefficients for situations (a) and (b) respectively; (e) and (f) effect of changing the phase of a terminal AO on the resonance integrals and NBMO coefficients; (g) calculation of energy of union with methyl for the situation indicated in (e) and (f).

the phases of the component AOs have always been chosen in such a way as to minimize the number of out-of-phase overlaps. Since the choice of phases is quite arbitrary, are we free to make this particular choice? The answer to this is that our argument is independent of the choice of phases. Consider for example the pentadienate system. If we invert the phase of one of the central AOs (Fig. 8.28a and b), we alter the signs of *two* of the resonance integrals; the effect of this is to leave the signs of the NBMO coefficients of the terminal AOs unchanged, so double union with methyl to form cyclohexatriene still gives an aromatic system (Fig. 8.28c and d). What happens if we invert the phase of a terminal AO? In this case (Fig. 8.28e) the relative signs of the terminal NBMO coefficients are indeed inverted (Fig. 8.28f). When, however, we consider union of this radical with methyl, we see that the relative phases of the methyl 2p AO and of one of the terminal AOs of the pentadiene system are the same, but the relative phases of the methyl $2p$ AO and the other terminal AO are opposite (see Fig. 8.28e); the resonance integrals for the two new bonds therefore have opposite signs, so the overall energy of union of methyl with the radical (Fig. 8.28g) is the same as in the other cases. Extending this argument, we can see that the situation is unchanged if the signs of overlap integrals for two, four, or any other even number of bonds in the ring are changed simultaneously. The essential factor is therefore the oddness or evenness of the number of out-of-phase overlaps. If the number is even, the system is of Hückel type; if it is odd, the system is of anti-Hückel type.

Secondly, it should be noted that the distinction between Hückel and anti-Hückel systems has been drawn previously in two other connections. Craig[30] pointed out that an analogous phase dislocation could occur in cyclic conjugated systems where one of the atoms contributes a d AO instead of a p AO (Fig. 8.29a). If the remaining AOs in the ring are all p AOs, the two AOs on each side of the d AO must have similar phases if the overlap between the p AOs are all to be in phase. In that case only one of the adjacent p AOs can overlap in phase with the d AO. Craig used this idea to explain certain properties of the phosphonitrile chlorides; however, as we shall see presently, his interpretation is probably incorrect, and it seems unlikely that the situation envisaged by him will ever prove significant in practice.

The other possible situation—and a very ingenious and entertaining one—has been pointed out by Heilbronner.[31] If we take an initially planar, linear π system, twist it so that one end turns 180° relative to the other, and join the ends to form a ring, the π MOs at the ends will join out of phase (Fig. 8.29b). The π MOs in the resulting structure, instead of forming two separate rings as in a normal cyclic conjugated system, form a single continuous ring, the topology of the resulting structure being that of a Moebius strip. Heilbronner pointed out that such Moebius strip compounds should be of anti-Hückel type in the sense that the orbital pattern predicted for them by the HMO method would lead one to expect aromaticity to be determined by the converse of Hückel's rule.

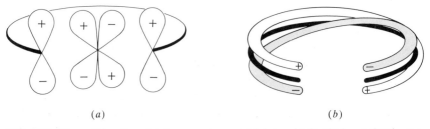

(a)   (b)

FIG. 8.29   Phase dislocation. (a) In a π system containing a d AO; (b) in a twisted π system of Moebius strip type.

This idea has been applied by Zimmerman[32] to the ring-opening reactions discussed in this section, using HMO theory to deduce whether or not a given transition state is aromatic.   However the HMO method cannot be used for this purpose, since it is known to be an unreliable guide to aromaticity (see Sec. 5.7).   Any argument of this kind must be based either on the SCF MO treatment or on the PMO method.

8.18   EE REACTIONS; ALTERNATIVE DESCRIPTIONS OF ELECTROCYCLIC REACTIONS

The reactions discussed in the three preceding sections are members of a class distinguished by having cyclic transition states in which electrons are delocalized round the ring.   Woodward and Hoffmann,[29] who suggested the convenient term *electrocyclic reaction* for processes of this kind, were primarily interested in explaining the stereospecificity of the ring-opening reactions considered in the last section; in their original communication, they discussed these reactions in terms of the following frontier-orbital argument (see Sec. 8.27[3]).

Consider the reverse reaction to the ring opening, e.g. the cyclization of hexatriene (XXXV) to cyclohexadiene (XXXVII).

XXXV   **XXXVI**   **XXXVII**

The transition state (XXXVI) is formed from XXXV by an interaction between the $2p$ AOs of the two terminal carbon atoms; in the frontier-orbital approach, it is assumed that the resulting change in energy is due mainly to the corresponding perturbation of the highest occupied MO ψ_μ (i.e. the frontier orbital) of the reactant.   If the terminal atoms in the reactant are atoms r and s, the perturbation $\mathbf{P}$ can be regarded, in HMO theory, as a change in the resonance integral between the AOs ϕ_r and ϕ_s from an initial value of zero in the reactant to β_{rs} in the transition state.   The change δE_μ in the energy of the MO ψ_μ is then given by:

$$\delta E_\mu = \int \psi_\mu \mathbf{P} \psi_\mu \, d\tau = a_{\mu r} a_{\mu s} \beta_{rs} \tag{8.89}$$

Since two electrons occupy this MO, the total change in energy δE is thus:

$$\delta E = 2\delta E_\mu = 2a_{\mu r} a_{\mu s} \beta_{rs} \tag{8.90}$$

If δE is negative, there will be a decrease in the total delocalization energy in passing to the transition state, and this of course should favor the reaction; likewise if δE is positive, the reaction will be correspondingly hindered.

The signs of the coefficients $a_{\mu r}$ and $a_{\mu s}$ are determined by an HMO calculation, while the sign of β_{rs} depends on the geometry of ring closure.   Since ring closure involves formation of a σ bond between atoms r and s, it must involve a prior twisting of the reactant to bring one lobe of the $2p$ AO ϕ_r into a σ-type overlap with one lobe of the $2p$ AO ϕ_s; this can come about in one of two ways (Fig. 8.30a and b). In the former case, ϕ_r and ϕ_s overlap in phase so that β_{rs} is negative; in the latter, the overlap is out of phase and β_{rs} positive.

The former type of ring closure (Fig. 8.30a) will lead to the converse of a disrotatory ring opening; since both reactions involve rotation of the ends of the chain in opposite directions, both can be classed as disrotatory. Likewise the other process (Fig. 8.30b) leads to a conrotatory ring closure. If then the product $a_{\mu r}a_{\mu s}$ in Eq. (8.90) is positive, δE will be negative if β_{rs} is negative and positive if β_{rs} is positive; here disrotatory ring closure will be favored. Likewise if β_{rs} is positive, conrotatory ring closure will be preferred.

This argument leads to the same conclusions as the PMO treatment of the previous section, and it can be applied equally to other electrocyclic reactions. It is, however, inferior to the PMO treatment in two respects. First, it depends on a treatment of doubtful validity; for as we shall see presently (Sec. 8.27.3), the frontier-orbital method has little to recommend it. Secondly, the treatment requires a knowledge of the coefficients in the frontier orbital of the reactant; these can be found only by a complete solution of the secular equations, whereas the PMO approach involves only a trivial pencil-and-paper calculation.

Later Longuet-Higgins and Abrahamson,[33] and Hoffmann and Woodward,[34] proposed an alternative approach to the problem, based on correlations of orbitals between the reactants and products. The idea here is that if a molecule has certain elements of symmetry, then its wave function must have corresponding symmetry. If the reactants, intermediates, and products in a reaction have a common symmetry element, e.g. a plane of symmetry, then the wave function of the system must throughout display the same behavior with respect to this element. Thus if the wave function of the reactants is symmetric with

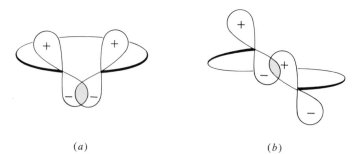

(a)   (b)

FIG. 8.30   The two ways in which the ends of a linear conjugated system can interact so as to lead to ring closure. (a) Disrotatory type; (b) conrotatory type.

respect to the plane of symmetry, the wave function of the transition state and products must likewise be symmetric. Moreover the same must apply to the individual MOs. As we alter the positions of the atoms in passing from reactants to products, the individual MOs must change continuously; in this way we can correlate individual MOs of the reactants with those of the products.

One example will illustrate this approach. Consider a concerted reaction in which two molecules of ethylene combine to form cyclobutane via a symmetrical rectangular transition state; i.e.

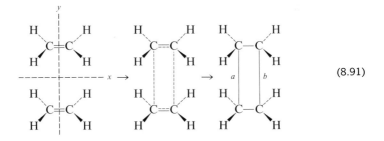

(8.91)

The reactants immediately before reaction, the transition state, and the products have two planes of symmetry; these are indicated for the reactants in Eq. (8.91), being designated x and y respectively. It follows that the MOs of all three systems must be either symmetric or antisymmetric for reflection in each of these two planes. Consider the four electrons that occupy the π MOs of the reactants and the CC σ MOs parallel to y in the product [a and b in Eq. (8.91)]. If we write the bonding π MOs of the two ethylene molecules as ψ_1 and ψ_2, and the corresponding antibonding MOs as ψ_1^* and ψ_2^*, we can combine these into the following symmetry orbitals for the reactants; the symbols ss, sa etc. designate their behavior with respect to reflection in the two planes of symmetry, the first letter referring to x and the second to y:

$$\phi_1 = \frac{1}{\sqrt{2}}(\psi_1 + \psi_2) \quad ss \qquad \phi_2 = \frac{1}{\sqrt{2}}(\psi_1 - \psi_2) \quad as$$

$$\phi_3 = \frac{1}{\sqrt{2}}(\psi_1^* + \psi_2^*) \quad sa \qquad \phi_4 = \frac{1}{\sqrt{2}}(\psi_1^* - \psi_2^*) \quad aa \qquad (8.92)$$

Since there is no interaction between the π MOs, the symmetry orbitals ϕ_1 and ϕ_2 have the same energy, and so likewise the orbitals ϕ_3 and ϕ_4 (Fig. 8.31). Next let us consider the analogous symmetry orbitals in the product. These (χ_i) can likewise be expressed in terms of localized two-center MOs for the σ bonds a and b in Eq. (8.91). Writing the bonding MOs of a and b as ξ_1 and ξ_2, and the corresponding antibonding MOs as ξ_1^* and ξ_2^*, we find:

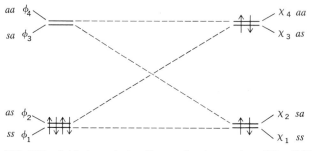

FIG. 8.31   Orbital correlation diagram for the reaction of Eq. (8.93).

$$\chi_1 = \frac{1}{\sqrt{2}}(\xi_1 + \xi_2) \quad _{ss} \qquad \chi_2 = \frac{1}{\sqrt{2}}(\xi_1 - \xi_2) \quad _{sa}$$

$$\chi_3 = \frac{1}{\sqrt{2}}(\xi^* + \xi^*) \quad _{as} \qquad \chi_4 = \frac{1}{\sqrt{2}}(\xi^* - \xi^*) \quad _{aa} \qquad (8.93)$$

Here again the symmetry orbitals χ_1 and χ_2 have the same energy since the bonds a and b do not interact with one another, and the same is true for the orbitals χ_3 and χ_4 (Fig. 8.31). If the system retains its symmetry throughout the reaction, the MOs for intermediate phases must show the same symmetry behavior as the MOs for reactants and products. Consequently there must be a correlation between each MO of the reactants and a MO of the products, such that each MO of the reactants passes continuously into the corresponding MO of the products as the reaction proceeds (see Fig. 8.31). If the orbital occupancy remains unchanged throughout the reaction, we can then predict the orbital occupancy in the products from that in the reactants. In the case of Fig. 8.31, we see that the ground state of the reactants is correlated in this way with a doubly excited state of the products. The transition state for the reaction will therefore be intermediate between the ground state of the reactants and a doubly excited state of the products; this should represent a very unfavorable situation, of high energy.

$$(8.94)$$

If on the other hand we carry out a similar analysis for the concerted reaction of butadiene with ethylene to form cyclohexene, we find that the bonding π MOs of the reactants correlate with bonding MOs of the products. Here the transition state should be intermediate in structure between the ground state of the reactants and the ground state of the products; its energy should therefore be much lower than the transition state of Fig. 8.31. One would then (correctly) conclude that the concerted reaction of Eq. (8.94) should take place much more easily than that of Eq. (8.91).

While this approach is elegant, ingenious, and original, it suffers from two major deficiencies in comparison with the PMO treatment.

In the first place, it can be applied only to systems which do have symmetry; this is a severe restriction. Woodward and Hoffmann have tried to extend it to other cases by assuming that they will follow a pattern analogous to that for symmetric reactions; they have derived in this way a set of rules for the sizes of rings that can be formed in concerted electrocyclic reactions. This extrapolation, however, has no basis other than intuition.

Secondly, the approach rests on the assumption that symmetry is maintained throughout the reaction; this obviously need not be so. Indeed, much evidence suggests that the transition states of some of these reactions are definitely unsymmetric; Diels-Alder reactions involving unsymmetric dienophiles (e.g. acrylonitrile) seem to be of this type. Unless symmetry is maintained, the correlation of orbitals between reactants and products loses its significance; for symmetry will be lost in the intermediate phases of the reaction. That effects of this kind are far from trivial is indicated by one classic example, the absorption spectrum of benzene. The band at 208 nm is due to a transition which is rigorously forbidden for a molecule with D_6 symmetry; it is observed only because the benzene molecule departs from this because it is vibrating. The resulting disturbance of symmetry is small; yet it is sufficient to give the "forbidden" band an extinction coefficient of nearly 10,000!

8.19   EE REACTIONS; EVANS' RULE AND SOME ADDITIONAL EXAMPLES OF ELECTROCYCLIC REACTIONS

The PMO treatment of electrocyclic reactions is based, as we have seen, on one very simple concept, the potential aromaticity of cyclic transition states. Reactions of this type take place only if the corresponding transition states are aromatic. Not only is this treatment much simpler, both conceptually and in practice, than the alternatives that have been suggested (Sec. 8.18), but it can also be summed up in one simple generalization, in place of a plethora of rules for individual systems. Since the basic idea behind this generalization was first discovered by Evans, we may term it *Evans' rule*.

Evans' Rule   Thermal electrocyclic reactions take place via aromatic transition states.

This rule applies not only to electrocyclic reactions of hydrocarbons but also to analogous reactions of compounds containing heteroatoms; examples will be found later (Sec. 9.17). Since many of these reactions involve unsymmetrical reactants and transition states, and since the frontier-orbital method fails catastrophically for compounds containing heteroatoms (see Sec. 8.27.3), it is fortunate that our PMO treatment can still be applied.

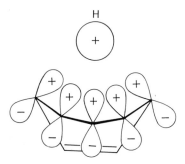

FIG. 8.32 Diagrammatic representation of orbitals in the transition state XXXIX.

A number of cases are known where hydrogen atoms migrate across aromatic systems; a classic example of this is cycloheptatriene (**XXXVIII**), which on heating undergoes autotropic rearrangements‡ by migrations of hydrogen [see Eq. (8.95)].

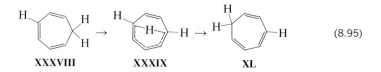

$$\qquad\qquad\qquad\qquad\qquad\qquad\qquad\qquad\qquad\qquad (8.95)$$

XXXVIII   XXXIX   XL

In the transition state (**XXXIX**), the migrating hydrogen must be partially bonded to two different carbon atoms; we can represent this situation in terms of MO theory by a model in which electrons occupy cyclic delocalized MOs derived from (possibly distorted) $2p$ AOs of the carbon atoms and the $1s$ AO of the hydrogen atom.   Assuming that the hydrogen AO overlaps with lobes of $2p$ AOs on the same side of the π system (see Fig. 8.32), it is easily seen that the delocalized system is of Hückel type.   If such a transition state is to be aromatic, it must then obey Hückel's rule.   The electrocyclic ring must therefore contain $4n + 2$ atoms, or $4n + 1$ carbon atoms.   Consequently migrations of this kind should occur between 1,5 positions, but not between 1,3 (i.e. allylic) positions. Detailed studies have shown that the migrations in cycloheptatriene take place as predicted (see Ref. 35) and the same is true of all other analogous migrations that have been studied.[35]

The reader may feel some concern regarding the possible effect of the two extra carbon atoms that have been represented in Fig. 8.32 as forming a localized ethylene unit; however one can see at once that this representation is correct if we consider the hypothetical conjugated hydrocarbon (**XLI**) that is isoconjugate

‡ An autotropic rearrangement is one in which a molecule is converted into an isomer differing from the original only by interchange of identical atoms.   Reactions of this kind can be detected and studied only if the atoms in them are suitably labeled, i.e. by the use of isotropic tracers.

with XXXIX. XLI can be constructed by union of the odd-AH radical (XLII) with methyl, as indicated below; it will be seen that XLII is cross-conjugated (Sec. 6.16), the lateral vinyl group forming an inactive segment. The energy of union is consequently the same as it would be if this group were absent, i.e. identical with the energy of union of the pentadienate radical (XLIII) with methyl to form benzene. The two extra carbon atoms in XLI therefore form a localized system, contributing nothing to the overall resonance energy.

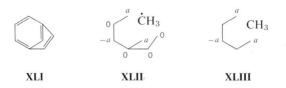

XLI   XLII   XLIII

Another very interesting, and possibly electrocyclic, reaction has been recently discovered by Doering[36] and his collaborators. Heptafulvalene (XLIV) reacts with tetracyanoethylene (TCNE) to give a single adduct (XLV) in which the TCNE, instead of adding across one of the 1,3-diene systems in XLIV, has added across two "*ortho*" positions in the seven-membered rings. Analogy with the Diels-Alder reaction might have led one to expect XLV to be formed by *cis* addition, and so to have the stereochemistry indicated in XLVI; in fact, however, the adduct proved to be XLVII, formed by *trans* addition of TCNE to XLIV.[37]

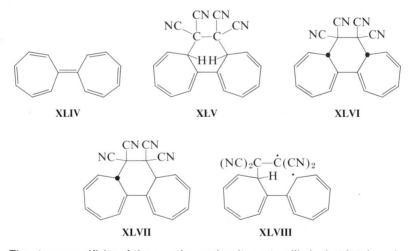

XLIV   XLV   XLVI

XLVII   XLVIII

The stereospecificity of the reaction makes it most unlikely that it takes place in two steps, via an intermediate biradical (XLVIII); besides, if XLVIII were an intermediate, one would certainly expect the product to be XLVI rather than XLVII.

If the reaction is concerted, the transition state (XLIX) will be isoconjugate with the tricyclic hydrocarbon (L). Now L can be derived by intramolecular union from the monocyclic AH LI, as indicated, by union between pairs of positions of like parity; L and LI should therefore have similar resonance energies, so L, like LI (which has $16 = 4 \times 4$ conjugated atoms), should be antiaromatic. The favored transition state for reaction of XLIV with TCNE should therefore be one where one end of the C=C π bond in TCNE overlaps in phase with the π MOs of XLIV, the other out of phase.

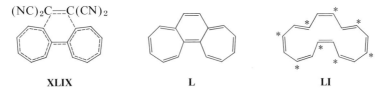

| XLIX | L | LI |

A little consideration will show that there are only two ways in which this can be achieved. Either one π MO of TCNE overlaps at one end with the upper π lobe of XLIX, and at the other end with the lower π lobe, leading to *cis* addition of XLIV to TCNE and *trans* addition of TCNE to XLIV; or one π lobe of XLIV overlaps with opposite π lobes of TCNE, leading to *trans* addition of XLIV to TCNE and *cis* addition of TCNE to XLIV.

This is as far as electronic considerations can take us; however examination of models suggests that the first alternative should be much the most favorable, leading to the (observed) product, XLVII. A recent structure analysis[38] has shown that XLIV has the S-shaped geometry indicated in Fig. 8.33; the point A on the upper π lobe and the point B on the lower π lobe lie close together, so they can easily overlap simultaneously with one of the C=C π lobes of TCNE.

These reactions deserve one final comment. In the preceding sections, we have considered only thermal electrocyclic reactions, and Evans' rule as stated at the beginning of this section therefore applied only to such thermal processes. Reactions of this kind can also take place under the influence of ultraviolet light, with, however, very different consequences. Since this book is specifically confined to ground-state chemistry, it would be out of place for us to consider processes of this kind in detail here. However the reader will find an extension of the PMO treatment outlined above to photochemical electrocyclic reactions in

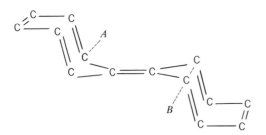

FIG. 8.33 Geometry of heptafulvalene.

a paper by the author;[21] this indicates that the rule governing the course of such reactions should be exactly the converse of Evans' rule; i.e.

Photochemical electrocyclic reactions take place through excited forms of anti-aromatic transition states.

Thus while the combination of two molecules of an olefine to a cyclobutane is forbidden as a thermal reaction on the grounds that the transition state would be antiaromatic, the corresponding photochemical reaction takes place very readily.   Indeed, it provides one of the best synthetic procedures for making derivatives of cyclobutane.   Numerous other examples have been reported and the rule now seems quite general.

8.20   EE REACTIONS; CONCERTED CYCLOADDITIONS

A number of reactions are known in which some reagent $X—Y$ adds to a carbon-carbon multiple bond;

$$\underset{\substack{b}}{\overset{\substack{a}}{\diagdown}}C=C\underset{\substack{d}}{\overset{\substack{c}}{\diagup}} + X—Y \rightarrow XabC—CcdY \qquad (8.96)$$

$$\textbf{LII} \qquad\qquad\qquad\qquad \textbf{LIII}$$

Let us see what predictions we might make concerning reactions of this type.

Evidently such a reaction cannot take place by a concerted *cis* cycloaddition; for if it did, the transition state would be isoconjugate with cyclobutadiene and consequently antiaromatic (see LIV).   The groups X and Y must therefore add either successively in two distinct stages via a stable intermediate or in one step by synchronous *trans* addition.

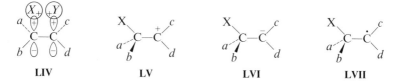

$$\textbf{LIV} \qquad\qquad\quad \textbf{LV} \qquad\qquad\quad \textbf{LVI} \qquad\qquad\quad \textbf{LVII}$$

If the reaction takes place in two distinct steps, the intermediate would nor-mally be expected to be a carbonium ion (LV), carbanion (LVI), or radical (LVII).   Processes of all three kinds are well recognized; in our terminology they are OE reactions and can be discussed in the same terms as for example aromatic substitution (Sec. 8.6).   Indeed, the formation of LV from LII is pre-cisely analogous to the formation of the arenonium intermediate during electro-philic substitution [see Eq. (8.27)].

Synchronous *trans* addition involves a different type of transition state, indi-cated in LVIII and LIX.   Here the delocalized system of the transition state contains two atoms more than that of the parent olefine (LII), while that of the product (LIII) contains two atoms fewer.   Reactions of this kind are therefore of EE type.

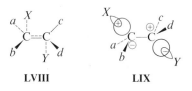

LVIII   LIX

Let us consider the effect of conjugated hydrocarbon substituents (e.g. phenyl) on the rates of the one-step and two-step reactions.   The delocalized system in the one-step transition state, represented by dotted lines in LVIII, is an even system; any interaction between this and the even substituent should be a small second-order effect, and should moreover be similar to that in the parent olefine (see Sec. 6.7).   On the other hand such a substituent should greatly facilitate the two-step reaction by stabilizing the intermediate ion or radical (LV to LVII); this can be seen at once by applying the arguments used in Sec. 8.10.   Substituents of this kind should therefore have little effect on the rates of additions taking place by the one-step mechanism, and different substituents should show similar effects; however they should greatly accelerate one-step additions, and the effect here should vary greatly from one substituent to another.

The addition of hydrogen halides to olefines seems to support these predictions nicely.   Addition to simple olefines takes place by stereospecific *trans* addition and almost certainly by the concerted one-step mechanism indicated in LVIII.[39]   Arylethylenes, on the other hand, add hydrogen halides in two steps via intermediate carbonium ions (LV); reactions of this type give mixtures of *cis* and *trans* adduct (since configuration is lost in the intermediate ion), and the ease of addition varies greatly with the nature of the aryl group.[40]

There is, however, one situation where addition to an olefine can take place by concerted *cis* addition; this is where the reagent is of the type XYZ, addition to the double bond taking place through X and Z.   If the Diels-Alder reaction is regarded as an addition to an olefine (XYZ being the diene), it would illustrate this situation; so also would the dipolar additions considered below (Sec. 9.17). However there are two important reactions of this type which fall into neither of these categories, viz. the *cis* hydroxylation of olefines by osmium tetroxide [Eq. (8.97)] and the *cis* addition of chlorine to olefines by treatment with iodobenzene dichloride [Eq. (8.98)].

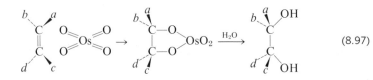

(8.97)

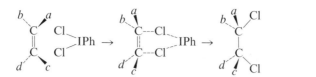

$$(8.98)$$

In the case of reactions of the type indicated in Eqs. (8.97) and (8.98), the same arguments should apply as in concerted *trans* addition; aryl groups should have little effect on the rate of the reaction, and substituents of this type should therefore tend to favor any alternative process taking place via intermediates such as LV, LVI, or LVII.   No such reaction is possible in the case of osmium tetroxide, but mechanisms of this type can easily be written for the reactions of PhICl$_2$; indeed, the concerted cycloaddition of chlorine has been established only for simple olefines, and at least one case is known (acenaphthylene, LX) where the reaction with PhICl$_2$ takes place in two steps via an intermediate carbonium ion;[40,41]

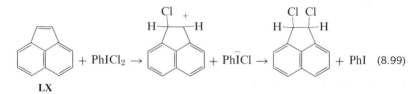

$$(8.99)$$

LX

Osmium tetroxide also reacts with bonds in aromatic hydrocarbons; thus phenanthrene (LXI) gives *cis*-9,10-dihydroxy-9,10-dihydrophenanthrene (LXII). Unlike the additions to olefines, reactions of this kind should depend critically on the bond being attacked; for the reaction destroys the conjugation in one ring of an aromatic system, so its ease should vary with the corresponding loss of delocalization energy.

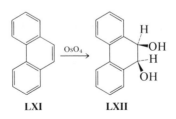

LXI   **LXII**

This loss of delocalization energy can of course be estimated by the SCF MO method; since it corresponds to the change produced by removal of two adjacent carbon atoms from the conjugated system of the parent hydrocarbon, it has been termed[25] the *ortholocalization energy*.   The point of attack in a given hydro-carbon should be the bond with the lowest ortholocalization energy; this is invariably the case.[25,42]   There should also be a relation between the rates of reaction of different hydrocarbons and the ortholocalization energies of the most reactive bonds in them; while quantitative data are lacking, this relationship certainly holds qualitatively.[25,42]

In the case of even AHs, ortholocalization energies δE_π can be estimated very simply by the PMO method.   Consider for example the bond between atoms s and t in an even AH.   The energy δE_π required to remove these atoms from conjugation can be found at once from Eq. (6.16):

$$\delta E_\pi = 2\beta\left(\sum_{r\neq t} p_{rs} + \sum_{u\neq s} p_{tu} + p_{st}\right) \tag{8.100}$$

where the sums are over bonds between atom s and adjacent atoms r other than t, and over bonds between atom t and adjacent atoms u other than s.   Now comparison of Eqs. (8.36) and (8.100) shows that to the approximation of PMO theory,

$$2\sum_r p_{rs} = N_s \qquad 2\sum_u p_{tu} = N_t \tag{8.101}$$

where the sums are now over all the adjacent atoms and N_s, N_t are the reactivity numbers of atoms t and u.   Hence:

$$\delta E_\pi = \beta(N_t + N_u) - 2\beta p_{st} \tag{8.102}$$

The bond order p_{st} can also be found approximately by using PMO theory [Eq. (6.147)], so Eq. (8.102) allows one to calculate ortholocalization energies. The results run parallel to those given by the SCF MO treatment and account equally well for the available experimental data.[42]

Equation (8.100) is interesting in another connection.   It has been known for some time that certain polycyclic aromatic hydrocarbons are carcinogenic, and that these can all be regarded as benzo, or polybenzo, derivatives of phenanthrene in which the 9,10 bond is insubstituted.   Some years ago Pullman and Pullman[43] drew attention to an apparent correlation between the carcinogenicity of such phenanthrene derivatives and a quantity which they described as the "total charge density of the K region," the K region being the 9,10-phenanthrene bond.   A typical example is benzo[a]pyrene (LXIII), one of the most active known carcinogens of this type.

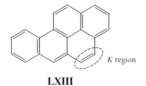

K region

LXIII

The total charge density of the K region is defined as a sum of the indices of free valence (see Sec. 8.27.1) of the two carbon atoms *plus* the bond order of the bond between them.   In the original work, these quantities were calculated by the valence-bond (VB) method, but it is known that there are close parallels between the values calculated in that way and by the MO method.   In the MO method, the free-valence number (equivalent to the VB index of free valence) f_s of atom s is defined by:

$$f_s = \sqrt{3} - \sum_r p_{rs} \tag{8.103}$$

where the sum is over atoms r directly bonded to s; with this definition, the total charge density Δ in the K region composed of atoms s and t is given by:

$$\Delta = f_s + f_t + p_{st} = \left(\sqrt{3} - \sum_r p_{rs}\right) + \left(\sqrt{3} - \sum_u p_{tu}\right) + p_{st}$$

$$= 2\sqrt{3} - \left(\sum_{r \neq t} p_{rs} - \sum_{u \neq s} p_{tu}\right) - p_{st} = 2\sqrt{3} - \delta E_\pi \tag{8.104}$$

where δE_π [see Eq. (8.100)] is the ortholocalization energy of the bond in the K region, between atoms t and u.   The correlation found by the Pullmans implies that the tendency to carcinogenicity is greater, the greater Δ; Eq. (8.104) shows that this corresponds to decreasing values of δE_π, that is to a greater tendency for the bond in the K region to undergo one-step synchronous addition.   In its original form, the correlation appeared as an apparently meaningless correspondence between carcinogenicity and a rather strange theoretical parameter; this revised interpretation suggests that carcinogenicity depends on some process in the cell where direct one-step addition takes place to the K-region bond.[42]

8.21   EE REACTIONS; CONCERTED ELIMINATIONS

A number of reactions are known which are the reverse of the reactions considered in Sec. 8.20, i.e. elimination reactions in which two groups, X and Y, are removed from a pair of adjacent saturated carbon atoms, leaving the latter doubly bound;

$$\underset{b}{\overset{a}{\diagdown}}\underset{Y}{\overset{X}{\underset{|}{C}}}-\underset{d}{\overset{c}{\underset{|}{C}}}\diagup \quad \rightarrow \quad \underset{b}{\overset{a}{\diagdown}}C{=}C\underset{d}{\overset{c}{\diagup}} \; + \; XY \tag{8.105}$$

since reactions of this type are the converse of additions, they must follow parallel mechanisms; the elimination can thus take place in two steps via an intermediate ion or radical (compare LV to LVII) or in one step by a concerted process. Reactions of both kinds can of course be analyzed by the same kind of procedures used to discuss addition (Sec. 8.20); there is, however, one further point of interest in the case of the concerted reactions.

   Consider for example the E_N2 elimination by base of hydrogen halide from an alkyl halide to form an olefine;

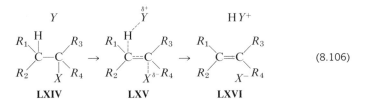

LXIV   LXV   LXVI

(8.106)

Since this reaction is the reverse of a one-step addition of HX to the olefine, it must take place through a transition state (LXV) in which the leaving hydrogen atom and halogen are *trans* to one another (compare LVIII and LIX). There is, however, no need for this transition state to be electronically symmetrical; in it the bonding to Y, and to X, may be very different.

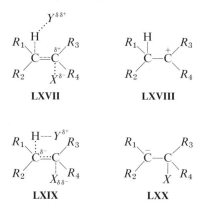

LXVII   LXVIII

LXIX   LXX

At one extreme, when the CH bond is barely weakened, the transition state (LXVII) will closely resemble that for an E_N1 elimination, taking place in two steps via the stable intermediate cation (LXVIII); at the other extreme, the transition state (LXIX) will approximate to that (LXX) for an $E1cB$ elimination, taking place in two steps via the stable intermediate anion (LXX). Suppose now that we introduce conjugated hydrocarbon substituents (e.g. phenyl) into the original halide (see LXIV). If the group is β to halogen (R_2 in LXIV), it will not affect the change in delocalization energy in passing from LXIV to the cation (LXVIII), but it will have a large effect on the conversion of LXIV to the anion (LXX). Such a substituent α to halogen (R_3 in LXIV) will have exactly the converse effect. Reactions of these two types should therefore be very sensitive to the nature of the substituent; the rates for the first type should run closely parallel to the rates of limiting S_N1 solvolysis of arylmethyl halides, R_2CH_2X (see Sec. 8.11), while those for the second should run closely parallel to the rates of base-catalyzed deprotonation of arylmethanes, R_3CH_3 (see Sec. 8.14).

If, however, the transition state is symmetrical, its resonance energy should not change with changes in the substituent; for as we saw in Sec. 8.20, the interaction between the substituent and the adjacent carbon atom is then a small second-order effect whose magnitude is independent of the substituent. There will, it is true, be a relative stabilization of the transition state (LXV), due to the changes in hybridization of the two carbon atoms in LXIV that are involved in the reaction; the bond between an aryl substituent and one of these carbon atoms will become stronger as the reaction proceeds (see Sec. 4.15), and this will facilitate the reaction.   However this effect will be independent of the aryl group.   If therefore we compare the rates of elimination of a series of halides leaving various conjugated hydrocarbon substituents, we should be able to infer the timing of bond breaking during the reaction.   If the transition state is symmetrical, the rates should vary little.   If it approaches the limiting structure LXVII and LXIX, variation in R_2 should have very little effect, while variation in R_3 should have a large one.

Experimental data concerning this point are lacking; nearly all the work on substituents has, as usual, made use of substituted phenyl groups.   Here the results are much harder to interpret, partly because groups of this kind are polar and reactions involving them are consequently subject to uncertain electrostatic effects, and partly because the theoretical treatment of systems containing heteroatoms, and in particular polar substituents, is much more difficult than that for hydrocarbons.   Few chemists seem as yet to have realized the potentialities of the approach indicated here, i.e. the use of unsubstituted, neutral, hydrocarbon substituents as a tool in studying reaction mechanisms.   Two very good examples of this technique have been outlined earlier in this chapter, i.e. the study of transition-state structures in aromatic substitution (Sec. 8.13) and the transition between the S_N1 and S_N2 mechanisms in aliphatic substitution (Sec. 8.12).   The reason for this neglect has been twofold.   First, organic chemists have been slow to appreciate the potentialities of MO theory as a practical aid in the laboratory; instead of learning how to use it themselves, they have preferred to accept the advice of "experts" whose chemical knowledge has all too often been scanty.   Secondly, organic chemists have tended to be hypnotized by the kind of approach embodied in the Hammett equation (see Sec. 9.15); they have consequently been dominated by a lemminglike urge to study systems amenable to ρ-σ plots.

8.22 OO REACTIONS; ELECTROCYCLIC RING OPENING AND RING CLOSURE

A number of reactions are known involving ring-opening and ring-closure processes analogous to those discussed in Sec. 8.17, but taking place in odd-numbered rings; many of them involve interconversions of odd-numbered delocalized systems and are consequently of OO type.   One example which has attracted much attention recently is the solvolysis of cyclopropyl halides and esters to allyl derivatives; this can be represented formally in terms of electrocyclic ring opening of an intermediate cyclopropyl cation to allyl, e.g.

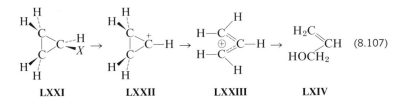

The conversion of LXXII to LXXIII is precisely analogous to the ring-opening reactions of cyclobutene and cyclohexadiene derivatives discussed above. In each case a single bond in a ring is ruptured to form an open-chain conjugated system, the reaction taking place with an extension of the π MOs over two additional atoms and involving rotation of two methylene groups through 90°. As before, there are two geometrically distinct ways in which this can happen, disrotatory and conrotatory. According to Evans' rule, the choice between them is determined by the consideration that the transition state should be aromatic.

Each such transition state is isoconjugate with an odd polymethine or with an odd anti-Hückel polymethine in which one pair of adjacent AOs overlap out of phase. In the reaction of Eq. (8.107), the transition state contains two delocalized electrons, i.e. those that link the methylene groups in LXXII and that occupy an allylic π MO in LXXIII. Such a transition state will be aromatic if it is of Hückel type; ring opening should therefore be disrotatory. Likewise the corresponding ring opening of an allyl anion (LXXV → LXXVI) should be conrotatory, since here there are four delocalized electrons in the transition state.

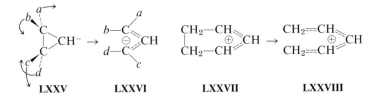

It is of course difficult to establish the stereochemistry of these reactions unambiguously; for the resulting ions combine with protons or bases to form allyl derivatives (e.g. LXXIV) in which the configuration of one atom is lost. It would be easier to study the reverse reactions, i.e. closure of allyl ions to cyclopropyl; unfortunately reactions of this kind do not take place. Fortunately the situation is different in the case of five-membered rings; here there is direct evidence that the stereochemistry of the reactions is as predicted.

Interconversion of 3-cyclopentenyl cation (LXXVII) and 1,3-pentadienyl cation (LXXVIII) involves a transition state with four delocalized electrons; both reactions should therefore take place by a conrotatory path, the transition state being of anti-Hückel type. Woodward and his collaborators[44] have devised an ingenious test of this prediction, by studying the acid-catalyzed ring closure of bis(1-cyclohexenyl) ketone (LXXIX) to a mixture of the decahydrofluorenones (LXXX and LXXXI):

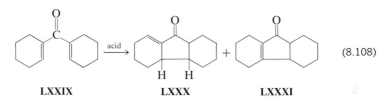

LXXIX   LXXX   LXXXI   (8.108)

These could be separated and the stereochemistry of LXXX determined.   The reaction almost certainly takes place via the conjugate acid (LXXXII) of LXXIX; since oxygen is so very much more electronegative than carbon, LXXXII must approximate in structure to the pentadienate ion (LXXXIII).   Cyclization of this to LXXXIV, followed by loss of a proton and ketonization, gives LXXX or LXXXI; if the cyclization is disrotatory, it should lead to LXXX, in which the ring junctions are *cis*, while if it is conrotatory, the ring junctions should be *trans*.   The observed stereochemistry was, as indicated below, *trans* (LXXXV), implying that the ring closure took place, as predicted, by the conrotatory path.

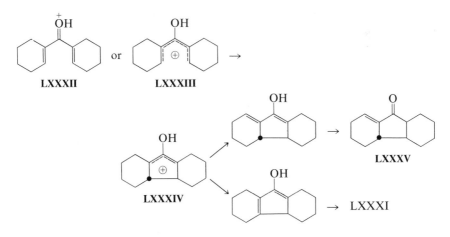

Let us now return to the cyclopropyl problem.

If the solvolysis of cyclopropyl derivatives took place via cyclopropyl cations (LXXII), it would be exceedingly difficult to draw any conclusions concerning the stereochemistry of ring opening.   However several lines of evidence suggest[45] that the reaction in fact takes place in a single converted step, ring opening accompanying ionization of the group X.   Thus the effect of I strain should be much greater in the ionization of LXXI to LXXII than in the analogous reaction of the corresponding 7-norbornyl derivative (LXXXVI), the CCC angles being 60° and 94° respectively; yet LXXI solvolyzes much faster than LXXXVI. Again, methyl substituents in the methylene groups of LXXII should have little stabilizing effect on the ion, and hence little effect on the rate of its formation from LXXI; in practice each such methyl substituent increases the rate a hundredfold. Both these results can be explained if the ionization of LXXI is accompanied by electrocyclic ring opening, this acting as a driving force and placing positive charges on the methylene carbon atoms.

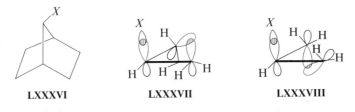

| LXXXVI | LXXXVII | LXXXVIII |

The transition state for the solvolysis of LXXI is consequently unsymmetrical, the methine carbon still being covalently bonded to the leaving group X. In this case there are two stereochemically nonequivalent ways in which disrotatory ring opening might take place, via transition states of the types indicated diagrammatically in LXXXVII and LXXXVIII. If these transition states differ in energy, we shall have an additional stereospecificity in the reaction; for if the methylene hydrogens are replaced by substituents, the two modes of ring opening give isomeric products. Thus ionization of the *cis-cis-cis*-dimethylcyclopropyl tosylate (LXXXIX) via a transition state of type LXXXVII will give XC, while if the transition state is of type LXXXVIII, the product will be XCI.

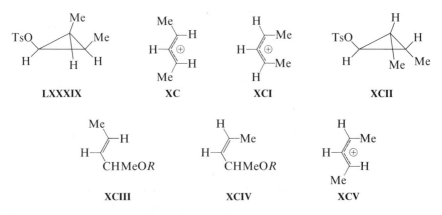

| LXXXIX | XC | XCI | XCII |

| XCIII | XCIV | XCV |

Likewise solvolysis of the *cis-cis-trans* tosylate (XCII) will give exactly opposite products, reaction via LXXXVII giving XCI and via LXXXVIII giving XC. The two ions can be distinguished by the products they give on reaction with solvent. That (XCIII) from XC is a derivative of *trans*-2-pentene, while that (XCIV) from XCI is a derivative of *cis*-2-pentene. If then one type of transition state is favored over the other, solvolysis of LXXXIX and XCII should give different products. If this is the case, it will not only establish that such a difference exists, and indicate the more favorable path, but it will also establish that the ring opening is indeed disrotatory; for conrotatory ring opening of LXXXIX or XCII would lead to the same intermediate allyl cation (XCV).

Schleyer and his collaborators[45] have carried out studies of this kind and found that one mode of disrotatory ring opening is not only favored, but favored to the complete exclusion of the other; the favored path is the one corresponding to the transition state LXXXVIII.   A very striking example of this is provided by the solvolysis of the *exo*-bicyclopentyl tosylate (XCVI).   Solvolysis via a transition state of type LXXXVII would give a virtually unstrained pentenyl cation (XCVII), while solvolysis via a transition state of type LXXXVIII would give the *trans* cation (XCVIII), which cannot exist in a planar configuration.   In spite of this handicap, the reaction does *not* proceed via XCVII, but through a distorted, nonplanar form of XCVIII; since this cannot react with solvent in the usual way to form an allyl ester or ether, which would be a derivative of the unknown *trans*-cyclopentene, it can react only by reversal of the ring-opening reaction to give a product (XCIX) derived from XCVI without rearrangement and with retention of configuration.   The extent of the stereospecificity is indicated by the rate of the solvolysis of XCVI, which is a millionfold less than that of the analogous dimethylcyclopropyl tosylate (XCII).

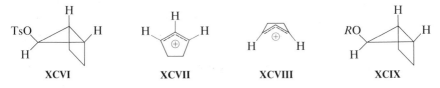

The origin of this additional kind of stereospecificity presents a very interesting problem, for which there is as yet no simple explanation.

8.23   THE THREE-CENTER BOND; π COMPLEXES

One of the classic problems of chemistry in the early days of electronic theory was to explain the existence of diborane, B_2H_6, a compound in which there are not enough valence electrons to link the atoms by normal two-center electron-pair bonds.   There seemed no good reason why BH_3 should not exist as a stable monomeric species, as do other trivalent boron compounds like BF_3 or BMe_3.

This problem was solved by Longuet-Higgins,[46] who pointed out the possibility of an entirely new kind of covalent bond, involving the sharing of a single pair of electrons between three nuclei.   The simplest example of this is provided by the stable ion H_3^+, where the two electrons occupy a three-center MO formed by mutual overlapping of $1s$ AOs of the three hydrogen atoms (C).   In C, each $1s$ AO overlaps with the AOs of both the other atoms; the resulting three-center MOs are therefore topologically equivalent to the π MOs of cyclopropenium (CI). Now we know that cyclopropenium is most stable (i.e. aromatic) if there are just two π electrons present; there is just one MO of low energy, capable of holding a single pair of electrons. The same situation should obtain in H_3^+, when the single pair of electrons can occupy the corresponding lower-energy MO (see CII). The structure of diborane can be interpreted (see CIII) in similar terms, the central hydrogen atoms being linked to both borons by three-center bonds; these in turn are formed by mutual overlap of the hydrogen $1s$ AO with hybrid AOs of the two boron atoms.

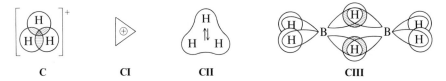

C   CI   CII   CIII

Bonds of this type have since proved the key to the chemistry of the boron hydrides, and of other "electron-deficient" molecules such as $Al_2(CH_3)_6$. Since the ion C^+ is isoelectronic with neutral B, one might expect similar "nonclassical" structures to be of importance in carbonium ion chemistry; this indeed has proved to be the case, although the types of bonding so far observed have been much more restricted.

Some time ago the author[47] pointed out that olefines should be able to form dative bonds to acceptors having vacant orbitals, the pair of bonding π electrons playing the same role as the pair of unshared valence electrons in for example ammonia or an amine. The rationale behind this was the consideration that AOs and MOs do not differ qualitatively; any orbital represents the possible motion of an electron in the field due to a number of other charged particles, and in this sense AOs and MOs are entirely equivalent. This basic idea can easily be put in a more rigorous form. Consider the MOs that can be formed by inter-action of the $2p$ AOs (ϕ_1 and ϕ_2) forming the π bond in ethylene with an AO ψ of an atom X that lies opposite the midpoint of the C=C bond (Fig. 8.34a). Since the resulting system still has a plane of symmetry, i.e. the plane bisecting the C=C bond, its MOs must be either symmetric or antisymmetric with respect to this plane P. The AO ψ is symmetric with reflection in P; let us then replace the AOs ϕ_1 and ϕ_2 by appropriate symmetry orbitals ξ_1 and ξ_2, given (compare Sec. 4.10) by:

$$\xi_1 = \frac{1}{\sqrt{2}} (\phi_1 + \phi_2) \qquad \text{symmetric} \qquad (8.109)$$

$$\xi_2 = \frac{1}{\sqrt{2}} (\phi_1 - \phi_2) \qquad \text{antisymmetric} \qquad (8.110)$$

Since ξ_1 and ξ_2 cannot interact, being of opposite symmetry, ξ_2 must be a MO of the complex (C_2H_4X) (Fig. 8.34b). The symmetric MOs are then combina-tions of ψ and ξ_1; it is easily seen that they are given by:

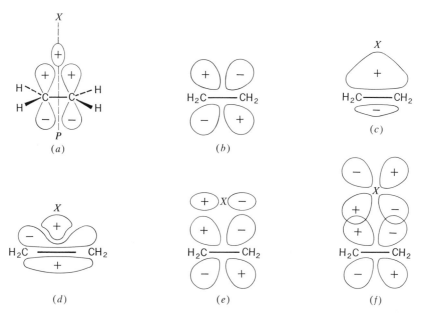

FIG. 8.34 (*a*) AOs interacting in formation of a simple π complex between ethylene and X; (*b*) antibonding π MO ξ_2 of ethylene; (*c*) bonding three-center MO in complex; (*d*) antibonding three-center MO in complex; (*e*) interaction of p AO of X with ξ_2; (*f*) interaction of d AO of X with ξ_2.

$$\chi_1 = A\psi + B\xi_1 \qquad\qquad (8.111)$$

$$\chi_2 = B\psi - A\xi_2 \qquad\qquad (8.112)$$

where A and B are the corresponding orbital coefficients. Thus χ_1 and χ_2 are precisely similar in form to the pair of MOs that would be formed by interaction of two AOs (ψ_1, ξ_1) of two adjacent atoms; this indicates very clearly that the symmetry orbital ξ_2, which is simply the bonding ethylene π MO, can be used to form bonds to a third center in just the same way as a simple AO can. The resulting symmetrical three-center MOs are illustrated in Fig. 8.34*c* and *d*; the former corresponds to the bonding two-center MO in a diatomic molecule, the latter to the corresponding antibonding MO.

The analogy is even closer if we consider that the MOs ξ_2 and χ_2 are antibonding (see Fig. 8.34); the resulting complex (C_2H_4X) will be stable only if there are but two electrons in the set of three-center MOs. The group X must therefore have an empty AO, so the bond is precisely analogous to the dative bond formed by a donor (e.g. NH_3) with an acceptor (e.g. BF_3), as in the typical coordination complex CIV. Olefines should therefore act as Lewis bases, forming dative bonds to acceptors (compare CIV with CV).

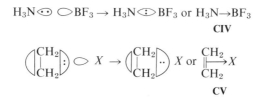

$$H_3N\odot\ \bigcirc BF_3 \rightarrow H_3N\odot BF_3 \text{ or } H_3N\rightarrow BF_3$$

CIV

CV

Compounds of this type were therefore termed π *complexes* and denoted by the conventional arrow symbol denoting a dative bond; compare CIV with CV. Numerous complexes of this kind are now known in inorganic chemistry; the term π complex, and its associated arrow symbolism, have been generally adopted by inorganic chemists.

A further complication arises[47] in cases where the *apical* group X in the π complex has electrons of π-type symmetry, i.e. where X has a pair of unshared p or d electrons, or forms part of a conjugated system. In this case the p, d, or π electrons occupy MOs that are antisymmetric to reflection in a plane of symmetry passing through X; if we orient X so that this plane coincides with the plane of symmetry P in the complex, the π-type orbitals can interact with the empty antisymmetric MO ξ_2 of Fig. 8.31b. This interaction can give rise to a second π-type dative bond (Fig. 8.34e and f) opposite in direction to the one considered previously; such a bond should strengthen the attachment of X greatly, for two reasons. First, X is attached to the olefine by a double bond rather than a single bond; secondly, any positive charge produced in the olefine by the primary dative bond of Fig. 8.34c will be counterbalanced by the negative charge set up by the reverse dative bond of Fig. 8.34e or f. Thus there can be strong bonding between the olefine and X without the need for concomitant charge separation.

Exactly the same situation arises in complexes formed between transition metals having unshared d electrons and donors (e.g. phosphines) having empty valence-shell d AOs. The resulting *back coordination* (compare CVI) greatly strengthens the binding in such complexes, and is responsible for the fact that phosphines form much more stable complexes to metals of this type (e.g. Pt) than do the corresponding amines, although the latter are much stronger bases. Indeed, olefines form isolable complexes only with metals that are capable of such back coordination, and there is conclusive independent evidence that back coordination is important in compounds of this kind. The situation can be conveniently represented by the self-explanatory double-arrow symbol shown in CVII.

$$Pt \leftarrow PR_3$$

CVI

$$\begin{matrix}CH_2\\ \| \\ CH_2\end{matrix} \rightarrow PtCl_3^-$$

CVII

The physical properties, and structures, of these π-complex coordination compounds of metals agree well with the description given above. Thus the metal is invariably opposite the midpoint of the CC bond, and the length and vibration frequency show that this bond is still double. Admittedly it is a good deal weaker than a normal double bond, but this would be expected; for the valence electrons are now shared between three nuclei instead of two, so their bonding effect on the carbon atoms must be correspondingly less than in the parent olefine, and back coordination places electrons in the MO ξ_2, which is antibonding between the carbon atoms.

In this discussion we have assumed that the olefine retains its planar geometry; in practice one would expect some distortion due to repulsions between the apical group X and the four atoms or groups attached to the *basal* carbon atoms. However any such distortions clearly have no great effect on the electronic structure of the resulting π complex, given that the carbon-carbon bond in it is still effectively double.

8.24 REACTIONS INVOLVING π-COMPLEX INTERMEDIATES; πA AND πR REACTIONS

Although the most definite evidence for the existence of π complexes comes from inorganic chemistry, the idea was in fact first introduced to explain the course of certain organic reactions. Although no organic π complex has as yet been isolated, there is now conclusive evidence that such structures play an important role as intermediates in various organic reactions.‡

Intermediates of this kind can be formed in one of two distinct ways. In the first, an acceptor adds to an olefine;

$$\begin{array}{c} R_2C \\ \| \\ R_2C \end{array} + X^+ \rightarrow \begin{array}{c} R_2C \\ \| \\ R_2C \end{array}\!\!\rightarrow X^+ \tag{8.113}$$

In the second, a carbonium ion rearranges to an isomeric π complex;

$$\begin{array}{c} R_2C{=}X \\ | \\ R_2C^+ \end{array} \rightarrow \begin{array}{c} R_2C \\ \| \\ R_2C \end{array}\!\!\rightarrow X^+ \tag{8.114}$$

Each of these reactions can occur as parts of a single concerted process. Thus a good example of a concerted π addition is provided by the solvolysis of 7-norbornenyl chloride (CVIII), which apparently takes place via an intramolecular nucleophilic S_N2 attack by the double bond to form the π complex (CIX); CVIII solvolyzes 10^{11} times faster than the saturated chloride CX. Likewise a concerted version of the rearrangement of Eq. (8.114) occurs in the solvolysis of *exo*-norbornyl chloride (CXI), this leading directly to the π complex (CXII).

‡ For a review see Ref. 48.

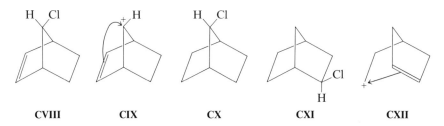

CVIII	**CIX**	**CX**	**CXI**	**CXII**

These reactions could be included in our general classification; thus Eq. (8.113) represents an EO reaction and Eq. (8.114) an OO one. However the reactions form a rather homogeneous group whose special characteristics are determined by the presence of π-complex intermediates; it is therefore convenient to classify them separately. We shall therefore term reactions of the type indicated in Eq. (8.113) *π-addition* (πA) reactions, and those of the type indicated in Eq. (8.114) *π-rearrangement* (πR) reactions. The same terms will of course also be applied to the associated concerted processes, e.g. CVIII → CIX or CXI → CXII.

Although these ideas were presented succinctly at an early date, and although the term π complex and its associated arrow symbolism have been generally accepted in inorganic chemistry (where alone such structures exist in the form of stable, isolable molecules), certain organic chemists have subsequently preferred to use alternative descriptions ("bridged ion," "nonclassical carbonium ion," "synartectic ion," etc.), together with a representation in terms of resonance theory, or a dotted-line notation for three-center bonds. This terminology and notation have unfortunately proved very misleading, and the literature has as a result become cluttered with a variety of mechanisms postulating novel "nonclassical" intermediates for which there are neither analogies nor theoretical justification. Since the matter has been discussed in detail in a recent review,[48] it need not be pursued here; there is as yet *no* definite evidence for the intervention of any type of "nonclassical carbonium ion" other than that described here as a π complex, and most of the confusions in the literature can be cleared up immediately by translating the authors' statements and formulas into π-complex terminology and symbolism.

8.25   FACTORS CONTROLLING THE STABILITY OF π COMPLEXES

Any reaction involving a π complex as an intermediate could equally well take place via a classical carbonium ion; for π complexes can be regarded as isomeric forms of carbonium ions [compare Eq. (8.114)]. Whether or not a given reaction takes place via a π complex therefore depends on the relative stabilities of the potential π complex and carbonium ion intermediates, i.e. the relative stabilities of a carbonium ion (CXIII) and a related π complex (CXIV). Let us consider the factors that would be expected to determine this choice.

CXIII   CXIV   CXV

8.25.1   EFFECT OF THE CR BOND ENERGY   In passing from CXIII to CXIV, the main effect is a replacement of two single bonds, CR and CC, by a CC double bond forming a dative bond to R.   If the bond energy of this dative bond is E_π, the change ΔE in bond energy in passing from CXIII to CXIV is given by

$$\Delta E = E_{C=C} - E_{C-C} - E_{C-R} + E_\pi \qquad (8.115)$$

where $E_{C=C}$, E_{C-C}, and E_{C-R} are bond energies of C=C, C—C, and C—R bonds respectively, and where we have neglected possible small changes in the bond energies of bonds to the other adjacent groups a to d due to changes in the hybridization of carbon.   Now the C—R bond in CXIII should be much stronger than the C$_2$—R bond in CXIV, because the AO of R will overlap better with a single sp^3 carbon hybrid AO than with half an ethylenic π MO (see Sec. 4.10). Therefore the greater E_{C-R}, the smaller ΔE, and the less favorable the π complex.   The rearrangement CXIII → CXIV should therefore occur more easily, other things being equal, the weaker the bond C—R in CXIII.   This effect is seen very clearly in the halogens.   The relative tendency for rearrangement to occur can be estimated from the relative rates of solvolysis of esters of the type CXV; synchronous rearrangement of the cation during separation of Y as Y^- acts as a driving force (*neighboring-group participation,* or *anchimeric assistance*).‡ Evidence of this kind shows that the tendency to rearrange increases in the order F < Cl < Br < I; the bond energies decrease in the order CF > CCl > CBr > CI.

8.25.2   EFFECT OF ELECTRONEGATIVITY OF R In CXIII, neutral R is linked by a covalent bond to a neutral carbon atom, whereas in CXIV, R^+ is linked by a dative bond to ethylene.   The bond in CXIV could be regarded equivalently as a covalent bond between neutral R and an ion-radical $C_2H_4{}^+$.   Now the π electron in $C_2H_4{}^+$ is much more tightly bound than an sp^3 electron in a neutral carbon atom; the second ionization potential of ethylene must be very much greater than the ionization potential of neutral carbon.   Consequently in the reaction CXIII → CXIV, R effectively becomes linked to a very much more electronegative group, and so becomes more positive.   This process will be more difficult, the more electronegative R; any increase in the electronegativity of R will therefore hinder the rearrangement.§   Thus the neutral group —OCH$_3$ is

‡ For a review, see Ref. 49.
§ For a justification of this intuitively obvious result, see Sec. 9.

much more electronegative than the ion $—O^-$; $—O^-$ is a much more effective "neighboring group" in solvolysis than $—OCH_3$ is. Again, *tert*-butyl is less electronegative than methyl, as is shown by the ionization potentials of the radicals ($CH_3\cdot = 9.84$ ev; $CMe_3\cdot = 7.19$ ev); if there is a choice between methyl and *tert*-butyl as the migrating group in a rearrangement of the type CXIII → CXIV, *tert*-butyl normally wins.

8.25.3 ARYL SUBSTITUENTS   One very common misunderstanding has been concerned with the effect of aryl substituents, in particular phenyl, on the stability of π complexes. The argument is based on a comparison, in terms of resonance theory, of the π complex and a corresponding arylmethyl cation. Consider for example the π complex CXVI. This can be represented as a hybrid of six contributing structures (CXVII to CXXII). The analogy between them and the four unexcited structures (CXIII to CXVII) for the benzyl cation is obvious. One would conclude that in both cases, charge should be delocalized onto phenyl with a parallel gain in stability. The benzyl cation is of course very much more stable than methyl, as is shown by the very much greater rate of S_N1 reactions of benzyl derivatives.

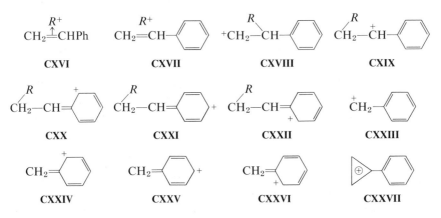

Let us now examine this problem in terms of PMO theory. The delocalized system in a π complex is, as we have seen, isoconjugate with the π MOs of cyclopropenium; CXVI is therefore isoconjugate with phenylcyclopropenium (CXXVII), a conclusion confirmed by the fact that we can write six unexcited resonance structures for CXXVII analogous to CXVII to CXXII. Any resonance stabilization due to phenyl should therefore be similar for CXVI and CXXVII.

We know that union of two even AHs R and S leads to no gain in resonance energy; for the π energy of union is automatically absorbed into the bond energy of the σ bond linking R to S in RS (see Sec. 6.7). The interactions involved are those between filled MOs of R and empty MOs of S, and conversely between filled bonding MOs of one component and empty antibonding MOs of the other.

Union of phenyl with methyl to give benzyl leads to a much greater change in π energy; this is because we are now dealing with interactions between bonding MOs of phenyl and the *nonbonding* AO of methyl.   This difference in energy is very much less than that between a bonding MO and antibonding MO, and the change in π energy correspondingly greater (Sec. 6.14).

However cyclopropenium is not an AH and consequently it does not have a NBMO; its empty MOs are antibonding.   Indeed, in a HMO treatment, they have the same energy $-\beta$ as the antibonding MO of ethylene.   Union of benzene and cyclopropenium should therefore lead to a change in π energy similar to that involved in the union of benzene with, say, ethylene; in this case there should be *no* change in resonance energy.   Phenyl groups should therefore *not* conjugatively stabilize cyclopropenium to any significant extent, in contrast to their effect on AH cations such as methyl or allyl; one might expect some inductive stabilization but this should be less than that due to alkyl.   In practice phenyl is much more efficient than alkyl at stabilizing an adjacent carbonium ion center, but much less efficient at stabilizing cyclopropenium.[50]

The same conclusion should of course apply to π complexes; here again the stabilizing effect of phenyl groups should be small, certainly much less than that of alkyl.   This argument can of course also be extended to other aryl groups.   If the choice is between a classical carbonium ion (CXIII) and a π complex (CXIV), an aryl substituent should favor CXIII.   This effect is seen very clearly in the case of addition of chlorine to olefines.   Addition to simple olefines is a πR process, taking place via a π-complex intermediate and leading to stereospecific *trans* addition [see for example Eq. (8.116)].   Addition to stilbene (CXXVIII) or acenaphthylene (CXXIX) on the other hand gives largely, or even predominantly, *cis* addition, via the "classical" carbonium ions (CXXX and CXXXI).[51]

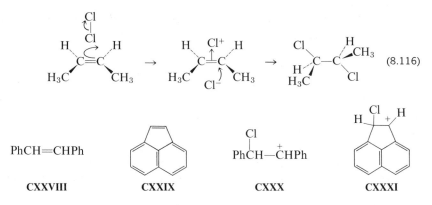

$$\text{(8.116)}$$

PhCH=CHPh

CXXVIII   **CXXIX**   **CXXX**   **CXXXI**

The situation here is indeed closely analogous to that involved in the polar addition of hydrogen halides to olefines, where a similar displacement of mechanism from concerted EE to nonconcerted $\overline{O}^+E$ is brought about by aryl substituents, for very similar reasons (see Sec. 8.20).

8.25.4   BACK COORDINATION   As we have seen, a π complex is greatly stabilized if the apical atom has p, d, or π electrons that can be used for back coordination; in organic chemistry, the most important case is the third, i.e. that where the apical group is unsaturated and has π electrons.

Consider for example a π complex where the apical group is phenyl (CXXXII). If the plane of the benzene ring is oriented perpendicular to the basal CC bond, the π electrons of the ring will overlap with the empty antibonding ethylenic MO (ξ_2 in Fig. 8.34b). The resulting conjugated system (CXXXIII) is isoconjugate with that in the benzyl cation (CXXXIV); the resulting increase in resonance energy will greatly stabilize the π complex.

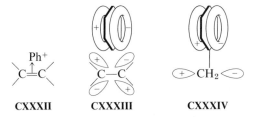

CXXXII   CXXXIII   CXXXIV

A π complex formed by migration of phenyl should therefore be more stable than one formed by migration of alkyl, where back coordination is not possible; on the other hand one can see very easily that the resonance energy of the π complex (CXXXIII) should be less than that of the benzyl cation (CXXXIV). First, the π MOs of phenyl overlap with only half the antibonding ethylenic π MO in CXXXIII but with both halves of the methylene $2p$ AO in CXXXIV; secondly, the antibonding π MO in CXXXIII has a much higher energy than the $2p$ AO in CXXXIV so the interactions with the filled benzene MOs will be much greater in the latter case.

The available experimental evidence suggests that simple carbonium ions are more stable than isomeric π complexes, at any rate in solution (see Sec. 8.25.5); on the other hand π complexes with apical aryl groups are at least comparable in stability with carbonium ions. However π complexes, even those with apical aryl groups, are less stable than arylmethyl cations, where the aryl group is attached to the positive center. Thus solvolyses taking place via benzylic esters invariably give products derived from classical cations, and the same is true of simple alkyl derivatives. On the other hand solvolysis of a β-arylalkyl ester often leads to a π complex; a classical example, first reported by Cram,[52] is the solvolysis of the 3-phenylbutyl 2-tosylate (CXXXV) which proceeds stereospecifically in the sense expected if the intermediate is the π complex (CXXXVI).

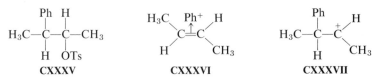

CXXXV   CXXXVI   CXXXVII

Here of course the choice is between a classical carbonium ion (CXXXVII), in which the phenyl is attached to the β position and so unable to provide any stabilization, and a π complex (CXXXVI) with an apical phenyl group.

The analogy between CXXXIII and CXXXIV is seen very clearly from the effect of substituents in the benzene ring.   Substituents that stabilize the benzyl cation (CXXXIV) should also stabilize the π complex (CXXXIII); however they will have little or no effect on the stability of a carbonium ion in which the phenyl group is attached β to the position center (compare CXXXVII).   Substituents which stabilize CXXXIV should therefore increase the tendency for a simple alkyl cation (e.g. CXXXVII) to rearrange to an isomeric π complex carrying an apical aryl group.   A good example of this is provided by the effect of p-methoxy (see Sec. 9.13.4).   β-Phenylethyl tosylate (CXXXVIII) shows hardly any signs of solvolyzing via a π-complex intermediate (CXXXIX); however the corresponding anisyl derivative (CXL) solvolyzes via the π complex CXLI.   Many other examples of this kind are now known.

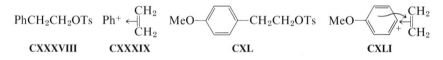

PhCH₂CH₂OTs   Ph⁺

CXXXVIII   **CXXXIX**   **CXL**   **CXLI**

8.25.5   _I_ STRAIN   One last vital factor in determining the relative stabilities of a π complex and an isomeric classical carbonium ion is _I_ strain,[53] i.e. strain effects arising from bending of bonds in such a way as to distort valence angles from their "normal" value.

Consider for example the solvolyses of 7-norbornenyl chloride (CVIII) and of 7-norbornyl chloride (CX).   In CX, the CCC valence angle (94°) at the 7 position is much less than the normal tetrahedral value (109°); the molecule is therefore strained.   If now we try to ionize the chlorine, thus leaving the ion CXLII, the strain increases greatly; for since the natural valence angle of sp^2 carbon is 120°, more energy is needed to reduce this to 94° than to reduce an angle whose equilibrium value is 109°   This increase in strain is the reason why CVIII solvolyzes about 10^7 times more slowly than a normal secondary alkyl chloride.

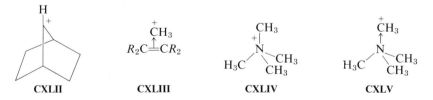

CXLII   **CXLIII**   **CXLIV**   **CXLV**

Consider now the unsaturated chloride (CVIII).   This can solvolyze to the π complex (CIX), which is stabilized not only by internal coordination, but also by the fact that there is no increase in _I_ strain in its formation; for the apical carbon atom (i.e., the carbon atom in the 7 position) is still effectively tetrahedral. The latter effect probably accounts for quite a large part of the observed difference in rates of solvolysis between CVIII and CX, i.e. a difference factor of no less than 10^{11}.

Attention needs to be drawn to this point because this is the one place where the π-complex notation can lead to misunderstanding. When we write a π complex with an apical alkyl group as for example CXLIII, we do *not* mean that the apical group is present as a carbonium ion, with planar geometry. The notation of CXLIII implies that the apical group is tetrahedral, being linked by covalent bonds to four other groups; the fact that one of these bonds is a bond to a molecule rather than to an atom is irrelevant from this point of view. Thus we can write the tetramethylammonium ion either as CXLIV, with four methyl groups covalently bonded to N^+, or as CXLV, with three methyl groups covalently bonded to N and one linked by a dative bond. The two descriptions are entirely equivalent, according to the standard conventions of nomenclature, so the possibility of writing CXLIV as CXLV in no way implies that one methyl group in CXLV differs from the rest.

Another very important *I*-strain effect arises in the case of strained polycyclic systems, e.g. CXI. In a π complex, the bond between the two basal carbons and the apical atom is relatively weak; we can therefore deform such a structure by moving the apical atom without greatly increasing the energy. In a strained system a π complex may therefore be selectively stabilized relative to an isomeric carbonium ion; for the strain may be relieved at little cost in the former case by distorting the bond to the apical group. Consequently we frequently find π complexes playing a role in "carbonium ion" reactions of strained condensed-ring systems (e.g. CXI), although they do not play such a role in the case of unstrained alkyl analogs. The reactions of *exo*-norbornyl esters provide a classic case.

8.25.6   SOLVATION   In a classical carbonium ion, the charge is concentrated on a single carbon atom; in a π complex, it is spread over three different atoms. The solvation energy of a classical cation is therefore greater than that of an isomeric π complex; the isomerization of classical cations to π complexes will therefore be hindered by preferential solvation of the former, when the reactions are carried out in solution.

This argument suggests that even simple classical carbonium ions might isomerize to π complexes in the absence of a solvent, i.e. in the gas phase; as yet there is no evidence concerning this. The only work reported in this connection has been concerned with the preparation of such ions by electron impact immediately prior to analysis by a mass spectrometer; measurements of this kind could be conclusive only if they showed that rearrangements to π complexes took place, and this was not the case.

8.26 MO CALCULATIONS FOR π COMPLEXES

Soon after the concept of π complexes had been developed, the author[54] reported some simple-minded HMO calculations for systems of this kind. Such calculations certainly suggest that π complexes might be as stable as, or even more stable than, isomeric classical carbonium ions; however it is easily seen that they cannot be taken seriously in a numerical sense, for reasons that were pointed out forcefully in a simultaneous publication by Coulson and Dewar.[55]

The difficulty here is one that was analyzed in some detail in Sec. 3.7. In the Hückel method, the total energy E of a molecule is set equal to a sum of the orbital energies ϵ_μ of the individual electrons. In a correct SCF MO treatment, however, the total energy is given by

$$E = \epsilon_\mu - \text{(electron repulsion)} + \text{(core repulsion)} \qquad (8.117)$$

Consequently the HMO method cannot even begin to give a valid estimate of E unless the two final terms in Eq. (8.109) cancel; for this to be even approximately true, it is essential that the sum of the core charges should be equal to the sum of the charges on the electrons, i.e. that the molecule should be neutral.

We may still be able to get some reasonable estimate of the relative energies of two forms of a given ion if they have the same geometry, on the grounds that the core repulsion will be the same for both; this would apply for example to calculations of resonance energies, or energies of union, where we compare systems of similar geometry, differing only in the distribution of electrons. Any attempts to compare energies of isomeric ions, in which the positions of the atoms differ, are, however, entirely unsound and no reliance whatsoever can be placed on any conclusion drawn from calculations of this kind.

Since these objections were stated very clearly in print, it seems strange that calculations of this kind should have been published by later authors without reference to them (e.g. Ref. 56), or indeed to the fact that HMO calculations had already been reported for such systems. The original calculations may have been of value in showing that the π-complex concept was at least reasonable; the later attempts to put such calculations on a quantitative basis must be dismissed as worthless.

Recently the situation has been further obscured by the publication of a paper comparing energies of various classical and nonclassical ions, using a more sophisticated version of the HMO method[57] (see Sec. 10.2). As the author points out very explicitly in his introduction, the use of his "extended Hückel method" for ions is open to precisely the same objections as the simpler versions used previously; the conclusions reached in this way are consequently equally worthless. It is perhaps surprising in view of this candid disclaimer that the paper should have appeared in print.

One must conclude that further theoretical work in this area will remain pointless unless, and until, some much better approach is available. It seems very likely that the SCF MO treatment outlined in Chap. 10 will prove the answer to this need.

8.27 MISCELLANEOUS CRITERIA OF REACTIVITY[58]

One major problem in calculating even the relative rates of chemical reactions is that of deducing the structures of transition states. Various attempts have consequently been made from time to time to circumvent this difficulty, by trying to relate the rates of chemical reactions to some calculated property of the reactants alone. Attempts of this kind have of course no theoretical justification; nevertheless they have attained a certain degree of acceptance because of their apparent practical success. The purpose of this section is to analyze these procedures in more detail, to see if they have any validity, and if not, to establish why they should work at all in practice. As we shall see, the reason for this success is in fact very simple. Nearly all applications of those techniques have been to AHs, where, as a result of the special orbital symmetry of AHs, all these various "indices of reactivity" correlate not only with each other, but also with the delocalization energies of activation calculated by the PMO method.

8.27.1 FREE VALENCE The use of free valence as a criterion of reactivity is an anachronism based on Thiele's theory of partial free valence. The idea here is that an atom in a conjugated system can exert only a certain maximum π-bonding power. If the actual bonding, as measured by a sum of the π-bond orders of bonds formed by it, falls below this limit, the difference should be a measure of the surplus valence available to bind other groups at that position. This quantity, the free-valence number, is therefore taken as a measure of the reactivity at that position. Free valence was originally defined in terms of Pauling bond orders, calculated by resonance theory or the valence-bond method; however it was later shown that HMO bond orders lead to similar results. In the HMO approximation, the maximum π-bonding power for a carbon atom in a conjugated hydrocarbon is $\sqrt{3}$; hence the free-valence number f_t of atom t is defined by:

$$f_t = \sqrt{3} - \sum_r p_{rt} \qquad (8.118)$$

where the sum is over atoms r directly linked to atom t.

In the HMO method, the ease of addition to atom t in an even AH is determined by the reactivity number N_t (Sec. 8.7), reaction taking place more easily, the smaller the reactivity number. Using the PMO estimate of bond orders in AHs [Eq. (8.36)], and Eq. (6.147),

$$N_t = 2\sum_r a_{0r} = 2\sum_r p_{rt} \qquad (8.119)$$

From Eqs. (8.118) and (8.119),

$$f_t = \sqrt{3} - \tfrac{1}{2}N_t \qquad (8.120)$$

Thus the smaller N_t, the greater f_t; hence the greater f_t, the greater the reactivity. The success of free valence as a criterion of reactivity depends on this relation, which of course holds only for AHs. For compounds of other types, e.g. nonalternant hydrocarbons or compounds containing heteroatoms, free valence ceases to be a useful criterion.

8.27.2 SELF-POLARIZABILITY The idea here is that in the reaction of a polar reagent with a neutral conjugated hydrocarbon, the ease of reaction at a given atom will depend on the extent to which the π electrons are polarized as the reagent approaches. Thus nitration of an aromatic AH by NO_2^+ involves formation of a bond from one carbon atom to the reagent, using a pair of electrons that originally occupied a π MO; the ease of this process might be expected to be related to the amount of negative charge induced at the atom in question as the positively charged ion approaches.

The effect of a positive charge adjacent to atom t will be to increase the binding energy of electrons there; in HMO terminology, this will be represented by a decrease $\delta\alpha_t$ in the corresponding coulomb integral. The resulting change in charge δq_t should then be given approximately by

$$\delta q_t = \frac{\partial q_t}{\partial \alpha_t} \delta\alpha_t = \pi_{t,t}\, \delta\alpha_t \qquad (8.121)$$

where $\pi_{t,t}$ is the self-polarizability of atom t.

The self-polarizability can be calculated approximately by PMO theory; it is given[58] (see Sec. 9.8) by

$$\pi_{t,t} \approx \frac{1}{2\beta \left| \sum_r a_{0r} \right|} \qquad (8.122)$$

where a_{0r} is the NBMO coefficient of atom r in the odd AH obtained by removing atom t from the even AH we are considering, and the sum is over atoms adjacent to atom t. From Eqs. (8.119) and (8.122),

$$\pi_{t,t} = \frac{1}{\beta N_t} \qquad (8.123)$$

Therefore the greater $\pi_{t,t}$, the smaller N_t, and the greater the reactivity.

Here again the correlation exists only for AHs; for other types of compound, $\pi_{t,t}$ proves a poor guide to reactivity. The premise on which this whole argument is based is in any case suspect; for the relative reactivities of AHs, and of different positions in a given AH, are the same for uncharged as for charged reagents.

8.27.3   THE FRONTIER-ORBITAL METHOD   In this approach the interaction between the reagent and the π electrons of a conjugated system is calculated by perturbation theory, the energy of interaction being analogous to the energy of union of two conjugated systems.   Since the perturbation of a given filled MO in the hydrocarbon depends inversely on the difference in energy between it and the empty orbitals of the reagent (compare Sec. 6.6), the most perturbable MO should be the highest occupied MO (HOMO).   The perturbation will also depend on the density of this orbital at the point of contact with the reagent, suggesting that the density of the HOMO or *frontier orbital* at the various positions in a molecule should serve as a measure of reactivity there.   This is the basis of the frontier-orbital method.[59]

The frontier-orbital method has even less to recommend it than the other approaches; for if we carry out the perturbation treatment properly, we find that the contributions of the frontier orbital are by no means dominant.   While the method gives quite good predictions of reactivity in AHs, this success is due once again to a fortuitous correlation between frontier-orbital density and localization energy.   In compounds of other types the method fails catastrophically. For example in 10,9-borazarophenanthrene the most reactive position is the one with the smallest frontier-orbital density,[60] and similar discrepancies appear in nonalternant systems and other compounds containing heteroatoms.

PROBLEMS

8.1   Predict the most reactive, and second most reactive, positions in the following aromatic AHs for substitution reactions in which steric effects are unimportant.

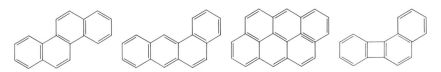

Using Fig. 8.12, predict approximate partial rate factors for methylation by methyl radicals.

8.2   Using Fig. 8.14*b*, predict approximate rate constants for the solvolyses of the following chlorides in formic acid at 25°:

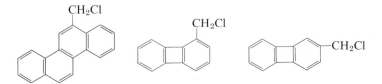

8.3   When pentaphene,

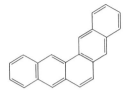

is treated with one molar equivalent of maleic anhydride, the only insolable products are unchanged pentaphene and an adduct formed from one molecule of pentaphene and *two* of maleic anhydride.   Interpret this, using PMO theory.

8.4   When the amine (A) is treated with nitrous acid in hydrochloric acid, the product is the covalent chloride (B).   Treatment with Lewis acids converts B into salts of dibenzotropylium(C), the chloride of which shows no tendency to revert to B.   What are the stereochemistries of A and B?

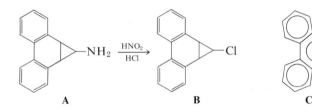

| A | B | C |

8.5   Olefines react as follows with B_2Cl_4:

$$R_2C \atop \| \atop R_2C \quad + \quad {BCl_2 \atop | \atop BCl_2} \quad \rightarrow \quad {R_2C-BCl_2 \atop | \atop R_2C-BCl_2}$$

By what mechanism would you expect this reaction to take place?

8.6   The dimer (D) of cyclobutadiene isomerizes to cyclooctatetraene (E) on heating, the half-life at 140° being 20 min.   In the presence of silver fluoborate, the half-life is only 5 min at 56°.

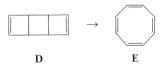

| D | E |

Evidently Ag^+ catalyzes electrocyclic opening of the four-membered rings in D, presumably by forming a π complex through one of the double bonds.   Explain the catalysis (*a*) in terms of the PMO theory of electrocyclic reactions; (*b*) in terms of orbital symmetry.

8.7 Of the two isomers F and G, one solvolyzes 10^{14} times faster than the other.

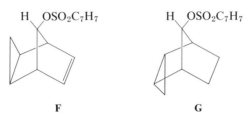

F   G

(*a*) Which isomer would you expect to solvolyze more rapidly? (*b*) The ratio of rates is greater than for the corresponding 7-norbornyl esters, in which the three-membered rings of F and G are replaced by double bonds. Explain this.

REFERENCES

1   Hammett, L. P.: "Physical Organic Chemistry," McGraw-Hill Book Company, New York, 1940.

2   Dewar, M. J. S., and R. J. Sampson: *J. Chem. Soc.* **1956,** 2789; **1957,** 2946.

3   Westheimer, F. H.: in M. S. Newman (ed.), "Steric Effects in Organic Chemistry," chap. 12, John Wiley & Sons, Inc., New York, 1956.

4   Evans, M. G., and M. Polanyi: *Trans. Faraday Soc.* **32,** 1340 (1936).

5   Bell, R. P.: *Proc. Roy. Soc.* (*London*) **A154,** 414 (1936); "Acid-Base Catalysis," Oxford University Press, Fair Lawn, N.J., 1941.

6   Warhurst, E.: *Quart. Rev.* (*London*) **5,** 44 (1951).

7   Dewar, M. J. S.: *Discussions Faraday Soc.* **2,** 261 (1947).

8   Bates, R. B., R. H. Carninghan, and C. E. Staples: *J. Am. Chem. Soc.* **85,** 3030 (1963).

9   Mackor, E. L., A. Hofstra, and J. H. van der Waals: *Trans. Faraday Soc.* **54,** 66 (1958).

10 Dewar, M. J. S., and C. de Llano: *J. Am. Chem. Soc.,* in press.

11 Dewar, M. J. S., T. Mole, and E. W. T. Warford: *J. Chem. Soc.* **1956,** 3581.

12 Barton, J. W., D. E. Henn, K. A. McLaughlan, and J. F. W. McOmie: *J. Chem. Soc.* **1963,** 1622; J. M. Blatchly, A. J. Boulton, and J. F. W. McOmie: *ibid.* **1965,** 4930.

13 Lay, M., and M. Szwarc: *J. Am. Chem. Soc.* **77,** 1949 (1955).

14 Kooyman, E. C., and E. Farenhorst: *Trans. Faraday Soc.* **49,** 58 (1953); A. D. Stefani and M. Szwarc: *J. Am. Chem. Soc.* **84,** 3661 (1962).

15 Dewar, M. J. S., T. Mole, and E. W. T. Warford: *J. Chem. Soc.* **1956,** 3581.

16 Brown, H. C., and K. L. Nelson: *J. Am. Chem. Soc.* **75,** 6292 (1953).

17 Dewar, M. J. S., and R. J. Sampson: *J. Chem. Soc.* **1956,** 2789; **1957,** 2946.

18 Streitwieser, A., Jr.: "Solvolytic Displacement Reactions," McGraw-Hill Book Company, New York, 1962; E. R. Thornton: "Solvolysis Mechanisms," The Ronald Press Company, New York, 1964.

19 Streitwieser, A., and W. C. Langworthy: *J. Am. Chem. Soc.* **85,** 1757, 1761 (1963).

20 Seltzer, S.: *J. Am. Chem. Soc.* **87,** 1534 (1965).

21 Dewar, M. J. S.: *Tetrahedron Suppl.* **8**(1), 75 (1966).

22 Evans, M. G.: *Trans. Faraday Soc.* **35,** 824 (1939).

23 Bartlett, P. D., L. K. Montgomery, and B. Seidel: *J. Am. Chem. Soc.* **86,** 616 (1964); L. K. Montgomery, K. Schneller, and P. D. Bartlett: *ibid.,* 622; P. D. Bartlett and L. K. Montgomery: *ibid.,* 628.

24 Dewar, M. J. S., and R. Scott Pyron: unpublished work.

25 Brown, R. D.: *J. Chem. Soc.* **1951,** 1612.

26 Vogel, E.: *Angew. Chem. Intern. Ed. Engl.* **2,** 1 (1963).

27 Gibson, D., and R. Pettit: *J. Am. Chem. Soc.* **87,** 2620 (1965).

28 Doering, W. von E., and W. R. Roth: *Tetrahedron* **18,** 67 (1962).

29 Woodward, R. B., and R. Hoffmann: *J. Am. Chem. Soc.* **87,** 395, 2511 (1965); R. Hoffmann and R. B. Woodward: *ibid.,* 2046, 4388, 4389.

30 Craig, D. P.: *J. Chem. Soc.* **1959,** 997.

31 Heilbronner, E.: *Tetrahedron Letters* **1964,** 1923.

32 Zimmerman, H. E.: *J. Am. Chem. Soc.* **88,** 1564 (1966).

33 Longuet-Higgins, H. C., and E. W. Abrahamson: *J. Am. Chem. Soc.* **87,** 2045 (1965).

34 Hoffmann, R., and R. B. Woodward: *J. Am. Chem. Soc.* **87,** 2048 (1965).

35 Woodward, R. B., and R. Hoffmann: *J. Am. Chem. Soc.* **87,** 2511 (1965).

36 Doering, W. von E.: personal communication.

37 Davis, R.: personal communication.

38 Coppers, P., and R. Thomas: American Crystallographic Association Meeting, Atlanta, Ga., 1967.

39 Fahey, R. C., and D.-J. Lee, *J. Am. Chem. Soc.* **89,** 2780 (1967), and personal communication from Dr. R. C. Fahey.

40 Dewar, M. J. S., and R. C. Fahey: *Angew. Chem. Intern. Ed. Engl.* **3,** 245 (1964).

41 Cristol, S. J., F. R. Stermitz, and P. S. Romey: *J. Am. Chem. Soc.* **78,** 4939 (1956).

42 Dewar, M. J. S.: *J. Am. Chem. Soc.* **74,** 3357 (1952).

43 Pullman, A., and B. Pullman: "Cancerisation par les substances chimiques et structure moléculaire," Masson et Cie, Paris, 1955.

44 Woodward, R. B.: Chemical Society Symposium on Aromaticity, Sheffield, 1966.

45 Schleyer, P. von R., G. W. Van Dive, U. Schöllkopf, and J. Paust: *J. Am. Chem. Soc.* **88,** 2568 (1966).

46 Longuet-Higgins, H. C.: *J. Chim. Phys.* **46,** 268 (1949).

47 Dewar, M. J. S.: *J. Chem. Soc.* **1946,** 406; *Bull. Soc. Chim.* **18,** C71 (1951).

48 Dewar, M. J. S., and A. P. Marchand: *Ann. Rev. Phys. Chem.* **16,** 321 (1965).

49 Streitwieser, A., Jr.: "Solvolytic Displacement Reactions," McGraw-Hill Book Company, New York, 1962.

50 Krebs, A. W.: *Angew. Chem. Intern. Ed. Engl.* **4,** 10 (1964).

51 Dewar, M. J. S., and R. C. Fahey: *Angew. Chem. Intern. Ed. Engl.* **4,** 10 (1964).

52 Cram, D. J.: *J. Am. Chem. Soc.* **71,** 3863 (1949).

53 Brown, H. C., R. S. Fletcher, and R. B. Jonassen: *J. Am. Chem. Soc.* **73,** 212 (1951); E. L. Eliel: "Stereochemistry of Carbon Compounds," p. 265, McGraw-Hill Book Company, New York, 1962.

54 Dewar, M. J. S.: *Discussions Faraday Soc.* **2,** 50 (1947).

55 Coulson, C. A., and M. J. S. Dewar: *Discussions Faraday Soc.* **2,** 54 (1947).

56 Simonetta, M., and S. Winstein: *J. Am. Chem. Soc.* **76,** 18 (1964).

57 Hoffmann, R.: *J. Am. Chem. Soc.* **86,** 1259 (1964).

58 Dewar, M. J. S.: *J. Am. Chem. Soc.* **74,** 3357 (1952).

59 Fukui, K., T. Yonezawa, and H. Shingu: *J. Chem. Phys.* **20,** 722 (1952); K. Fukui, T. Yonezawa, C. Nagata, and H. Shingu, *ibid.* **22,** 1433 (1954).

60 Dewar, M. J. S.: unpublished work; see *Progr. Boron Chem.* **1,** 260 (1964).

CHAPTER NINE

CONJUGATED SYSTEMS
CONTAINING HETEROATOMS

9.1 INTRODUCTION

The preceding chapters have been concerned solely with conjugated hydrocarbons; here we shall extend the same treatment to systems containing heteroatoms. Since the primary purpose of this book is to cover the principles of quantum chemistry rather than their detailed application to specific problems, the discussion of heteroconjugated systems will be centered primarily on those respects in which the treatment differs from that of hydrocarbons.

As regards the Pople SCF MO method, heteroatoms present additional problems in two respects. First, the number of parameters is greater, and their determination more difficult; for thermochemical data for heteroconjugated molecules are scanty. Secondly, one may not be able any longer to treat the core as an assemblage of atoms carrying integral charges, because the σ bonds between dissimilar atoms are polar. For example the α carbon atoms in the core of pyridine will carry positive charges greater than $+e$, and the nitrogen atom a charge less than $+e$, as a result of the polarity of the σ bonds linking them.

The PMO treatment also runs into problems, because of its inadequate treatment of charges in conjugated systems. This point was emphasized earlier (Sec. 5.11), in connection with the behavior of odd-AH ions; similar problems arise in systems containing heteroatoms, where again the SCF MO method predicts charge distributions which differ qualitatively from those given by the simple HMO or PMO methods.

A final problem is presented by atoms containing d orbitals in their valence shells; these can be used to form π bonds of $p\pi\text{-}d\pi$ type, a phenomenon which will be discussed in the last section of this chapter. However conjugation of this type seems to play only a minor role in organic chemistry proper, its main field of activity involving organometallic compounds, in particular those formed by transition metals. Since this topic has been covered very thoroughly in recent inorganic texts,[1] we need not pursue it here.

9.2 PARAMETERS FOR HETEROATOMS IN THE
POPLE SCF MO TREATMENT

The parameters in the Pople treatment fall into three groups: (1) the "atomic" parameters W_i and (ii,ii); these refer to the behavior of electrons on isolated atoms and are independent of the molecules in which the atoms appear; (2) the two-center integrals (ii,jj); and (3) the core resonance integrals $\beta_{ij}{}^c$.

The atomic parameters are usually determined by the Pariser-Parr method (Sec. 5.3), from valence-state ionization potentials I_x and electron affinities A_x; that is

$$W_x = -I_x \qquad (xx,xx) = I_x - A_x \qquad (9.1)$$

The problem in applying this procedure lies in the estimation of the quantities I_x and A_x. These cannot be estimated directly from spectroscopic data, because valence states of atoms do not correspond to any "true" spectroscopic states. The calculation of valence-state ionization potentials and electron affinities from spectroscopic data is therefore by no means trivial. We ignored this problem in the case of hydrocarbons because our primary object is to calculate heats of formation of molecules, and in the case of hydrocarbons, the heat of formation does not depend on the value of W_c. Since this is no longer the case in molecules where heteroatoms are present, the calculation of valence-state ionization potentials becomes a matter of vital significance.

The reason for this distinction between conjugated hydrocarbons and hetero-conjugated molecules can be seen at once from Eqs. (5.40) and (5.44). The contribution $E(W)$ of terms involving W_i to the total energy of a molecule is given by:

$$E(W) = \sum_i q_i W_i \qquad (9.2)$$

where q_i is the π-electron charge density at atom i. The corresponding contribution $E(W')$ to the energy of the atoms from which the molecule is composed is given by:

$$E(W)' = \sum_i n_i W_i \qquad (9.3)$$

where n_i is the total number of electrons (0, 1, or 2) in the appropriate p AO of atom i. Since the total number of such p electrons is equal to the number of π electrons in the molecule,

$$\sum_i n_i = \sum_i q_i \qquad (9.4)$$

If all the atoms are identical, so that the W_i all have a common value, $E(W) = E(W)'$, and the contribution of such terms to the heat of atomization is zero. In the case of compounds containing heteroatoms, this condition can be met only by coincidence in cases where $q_i = n_i$ for each heteroatom present, a condition which is never met in practice.

Let us then consider in more detail the calculation of valence-state ionization potentials and electron affinities. In our localized-bond model, an atom in a conjugated system is supposed to be in an sp^2-hybridized state. Thus a conjugated carbon atom is in a state which would be represented, in an orbital approximation, by the symbol:

C: $$(1s)^2(tr_1)(tr_2)(tr_3)(2p_z) \tag{9.5}$$

where tr_1, tr_2, tr_3 are trigonal hybrids formed from the $2s$, $2p_x$, and $2p_y$ AOs. The valence-state ionization potential and electron affinity are defined as the differences in energy between neutral carbon in this configuration and the ions C^+ and C^- respectively in the configurations:

C$^+$: $$(1s)^2(tr_1)(tr_2)(tr_3) \tag{9.6}$$

C$^-$: $$(1s)^2(tr_1)(tr_2)(tr_3)(2p_z)^2 \tag{9.7}$$

One might perhaps expect the configuration of Eq. (9.5) to be equivalent to that implied by the symbol $(2s)(2p_x)(2p_y)(2p_z)$, on the grounds that three electrons occupying AOs that are one-third s and two-thirds p should be equivalent to one electron occupying the s AO and two occupying p AOs; however this conclusion, which incidentally is to be found in most elementary texts, is incorrect. We can see this in two ways. First, a little reflection will show that the configurations of Eqs. (9.5) to (9.7) cannot possibly represent real states of C, C^+, or C^-, because the corresponding wave functions are not eigenfunctions of the operator $\mathbf{M}_z$. Hybrid AOs are not eigenfunctions of the one-electron operators $\mathbf{M}_{zi}$. Secondly, it can be shown very easily that the energy calculated for a configuration such as that of Eq. (9.5) differs from the value from an analogous configuration involving "pure" s and p AOs. This point can be best illustrated by a simple example, the state $(2s)(2p)$ of helium, and an "equivalent" configuration $(d_i^+)(d_i^-)$, where d_i^+ and d_i^- are diagonal sp hybrids defined by:

$$d_i^+ = \frac{1}{\sqrt{2}}(s+p) \qquad d_i^- = \frac{1}{\sqrt{2}}(s-p) \tag{9.8}$$

where s and p are the $2s$ and $2p$ AOs respectively. Consider first the "normal" configuration $(2s)(2p)$. The total energy E of this is given by:

$$E = E_s + E_p + (ss,pp) \tag{9.9}$$

where (ss,pp) is the usual electron repulsion integral, and where

$$E_s = \int s\mathbf{H}^c s\, d\tau \qquad E_p = \int p\mathbf{H}^c p\, d\tau \tag{9.10}$$

$\mathbf{H}^c$ being the core part of the hamiltonian. Likewise for the configuration $(d_i^+)(d_i^-)$, the total energy E' is given by:

$$E' = \int d_i^+\mathbf{H}^c d_i^+\, d\tau + \int d_i^-\mathbf{H}^c d_i^-\, d\tau + \int\int [d_i^+(1)]^2\frac{e^2}{r_{12}}[d_i^-(2)]^2\, d\tau_1\, d\tau_2 \tag{9.11}$$

Using Eq. (9.9),

$$\int d_i{}^+ \mathbf{H}^c d_i{}^+ \, d\tau = \tfrac{1}{2}\int (s + p)\mathbf{H}^c(s + p) \, d\tau = \tfrac{1}{2}(E_s + E_p) \qquad (9.12)$$

since the integrals $\int s\mathbf{H}^c p \, d\tau$ and $\int p\mathbf{H}^c s \, d\tau$ vanish, through symmetry.‡

Likewise:

$$\int d_i{}^- \mathbf{H}^c d_i{}^- \, d\tau = \tfrac{1}{2}(E_s + E_p) \qquad (9.13)$$

The final integral in Eq. (9.11) can also be expanded in terms of integrals over s and p;

$$\iint [d_i{}^+(1)]^2 \frac{e^2}{r_{12}} [d_i{}^-(2)] \, d\tau_1 \, d\tau_2 = \tfrac{1}{4}\iint [s(1) + p(1)]^2 \frac{e^2}{r_{12}} [s(2) - p(2)]^2 \, d\tau_1 \, d\tau_2$$

$$= \tfrac{1}{4}[(ss,ss) + (pp,pp) + 2(ss,pp)] - (sp,sp) \qquad (9.14)$$

Here again the remaining integrals vanish, through symmetry.§   From Eqs. (9.11) to (9.14),

$$E' = E_s + E_p + \tfrac{1}{4}[(ss,ss) + (pp,pp) + 2(ss,pp)] - (sp,sp) \qquad (9.15)$$

Thus the energies of the two configurations, E and E', are not the same.   The physical reason for this is, incidentally, easy to see.   The configuration $(2s)(2p)$ represents a situation where one electron spends all its time in the AO s, the other all its time in p.   The configuration $(d_i{}^+)(d_i{}^-)$, on the other hand, represents a situation where each electron spends half its time in the AO s, and half in the AO p.   Half the time the electrons are in different AOs, but half the time they are in the same AO (s or p); the average repulsion between them is therefore different from what it is in the former case.

The energies of valence states could be found directly by this kind of procedure, assuming suitable forms for the AOs and determining the necessary integrals by direct quadrature.   Since, however, the orbital picture is known to be a very crude approximation and to give very poor values for energies, it would be much better if we could find some more reliable way of assessing the energies of valence states.   Now although these differ from the energies of "normal" configurations built up from standard AOs, the differences are not likely to be very great.   Thus the one-electron terms in E and E' [compare Eqs. (9.9) and (9.15)] are identical, and the two-electron terms differ only inasmuch as there are differences between the electronic repulsions, depending on the precise orbitals occupied by the electrons; these differences must be small.   There is therefore good reason to hope that we may get satisfactory estimates of the dif-

---

‡ $\mathbf{H}^c$ is a totally symmetric function, so the integral must vanish unless the integrand is invariant for all symmetry operations, i.e. is also totally symmetric. The $2s$ AO s is totally symmetric, but the $2p$ AO p is not, being antisymmetric for reflection in its nodal plane. Integrals of the type $\int s\mathbf{H}^c p \, d\tau$ must therefore vanish.

§ Although the function p is not totally symmetric, its square, p^2, is; the integrand of the integral (sp,sp) is therefore totally symmetric, so this integral does not vanish.

ferences in energy between valence states and normal (spectroscopic) states, if we calculate *both* by the orbital approximation. The absolute energies of valence states can then be found to a much better approximation by adding these differences to the energies determined experimentally for the normal states.

Here another problem arises, closely analogous to that encountered in our treatment of radicals. A single configuration, constructed from standard AOs, will be an eigenfunction of the operator M_z, representing the component of total orbital angular momentum of the atom along the z axis; for M_z is simply a sum of the corresponding one-electron operators M_{zi},

$$M_z = \Sigma M_{zi} \tag{9.16}$$

while the individual AOs are all eigenfunctions of the M_{zi}. However the same will not necessarily be true for the operator L^2, representing the total orbital angular momentum of the atom; for L^2 is *not* a simple sum of the one-electron operators L_i^2. This point was discussed in general terms in Sec. 4.2; here we shall illustrate it by a detailed discussion of one specific case, i.e. the states of carbon corresponding to configurations of the type $(1s)^2(2s)^2(2p)^2$. There are three real states of the atom that correspond to this orbital picture; let us consider how they can be represented in terms of single Slater determinants corresponding to the orbital picture indicated above.

All configurations of this type have their $1s$ and $2s$ AOs filled; we can therefore confine our attention to the two remaining electrons. Furthermore, since we are concerned here with angular momentum, we must not use the usual real forms of p AOs [see Eqs. (2.34) to (2.39)]; we must use the "correct" complex forms $2p_1$, $2p_0$, and $2p_{-1}$, corresponding to components of angular momentum along the z axis of $\hbar$, 0, and $-\hbar$ respectively.

There are 15 distinct ways in which two electrons can be assigned to this set of three $2p$ AOs; these are illustrated in Fig. 9.1.

The real states of the atom are to be written as linear combinations Ψ_μ of the 15 Slater determinants ψ_i corresponding to the 15 individual configurations;

$$\Psi_\mu = \sum_i a_{\mu i}\psi_i \tag{9.17}$$

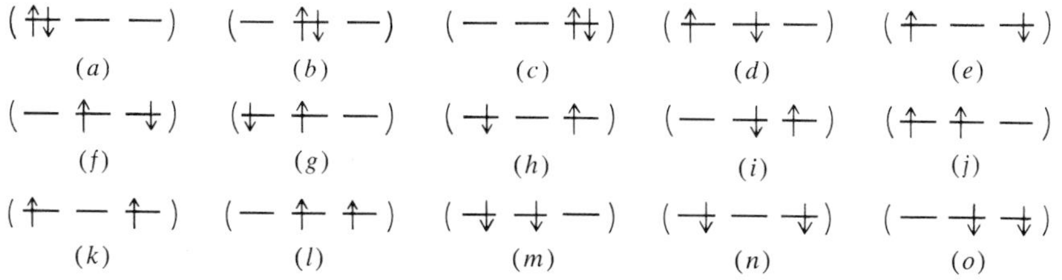

$(\uparrow\downarrow - -)$ $(- \uparrow\downarrow -)$ $(- - \uparrow\downarrow)$ $(\uparrow \downarrow -)$ $(\uparrow - \downarrow)$
  (a) (b) (c) (d) (e)

$(- \uparrow \downarrow)$ $(\downarrow \uparrow -)$ $(\downarrow - \uparrow)$ $(- \downarrow \uparrow)$ $(\uparrow \uparrow -)$
  (f) (g) (h) (i) (j)

$(\uparrow - \uparrow)$ $(- \uparrow \uparrow)$ $(\downarrow \downarrow -)$ $(\downarrow - \downarrow)$ $(- \downarrow \downarrow)$
  (k) (l) (m) (n) (o)

FIG. 9.1 The 15 configurations of carbon of the type $(1s)^2(2s)^2(2p)^2$. The arrows represent the two p electrons and their spins; the horizontal lines in each group represent AOs with $m = 1$, 0, and -1 respectively.

The coefficients $a_{\mu i}$, and the energies corresponding to the functions Ψ_μ, are given as usual by the variation equations:

$$\sum_j a_{\mu j}(H_{ij} - E_\mu \delta_{ij}) = 0 \qquad (9.18)$$

where

$$H_{ij} = \int \psi_i \mathbf{H} \psi_j \, d\tau \qquad (9.19)$$

and E_μ is one root of the secular equation

$$|H_{ij} - E\delta_{ij}| = 0 \qquad (9.20)$$

The basis-set functions ψ_i are of course mutually orthogonal, being constructed from an orthogonal set of spin-orbitals.

As usual, we neglect spin-orbital interactions; the hamiltonian operator $\mathbf{H}$ is therefore a function of the space coordinates alone [Eq. (2.43)]. $\mathbf{H}$ therefore commutes with the operators $\mathbf{S}^2$ and $\mathbf{S}_z$; any eigenfunction of $\mathbf{H}$ must therefore also be an eigenfunction of $\mathbf{S}_z$ and $\mathbf{S}^2$, as well as being an eigenfunction of the orbital-angular-momentum operators $\mathbf{M}_z$ and $\mathbf{M}^2$. Now the component S_z of total spin momentum along the z axis is given by a sum of the contributions of individual electrons, and the same is true of the corresponding component M_z of the total orbital angular momentum. Each of the configurations in Fig. 9.1 is then seen to be an eigenfunction of $\mathbf{M}_z$ and $\mathbf{S}_z$, with eigenvalues that can be deduced by inspection. Consider for example configuration f. In this the electrons have opposite spins, so their contributions to S_z are $+\frac{1}{2}\hbar$ and $-\frac{1}{2}\hbar$ respectively; the component S_z of total spin momentum is $\frac{1}{2}\hbar - \frac{1}{2}\hbar$, or zero. Likewise one electron occupies the AO $2p_0$, with $M_z = 0$, the other the AO $2p_{-1}$ with $M_z = -\hbar$; the component M_z of total orbital angular momentum is therefore $0 - \hbar$, or $-\hbar$.

Consider now the set of equations (9.18) to (9.20). Since $\mathbf{H}$ commutes with $\mathbf{M}_z$ and $\mathbf{S}_z$, it is very easily seen that the matrix element H_{ij} vanishes unless ψ_i and ψ_j are configurations with the same value for M_z, and the same value for S_z.‡ The secular equation consequently factorizes into a series of smaller equations, and the values of $a_{\mu i}$ in Eq. (9.18) are such as to make each Ψ_μ a function only of configurations with identical values both for M_z and S_z. Table 9.1 shows the corresponding classifications of the 15 configurations. Eight of these are unique, and so must correspond to real states of the atom; the other real states will be combinations of two, or three, individual configurations, the coefficients $a_{\mu i}$ in Eq. (9.18) being found by solving two 2-row secular equations and one 3-row one.

The individual states of the atom are also distinguished by the quantum numbers L and S, denoting respectively the number of units of total orbital angular momentum and of total spin orbital momentum. Since each p electron has one

---

‡ The argument is exactly the same as that used in Sec. 2.11, the operators $\mathbf{M}_z$ and $\mathbf{S}_z$ being substituted for the symmetry operator $\boldsymbol{\sigma}$.

TABLE 9.1 Classification of the configurations of Fig. 9.1, according to their values for M_z and S_z

S_z	M_z				
	$2\hbar$	$\hbar$	0	$-\hbar$	$-2\hbar$
h		j	k	l	
0	a	d, g	b, e, h	f, i	c
$-\hbar$		m	n	o	

unit of orbital angular momentum, and since the total orbital angular momentum is a vector sum of contributions by the individual electrons, L can have the values 2, 1, or 0, corresponding respectively to D, P, and S states. Likewise since each electron has one-half unit of spin momentum, S can be unity or zero (triplet and singlet states respectively).

Inspection of Table 9.1 shows that there are just two configurations (a and c) with $M_z = \pm 2\hbar$; these must therefore be substates of a single D state. Since $S_z = 0$ in each case, the state is a singlet (^1D). The remaining states must therefore have $L = 1$ or 0. Likewise there is just one configuration (j) with $S_z = M_z = \hbar$; this must be a substate of a triplet P state (^3P). A triplet P state has nine substates, with values of $\pm \hbar$ or 0 for both M_z and S_z; evidently the configurations j to o represent six of these. Consider now the configurations d and g, with $M_z = \hbar$ and $S_z = 0$. Combinations of these [Eq. (6.18)] will represent two real states of the atom. Now the ^1D state, and also ^3P, have substates with $M_z = \hbar$ and $S_z = 0$; these must therefore be the states that are represented by combinations of d and g. Likewise combinations of f and i represent substates of ^1D and ^3P with $M_z = -\hbar$ and $S_z = 0$. We have now accounted for 14 of the 15 real states of the atom that correspond to the configurations of Fig. 9.1 and Table 9.1; the remaining state is one arising from the interaction of the configurations b, e, and g, and so must have $M_z = S_z = 0$. Since it is unique, this must be a ^1S state.

This procedure can easily be extended to other atoms and other states. If we assume suitable forms for the individual AOs, we can evaluate the integrals in Eqs. (9.19) to (9.21) and so estimate the energies of the resulting states in a straightforward manner. The *promotion energies* of valence states, i.e. the difference in energy between such a state and the real ground state of the atom in question, can then be estimated by comparing the energy calculated for the valence state with that calculated for the ground state. In the case of carbon, the ground state is the ^3P state derived above. Extensive calculations of this kind have been reported by Hinze and Jaffé;[2] these represent the best source of promotion energies at present available. The energies of valence states can be found by adding their promotion energies to the experimentally determined values for the energies of ground states.

Given the "atomic" parameters, the remaining parameters for heteroatoms can be found by the same procedures as in the case of hydrocarbons. The two-center electron repulsion integrals can be found by any of the usual formulas; for ground-state calculations, an approximation analogous to that of Eq. (5.17) has been found convenient,[3] i.e.

$$(ii,jj) = \frac{e^2}{\{r_{ij}^2 + \frac{1}{4}[(ii,ii) + (jj,jj)]^2\}^{1/2}} \tag{9.21}$$

In the case when atoms i and j are identical, this reduces to Eq. (5.17).

The core resonance integrals β_{ij}^c are treated as disposable parameters; if we are interested in ground states, their values must be determined empirically from some suitable property of ground states. In cases where the necessary thermochemical data are available, the thermocycle method indicated in Eq. (5.30) is probably the best choice. This can be applied without modification to bonds involving heteroatoms, provided the necessary bond energies, etc., are known. Such data are available for bonds involving carbon, oxygen, and nitrogen. The treatment cannot be extended to boron or fluorine since no compounds are known in which these elements form simple double bonds. Possible approaches to the problem of extending the Pople method to such elements will be considered presently (Sec. 9.20).

9.3 APPLICATION OF THE POPLE METHOD TO COMPOUNDS CONTAINING NITROGEN OR OXYGEN; ELECTRONEGATIVITY AND σ POLARIZATION

Most of the published work on systems containing heteroatoms, using the Pople method, has been primarily concerned with the interpretation of ultraviolet-visible absorption spectra; the parameters, in particular the one-electron resonance integrals β_{ij}^c, have been chosen accordingly. In cases where such calculations have been extended to ground states, the results have consequently been unsatisfactory; for the parameters appropriate to calculations of excitation energies are not those best suited to calculations for ground states.

This distinction has been noted above in general terms, in Secs. 3.10 and 5.3; since, however, the point is a very important one, we may consider it again in rather more detail. We have seen (Sec. 3.10) that excited states cannot be represented by single Slater determinants constructed from MOs found by applying the Roothaan method to the ground states; this is because a direct SCF treatment of any one excited state would give MOs different from the ground-state MOs. If we used the excited-state SCF MOs, then we could legitimately represent the excited states by the corresponding single Slater determinant; equally, we could no longer represent the ground state by a single Slater determinant, using the new set of (excited-state) SCF MOs. Calculations of this kind have been carried out for simple diatomic molecules; it appears that the excited electron occupies a MO which is more diffuse, and of higher energy, than calculations for the ground state would suggest. This difference can be accommodated in the Roothaan method by using different AOs to construct bonding and antibonding MOs; the antibonding MOs are built up from AOs with smaller values for Z, the effective nuclear charge, and consequently larger than the AOs used to construct the bonding MOs.

If we ignore this distinction, using a single set of MOs to calculate excitation energies, we shall inevitably overestimate the tightness of binding of an electron that has been excited into an originally empty antibonding MO. We shall therefore arrive at an estimate of the excitation energy which is too small. If, however, we are using a semiempirical procedure to estimate the orbital energies, we can correct the situation by suitable adjustment of parameters. This is what we do in effect in the Pople and Pariser-Parr treatments of light absorption, the parameters, in particular the one-electron resonance integrals $\beta_{ij}{}^c$, being chosen to give the best fit to the observed light absorption of some chosen compound or compounds. If we now try to calculate ground-state energies, using these "spectroscopic" values for the parameters, we shall clearly run into troubles of a converse kind; the calculated binding energies will inevitably be too large. If therefore we wish to calculate ground-state properties of molecules, we must choose our parameters by fitting some ground-state property, not by fitting excitation energies deduced from spectroscopic measurements.

The first calculations of this kind were reported by Dewar and Gleicher,[3] using the procedure outlined in Sec. 5.3. Here the Pople method was used to estimate the total π-binding energy, while the contribution of the σ bonds was assumed to be a sum of individual bond energies, a given σ bond making a constant contribution regardless of the molecule in which it appears. Since the compounds treated were all heteroaromatic, this seemed a reasonable first approximation; for the lengths of bonds in aromatic compounds do not vary much. A distinction had of course to be drawn between two different types of nitrogen in such compounds, i.e. nitrogen that is written as doubly bound in a classical structure [compare pyridine (I)], and nitrogen that is written as singly bound [compare pyrrole (II)]; for the lengths of σ bonds are very different in the two cases. This difference is also reflected in the F matrix. In pyridine, the six π electrons move in the field of a core composed, like that of benzene, of six atoms, each carrying unit positive charge (III); in pyrrole, however, removal of the six π electrons leaves a core in which each carbon atom carries one unit of charge, but nitrogen carries two (IV). The quantity c_j in Eq. (3.64) is therefore no longer equal to unity in the case of pyrrole-type nitrogen, but rather to 2. Furthermore, the valence-state ionization potential W is not the same for the two types of nitrogen. For pyridine-type nitrogen, W refers to the process $N \rightarrow N^+$, but for pyrrole-type nitrogen to the process $N^+ \rightarrow N^{++}$. The one-center repulsion integrals differ correspondingly, since the quantities I and A in Eq. (5.13) refer to different processes.

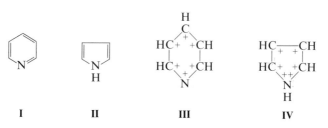

| I | II | III | IV |

Dewar and Gleicher treated the various σ-bond energies as parameters, to be determined by fitting the heats of atomization of some appropriate compound or compounds.   Given these, they were able to calculate heats of atomization of a wide range of nitrogen and oxygen heteroaromatic compounds, with the results shown in Table 9.2.   The agreement with experiment, while inferior to that obtained for hydrocarbons (Sec. 5.4), is still reasonably good.

This treatment suffered, however, from two quite serious defects.   In the first place, it could be applied only to compounds where the bonds have lengths close to some mean value; for each type of σ bond is supposed to have a bond energy independent of its environment, and this can be so only if the lengths do not vary appreciably.   Secondly, the treatment suffered from an annoying internal inconsistency in that these empirical σ-bond energies did not correspond to the values calculated from the thermocycle used to estimate β^c [Eq. (5.30)];

TABLE 9.2   Heats of atomization of heteroaromatic compounds[3]

Compound	Heat of atomization, ev		
	Calc.[a]	Obs.	Difference
PYRIDINE	52.01	52.00	0.01
PYRIMIDINE	46.44	46.61	−0.17
PYRAZINE	46.78	46.62	+0.16
QUINOLINE	85.55	85.55	0
PYRROLE	44.96	44.94	0.02
INDOLE	78.27	78.39	−0.12
CARBAZOLE	112.00	112.00	0
PYRAZOLE	39.28	39.39	−0.11
IMIDAZOLE	39.19	39.79	−0.60
1,2,4-TRIAZOLE	34.30	34.38	−0.08
TETRAZOLE	27.46	28.11	−0.65
BENZO[d]PYRAZOLE	73.15	72.94	0.21
BENZO[d]IMIDAZOLE	73.06	73.53	−0.47
BENZO[d]TRIAZOLE	66.97	67.21	−0.24
FURAN	41.44	41.68	−0.24
DIBENZOFURAN	109.45	109.21	0.24

[a] Values quoted for variable β, PPP method (i.e. the approximation described above, in which allowance is made for variation of integrals with bond length, but the σ-bond energies are assumed independent of bond length).

Table 9.3 illustrates this point very clearly, the values calculated from the thermocycle being very significantly different from those deduced by Dewar and Gleicher.[3]

Preliminary work on hydrocarbons[4] had adopted this same procedure, although the inconsistency between the empirical values for the "aromatic" C—C σ-bond energy and that found from the thermocycle was small. Later it was found possible (Sec. 5.3) to eliminate this inconsistency, so that the calculations could be applied to bonds of different length and without the need for an independent parameter (i.e. the σ-bond energy). Attempts have therefore been made to modify the treatment of heteroatoms in an analogous manner.

This, however, proved an awkward problem; for the heats of formation of compounds containing the same atom with different coordination numbers (e.g. pyridine-type nitrogen and pyrrole-type nitrogen) could not easily be fitted with the same set of parameters. The first successful approach[5] followed the suggestion made at the beginning of this chapter, that in molecules containing heteroatoms, allowance should be made for the polarity of σ bonds. Since the simple-minded HMO treatment of σ bonds in Sec. 4.6 suggests that the charges on the terminal atoms should be proportional to the difference between their coulomb integrals α, it was assumed as a first approximation that the total formal charge δq_{ij} on atom i, due to the presence of a polar σ bond to atom j, can be written as

$$\delta q_{ij} = A(\alpha_i - \alpha_j) \tag{9.22}$$

where A has the same value for all bonds. The net formal charge on atom i is then found by summing contributions for the various σ bonds involving it in a given molecule.

In an SCF MO treatment, the HMO coulomb integrals α have of course to be replaced by the appropriate diagonal F-matrix elements. As a first approximation, we may set these diagonal F-matrix elements, F_{11} or F_{22}, equal to the values that they would have if the bond were homopolar, so that the charge den-

TABLE 9.3 Comparison[3] of "aromatic" σ-bond energies from heats of formation and from thermocycle

Bond	σ-bond energy, ev	
	From ΔH_f	From thermocycle
C—C	3.812	4.043
C—N (pyridine)	2.911	3.248
C—N (pyrrole)	3.189	3.433
C—O (furan)	3.775	3.882
N—N (pyridazine)	2.232	2.532
N—N (pyrazole)	2.570	2.745

sities, q_1 and q_2, at the two atoms are both equal to unity. In that case, from Eq. (3.64),

$$F_{11} = W_1 + \tfrac{1}{2}(11,11) = -\tfrac{1}{2}(I_1 + A_1) \qquad (9.23)$$

$$F_{22} = W_2 + \tfrac{1}{2}(22,22) = -\tfrac{1}{2}(I_2 + A_2) \qquad (9.24)$$

where I_1 and A_1 are respectively the valence-state ionization potential and electron affinity of atom 1, and I_2 and A_2 are the corresponding quantities for atom 2. Thus the quantity α appearing in the HMO treatment is not a measure of the valence-state ionization potential of a given atom, as is often stated in texts discussing the HMO method; it represents rather a mean of the valence-state ionization potential and electron affinity. This quantity clearly serves as a measure of the affinity for electrons that a given atom shows in forming bonds; in conventional terminology, it provides a quantitative measure of the *electronegativity*. Various definitions of electronegativity have appeared from time to time in the literature (compare Sec. 4.6); the one embodied in Eqs. (9.23) and (9.24), due to Mulliken, is clearly the most appropriate in the present connection.

Accepting this definition, and writing the electronegativity of atom i as ν_i, Eq. (9.22) becomes:

$$\delta q_{ij} = A(\nu_i - \nu_j) \qquad (9.25)$$

Strictly, we should also include a dependence on the bond energy of the σ bond in question; for the polarity of a given bond will depend both on the difference in electronegativity between the atoms forming it and on its polarizability. The polarizability is less, the stronger the bond [see Eq. (4.46)]. In the cases we are considering, however, the variations in σ-bond energy are small and can be neglected, as a first approximation.

Knowing the formal charges on the atoms forming the core of our molecule, the next problem is to estimate the corresponding changes in the valence-state ionization potentials, and one-center repulsion integrals (ii,jj), for the p AOs contributing to our π system. This can be done by the following procedure, due to Hinze, Whitehead, and Jaffé.[6] The "standard" values for valence-state ionization potentials I_i and electron affinities A_i of p AOs refer to valence states in

TABLE 9.4 Atomic parameters used in the π treatment of heteroconjugated molecules

Atom	W_i, ev	(ii,ii), ev	A^a	B^a	C^a
C	−11.16	10.88	−55.9860	18.7385	−1.2655
N (pyridine)	−14.12	10.81	−101.363	30.6085	−2.1995
N (pyrrole)	−28.586	14.47	−89.402	24.6265	−1.4515
O (ether)	−33.901	16.20	−136.787	33.3355	−1.9035
O (ketone)	−17.697		−101.597	16.780	0

^{a} Parameters relating W to the charge density q; $W = A + B_q + C_q{}^2$.

TABLE 9.5   Molecular parameters used in the π treatment of heteroconjugated molecules

Bond	Bond energy, ev	Bond length, Å	Force constant, dynes/nm	a^a, Å^{-1}
C—N	3.3463	1.448	0.3956	1.9209
C=N	5.1766	1.270	1.050	2.5161
C—O	3.9987	1.395	0.4902	1.7870
C=O	7.1011	1.230	1.080	2.1787
N—N	2.3017	1.417	0.4717	2.5290
N=N	4.0926	1.240	1.325	3.1787

^{a} Constant in the Morse equation.

which each atom carries an integral number of electrons.   In the cases we are considering, this is no longer so.   However it may reasonably be assumed that the I's and A's will be continuous functions of the numbers of electrons present; for fractional numbers of electrons, we can then estimate I and A by interpolation.   Consider for example the case of nitrogen.   We can estimate valence-state ionization potentials from spectroscopic data[2] for three states of nitrogen (N^-, N, and N^+) with different integral numbers of electrons.   These values can be fitted to a quadratic expression relating the charge q on nitrogen to its ionization potential;

$$I = a_0 + a_1q + a_2q^2 \qquad (9.26)$$

Equation (9.26) can then be used to estimate I in cases where the charge is fractional.

This approach[4] has proved successful for conjugated molecules containing nitrogen and oxygen.   Assuming σ-bond energies calculated from the same thermocycles used to determine β^c, good estimates were obtained for the heats of formation of a wide range of compounds including both heteroaromatics and systems containing "localized" bonds.   The various parameters assumed in this treatment are shown in Tables 9.4 and 9.5, while Table 9.6 compares calculated and observed heats of atomization for a number of compounds where reasonably reliable thermochemical data are available.‡

The results in Table 9.6 seem to suggest that σ polarization should be taken into account in treating heteroconjugated molecules, using the Hückel approximation.   Even so, the agreement is still inferior to that achieved in the corresponding treatment of hydrocarbons (Chaps. 5 to 7).   This is not surprising; for the introduction of σ polarization into treatments of this kind is by its very nature a makeshift.   As soon as we start to introduce interactions between σ and π electrons explicitly into our treatment, it becomes logically inconsistent to

‡ A major handicap here is the lack of accurate thermochemical data for conjugated systems containing heteroatoms but free from saturated substituents such as alkyl.

TABLE 9.6 Comparison of calculated and observed heats of atomization
for heteroconjugated molecules

Compound	Heat of atomization, ev		
	Calc.	Obs.	Difference
PYRIDINE	51.87	51.78	0.09
QUINOLINE	85.32	85.18	0.14
PYRIMIDINE	46.86	46.99	−0.13
PYRAZINE	46.27	46.44	−0.17
PYRIDAZINE	45.74	45.59	0.15
PYRROLE	44.77	44.77	0
INDOLE	78.44	78.06	0.38
CARBAZOLE	112.18	111.91	0.27
PYRAZOLE	39.32	39.26	0.06
1,2,4-TRIAZOLE	34.54	34.29	0.25
TETRAZOLE	28.01	28.06	−0.05
IMIDAZOLE	39.74	39.66	0.08
BENZPYRAZOLE	72.89	72.65	0.24
BENZIMIDAZOLE	73.41	73.23	0.18
BENZTRIAZOLE	67.14	66.96	0.18
ANILINE	64.39	64.31	0.08
DIPHENYLAMINE	116.62	116.53	0.09
α-NAPHTHYLAMINE	97.81	97.79	0.02
β-NAPHTHYLAMINE	97.81	97.78	0.03
FURAN	41.56	41.52	0.04
DIBENZOFURAN	109.22	109.18	0.04
ANISOLE	73.28	73.35	−0.07
DIPHENYL ETHER	113.78	113.84	−0.06
p-BENZOQUINONE	60.10	59.94	0.16
FORMALDEHYDE	15.71	15.71	0
BENZALDEHYDE	68.51	68.27	0.24
BENZOPHENONE	121.24	120.98	0.26

use the Hückel σ-π approximation.   The only satisfactory procedures would be
ones in which all the valence electrons, both σ and π, are included in the SCF MO
calculations; approaches of this kind will be considered in the following chapter.

9.4   CHARGE DISTRIBUTIONS AND DIPOLE MOMENTS

The π-electron charge distributions given by the Pople method are very different from the corresponding HMO values, the differences being analogous to
those observed in the case of carbonium ions and carbanions (Sec. 5.11) and
due to the same factors.   Figure 9.2 shows this distinction very clearly.   Note
that while both procedures agree in predicting large positive formal charges
($q < 1$) at the α,γ positions in pyridine, the Pople method[4] differs in predicting
comparable *negative* formal charges ($q > 1$) at the β positions.

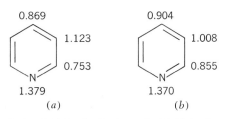

FIG. 9.2 π-electron densities for pyridine calculated (*a*) by the Pople method;[4] (*b*) by the HMO method, with $\beta_{CN} = \beta_{CC}$ and $\alpha_N = \alpha_C + \beta_{CC}$.

The situation is clearly very similar to that appearing in the odd-AH polyene ions of Fig. 5.9. Figure 9.2*b* shows the kind of π-electron distribution that pyridine would have if the atoms in it had electronegativities that were independent of charge; for this is one of the basic assumptions underlying the HMO method. The large formal charges on the α,γ positions lead to an increase in electronegativity at those atoms, but they also lead to a much larger increase in electronegativity at the intermediate β positions, for reasons that were analyzed in detail in the discussion of odd-AH ions in Sec. 5.11. Consequently there is a drift of electrons to the β positions which acquire significant negative formal charges as a result.

There is no method by which charge distributions can be measured directly; however there is evidence[7] that, other things being equal, the nmr chemical shifts of protons in aromatic systems depend on the density of π electrons at the adjacent carbon atoms. "Other things being equal" implies that allowance can be made for differential effects due to long-range diamagnetic shielding, in particular by ring currents[8] in the aromatic system, and by "inductive" effects in cases where the carbon atom forms a polar bond or bonds to neighbors in the ring. On this basis, an interesting check of the SCF results is provided by a comparison of the proton nmr spectra of naphthalene (V), and of 10,9-borazaronaphthalene (VI),[8,9] two compounds which are isoelectronic with each other and in which ring-current effects might consequently be expected to play similar roles.

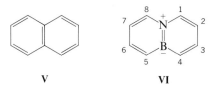

V   VI

The inductive effects of boron and nitrogen can be estimated from a comparison of the methyl chemical shifts in compounds of the type R_2CHCH_3, R_2BCH_3, and R_2NCH_3; on this basis one might expect the 1 proton in VI to be shifted about 2 ppm downfield relative to that in V, and the 4 proton to be shifted a similar amount upfield. Table 9.7 shows π-electron charge densities calculated for VI by the HMO method. Since the lowest charge is at the 1 position, and

TABLE 9.7 Calculated π-electron densities,
in 10,9-borazaronaphthalene

Position	HMO	Pople
1	0.907	0.985
2	1.056	1.022
3	0.944	0.951
4	1.093	0.971

since the proton there should be strongly deshielded by the inductive effect of nitrogen, the corresponding signal should appear far downfield relative to those for the remaining protons.   It should moreover be a doublet, since there is only one proton *ortho* to the proton in question, and coupling constants between protons in an aromatic ring are large only if they are *ortho* to one another.   A similar argument shows that the signal for the 4 proton should lie far upfield, being also a doublet.   The signals for the 2 and 3 protons should be quartets, that for the 2 proton lying upfield relative to that for the 3 position since the π-electron density is much greater there.   The spectrum should on this basis follow the pattern indicated in Fig. 9.3a.

The observed proton nmr spectrum is entirely different from this; it is shown in Fig. 9.3b.   One proton absorbs far upfield from the rest; the corresponding signal is, however, not a doublet but a triplet, implying that the proton in question is in the 2 or 3 position.   Various lines of argument suggest that it is in fact in the 2 position, and that the two downfield peaks are due, as indicated in

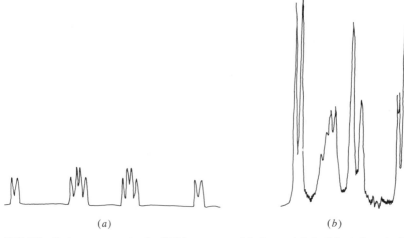

(a)   (b)

FIG. 9.3 Proton nmr spectra for 10,9-borazaronaphthalene. (*a*) Anticipated on the basis of HMO calculations; (*b*) observed.[9]

Fig. 9.3*b*, to the 1 proton. The intermediate multiplet is then due to the 3 and 4 protons.

Since the 4 proton would be expected to absorb about 2 ppm upfield relative to the 3 proton if the π-electron densities of the adjacent carbon atoms were the same, it is evident that the π-electron density of the 4 position must in fact be very low, in complete contradiction of the HMO results, which predict it to be the highest; likewise the π-electron density at the 1 position must be large, certainly much greater than that of the 3 or 4 positions. The last column of Table 9.7 shows π-electron densities calculated by the Pople method. These are admittedly somewhat uncertain since, for reasons indicated above, it is not easy to determine the parameters for boron; however calculations using a range of values led to the same general result. Note that the π-electron densities follow a pattern qualitatively different from that predicted by the HMO method, but in general agreement with the nmr spectrum. Thus the π density at the 1 position, instead of being the smallest of the four, is nearly the greatest, and that at the 4 position, instead of being the greatest, is nearly the least. These results provide an amusing vindication of the SCF treatment.

A further test might be provided by comparisons of calculated and observed dipole moments; however comparisons of this kind are not really meaningful since there is no satisfactory way of estimating the contributions of the σ electrons. The procedure used to allow for σ polarization is frankly somewhat of a makeshift; if such allowances have to be made, then the only satisfactory way to make them is to abandon the Hückel approximation altogether and include the σ electrons explicitly in the calculation. Such an approach will be discussed in detail in the following chapter.

9.5 CHEMICAL REACTIVITY OF HETEROCONJUGATED MOLECULES

The method outlined above can be applied to reactions of heteroconjugated molecules, following the same procedures as those used in the corresponding treatment of hydrocarbons in Chap. 8. Since no new principles are involved, a few examples will suffice.

9.5.1 SALT FORMATION   Carbonyl compounds (VII) act as bases, albeit weak ones;

$$R_2C{=}O + H^+ \rightleftarrows R_2C{=}\overset{+}{O}H \tag{9.27}$$
$$\text{VII} \qquad\qquad\qquad \text{VIII}$$

The pK_A of the conjugate acids (VIII) can be measured by standard techniques; following the argument of Sec. 8.5, we would expect them to follow a relation of the form:

$$pK_a = A + B[\Delta H(R_2\overset{+}{C}OH) - \Delta H(R_2CO)] \tag{9.28}$$

where $\Delta H(R_2\overset{+}{C}OH)$ is the calculated heat of formation of the conjugate acid (VIII) and $\Delta H(R_2CO)$ that of the parent base (VII).   Data are available for a wide range of compounds of this type, including aldehydes, ketones, pyrones, and tropones, and covering a range of pK_A of 12 units.   Figure 9.4 shows a plot of the measured pK_A against the calculated[5] differences in heats of formation. With one exception (diphenylcyclopropenone) all the points lie close to a straight line.

9.5.2   ELECTROPHILIC SUBSTITUTION   Rates of aromatic substitution can be discussed in terms of our present approximation by using the arguments outlined in Sec. 8.7.   The rate constants k should follow a relation of the form

$$\log k = A + B\,\Delta E_{\text{loc}} \tag{9.29}$$

where ΔE_{loc} is the localization energy, i.e. the difference in energy between the aromatic compound and the appropriate Wheland intermediate for substitution. Figure 9.5 shows a plot of this kind for nitration both of a number of aromatic hydrocarbons (compare Sec. 8.7) and of various heteroaromatics.   Not only do the points nearly all lie close to a straight line, but the line is the one previously plotted in Fig. 8.9, from data for hydrocarbons alone.   Note also that the rate constants cover an enormous range, about $10^{13}:1$.

The only significant deviations in Fig. 9.5 are for carbazole (IX) and diphenylamine (X); a possible explanation of this will be suggested presently (Sec. 9.10).

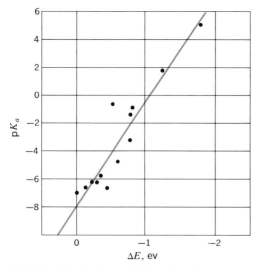

FIG. 9.4   Plot of pK_a vs. ΔE for carbonyl compounds.

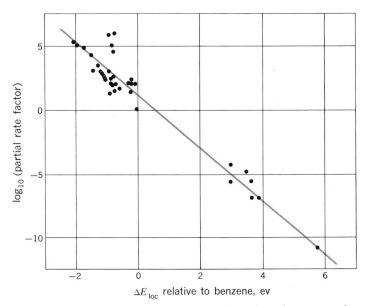

FIG. 9.5 Plot[4] of log k vs. ΔE_{loc} for nitration of aromatic hydrocarbons, heteroaromatics, ethers, and amines.

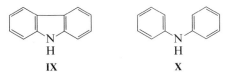

9.5.3 TAUTOMERIC EQUILIBRIA

Many heteroaromatic compounds containing hydroxy or amino groups can exist in tautomeric forms. A classic example of this is provided by the equilibria between 2-hydroxypyridine (XI) and α-pyridone (XII) and between 2-aminopyridine (XIII) and 2-imino-1,2-dihydropyridine (XIV).

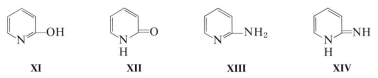

While no equilibrium constants have been measured for simple systems of this kind, it is known in many cases which of the two tautomers is the more stable, and this information provides an obvious further check of our SCF calculations. Admittedly complications may arise in practice from hydrogen bonding, which our treatment ignores, and which may lead to a displacement of equilibrium in hydrogen-bonding solvents; however this is unlikely to be serious, given that the equilibria seem in most cases to lie very far over on one side or the other.

Table 9.8 shows heats of isomerization calculated by the Pople method; note that these are differences between the total heats of formation for the pairs of tautomers, not differences in π energy.   The distinction here is very important since the tautomers have significantly different geometries; it would be entirely incorrect to ignore the corresponding changes in energy of the σ bonds.   The results in Table 9.8 lead to the prediction that compounds with a hydroxy group α or γ to nitrogen should exist preferentially as the ketonic tautomers (e.g. XII), while the reverse should be true of the amines; all the available chemical evidence seems to support this conclusion.

9.5.4   RADICALS CONTAINING HETEROATOMS   The heats of formation of radicals containing heteroatoms can be calculated by the closed-shell Pople method of Sec. 7.7; experimental data for such systems are unfortunately

TABLE 9.8   Heats of isomerization in prototropic systems[4]

Tautomer A	Tautomer B	$\Delta H(A \rightarrow B)$, ev
		0.054
		1.000
		0.120
		1.135
		0.964
		1.101

TABLE 9.9   Calculated[10] and observed heats of atomization of radicals containing nitrogen or oxygen

Radical	Heat of atomization, ev		
	Calc.	Obs.	Difference
PhO·	58.09	57.91 ± 0.26	0.18
PhCOO·	68.71	69.25 ± 0.24	0.54
$CH_3COO·$	28.88	28.72 ± 0.22	0.16
$CH_3COCH_2·$	36.99	36.59 ± 0.16	0.40
PhHN·	60.96	60.86 ± 0.26	0.10
PhMeN·	65.64	65.78 ± 0.29	−0.14

scanty, so it is difficult to say much concerning the accuracy of the calculated values.   Table 9.9 shows some comparisons of this kind.

The agreement between the calculated and observed heats of atomization is satisfactory, especially in view of the uncertainties in the experimental values; the estimated limits of error are certainly not conservative in most cases.

9.6   PMO TREATMENT OF HETEROCONJUGATED SYSTEMS

The Pople treatment outlined above seems to provide a very satisfactory account of the ground-state properties of conjugated compounds containing heteroatoms; calculations of this kind do, however, require the use of a fairly large digital computer, so there is also a need for some simpler approach that could be used as an immediate adjunct to chemical thinking.   In the case of hydrocarbons, the PMO method provided an ideal solution of this kind; here we shall consider its extension to compounds containing heteroatoms.

The general approach to this problem was outlined in Chap. 6.   A heteroconjugated molecule is regarded as a perturbed form of the isoconjugate hydrocarbon,‡ differing from it in that the coulomb integral of each heteroatom, and the resonance integral of each bond formed by a heteroatom, may differ from the corresponding values for carbon and for a carbon-carbon bond.   The corresponding change δQ in some property Q on passing from the hydrocarbon to the heteroconjugated molecule can be written, to a first approximation, as:

$$\delta Q = \sum_i \frac{\partial Q}{\partial \alpha_i} \delta \alpha_i + \sum_{i,j} \frac{\partial Q}{\partial \beta_{ij}} \delta \beta_{ij} \tag{9.30}$$

‡ Two molecules are defined as isoconjugate if they contain the same number of conjugated atoms linked analogously by σ bonds, and the same number of π electrons.   Thus benzene and pyridine are isoconjugate, and so are pyrrole and the cyclopentadienate ion, $C_5H_5^-$, since in each pair we have the same number of conjugated atoms linked analogously (i.e. in a single ring) and the same number (i.e. six) of π electrons.

where $\delta\alpha_i$ is the difference between the coulomb integral of atom i and that of carbon, and $\delta\beta_{ij}$ the corresponding difference in the resonance integral of the bond between atoms i and j. The values of the differential coefficients for various molecular properties, in particular the total energy, π-charge densities, and π-bond orders, were deduced in the earlier sections of Chap. 6; their use will now be illustrated by applying them to some specific problems.

9.7   RESONANCE ENERGIES OF EVEN SYSTEMS

The resonance energy RE of a conjugated hydrocarbon is defined (Sec. 5.6) by:

$$RE = -(\Delta H - \Delta H_{cl}) \qquad (9.31)$$

where ΔH is its heat of formation and ΔH_{cl} the heat of formation it would have if the bonds in it were localized. (The *minus* sign follows from the convention that resonance energies are treated as positive quantities, but heats of formation as negative ones.) Our first problem is to deduce how RE will change if one or more carbon atoms are replaced by heteroatoms.

As a first approximation, we may ignore the effect of changes in resonance integrals, for three reasons: (1) the π bonds in question are all of comparable strength, so that the resonance integrals all have similar values; (2) changes in resonance integrals will alter the energies of the hydrocarbon, and of the analog with localized bonds, to comparable extents; (3) the coefficients $\partial Q/\partial\beta_{ij}$ in Eq. (9.30) are harder to estimate in the kind of way we shall be using than are the corresponding coefficients involving coulomb integrals.

From Eq. (6.16), the required coefficients in Eq. (9.30) are seen to be:

$$\frac{\partial\Delta H}{\partial\alpha_i} = q_i \qquad \frac{\partial\Delta H_{cl}}{\partial\alpha_i} = q_i' \qquad (9.32)$$

where α_i is the coulomb integral of atom i, and q_i and q_i' are the charge densities in the actual hydrocarbon and in the localized-bond analog respectively. The energy relationships we need are then as illustrated in Fig. 9.6. The resonance energy RE′ of the heteroconjugated molecule is defined by:

$$RE' = -(\Delta H' - \Delta H_{cl}') \qquad (9.33)$$

where $\Delta H'$ is its heat of formation, and $\Delta H_{cl}'$ that of the corresponding localized-bond analog. From Fig. 9.6,

$$RE' = RE + \sum_i q_i'\,\delta\alpha_i - \sum_i q_i\,\delta\alpha_i = RE + \sum_i (q_i' - q_i)\,\delta\alpha_i \qquad (9.34)$$

Consider first an even-AH or odd-AH radical. From the pairing theorem, the π-charge density at each position in such a molecule is unity. Moreover the same will be true for the localized-bond analog, this being also a neutral AH.

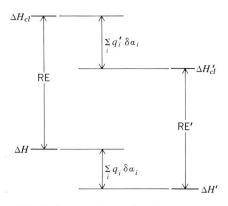

FIG. 9.6   Calculation of the resonance energy RE′ of a heteroconjugated molecule in terms of that RE of the isoconjugate hydrocarbon.

Consequently

$$RE' = RE + \sum_i (1 - 1)\, \delta\alpha_i \equiv RE \qquad (9.35)$$

The resonance energy of an even heteroconjugated compound, or of an odd heteroconjugated radical, should therefore be the same, to this first approximation, as that of the isoconjugate AH.   The available evidence certainly seems to support this conclusion.   Thus the resonance energies of the various monocyclic azines, e.g.

all seem to be similar to that of the isoconjugate AH, i.e. benzene, and the same relation holds between the various bicyclic azines (quinoline, isoquinoline, quinazoline, etc.) and naphthalene.

In the case of nonalternant hydrocarbons, e.g. azulene, the situation is different.   A structure with localized bonds will of course be effectively alternant, regardless of the way in which the individual localized double bonds are linked together; hence q_i' in Eq. (9.36) will still be equal to unity.   However in the case of a nonlocalized, nonalternant hydrocarbon, the charge densities q_i will normally differ from unity.   Hence:

$$RE' = RE + \sum_i (1 - q_i)\, \delta\alpha_i \qquad (9.36)$$

If the heteroatom in question is more electronegative than carbon (e.g. N or O), $\delta\alpha$ will be negative; in that case RE′ > RE if the heteroatom is at a position with a negative formal charge (that is $q_i > 1$), while RE′ < RE if $q_i < 1$.   The charge densities in nonalternant hydrocarbons cannot of course be estimated in any

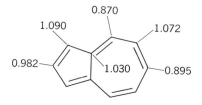

FIG. 9.7 π-charge densities calculated for azulene (see Chap. 5).

simple way; it is necessary to calculate them, preferably by an SCF MO method. Figure 9.7 shows the π-charge densities calculated for azulene by the method of Chap. 5; it will be seen that there are quite large negative formal charges in the five-membered ring, in particular at the 1,3 positions, and positive formal charges in the seven-membered ring.   We would therefore expect azaazulenes to be more stable than azulene if the heteroatoms are in the five-membered ring; several compounds of this type have indeed been prepared (e.g. Ref. 11). Analogous azines with nitrogen in the seven-membered rings should on the other hand be less stable; it is perhaps significant that no compounds of this type have as yet been reported.

9.8   ODD ALTERNANT RADICALS AND IONS
Our definition of resonance energy does not extend to odd-AH radicals or ions, because there is no satisfactory way of defining a suitable "localized" reference system for compounds of this type.   From a chemical standpoint, however, this is not a serious omission; for in chemistry we are concerned not so much with the absolute heats of formation of systems of this kind as with the ease of form-ing them from related "normal" even systems.   Consider for example the bond-dissociation energy of the central bond in bibenzyl, i.e. the energy absorbed in the process

$$PhCH_2—CH_2Ph \rightarrow Ph\dot{C}H_2 + \dot{C}H_2Ph \qquad (9.37)$$

This energy is less by 36 kcal/mole than the corresponding value for the CC bond in ethane.   The difference is mainly due to the fact that the total π-bond energy of two benzyl radicals is greater than that of two phenyl groups.   The difference in π-bond energy between benzyl and phenyl is often referred to as "resonance energy"; however this seems an unfortunate misuse of the term since it depends on an *ad hoc* definition.   Bond rupture in bibenzyl is facilitated by the increase in π-bond energy accompanying it; a similar phenomenon is observed in the case of *n*-alkyl radicals, which can readily fragment into ethylene and a smaller radical, i.e.

$$R—CH_2—CH_2\cdot \rightarrow R\cdot + CH_2{=}CH_2 \qquad (9.38)$$

The bond-dissociation energy of the R—C bond in this process (which of course is simply the reverse of the propagation step in a corresponding vinyl polymerization) is very low, of the order of 20 kcal/mole; this is because rupture is accompanied by an increase in π-bond energy, the original radical being saturated while one of the products has a double bond. We do not find it necessary to describe this increase in π-bond energy as an increase in resonance energy; it is difficult to see any justification for treating the bibenzyl case any differently.

Our object is to examine the effect of heteroatoms on the ease of interconversion of odd and even alternant systems.   The corresponding changes in π energy were discussed in detail in terms of PMO theory in Secs. 8.6 to 8.14.   The change in π energy in an OE process involving addition of an extra carbon atom t to an odd AH is given approximately by:

$$\delta E_\pi^{\mathrm{OE}} = 2\beta \sum_r a_{0r} \tag{9.39}$$

where the sum is over atoms r that are directly linked to atom t in the product; the corresponding π-energy change in an EO reaction, involving removal of atom t from an odd AH, is given approximately by:

$$\delta E_\pi^{\mathrm{EO}} = 2\beta(1 - a_{0t}) \tag{9.40}$$

where a_{0t} is the NBMO coefficient at atom t in the odd AH. We wish to deduce the corresponding energy changes for cases where heteroatoms are present, subject once again, at any rate initially, to the assumption that the resonance integrals of all π bonds are the same.

Consider first the case of an odd AH undergoing an OE reaction. Here the energy change $\delta E_\pi^{\mathrm{OE}}$ is the difference in energy between the final even AH S and the initial odd AH R. Suppose we replace one or more carbon atoms in R and S by heteroatoms. The effect on their energies can be deduced at once from the argument in Sec. 9.7 and Fig. 9.6. We can use this figure directly if we identify "ΔH_{cl}" with the energy of the odd AH, "ΔH" with the energy of the even AH, and "RE" with $\delta E_\pi^{\mathrm{OE}}$. The corresponding energy difference $(\delta E_\pi^{\mathrm{OE}})_H$ for the heteroconjugated system is then given by

$$(\delta E_\pi^{\mathrm{OE}})_H = \delta E_\pi^{\mathrm{OE}} + \sum_i (q_i - q_i') \,\delta\alpha_i \tag{9.41}$$

where q_i is the π-charge density at atom i in S, and q_i' the π-charge density at atom i in R. Since moreover S is by definition an even AH in which $q = 1$ at each position, this becomes:

$$(\delta E_\pi^{\mathrm{OE}})_H = \delta E_\pi^{\mathrm{OE}} + \sum_i (1 - q_i') \,\delta\alpha_i \tag{9.42}$$

Consider first the case where R is an odd-AH radical, where $q' = 1$ at each position. From Eq. (9.42):

$$(\delta E^{\mathrm{OE}})_H = \delta E^{\mathrm{OE}} \tag{9.43}$$

Reactions involving odd alternant heteroconjugated radicals should therefore take place just about as readily as corresponding reactions of the isoconjugate AHs.   The experimental evidence seems to support this conclusion.

Consider for example the addition of a radical X' to a vinyl derivative XCH=CH$_2$, when X is an even conjugated group;

$$X\text{CH}=\text{CH}_2 + X' \rightarrow X\dot{\text{C}}\text{H}\text{---}\text{CH}_2X' \tag{9.44}$$

Addition removes the terminal atom from conjugation, so this is an $\overline{O}{}^R\overline{E}$ reaction. Reactions of this type occur as the propagation steps in radical-catalyzed vinyl polymerizations, and the relative rates of many such reactions have been studied. It appears that the rates are very much the same for groups X containing heteroatoms (e.g. α-pyridyl or —COR) as they are for the isoconjugate AH groups (e.g. phenyl or —CH=CH$_2$).‡   Another example is provided by radical substitution in aromatic compounds.   The rates of reaction of heteroaromatics such as pyridine or quinoline are very similar to those for the isoconjugate AHs.

Next let us consider an analogous process in which the odd AH occurs as an anion.   Here the π-charge density q'_i at atom i is given by

$$q'_i = 1 + a_{0i}{}^2 \tag{9.45}$$

where a_{0i} is the NBMO coefficient at atom i.   From Eqs. (9.42) and (9.45),

$$(\delta E_\pi{}^{OE})_H = \delta E_\pi{}^{OE} - \sum_i a_{0i}{}^2 \, \delta\alpha_i \tag{9.46}$$

In cases where $\delta\alpha_i$ is negative, as is true for most typical heteroatoms, $(\delta E_\pi{}^{OE})_H$ will then be numerically less than $\delta E_\pi{}^{OE}$; the conversion of the odd ion to an even system with one additional carbon atom should therefore be inhibited by the presence of heteroatoms, provided that at least one of these occupies an active position in R, where the NBMO coefficient a_{0i} differs from zero.   O–E reactions should therefore be inhibited by appropriately placed heteroatoms, and $\overline{O}$–$\overline{E}$ reactions correspondingly facilitated.

This prediction is again supported by the available experimental evidence, most of which refers to reactions of $\overline{O}$–$\overline{E}$ type.   A classical example is provided by nucleophilic aromatic substitution, e.g. the Chichibabin reaction [amination by sodamide; Eq. (9.47)], and displacement of halogen by nucleophiles [Eq. (9.48)].

$$\text{(pyridine)} + \text{NH}_2{}^- \rightarrow \text{(intermediate)} \rightarrow \text{(2-aminopyridine)}\text{---NH}_2 + \text{H}^- \tag{9.47}$$

XV

‡ For general accounts, see Ref. 12.

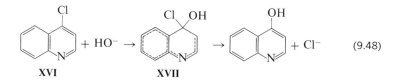

$$\text{XVI} \qquad\qquad \text{XVII} \qquad\qquad\qquad (9.48)$$

Reactions of this type take place only with great difficulty in the case of aromatic hydrocarbons, but readily with nitrogen heterocycles. Comparison of Eqs. (8.35) and (9.46) shows that the quantity ΔE_{deloc} that measures the ease of substitution is given in the case of nucleophilic substitution of a heteroaromatic by:

$$\Delta E_{\text{deloc}} = -\beta N_t + \sum_i a_{0i}{}^2 \, \delta\alpha_i \qquad (9.49)$$

Thus ΔE_{deloc} is less than it would be for the isoconjugate AH (that is $-\beta N_t$) by the final sum in Eq. (9.49). Evidently this sum is the determining factor in reactions of this kind, seeing that they take place easily only if at least one heteroatom occupies a position which in the Wheland intermediate (e.g. XV or XVII) has a numerically large NBMO coefficient. This condition can be met only if there is at least one heteroatom in the ring where attack takes place, in a position *ortho* or *para* to the point of attack. Likewise compounds with two or three heteroatoms in these strategic positions are much more reactive than compounds with only one; for instance 4-chloroquinoline (XVI) hydrolyzes with some difficulty, the reaction requiring the use of hot aqueous alkali; 4-chloroquinazoline (XVIII) on the other hand hydrolyzes easily with water in the cold; and cyanuric chloride (XIX) reacts as easily with water as do many acid chlorides.

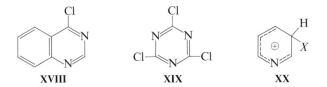

XVIII   XIX   XX

The third case, i.e. that where R is an odd-AH cation, can be treated likewise. We find [compare Eqs. (9.45) and (9.46)] that:

$$q_i' = 1 - a_{0i}{}^2 \qquad (9.50)$$

$$(\delta E_\pi{}^{OE})_H = \delta E_\pi{}^{OE} + \sum_i a_{0i}{}^2 \, \delta\alpha_i \qquad (9.51)$$

Here the even structure S is greatly favored in comparison with the situation in the isoconjugate AH; O^+E reactions should therefore be facilitated by heteroatoms, and $\overline{O}{}^+\overline{E}$ ones inhibited. Examples of the first kind are rare, the destabilization of odd-AH cations by heteroatoms being so great that systems of this kind are hard to come by; the second case is again well illustrated by electrophilic aromatic substitution, a typical $\overline{O}{}^+E$ process.   Here, following the same argument as before, we find that:

$$\Delta E_{\text{deloc}} = -\beta N_t - \sum_i a_{0i}{}^2\, \delta\alpha_i \tag{9.52}$$

so the typical heteroatoms (for example N, O) should have a deactivating effect. This effect is not only observed but is so great that pyridine undergoes substitution only under extreme conditions; when it does so, the products are formed by β substitution so that the nitrogen atom is at least at an inactive position in the arenonium intermediate (XX).   [The reader may wonder why the nitrogen atom should have any effect at all on β substitution, since the final sum in Eq. (9.52) then vanishes; the reason for this apparent anomaly will be considered presently (Sec. 9.16).]

When possible, substitution takes place in some ring that is free from heteroatoms; thus nitration of quinoline, or of isoquinoline, gives mainly a mixture of the 5- and 8-nitro derivatives (XXI to XXIV).

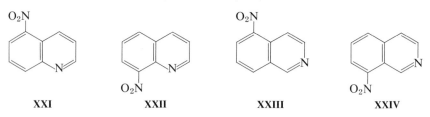

| XXI | XXII | XXIII | XXIV |

The NBMO coefficients in a ring removed from the point of substitution are numerically much smaller than those in the ring where substitution is taking place; this is illustrated by the values of the squares of NBMO coefficients for the intermediates in α and β substitution of naphthalene (XXV and XXVI).

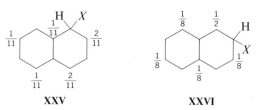

XXV   XXVI

The results in XXI to XXIV raise a further interesting point.   Substitution at the 8 position in quinoline (XXII), or in the 5 position in isoquinoline (XXIII), takes place via an intermediate ion in which the nitrogen atom occupies an inactive position.   This is not true for the two remaining isomers (XXI and XXIV).   Why does not quinoline prefer to substitute in the 6 position, and isoquinoline in the 7 position, reactions which would again take place via intermediates when a_{0i} vanishes?   The answer lies in the expression for ΔE_{deloc} [Eq. (9.52)].   This contains a term $-\beta N_t$, measuring the ease of attack at the corresponding point in the isoconjugate AH.   Now N_t is much less ($= 1.81$) at the

α position of naphthalene than at the β position ($= 2.12$); this is why attack takes place at the α position preferentially. The same preference will be carried over to quinoline and isoquinoline; hence β substitution will predominate only if the contributions of the final terms in Eq. (9.54) outweigh this difference. Evidently they do not, so the α positions still win out. The effect of nitrogen does, however, appear as a minor correction in that nitration of isoquinoline gives more XXIII than XXIV (85:15), whereas in quinoline, the 5 and 8 isomers are formed in equal amounts.‡

Another interesting case is provided by 10-methyl-10,9-borazarophenanthrene (XXVII), a compound isoelectronic with 9-methylphenanthrene (XXVIII) and containing a heteroatom (i.e. boron) that is *less* electronegative than carbon. Here electrophilic substitution should be *accelerated* if boron occupies an active position in the intermediate. This condition is met if substitution takes place at the 2, 4, 6, or 8 positions in XXVII. Since 1 and 3 positions of XXVIII are much more reactive than the 2 or 4 positions, we would predict that XXVII should not only undergo substitution much more easily than XXVIII, but also that attack should take place preferentially at the 6 and 8 positions; both these predictions agree with experiment.[13]

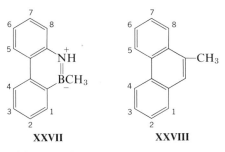

XXVII   XXVIII

The reactions considered so far in this section have involved the interconversion of an odd system with an even one containing an additional atom; let us now turn to corresponding reactions when the odd system has the additional atom, i.e. reactions of EO type. It is very easily seen, following arguments analogous to those used for OE reactions, that in the case of heteroconjugated systems, the π-energy differences of Eq. (9.40) become:

Radicals: $(\delta E_\pi^{EO})_H = \delta E_\pi^{EO}$ (9.53)

Anions: $(\delta E_\pi^{EO})_H = \delta E_\pi^{EO} + \sum_i a_{0i}^2\, \delta \alpha_i$ (9.54)

Cations: $(\delta E_\pi^{EO})_H = \delta E_\pi^{EO} - \sum_i a_{0i}^2\, \delta \alpha_i$ (9.55)

‡ It might seem at first sight surprising that the 8 isomer does not predominate. However the nitration is carried out in concentrated sulfuric acid when the nitrogen atom of quinoline must be completely protonated; the resulting positively charged $\overset{\displaystyle \sim +}{>}NH$ group will be surrounded by solvent molecules and gegenions, so sterically hindering attack at the position *peri* to it.

Here again the odd anion should be favored by the presence of heteroatoms, and the odd cation rebuffed, while radicals should remain unaffected. The experimental evidence again supports our conclusions.

9.8.1 EO^R REACTIONS   A good example is provided by the thermal dissociation of hydrazobenzene into radicals;

$$PhNH—NHPh \rightarrow PhNH\cdot + \cdot HNPh \tag{9.56}$$

The energy required to bring this about, i.e. the NN bond-dissociation energy, is much less (35.5 kcal/mole[14]) than the corresponding value for hydrazine (61 kcal/mole[15]). As in the case of bibenzyl [Eq. (9.39)], the difference can be attributed to an increase in π-bond energy during the reaction; on this basis, the extra π energy of the radical PhNH$\cdot$ relative to benzene and that of benzyl relative to benzene are very similar, as Eq. (9.55) requires.‡

9.8.2 EO$^-$ REACTIONS   The best examples of EO$^-$ reactions involve deprotonation at a saturated carbon atom adjacent to a heteroconjugated system. For example the methyl protons in α-picoline (XXIX), or 4-methylquinoline (XXX), are much more acidic than those in the isoconjugate hydrocarbons; in each case the product is an odd alternant ion (XXXI or XXXII), where nitrogen occupies an active position. The methyl protons in β-picoline (XXXIII) are much less acidic than those in XXIX or XXX; here the anion (XXXIV) has its nitrogen atom at an inactive position.

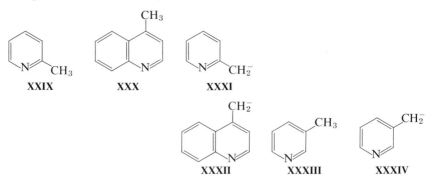

The best-known cases are those when the heteroconjugated system contains oxygen. Thus protons α to a carbonyl group are enormously more acidic than

---

‡ The situations are not entirely comparable in that the nitrogen atoms in hydrazobenzene can interact with the π electrons of the rings, unlike the methylene groups in bibenzyl. This would make the difference in bond-dissociation energies between hydrazobenzene and hydrazine less than twice the quantity $(\delta E_\pi{}^{EO})_H$ for the PhNH$\cdot$ radical. The resonance energy of hydrazobenzene is probably quite small, judging by calculations using the method of Sec. 9.3; in any case the correction is in the right direction, given that the difference in bond-dissociation energies between hydrazobenzene and hydrazine is less than that between bibenzyl and ethane.

ones α to a carbon-carbon double bond, and the same is true of more extended systems of this kind. The methyl protons in crotonaldehyde, CH_3—CH=CH—CHO, are, for example, far more acidic than those in piperylene, $CH_3CH=CH$—CH=CH_2.

9.8.3 EO$^+$ REACTIONS The best examples here are provided by reactions analogous to those of Sec. 9.8.2, but in which a conjugated cation is formed by separation of a suitable "leaving" group as an anion. Here heteroatoms should and do hinder the reaction. Thus while allyl chloride solvolyzes very easily indeed by the limiting S_N1 mechanism, involving ionization of chlorine (see Secs. 8.11 and 8.12),

$$CH_2=CHCH_2Cl \rightarrow [CH_2\text{---}CH\text{---}CH_2]^+ \; Cl^- \tag{9.57}$$

the isoconjugate chloride, chloracetone, O=$CMeCH_2Cl$, does not undergo reactions of this type at all. Many other examples could be quoted, but it will be convenient to reserve further discussion until a later part of this chapter (Sec. 9.13).

9.9 BOND ORDERS AND CHARGE DENSITIES IN EVEN SYSTEMS

Given that the resonance energies of even alternant heteroconjugated molecules are the same, to a first approximation, as those of the isoconjugate AHs (Sec. 9.7), one might expect the bond orders to follow a similar pattern and so also the rules for bond localization. We shall now show that this situation is indeed correct. To do this, we first need to prove the following theorem.

Theorem 9.1 In an even AH, atom-bond and bond-atom polarizabilities vanish.

The expression for the bond-atom polarizability in an even system is [see Eq. (6.30)]:

$$\pi_{kl,i} = 2 \sum_{\mu}^{\text{occ}} \sum_{\nu}^{\text{unocc}} \frac{a_{\mu i} a_{\nu i} (a_{\mu k} a_{\nu l} + a_{\mu l} a_{\nu k})}{E_\mu - E_\nu} \tag{9.58}$$

Since we are concerned only with changes in the lengths of real bonds in the molecule we can confine our attention to cases where the atoms k and l are directly linked. In an AH, atoms which are directly linked are necessarily of opposite parity; atoms k and l are therefore of opposite parity. One of these, which we may take to be l, will be of the same parity as atom i; since starring is arbitrary, we may assume atoms i and l to be starred, and atom k consequently unstarred. From Theorem 6.1, we may then replace the summation over unoccupied MOs ν in Eq. (9.58) by one over occupied MOs if we reverse the signs of E_ν and of the unstarred coefficient $a_{\nu k}$; hence:

$$\pi_{kl,i} = 2 \sum_{\mu}^{\text{occ}} \sum_{\nu}^{\text{occ}} \frac{a_{\mu i} a_{\nu i} (a_{\mu k} a_{\nu l} - a_{\mu l} a_{\nu k})}{E_\mu + E_\nu} = 0 \tag{9.59}$$

The double sum vanishes since each term in it occurs twice over, with opposite signs. This proves the theorem.

It follows from the definition of bond-atom polarizabilities [Eq. (6.30)] that the bond orders in an even AH will not be affected, to a first approximation, by changes in the electronegativities of the conjugated atoms. To this approximation, and neglecting once more the possible effects of changes in resonance integrals, we can deduce that the bond orders in an alternant heteroconjugated molecule should be the same as those in the isoconjugate AH. The most important consequence is that the rules for bond localization are the same in both cases; essential single bonds, and essential double bonds, are localized in even heteroconjugated molecules. The available experimental evidence suggests that bonds of this type (e.g. the central bond in bipyridyl) are indeed similar to those in the isoconjugate hydrocarbon.

The parallel does not, however, hold for even nonalternant systems. Here the bond-atom polarizabilities do not vanish, so the properties of heteroconjugated molecules of this type may differ significantly from those of the isoconjugate AHs. A good example is provided by tropone (XXXV), a compound isoconjugate with heptafulvene (XXXVI). In heptafulvene, the bonds are effectively localized single and double bonds (see Table 5.4, Fig. 5.7, and Sec. 6.8), and the molecule is predicted to have only a small dipole moment (0.46 D). Tropone, on the other hand, has quite a large dipole moment (4.17 D)[16] and the carbonyl stretching frequency is unusually low (1,638 cm^{-1});[17] calculations support the conclusion that tropone is significantly perturbed from the classical structure (XXXV) in the direction of the dipolar structure (XXXVII).

XXXV   XXXVI   XXXVII

The effect of heteroatoms on the π-electron distribution in an even alternant system can be found in two different ways. The first makes use of the atom-atom polarizabilities defined in Eqs. (6.22), (6.23), (6.26), and (6.27). The following theorems can be proved by the procedure used for Theorem 9.1.‡

Theorem 9.2 In any conjugated hydrocarbon, the self-polarizabilities of all atoms are negative.

Theorem 9.3 In an even AH, the atom-atom polarizability $\pi_{j,i}$ is positive if atoms i and j are of opposite parity but negative if they are of the same parity.

‡ For a detailed discussion of this approach, and some additional theorems of the same kind, see Ref. 18.

Theorem 9.2, together with Eq. (6.22), shows that a heteroatom that is more electronegative than carbon (i.e. one for which $\delta\alpha$ is negative) will have a negative formal charge if it forms part of an even conjugated system; for the product $\pi_{i,i}\,\delta\alpha_i$ in Eq. (6.22) will be positive, and $q_i = 1$ for an even AH.   This result agrees with chemical intuition and the available experimental evidence; e.g. the basic strength of pyridine indicates very strongly that the nitrogen atom in it has a formal negative charge.

Theorem 9.3 shows that positions of opposite parity to a heteroatom in an even conjugated molecule likewise acquire positive formal charges, while positions of like parity acquire negative ones.   The first conclusion agrees with current chemical intuition based on resonance theory; thus the carbon atoms α,γ to nitrogen in pyridine are supposed to have positive charges, due to contributions by dipolar resonance structures such as XXXVIII.

XXXVIII

The second statement has no convincing counterpart in terms of resonance theory; together with the first, it amounts to a modern version[18] of the "law of alternating polarity" that organic chemists devised in the preelectronic era.   In practice, however, the atom-atom polarizabilities between positions of like parity are invariably small, so the negative charges calculated in that way for, say, the β positions in pyridine are trivial.   This leads to a rather paradoxical position, given that the SCF MO method predicts large negative charges in such positions (compare Fig. 9.2).   These arise, in the terminology of this section, from changes in the coulomb integrals α of atoms, due to formal charges at them and at their neighbors.   Allowance could be made for these changes by an iterative procedure, using Eqs. (6.23) and (6.27) to calculate the formal charges, deducing from these the corresponding changes in the α_i [compare Eq. (3.64); the quantities α_i correspond to diagonal elements F_{ii} of the F matrix], recalculating the charges, and continuing the cycle until the results converge.   Whether such a refinement would be worth attempting, given that the basic approach itself represents only a first approximation, seems doubtful; no one as yet seems to have tried it.

There is, however, an alternative PMO treatment which has the advantage of providing simple estimates of the quantities $\pi_{j,i}$.   Consider a heteroconjugated molecule S, formed by union of a heteroatom T, of coulomb integral $\delta\alpha$, with an odd-AH radical R (Fig. 9.8a).   Suppose first that union takes place through a single atom r in R.   If $\delta\alpha$ is small, the interaction between the AO ψ of T and the MOs of R will be small second-order effects except for that involving the NBMO Φ_0 of R; for Φ_0 and ψ will be nearly degenerate.   We can therefore represent the

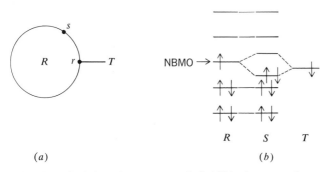

FIG. 9.8 Calculation of atom-atom polarizabilities in an even heteroconjugated molecule S. (a) Formation of S by union of an odd AH R with a heteroatom T; (b) corresponding first-order changes in the energies of MOs.

interaction, to a first approximation, by ignoring all the other MOs and so treating the interaction as a two-orbital problem (see Fig. 9.8b). The corresponding secular equation is as follows:

$$\begin{vmatrix} \int\Phi_0\mathbf{H}\Phi_0\,d\tau - E & \int\Phi_0\mathbf{H}\psi\,d\tau \\ \int\psi\mathbf{H}\Phi_0\,d\tau & \int\psi\mathbf{H}\psi\,d\tau - E \end{vmatrix} = 0 \tag{9.60}$$

Taking the energy of a NBMO to be zero, as usual, and following the procedure of Eqs. (6.74) to (6.77), this becomes:

$$\begin{vmatrix} -E & a_{0r}\beta \\ a_{0r}\beta & \delta\alpha - E \end{vmatrix} = E^2 - E\,\delta\alpha - a_{0r}^2\beta^2 = 0 \tag{9.61}$$

where β is the r—T resonance integral and a_{0r} the NBMO coefficient of atom r. The solutions of this equation are:

$$E = \tfrac{1}{2}[-\delta\alpha \pm \sqrt{(\delta\alpha)^2 + 4a_{0r}^2\beta^2}] \tag{9.62}$$

We write the corresponding MO ξ in the form:

$$\xi = A\Phi_0 + B\psi \tag{9.63}$$

The coefficients A and B are given by the usual equation:

$$A\left(\int\Phi_0\mathbf{H}\Phi_0\,d\tau - E\right) + B\int\Phi_0\mathbf{H}\psi\,d\tau = 0 \tag{9.64}$$

which becomes:

$$-AE + a_{0r}\beta B = 0 \tag{9.65}$$

The energy of the bonding MO is given by Eq. (9.62) with the negative square root; substituting this in Eq. (9.65):

$$\tfrac{1}{2}A[\delta\alpha + \sqrt{(\delta\alpha)^2 + 4a_{0r}^2\beta^2}] + a_{0r}\beta B = 0 \tag{9.66}$$

We are assuming that $\delta\alpha$ is small; let us as a first approximation neglect $(\delta\alpha)^2$. Equation (9.66) then becomes:

$$B = \frac{A}{2|a_{0r}|\beta}(\delta\alpha + 2|a_{0r}|\beta) = A(1+y) \tag{9.67}$$

where

$$y = \frac{\delta\alpha}{2|a_{0r}|\beta} \tag{9.68}$$

Using the normalizing condition for this MO,

$$A^2 + B^2 = 1 = A^2[1 + (1+y)^2] = 2A^2(1+y) \tag{9.69}$$

since we are neglecting terms involving $(\delta\alpha)^2$, and hence likewise y^2. From Eqs. (9.67) and (9.69),

$$A^2 = \frac{1}{2(1+y)} \qquad B^2 = \frac{1+2y}{2(1+y)} \tag{9.70}$$

The total π-charge density q_T at atom T in S is given by $2B^2$; if y^2 is neglected, this becomes:

$$q_T = 2B^2 = (1+2y)(1+y)^{-1} \approx (1+2y)(1-y)$$
$$\approx 1 + y \equiv 1 + \frac{\delta\alpha}{2|a_{0r}|\beta} \tag{9.71}$$

But from Eq. (6.22), since S is an even alternant system containing a single heteroatom T,

$$q_T = 1 + \pi_{T,T}\,\delta\alpha \tag{9.72}$$

where $\pi_{T,T}$ is the self-polarizability of atom T in the AH isoconjugate with S. Comparing Eqs. (9.71) and (9.72),

$$\pi_{T,T} = \frac{1}{2|a_{0r}|\beta} \tag{9.73}$$

This result can be generalized [compare Eq. (6.82)] to atoms which are multiply linked. Consider such an atom t in an even AH. Its self-polarizability is easily seen to be given by:

$$\pi_{t,t} = \frac{1}{\left|2\beta\sum_r a_{0r}\right|} \tag{9.74}$$

where the sum is over atoms r that are directly linked to atom t. Since β is negative, so also is $\pi_{t,t}$; this provides an alternative proof of Theorem 9.2.

Atom-atom polarizabilities can be deduced in an analogous manner. Let us return to the system of Fig. 9.8. The charge density at atom s in R is given by:

$$q_s = 2\sum_{\mu}^{B} a_{\mu s}^2 + a_{0s}^2 = 1 \tag{9.75}$$

since R is an odd-AH radical. In T, the MOs Φ_μ remain unchanged; the new charge density q'_s is then given by

$$q'_s = 2 \sum_{\mu}^{B} a_{\mu s}^2 + 2A_s^2 \tag{9.76}$$

where A_s is the coefficient of the AO ϕ_s in the bonding MO ξ formed by interaction of the NBMO Φ_0 with the AO ψ of T. From Eq. (9.63),

$$\xi = A\Phi_0 + B\psi = \sum_i (Aa_{0i}\phi_i) + B\psi \tag{9.77}$$

Hence:

$$A_s = Aa_{0s} \tag{9.78}$$

From Eqs. (9.76), (9.75), (9.78), (9.70), and (9.68),

$$q'_s = 1 - a_{0s}^2 + 2A^2a_{0s}^2 = 1 - a_{0s}^2 + \frac{a_{0s}^2}{1+y}$$

$$= 1 - a_{0s}^2 y = 1 - \frac{a_{0s}^2 \, \delta\alpha}{2|a_{0r}|\beta} \tag{9.79}$$

Comparison with Eq. (6.26) shows that the atom-atom polarizability $\pi_{T,s}$ is given by:

$$\pi_{T,s} = -\frac{a_{0s}^2}{2\beta|a_{0r}|} \tag{9.80}$$

In the general case of an even AH S,

$$\pi_{t,s} = -\frac{a_{0s}^2}{2\beta\left|\sum_r a_{0r}\right|} \tag{9.81}$$

where the sum is over atoms r directly linked to atom t and a_{0i} is the NBMO coefficient of atom i in the odd AH R formed by removing atom t from S.

Now atom r is by definition a starred atom in the odd AH R; for it must be a member of the more numerous set. Thus a_{0s} vanishes unless atoms r and s are of like parity. Since atom r is by definition of opposite parity to its neighbor t in the even-AH S, we conclude that $\pi_{t,s}$ vanishes if atoms s and t are of like parity. If they are of opposite parity, then $\pi_{t,s}$ must be positive. This leads to an alternative version (Theorem 9.4) of Theorem 9.3:

Theorem 9.4   In an even AH, the atom-atom polarizability $\pi_{j,i}$ is small if atoms i and j are of like parity, and positive if they are of opposite parity.

9.10 BOND ORDERS AND CHARGE DENSITIES IN ODD SYSTEMS
Odd systems can be treated by procedures precisely analogous to those used in Sec. 9.9; since no new principles are involved, most of the derivations can be

left to the reader as an exercise. It can, for example, be shown that Theorem 9.1 applies equally to odd-AH radicals; the introduction of a heteroatom into such a system has little effect either on its stability or on the bond lengths in it. Theorem 9.1 should also hold for odd ions in which heteroatoms occupy inactive positions.

The most important case, however, concerns neutral molecules isoconjugate with odd-AH anions and containing at least one heteroatom at an active position; aniline, $PhNH_2$, is a good example, being isoconjugate with the benzyl anion, $PhCH_2^-$. We can see qualitatively what will happen in such a system from Fig. 9.9, which illustrates its formation by union of an even AH R with an additional atom T. From our previous discussion, we know that the mutual interactions of filled orbitals have no effect either on the total energy or on any other collective property; any changes must therefore arise from interactions between the filled AO of T and empty antibonding MOs of R. If T is carbon (Fig. 9.9a), the combination RT is an odd-AH anion; we know that the charge in this is strongly delocalized, and that the bond orders all have intermediate values. As we make T more electronegative (Fig. 9.9b and c), the interactions decrease; for in perturbation theory, they are given by expressions containing the factor $(\alpha - E_\mu)^{-1}$, α being the coulomb integral of T and E_μ the energy of one of the empty MOs of R. This factor becomes progressively smaller, the more negative α.

In the extreme case, where T is very much more electronegative than carbon, the interactions will become very small; the bond order between R and T will then become negligible, and the perturbed orbital ψ', corresponding to the AO ψ of S, will become almost indistinguishable from ψ itself. In this case the bond orders and π-charge densities in R will be essentially the same as if T were absent, while the π-charge density on T will be close to 2. In other words the situation will resemble closely one in which there are *no* interactions between R and T.

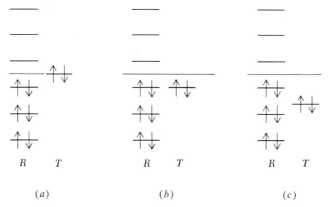

$$R \qquad T \qquad\qquad R \qquad T \qquad\qquad R \qquad T$$

$$(a) \qquad\qquad\qquad (b) \qquad\qquad\qquad (c)$$

FIG. 9.9 Perturbation of an even AH R by union with an extra atom T. (a) T is carbon; (b) and (c) T is a heteroatom of increasing electronegativity.

Molecules of the type we are considering come close to this extreme; for the differences in electronegativity are very great. Consider aniline. The π electrons move round a core $(C_6H_7N)^{8+}$ in which each carbon atom has one unit of charge, but nitrogen has two. The term W_N in the diagonal F-matrix element for nitrogen corresponds to the process $N^+ \rightarrow N^{++}$; this, the second ionization potential of nitrogen in the sp^2 valence state, has a value of about 27 ev, enormously larger than that (≈ 11 ev) for neutral carbon. The π interaction between nitrogen and the ring in aniline is therefore quite small.

We can estimate the magnitude of this interaction experimentally by an ingenious method due to Wepster.[19] When dimethylaniline (XXXIX) forms a salt,

$$PhNMe_2 + H^+ \rightleftarrows Ph\overset{+}{N}HMe_2 \qquad (9.82)$$
XXXIX

the nitrogen atom becomes quadrivalent and is consequently removed from conjugation with the ring ($\overline{EO}$ reaction). The resulting decrease in π energy should lead to a corresponding decrease in the equilibrium constant. In order to estimate the importance of this, Wepster examined benzoquinuclidine (XL), a compound in which the unshared electrons of nitrogen lie in the plane of the ring, occupying an AO which is symmetrical with respect to reflection in the node of the π system. Here π interactions between nitrogen and the ring are forbidden by symmetry, so the pK of XL tells us what the corresponding value would be for XXXIX if it too had a pair of electrons localized on nitrogen.‡

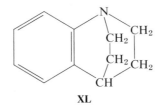

XL

In practice dimethylaniline turned out to be the weaker base by about 2.8 pK units, corresponding to a π-interaction energy of about 4 kcal/mole; this is very much less than the corresponding value for the benzyl anion, estimates of which vary from 13 to 30 kcal/mole.

9.11 STEREOCHEMISTRY OF TRIVALENT NITROGEN IN CONJUGATED MOLECULES

At one time it was commonly assumed that the nitrogen atom in compounds such as aniline must be coplanar, on the grounds that it could not otherwise

‡ Dimethylaniline was used for this comparison since any "inductive" effects of the methyl groups should be similar to those of the adjacent saturated rings in XXXIX.

undergo π interactions with the adjacent conjugated system.   This idea, based on naïve resonance theory, is incorrect.

Consider a compound $X\mathrm{NH_2}$, where X is some unsaturated group.   Consider the change δE_π in π energy, due to interactions of the unshared electrons of nitrogen with the π electrons of X.   Following the argument outlined in the preceding section, we can easily see that this is given, to the approximation of second-order perturbation theory, by:

$$\delta E_\pi = 2 \sum_{\mu}^{\mathrm{unocc}} \frac{a_{\mu r}{}^2 \beta^2}{\alpha - E_\mu} \tag{9.83}$$

where $a_{\mu r}$ is the AO coefficient at atom r (to which nitrogen is linked to X in $X\mathrm{NH_2}$) in the MO Φ_μ of X of energy E_μ, and α is the coulomb integral for nitrogen.   If then we alter the interaction between X and N in some way, either by altering the geometry of N or perhaps by twisting the XN bond, the changes in δE_π will run parallel to the corresponding changes in β^2.   If we use the Mulliken approximation for resonance integrals [see Eq. (3.24)], δE_π should then be proportional to the square of the overlap integral for the π-like bond between nitrogen and the atom adjacent to it, in $X\mathrm{NH_2}$.

Suppose that the adjacent atom is carbon, and that the nitrogen atom is pyramidal, with a geometry corresponding to sp^3 hybridization.   The required overlap integral will be one between a carbon $2p$ AO ϕ and an sp^3 hybrid AO ψ of the adjacent nitrogen atom (Fig. 9.10a).   Now by definition, ψ can be written as a combination of an s AO s and a p AO p (Fig. 9.9b), the axis of the latter lying along the axis of the hybrid, and the coefficients being respectively $\sqrt{\tfrac{1}{4}}$ and $\sqrt{\tfrac{3}{4}}$ since the density of ψ (that is ψ^2) is the sum of one-quarter the s density (that is s^2) and three-quarters the p density (that is p^2);

$$\psi = \tfrac{1}{2}s + \sqrt{\tfrac{3}{4}}\,p \tag{9.84}$$

The $2p$ AO p can in turn be represented as a combination of p AOs x and y whose axes lie respectively parallel and perpendicular to that of ϕ (Fig. 9.9c).   Since p AOs transform like vectors,

$$p = x \sin\theta + y \cos\theta \tag{9.85}$$

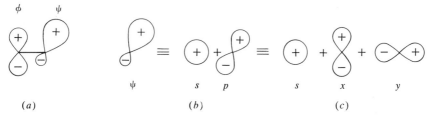

FIG. 9.10   Calculation of overlap between a sp^3 hybrid AO ψ and an adjacent p AO ϕ.

Here θ is $70°10'$, being $180°$ *less* the tetrahedral angle. Combining Eqs. (9.84) and (9.85),

$$\psi = \tfrac{1}{2}s + (\sqrt{\tfrac{3}{4}}\cos\theta)x + (\sqrt{\tfrac{3}{4}}\sin\theta)y \tag{9.86}$$

Consider now the overlap integral s between ϕ and ψ:

$$s = \int\phi\psi \, d\tau = \int\phi[\tfrac{1}{2}s + (\sqrt{\tfrac{3}{4}}\sin\theta)x + (\sqrt{\tfrac{3}{4}}\cos\theta)y] \, d\tau \tag{9.87}$$

The integrals $\int\phi s \, d\tau$ and $\int\phi y \, d\tau$ vanish through symmetry, since s and y are symmetric for reflection in the nodal plane of ϕ. The integral $\int\phi x \, d\tau$ is just the standard overlap integral S_0 for a C—N π bond. Hence:

$$S = (\sqrt{\tfrac{3}{4}}\sin\theta)S_0 \tag{9.88}$$

The π energy of interaction δE_π in pyramidal XNH_2 is therefore given in terms of that $[(\delta E_\pi)_0]$ for planar XNH_2 by:

$$\delta E_\pi \approx (\sqrt{\tfrac{3}{4}}\sin\theta)^2(\delta E_\pi)_0 \approx 0.66(\delta E_\pi)_0 \tag{9.89}$$

Thus so far from being negligible, the interaction energy is about two-thirds that for the planar structure. Evidence for π interaction in a compound of this type is therefore no evidence that the nitrogen atom in it is planar; indeed, the gain in π energy due to planarity may not even be enough to make the planar form the more stable, given that trivalent nitrogen prefers to be pyramidal.

This argument can be put more quantitatively as follows. Our object is to establish the change in energy when the pyramidal form of XNH_2 passes over into the planar form; we can carry out this transformation in the following three steps:

1   First we interrupt the π interaction between X and nitrogen, perhaps by twisting the system about the X—N bond [compare benzoquinuclidine (XL)]. To do so, we must supply the necessary π energy δE_π [Eq. (9.89)].

2   Next we flatten out the nitrogen atom; the energy required can be assumed to be the same as in the case of ammonia, 6 kcal/mole.

3   Finally, we allow the molecule to revert to a normal "resonating" state; here we gain the π-energy term $(\delta E_\pi)_0$. The overlap energy change ΔE in the process is then given by:

$$\Delta E = \delta E_\pi + 6 - (\delta E_\pi)_0 \approx 6 - \tfrac{1}{3}(\delta E_\pi)_0 \tag{9.90}$$

[using Eq. (9.89)].

Thus unless $(\delta E_\pi)_0 > 18$ kcal/mole, the pyramidal form of XNH_2 should be the more favorable. We have seen that this condition is not met even approximately in the case of aniline; many lines of evidence indicate unambiguously that the nitrogen atom in aniline is pyramidal.

The same should be true for all compounds where the π interactions are not very strong; even amides seem to fall in this category, though only just. If we take the barrier to rotation about the CO—N bond as a measure of δE_π for compounds of this type, the values deduced by nmr methods (7 to 18 kcal/mole[20]) are less than our estimate of the critical value. Admittedly this estimate is based on a very crude argument, but simple amides do seem to be nonplanar in the gas phase.[21] In the solid state, typical amides are coplanar, but this may very well be due to the complicating effects of hydrogen bonding in the crystal. We would certainly predict that even if amides are noncoplanar, the barrier to flattening them must be extremely small.

These arguments can be extended to other similar systems. For example one would expect simple carbanions R_3C^- to be pyramidal, like the corresponding isoelectronic amines R_3N; what will happen if we introduce unsaturated groups? Here the answer seems fairly clear in the sense that ions of this type can be prepared only if they have large π-interaction energies; paraffin hydrocarbons are virtually nonacidic, with pK_A estimated[22] to be of the order of 80, so any compound in which saturated CH undergoes ionization must be one in which the resulting anion is highly stabilized. Ions of this type must undoubtedly be coplanar. Similar considerations may account for the apparently anomalously high reactivity of aromatic amines to electrophilic substitution (see Sec. 9.5.2). The nitrogen in diphenylamine (XLI) is undoubtedly pyramidal; however in the Wheland intermediate (XLII) for *para* nitration, there will be a very strong π interaction between the unshared electrons of nitrogen and the adjacent carbonium ion. If the nitrogen atom changes its geometry accordingly, there will be a considerable increase in the total π-bond energy. In the treatment of Sec. 9.5.2, it was assumed that the parameters for nitrogen are the same in both systems; if we are right, the reactivities so calculated should be too small, as indeed they are.

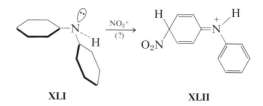

XLI   XLII

If this argument is correct, it poses in turn a further very interesting question; are the nitrogen atoms in five-ring heteroaromatics (e.g. pyrrole or carbazole) planar? It has always been assumed that they must be, on the grounds that otherwise compounds of this type would not be aromatic. The argument given above shows this conclusion to be unsound. It has been claimed that microwave spectroscopy shows pyrrole to be planar;[23] however the authors clearly did not seriously consider any other possibility, and a nonplanar form, with rapidly inverting nitrogen, might fit their results equally well. In our case (see Fig. 9.5) carbazole shows the same anomalously high reactivity to nitration as diphenylamine, a result which could likewise be explained if its equilibrium state were nonplanar.

9.12 SUBSTITUENTS

Organic chemists, in their classification of structure and chemical reactivity, have found it convenient in many cases to regard molecules as being composed of a central kernel with one or more groups (*substituents*) attached to it. For example, in considering the reactions of derivatives of benzene, it is natural to regard these as being formed from benzene by the replacement of hydrogen atoms by appropriate substituents (halogen, —OH, —NH_2, —NO_2, —COOH, etc.). The reactivity of such a molecule is regarded as a superposition of two factors, one the reactivity of the corresponding parent molecule with no substituents, the other the changes in reactivity brought about the substituents. If our PMO treatment of reactivity is to be of practical value to chemists, it must be able to reproduce the spectrum of substituent effects that have been observed experimentally.

In a conjugated system, substituents can act in two distinct ways. In the first, the substituent forms a polar σ bond to the adjacent conjugated carbon atom; the carbon atom in this way acquires a positive or negative formal charge which in turn alters its electronegativity. In our approach, this will be represented by a change in the coulomb integral of the carbon atom, leading to a polarization of the π electrons entirely analogous to that brought about by replacement of carbon by a heteroatom. Substituents of this type are termed *inductive* (e.g. —CF_3), and the π polarization brought about by the mechanism indicated above is termed the *π-inductive effect*.

Substituents exerting this effect can be denoted by the symbol I. We also need to distinguish between substituents that confer a positive charge on an adjacent carbon atom and those that confer a negative charge. Following the usual conventions of physics,‡ we term substituents of the former type $+I$, since they behave as though they were deficient in electrons, and substituents of the latter type $-I$, since they behave as though they had an excess of electrons.

The second class of substituents are ones with p or π electrons, that can interact with the π electrons of an adjacent conjugated system. Interactions of this kind were originally termed *electromeric* by Lapworth and Robinson, a term

‡ This sign convention was the one proposed in the early days of electronic theory by Lapworth and Robinson, and it has the further advantage of agreeing with the sign convention for σ constants in the Hammett treatment (see Sec. 9.13). Unfortunately Ingold, at a later date, introduced the opposite, and less logical convention, for no very good reason, and as a result the literature has been for many years in a chaotic state in this respect. There seems to be no good reason for not retaining the prior, and more logical, convention of Lapworth and Robinson.

which seems entirely satisfactory; we therefore denote them by the symbol E. Three groups of E substituents will be distinguished below, designated by the symbols $+E$, $-E$, and $\pm E$.

The effect of substituents on chemical reactions can be most conveniently analyzed in terms of the classification of Sec. 8.7.   Consider first an EE reaction.   We know that the resonance energy of an even alternant system is unaffected by changes in the electronegativity of the constituent atoms; I substituents should therefore have little effect on the rates of reactions in which both reactants and products are even.   The same applies to E substituents, since the bond linking an even conjugated system to another group is normally an essential single bond; an E substituent will therefore change the energies of different even systems to much the same extent.   Substituents will therefore exercise specific effects mainly in reactions of OE or EO type, and they will do so through specific interactions with the odd system.   Our classification should therefore be based on the effects of substituents on such processes, i.e. on the relative changes in energy when a substituent is attached to an odd system, or to a related even one.   The substituent must of course be attached to an active atom in the odd system; for the special properties of an odd-AH ion or radical are due entirely to the presence in it of a NBMO.   A system of this kind will look no different from an even AH to a group attached to an inactive position.

9.13   CLASSIFICATION OF SUBSTITUENTS

9.13.1 I SUBSTITUENTS   Inductive substituents, so far as our present treatment is concerned, are assumed to act entirely by the π-inductive effect.   Thus a $+I$ substituent at position i will have qualitatively the same effect as replacement of carbon atom i by a more electronegative heteroatom (e.g. N or O), while a $-I$ substituent will have the same effect as corresponding replacement by a less electronegative heteroatom (e.g. B).   The effects of such substituents can be deduced at once from the arguments of Sec. 9.8.   Substituents of this type should have no effect on $O^R E$ or EO^R reactions, since the stabilities of radicals relative to analogous even systems are not affected by changes in electronegativity.   On the other hand $+E$ substituents should facilitate the formation of odd anions from even systems, i.e. $\overline{O}^- E$ or EO^- reactions, and hinder analogous reactions leading to cations, whereas $-I$ substituents should have exactly the converse effect.   These conclusions agree with conventional theory and with experiment so it is unnecessary to discuss them in detail.   A simple example is the effect on the basicity of aniline of a $+I$ (CF_3) or $-I$ (CH_3) substituent in the *para* position;

$$R\!-\!\!\underset{}{\bigcirc}\!\!-\!NH_2 + H^+ \rightleftharpoons R\!-\!\!\underset{}{\bigcirc}\!\!-\!NH_3^+ \qquad (9.91)$$

salt formation by aniline is an $\overline{E}\overline{O}^-$ reaction and so should be inhibited by $+I$, and facilitated by $-I$, substituents. As expected on this basis, p-toluidine is a stronger base than aniline, while p-trifluoromethylaniline is weaker.

The relative effects of a given substituent at various positions in different odd systems can be deduced semiquantitatively from the arguments of Sec. 9.8; the stabilizing, or destabilizing, effect on an odd-AH ion, or on a heteroconjugated molecule isoconjugate with such an ion, should be proportional to the square of the NBMO coefficient at the point of attachment [compare Eqs. (9.54) and (9.55)].

9.13.2 $\pm E$ SUBSTITUENTS

A $\pm E$ substituent is one derived from an even AH by loss of a hydrogen atom; phenyl, vinyl, and naphthyl are obvious examples. When therefore a substituent of this type is attached to an AH, the product is another larger AH. In the PMO approximation, the π energy of a given AH is the same, regardless of whether it occurs as an ion or radical; substituents of this type will therefore have similar effects on OE or EO reactions, regardless of the nature of the odd species. They are accordingly classed as $\pm E$.

To deduce this effect, let us consider a specific case; the effect of a phenyl substituent on substitution in benzene. Figure 9.11 shows the NBMO coefficients of the various Wheland intermediates and the corresponding reactivity numbers; it will be seen that phenyl reduces the reactivity number, and so should facilitate substitution, if it is attached to an active position (*ortho* or *para*) in the intermediate, but has no effect at an inactive position (*meta*). The reason for this is also clear from the figure. When an even AH R is united with an odd AH S through an active position in the latter, the NBMO spreads over R; the ratios of the NBMO coefficients in S remain unchanged, but their absolute values are decreased.

The transition state for *meta* substitution (Fig. 9.11c) raises an interesting point. It will be seen that all positions in the phenyl substituent, both starred and unstarred, are inactive. The substituent consequently has no effect on the course of the reaction. In the PMO treatment, this is the factor that corresponds to, and accounts for, the classical phenomenon of *cross conjugation*. We may therefore term an odd AH cross-conjugated if it contains an *inactive segment* of atoms all of which are inactive; such an inactive segment plays no part in reactions involving that particular odd AH (see p. 230).

For substitution in even AHs in general, it can be shown[24] that the effect of a $\pm E$ substituent on the reactivity number is given by:

$$N_t = (N_t)_0(1 + a_{0r}{}^2A^{\pm})^{-1/2} \tag{9.92}$$

where a_{0r} is the NBMO coefficient at the point of attachment of the substituent, $(N_t)_0$ is the reactivity number in the absence of the substituent, N_t that with it, and $A^{\pm}$ the $\pm E$ *activity* of the substituent, defined as follows. Consider the odd AH RCH_2 formed by union of the $\pm E$ substituent R with methyl. Calculate the NBMO coefficients in this by the normal procedure, but instead of normaliz-

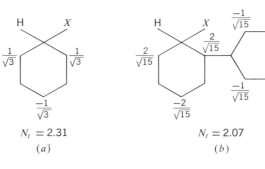

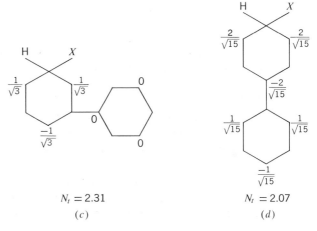

FIG. 9.11   Wheland intermediates, NBMO coefficients, and reactivity numbers for substitution in benzene and biphenyl.

ing the MO, scale the coefficients b_{0j} so that the coefficient of the methylene AO is unity.   Then:

$$A^{\pm} = \sum_{j} b_{0j}^{2} \tag{9.93}$$

Figure 9.12 illustrates the procedure for phenyl and α- and β-naphthyl.   The quantity $A^{\pm}$ should be a measure of the "conjugating power" of the substituent. A simple test of this is provided by the basicities of the corresponding arylamines. As we have seen (Sec. 9.10), salt formation in such amines is hindered by the loss of π energy when the amino nitrogen becomes protonated and so loses its pair of unshared electrons.   The effect should be greater, the greater the conjugating power of the aryl group.   As expected on this basis from the data in Fig. 9.12, basicity decreases in the order aniline $> \beta$-naphthylamine $> \alpha$-naphthylamine.

Equation (9.92) shows the effect of a $\pm E$ substituent on reactions of OE type;

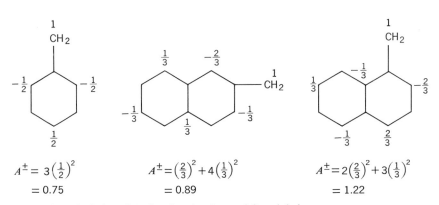

FIG. 9.12 Calculation of $A^{\pm}$ for phenyl and α- and β-naphthyl.

it is easily seen that the corresponding expression for the delocalization energy of reaction [see Eq. (8.49)] for an EO reaction is:

$$\Delta E_{\mathrm{deloc}} = (\Delta E_{\mathrm{deloc}})_0 (1 + a_{0r}{}^2 A^{\pm})^{-1/2} + 2\beta[1 - (1 + a_{0r}{}^2 A^{\pm})^{-1/2}] \quad (9.94)$$

Here, as in Eq. (9.92), the effect of the substituent appears as a product $a_{0r}{}^2 A^{\pm}$ of two factors, one ($a_{0r}{}^2$) representing the density of the NBMO at the point of attachment of the substituent, the other the E activity of the substituent.

9.13.3 $+E$ SUBSTITUENTS A $+E$ substituent is one derived from a $\pm E$ substituent by replacing one or more carbon atoms by heteroatoms; examples, with the isoconjugate $\pm E$ substituents in parentheses, are as follows:

$$-\mathrm{CHO}\ (-\mathrm{CH}{=}\mathrm{CH}_2);\quad \text{⬡N}\ (-\mathrm{Ph});$$
$$-\mathrm{CH}{=}\mathrm{CH}{-}\mathrm{CO}R\ (-\mathrm{CH}{=}\mathrm{CH}{-}\mathrm{CH}{=}\mathrm{CH}_2).$$

We can deduce the effect of a $+E$ substituent by the procedure used to analyze heteroconjugated molecules (Sec. 9.7), i.e. by examining first the effect of the isoconjugate $\pm E$ substituent, and next the modification introduced by the heteroatom.

When a substituent of this type is attached to an odd AH, the result is an odd heteroconjugated molecule. The effect of the heteroatom can therefore be deduced immediately from the results of Sec. 9.8. In comparison with the isoconjugate $\pm E$ substituent, a given $+E$ substituent should have a greater stabilizing effect on odd-AH anions, a similar effect on odd-AH radicals, and a smaller effect on odd-AH cations. Parallel effects should be observed in the case of odd systems that are isoconjugate with odd-AH ions or radicals.

Numerous lines of evidence illustrate the similar efficiency of $+E$ and $\pm E$ substituents in stabilizing odd-AH radicals. The rates of radical substitution in substituted benzenes differ little from that of benzene itself, and the same is true for radical addition to the exocyclic double bond of substituted styrenes (as measured for example by the ease with which they add radicals during vinyl polymerization). Compounds of this type differ little from styrene in reactivity, unless of course they contain *ortho* substituents that can exercise steric effects.

Likewise the greater efficacy of $+E$ substituents over isoconjugate $\pm E$ ones in stabilizing odd-AH anions is commonplace. Whereas, for example, the chlorine in chlorobenzene does not undergo direct nucleophilic replacement under any conditions, that in *p*-chloronitrobenzene‡ or 2,4-dinitrochlorobenzene can be displaced quite easily; e.g.

$$O_2N-\!\!\bigcirc\!\!-Cl + HO^- \rightarrow O_2N-\!\!\bigcirc\!\!-OH + Cl^- \qquad (9.95)$$

This is a typical nucleophilic aromatic substitution, of $\overline{O}-\overline{E}$ type. Another example is provided by the prototropic reactions of methyl groups adjacent to aromatic rings. Compounds of the type $Ar\text{CH}_3$, where ArH is an even AH, undergo reactions of this type only under drastic conditions since the anions $Ar\text{CH}_2^-$ are not very highly stabilized, while *p*-nitrotoluene undergoes base-catalyzed prototropic reactions, e.g. deuterium exchange or aldol condensation, quite readily; e.g.

$$O_2N-\!\!\bigcirc\!\!-CH_3 + D_2O \xrightarrow{\ HO^-\ } O_2N-\!\!\bigcirc\!\!-CD_3 \qquad (9.96)$$

$$O_2N-\!\!\bigcirc\!\!-CH_3 + Ar\text{CHO} \xrightarrow{\ HO^-\ } O_2N-\!\!\bigcirc\!\!-CH{=}CHAr \qquad (9.97)$$

A third example is provided by nucleophilic addition to double bonds (Michael reaction), a process which takes place easily only if the bond in question carries a $+E$ substituent. A simple example is the 1,4 addition of Grignard reagents to α,β-unsaturated ketones;

$$R\text{MgBr} + CH_2{=}CH-CR{=}O \rightarrow$$
$$RCH_2-CH{\cdots}CR{\cdots}\overline{O}\ \text{MgBr} \xrightarrow{\ H_2O\ } RCH_2CH_2COR \qquad (9.98)$$

The effects of $+E$ substituents on odd-AH radicals or anions are therefore straightforward; in the case of cations, however, an ambiguity arises. A $\pm E$ substituent has a stabilizing effect on an odd-AH cation, while introduction of a heteroatom into such a system has a destabilizing effect. The net effect of a $+E$ substituent is therefore a sum of two factors, one (stabilizing) representing the effect of the isoconjugate $\pm E$ substituent, the other (destabilizing) being due to replacement of carbon by a more electronegative atom. Different substituents of this type may therefore exert either a net stabilizing effect or a net destabilizing effect on odd-AH cations.

‡ The nitro group is properly classed as a $+E$ substituent; see Sec. 9.14.

The situation can be simply visualized.   When a $\pm E$ or $+E$ substituent is attached to an active position in an odd-AH cation R^+, the NBMO expands over the substituent (compare Fig. 9.11).   This "dilutes" the part of the NBMO in R^+ and so reduces the numerical values of the NBMO coefficients; Eqs. (8.35) and (8.49) show that this has the effect of stabilizing the odd AH relative to an analogous even system with one atom more or one atom less.   However in the case of an odd-AH cation, expansion of the NBMO also places formal positive charges on various atoms in the substituent; if these include the heteroatom of a $+E$ substituent, the result will be a decrease in the relative stability of the odd AH cation.   Clearly the charges at individual positions will tend to be greater, the less dispersed the NBMO, i.e. the smaller the $+E$ substituent; on the other hand the $\pm E$ activity of a $\pm E$ substituent should in general be greater, the bigger it is, and the more the original NBMO is consequently diluted.   This argument can be put in a numerical form,[24] but without any particular gain. Large $\pm E$ substituents should stabilize odd-AH cations, and one would expect the stabilization to decrease as the substituent becomes smaller.   This is observed in practice.   Thus γ-pyridylbenzene (XLIII) and ω-benzoylstyrene (XLIV) nitrate *ortho-para* to the substituent (i.e. pyridyl or —CH=CH—COPh), because these large substituents have a net stabilizing effect on odd-AH cations.   If nitration had taken place *meta*, the Wheland intermediate would be cross-conjugated (see Fig. 9.11c); the substituent would then exercise no net effect on the reaction, being attached to an inactive position in the intermediate.

XLIII	**XLIV**

Conversely, with small $+E$ substituents such as —CHO, —NO$_2$, or —COCH$_3$, nitration *does* take place in the *meta* position.   Here the deactivating effect of the heteroatom wins out, so that the substituent has on balance a deactivating effect on odd-AH cations.   Substitution therefore takes place *meta*, when the effect of the substituent is minimized.

9.13.4 $-E$ SUBSTITUENTS   A $-E$ substituent is defined as a group derived from a system isoconjugate with an odd-AH anion and attached through an active position; typical examples are MeO— and Me$_2$N— (isoconjugate with the simplest odd-AH anion, —CH$_2^-$), and H$_2$N —⬡— (isoconjugate with the odd-AH anion CH$_2^-$ —⬡—).

When an odd-AH cation and an odd-AH anion unite, the product is an even AH, formed with a great increase in total π-bond energy.   The process differs from union of two odd-AH radicals (compare Fig. 6.6) only in that both nonbonding

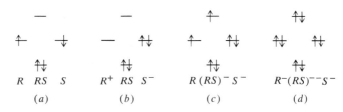

FIG. 9.13 Perturbations of the NBMO electrons on union of (*a*) two odd-AH radicals; (*b*) an odd-AH cation with an odd-AH anion; (*c*) an odd-AH radical with an odd-AH anion; (*d*) two odd-AH anions.

electrons occupy the NBMO of one component; the total π energy of union is the same in both cases, to the approximation of PMO theory (Fig. 9.13*a* and *b*). Similar considerations should apply to a lesser degree when an odd-AH cation unites with a heteroconjugated molecule isoconjugate with an odd-AH anion; the change in π energy should again be a large first-order effect.

Union of an odd-AH anion with an odd-AH radical should also lead to a first-order stabilization (Fig. 9.13*c*), which, however, should be less than for the cation since there is now one electron too many to be accommodated in the normal bonding MOs. Two electrons decrease in energy during union, as in the previous cases (Fig. 9.13*a* and *b*), but one increases. Finally union of two odd-AH anions (Fig. 9.13*d*) should lead to no first-order change in π energy; the change in π energy should be the second-order effect that is automatically taken into account in the bond energy of the "localized single" bond between R and S in RS.

$-E$ substituents should therefore have a large stabilizing effect on odd-AH cations, a smaller one on odd-AH radicals, and none on odd-AH anions; the available experimental evidence very strongly supports these conclusions. Substituents of this type greatly facilitate reactions in which an even-AH is converted to an odd-AH cation. Aniline, for example, undergoes electrophilic substitution with enormously greater ease than benzene, and the solvolysis of benzyl chloride is enormously accelerated by $-E$ substituents in the *para* position. Thus aniline readily couples with aryldiazonium ions, an electrophilic substitution that is unknown in the case of benzene itself;

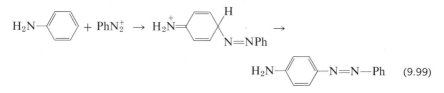

$$H_2N\!\!-\!\!\langle\ \rangle\!\!-\!\!N\!=\!N\!-\!Ph \qquad (9.99)$$

Again, whereas benzhydryl chloride, Ph_2CHCl, can be induced to ionize to Ph_2CH^+ only in the total absence of nucleophiles, the corresponding bis(p-dimethylamino) derivative [Michler's Hydrol Blue (XLV)] gives stable ionic solutions in water and the solid chloride forms ionic crystals.

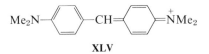

XLV

The effect on radical reactions is much less marked.   Vinyl ethers and esters do, however, add radicals more easily than ethylene does, as is shown by the much greater ease of radical-catalyzed polymerization; such additions are typical $\overline{O}^R\overline{E}$ reactions,

$$ROCH{=}CH_2 + X{\cdot} \rightarrow RO\overset{\cdot}{C}H{-}CH_2X \qquad (9.100)$$

Again, ethers autooxidize much more easily than the corresponding paraffins; this is because abstraction of hydrogen atoms (an EO^R reaction) is facilitated by the adjacent $-E$ alkoxy group;

$$RO{-}\overset{|}{\underset{|}{C}}{-}H + {\cdot}O_2R' \rightarrow RO{-}\overset{|}{\underset{|}{C}}{\cdot} + HO_2R' \qquad (9.101)$$

Finally, substituents of this type have little or no effect on reactions involving odd-AH anions.   For example the methylene protons in ω-methoxyacetophenone, $PhCOCH_2OMe$, differ little in acidity from those in the methyl group of acetophenone.

9.13.5   SUMMARY OF SUBSTITUENT EFFECTS   The discussion in the previous section can be summed up succinctly in a table (Table 9.10), showing the qualitative effects of substituents on the stabilities of odd-AH radicals and ions relative to their effects on analogous even systems with one more, or one less, conjugated carbon atom.

This treatment can be put on a quantitative basis;[24] in each case, the effect of a substituent appears as the product of two factors, one the NBMO density at the point of attachment to the odd AH, the other a measure of the activity of

TABLE 9.10   Effect of substituents of various types on the stabilities of odd-AH radicals and ions, relative to their effects on analogous even systems (+ + very strong stabilization, + significant stabilization, − significant destabilization, 0 no effect)

Substituent	Odd-AH cation	Odd-AH radical	Odd-AH anion
$+I$	−	0	+
$-I$	+	0	−
$+E$	+	+	+
$+E$	?	+	+ +
$-E$	+ +	+	0

the substituent [compare Eqs. (9.92) and (9.94)].   Whether this kind of approach would be successful in a quantitative sense is uncertain since it has not been tried, mainly because experimental data to test it are lacking.   For example one obvious check would be to compare the effects of substituents on rates of sub-stitution in benzene and in other aromatic hydrocarbons; although an enormous amount of work has been done on the further substitution of substituted ben-zenes, there are no comparable rate data for other systems, not even for naphthalene.

The treatment would in any case have to be modified to allow for the field effects of substituents, which have been neglected in this simple first-order approach.   The field effect, and procedures for estimating it, will be found below (Sec. 9.14).

9.13.6   ADDITIVITY OF SUBSTITUENT EFFECTS; MUTUAL CONJUGATION

The treatment of substituent effects in Secs. 9.13.1 to 9.13.4 was based on the use of first-order perturbation theory; since first-order perturbations are addi-tive, one might expect the effects of substituents to be likewise additive.   A de-tailed study[25] shows that this is the case, with two exceptions.

When a $-E$ substituent is attached to an even AH, the resulting system is isoconjugate with an odd-AH anion; if a $+E$ substituent is attached to an active position in this, its stabilizing effect will be greater (see Table 9.10) than if it were attached to the even AH alone.   The total stabilization when both substitu-ents are present will therefore be greater than the sum of the stabilizations due to each separately.   This effect, which may be termed *mutual conjugation*, there-fore arises when we have a $+E$ substituent and a $-E$ substituent attached to positions of opposite parity in an even AH.   The effect has long been familiar to organic chemists and manifests itself in a variety of ways.   A simple example is provided by *p*-nitraniline (XLVI), which has a much larger dipole moment than would be expected from the values for aniline and nitrobenzene, and which is a much weaker base than aniline, implying that the π interaction of the nitro group with the ring is greater in XLVI than it is in the ion (XLVII), where the amino nitrogen has been removed from the conjugated system.

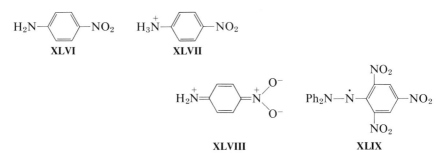

In conventional texts, this interaction is represented in resonance terminology as being due to contributions by the dipolar resonance structure (XLVIII). This kind of explanation cannot, however, be extended to odd systems. A detailed PMO analysis,[25] which need not be reproduced here, shows that the rules for mutual conjugation in odd AHs are different from those in even ones. In an odd AH, mutual conjugation should be observed when a $-E$ substituent and a $+E$ substituent are both attached to active atoms, i.e. atoms of *like* parity, exactly the inverse of the rule for even AHs. This condition is met in diphenyl-picrylhydrazyl (XLIX), a compound noteworthy in that it is one of the most stable organic free radicals known. In our terminology, this can be regarded as a substituted version of the phenylimino radical, $Ph\dot{N}H$, in which a $-E$ substituent (Ph_2N-) and three $+E$ substituents ($-NO_2$) are all attached to positions that are active in the isoconjugate hydrocarbon radical $PhCH_2\cdot$. Both these features are essential if radicals of this type are to exist in a stable monomeric form.

9.14 SOME SPECIAL SUBSTITUENTS; THE NITRO AND CARBOXY GROUPS

One group of substituents seems to play an anomalous role in our scheme, viz. the nitro group and carboxy derivatives (e.g. $EtOOC-$). These have odd conjugated systems containing three atoms and four π electrons, isoconjugate with the allyl anion. They are *not*, however, $-E$ substituents; for they are attached to adjacent systems through the central, inactive atom of the allylic system.

Consider a system formed by union of allyl, through its central atom, with some conjugated molecule R (Fig. 9.14a). The system has a plane of symmetry (indicated by the dashed line) bisecting the allyl group. Let us then construct the allyl π MOs from an appropriate set of symmetry orbitals, constructed from the three $2p$ AOs ϕ_1, ϕ_2, and ϕ_3 (see Sec. 4.9). The symmetry orbitals are indicated in Fig. 9.14b, and the allyl MOs in Fig. 9.14c.

It will be seen that the MOs ψ_1 and ψ_2 have *exactly* the same form as the MOs

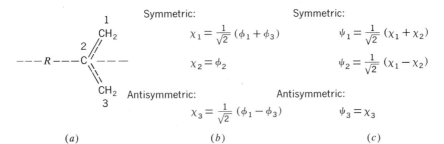

FIG. 9.14 (a) Compound formed by union of RH with allyl, via its central atom; (b) symmetry orbitals of allyl; (c) MOs of allyl.

of a homopolar diatomic molecule, the symmetric grouping of AOs ϕ_1 and ϕ_3 in allyl playing the role of one of the AOs in the latter.   The π interactions between R and these MOs will therefore be precisely analogous to those in the corresponding ethylene derivative, RCH$=$CH$_2$.   Since there is no π interaction between R and the NBMO of allyl, R lying on the nodal plane of the latter, we can see that the effect of allyl on R in R—allyl should be precisely analogous to the effect of the vinyl group on R in RCH$=$CH$_2$.   Thus the 2-allyl group is to all intents and purposes a $\pm E$ substituent; it follows that the corresponding isoconjugate groups —NO$_2$ and —COO$^-$ are $+E$ substituents.

The situation is less clear with unsymmetrical groups such as —COOEt, —CONH$_2$, or —COCl.   Since, however, the carbonyl group is itself of $+E$ type, one might anticipate (correctly) that these groups should also show $+E$ behavior.

9.15 INDUCTIVE AND FIELD EFFECTS; THE HAMMETT EQUATION

In Sec. 9.13 we considered those effects of substituents that arise from polarization of the π electrons in an adjacent conjugated system.   It has long been recognized, however, that other effects must also operate, since a substituent can also influence reactions at centers "insulated" from it by intervening saturated atoms across which conjugative effects cannot be directly transmitted.   In the early days of electronic theory, Lapworth and Robinson[26] recognized two possible effects of this kind, the *field effect*, in which a charged or dipolar substituent influences a distant reaction center by direct electrostatic interaction across space, and the *inductive effect* (which we shall here call the σ-inductive effect, to distinguish it from the π-inductive effect of Sec. 9.13.1), in which σ bonds were supposed to be successively polarized by the same mechanism as that invoked in the π-inductive effect.   The idea here is that if a given carbon atom forms a polar bond to some substituent, the resulting charge on the carbon atom will alter its electronegativity; this in turn will lead to polarization of the σ bond attaching it to an adjacent carbon atom, and successive polarizations of this kind can clearly propagate the effect along a chain of carbon atoms by successive polarization of bonds.   At the time these ideas were proposed, there was no evidence or theory favoring one mechanism over the other.   Since either could account for the available evidence, it was clearly redundant to postulate both.   Lapworth and Robinson decided to adopt the σ-inductive effect rather than the field effect, and this decision had until recently been almost universally adopted by organic chemists.

It is, however, now known that the field effect can be very important.   The classic work in this connection is that of Kirkwood and Westheimer,[27] who showed that the large differences between the first and second dissociation constants of dibasic acids, such as malonic or succinic, could be accounted for quantitatively, in such terms.   Loss of the first proton leaves a conjugate base of the type $HOOC—R—COO^-$; the field effect, due to the charged $—COO^-$ group, hinders ionization of the second proton.

There is, on the other hand, no evidence that the σ-inductive effect can be propagated over more than one, or at the most two, bonds, and there are now good reasons for believing that it cannot. The effect should die off exponentially with the number of bonds traversed, being attenuated by a factor ϵ^n after passage through n bonds where ϵ is the so-called *falloff factor*. Unless ϵ is large, the quantity ϵ^n will obviously become negligible when n is still small. A large value of ϵ is therefore necessary to explain observed long-range effects. The available evidence indicates, however, that ϵ is in fact small. Thus since ϵ is effectively a measure of the extent to which a CC bond is polarized when one of the carbon atoms changes its electronegativity, a high value of ϵ would imply a high bond polarizability. This in turn would imply that hydrocarbons, containing numerous very polarizable CC bonds, should have large dielectric constants; such is not the case. As a further argument, consider a homologous series of compounds of the type $H(CH_2)_nX$, where the bond CX is polar. If CC bonds are very polarizable, the dipole moment should increase greatly on passing from CH_3X to the higher homologs, because of the successive polarization of CC bonds. No such effect is observed. The available data for dipole moments in homologous series show that ϵ cannot possibly be as great as 0.2,‡ a value which would imply very rapid attenuation of the σ-inductive effect along a chain.

A further approach to this problem is provided by the use of linear free-energy relationships, of which the Hammett ρ-σ relation is perhaps the best known. In his discussion of the role of entropy (see Sec. 8.2), Hammett concluded that structure and reactivity could be related to one another only for a series of reactions in which the entropies of activation or reaction are constant. One case satisfying this condition is provided by reactions of *meta*- or *para*-disubstituted benzene derivatives of the type C_6H_4XY, where Y is a side chain that undergoes some specified reaction, while X is a variable substituent. Hammett showed that the rate and equilibrium constants for many such reactions follow a very simple pattern. The constant k is given by the equation

$$\log k = \rho\sigma \tag{9.102}$$

where ρ is a constant characteristic of Y and the same for all substituents X, while σ is a constant characteristic of a given substituent X and the same for all reactions. In order to fix the scales of ρ and σ, Hammett set $\rho = 1$ for the case where k is the acid dissociation constant of a substituted benzoic acid, XC_6H_4COOH, in water.

Hammett's sole object was to show that in one specific instance, where en-

‡ For this and additional arguments, see Ref. 28.

tropy effects are constant, a simple relationship could exist between structure and reactivity. The Hammett relation achieved immediate popularity, and it became a fashionable pastime to measure k for some reaction involving a series of benzene derivatives and to publish a corresponding "Hammett plot." Data of this kind are now available for nearly 1,000 systems. A kind of mystique came to surround Eq. (9.102), so much so that when systems failed to obey it exactly, many chemists felt it necessary to "correct" these imperfections by appropriate modifications. A whole series of alternative sets of σ constants (σ^+, σ^-, σ^*, $\sigma^\dagger$, etc.) were developed to bring the recalcitrants back into line, and the situation finally came to border on the ridiculous. Looking back, it is difficult to see why so much effort should have been put into such an utterly unproductive area; for an empirical relation is of value in science only in so far as it stimulates efforts to interpret it theoretically. Most of the authors in question clearly felt Eq. (9.102), and efforts to extend its scope, an end in itself.

As van Bekkum, Verkade, and Wepster[29] pointed out some time ago, the Hammett relation can be expected to hold only when there is no mutual conjugation between the substituent and the reaction center. The deviations noted above arise in cases where there is such mutual conjugation. If they are to be brought into line, this must be done by taking mutual conjugation explicitly into account, rather than by introducing more parameters (i.e. new kinds of σ constants).

In cases where there is no mutual conjugation in the reactants, or in the products, or in the transition state, the resonance interactions between the substituent and the ring will be the same throughout, and the same for different reactions. One can see very easily why the Hammett relation holds in such cases.[30] Charges and/or dipoles in the substituent, and charges induced in the ring by π interactions or the π-inductive effect, will set up an electrostatic field in the region occupied by the reacting side chain. This field will interact with charges and/or dipoles in the latter. The resulting interaction energy will be of the form QA, where Q is the electrostatic potential at the side chain due to the charges and dipoles in the substituent and the ring, while A is a measure of the change in energy of the side chain when it is placed in an electrostatic field where the potential is unity. The total interaction energy is therefore a product of two factors, one depending only on the substituent, one only on the side chain. Consider now the effect of the substituent on an equilibrium. The difference in energy between the reactants with and without the side chain will be QA_R, where A_R is the value of A for the reactants. Likewise the corresponding change in energy of the products will be QA_P, when A_P is the value of A for the products. The difference δE between the energies of reaction for the substituted and unsubstituted cases will then be:

$$\delta E = Q(A_P - A_R) \qquad (9.103)$$

Using the argument of Sec. 8.2, the ratio of the corresponding equilibrium constants k and k_0, should be given by

$$RT \log \frac{k}{k_0} = Q(A_P - A_R) \qquad (9.104)$$

This is of exactly the same form as Eq. (9.102).

In cases of this kind, the effect of a standard substituent can therefore provide information concerning the change in charge distribution at the reaction center during the reaction; for the Hammett ρ constant should be proportional to $A_P - A_R$ in Eq. (9.104).   Much useful information has been obtained in this way.   However most authors seem to have felt under an obligation to study a whole range of substituents in order to be able to produce Hammett plots for the reactions they are studying; this is quite unnecessary, because the same information can be obtained by using one, or at most two, substituents with numerically large σ constants.   One cannot after all achieve anything more than a rough indication of the changes in polarity during the reaction, given that the treatment is an empirical one in which the proportionality factor between charges and equilibrium constants is not known.   The same of course applies to the analogous treatment of rates of reaction.

As we have seen, the polarization of π electrons by a substituent should follow the same general pattern, regardless of whether the polarization is due to a π interaction or a π-inductive effect.   The electrostatic potential in Eq. (9.104) should therefore be approximately of the form

$$Q = MT \qquad (9.105)$$

where M is a constant characteristic of the substituent and indicates its ability to polarize an adjacent π system, while T measures the field produced at the side chain when the π system is subject to unit polarization.   The only other effect brought about by the substituent will be that due to direct electrostatic interactions between it and the reaction center (field effect); these will be of the form Fr^n, where r is the distance between the substituent and the reaction center, and n will depend on the nature of the field[28] (i.e. point charge, dipole, etc.).   On this basis, the Hammett σ constant will, apart from a proportionality factor, be given by

$$\sigma = MT + Fr^n \qquad (9.106)$$

Note that this result provides a generalized version of the Hammett relation, that can in principle be applied to molecules of all kinds, and not merely to benzene.

The next problem is to determine the quantities in Eq. (9.106).   As a first approximation, we may treat M and F as parameters to be determined from data for the effects of a given substituent in the *meta* and *para* positions of benzene.

If we can decide on a value for n, and on some method for estimating T, we should then be able to calculate σ for various positions in other ring systems.

If an approach of this kind is to be effective, it must of course be possible to compare its predictions with experiment. Curiously enough, in view of the fact that nearly a thousand series of benzene derivatives had been studied, there was until recently *not a single case* where the effects of substituents in some other ring system had been systematically investigated. Eventually Dewar and Grisdale[28] provided data of this kind for the pK_A of α-naphthoic acids carrying a variety of substituents in the five unhindered positions, and Wells and Adcock[31] have reported a similar study of the β-naphthoic acids. The observed σ constants agreed quite well with those calculated from Eq. (9.106), using a very simple-minded PMO method[28] to estimate T. Since this treatment was essentially preliminary in nature, the reader is referred to the original paper for details.[28] This same kind of analysis has also been used to interpret the effects of substituents on the ^{19}F nmr chemical shifts of substituted aryl fluorides, T in this case being estimated by the Pople method.[32]

It must be admitted that this area of chemistry is not a very fundamental one, for three reasons. First, the effects of substituents on the rates of reactions following the Hammett relation are small. The overall spread of rate constants, or equilibrium constants, rarely covers a range of more than two or three powers of 10. This is trivial compared with the differences in reactivity observed in other cases. Thus fluorobenzene fails to react with amines even under rather drastic conditions, whereas 2,4-dinitrofluorobenzene reacts so readily that it is used to label free amino groups in proteins and polypeptides in cold aqueous solution. The ratio of rate constants for reaction with a given amine must amount to many powers of 10.‡

Secondly, the use of the Hammett relation as an aid to studying reaction mechanisms suffers from the uncertainty in relating the observed ρ constants to structures of, for example, transition states. Information of the same kind can usually be gained more directly, and less ambiguously, by using a series of unsubstituted aryl groups rather than substituted phenyls; for the effects of unsubstituted aryl groups are much easier to treat theoretically. This leads to the third point. Substituents normally contain heteroatoms in environments where the role of σ bonds cannot realistically be neglected; treatments of σ-bonded systems (see Chap. 10) are only just beginning to reach a level of precision where they can be usefully applied to chemical problems. When it becomes possible to treat molecules (and transition states) in this kind of way with the precision that has already been attained in the treatment of conjugated systems, stopgap measures such as those based on the Hammett relation will lose all significance.

‡ Aromatic substitution is of course a case when the Hammett relation fails because the aromatic ring does not maintain its integrity during the formation of the arenonium intermediate.

9.16 INDIRECT ELECTROMERIC EFFECTS

We noted earlier (Sec. 9.8) that electrophilic substitution in pyridine takes place very much less readily than in benzene, although the PMO method predicts equal reactivity for benzene and the β positions in pyridine. It is true that many of these reactions (e.g. nitration in sulfuric acid) involve attacks on the pyridinium ion rather than pyridine itself and that in such cases the decreased reactivity is undoubtedly due primarily to a field effect of the positively charged NH group; however reactions involving relatively nonacidic conditions also take place less readily in the case of pyridine than benzene. The phenomenon is in any case a rather general one. For example β-picoline (XXIII) is much more acidic than toluene[33] although the simple PMO method would predict these to be acids of comparable strength; for in the conjugate base (XXIV), nitrogen occupies an inactive position. Again, similar anomalies are observed in the strengths of phenols and aromatic amines when the hydroxyl or amino group occupies a position *"meta"* to a nitrogen atom in the ring.

The explanation of these results seems to lie in a π-inductive effect, due to polarity of the bonds linking the nitrogen to neighboring carbon atoms in the ring.[34] Thus the polarity of the CN σ bonds in pyridine increases the electronegativity of the α carbon atoms; these can then exert qualitatively the same effects on the positions *ortho-para* to them (i.e. the β positions) as the nitrogen atom itself does on the α,γ positions.

Another kind of indirect electromeric effect is observed in the case of Hammett-type systems where there is no direct interaction between the substituent and the reaction center. Thus the σ constant for *meta* NH_2 is negative, implying electron release by the substituent, although one would expect the field and/or inductive effect of NH_2 to be in the opposite direction; this moreover is seen to be the case in saturated molecules, where NH_2 exerts electron withdrawal. Clearly the special effect of NH_2 in benzene (and also in other aromatic systems[28]) must be due to an electromeric interaction with the π electrons of the ring.

This interaction cannot, however, operate by inducing formal π charges in the positions *meta* to nitrogen; for these are *positive,* not negative. The primary effect of the interaction between NH_2 and the ring in benzene is to transfer electrons from nitrogen to the positions *ortho-para* to it, leading to formal negative charges at them; the intervening (*meta*) positions consequently carry positive charges, for the same reason that positive charges appear at the inactive positions in alternant carbanions (Sec. 5.11).

The explanation seems to lie[35] in the fact that the chemically reactive center in a side chain (e.g. the proton in a carboxyl group, in the case where we are considering the effects of substituents on acid strength) is not much further away from the carbon atoms *ortho* to it than it is from the atom in the ring to which it is attached (see Fig. 9.15a). In the case of a *meta* amino substituent, the *ortho* positions carry large formal negative charges, while the atom *meta* to

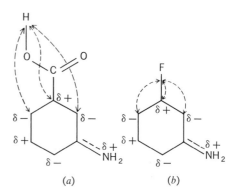

FIG. 9.15   Electromeric-field effects in the *meta* positions of aniline. (*a*) For chemical reaction in a side chain, *meta* NH_2 exerts a $-E$ effect; (*b*) for ^{19}F chemical shifts of fluorine attached to the ring, *meta* NH_2 exerts a $+E$ effect.

nitrogen carries a smaller positive one.   Since there are *two* positions of the former type, and only one of the latter, and since all are at comparable distances from the reaction center, the field effect at the reaction center is dominated by the charges at the *ortho* positions.   This indirect electromeric field effect therefore corresponds to electron release by the nitrogen.

The situation would of course be entirely different for a reaction center very close to the adjacent atom in the ring; for here the positive charge of the latter might play a dominant role.   This situation seems to arise in the effect of substituents on the ^{19}F nmr chemical shifts of aryl fluorides,[35] where substituents *meta* to fluorine exert anomalous effects.   Here the substituent acts by polarizing the electrons in the CF bond, and these of course are very much closer to the carbon atom forming the bond than they are to the carbon atoms *ortho* to fluorine (Fig. 9.15*b*).

9.17   HETEROELECTROCYCLIC REACTIONS
In Sec. 8.17 we considered a class of EE reactions, distinguished by the fact that they proceed via transition states in which the delocalized electrons occupy cyclic MOs.   The reactions discussed were ones in which the pseudo-conjugated ring consisted of only carbon atoms; however parallel reactions are also known in which heteroatoms play a part.   We may term reactions of this type *heteroelectrocyclic* reactions.

The large majority of heteroelectrocyclic reactions follow a common pattern, involving addition of a compound isoconjugate with the allyl anion to a double or triple bond.   Two typical examples follow:

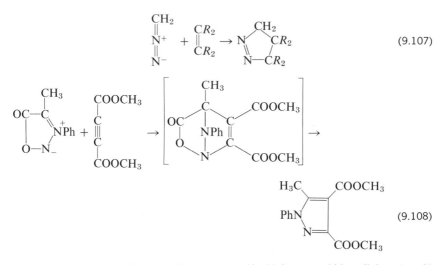

$$(9.107)$$

$$(9.108)$$

Numerous other examples have been reported by Huisgen and his collaborators,[36] who have termed reactions of this type *dipolar additions*.

The reason why reactions of this type take place readily can be seen at once from the arguments of Sec. 8.17. The transition state for such a reaction is one (see Fig. 9.16*a*) in which the delocalized MOs arise from overlap of five AOs in a ring, the overlap being everywhere in phase; the transition state is therefore isoconjugate with the cyclopentadienate anion (Fig. 9.16*b*) and so aromatic. One can conclude that analogous reactions leading to seven-membered rings should not take place, at least not in a single concerted step, since the transition state would then be isoconjugate with the antiaromatic tropylium anion, $C_7H_7^-$. No example of such reactions has been reported.‡

9.18 MUTUAL CONJUGATION IN THE TRANSITION STATE

In the transition state for a reaction between two molecules R and S, the MOs of R and of S interact; consequently the transition state may, and often does, have a delocalized system that differs in important respects from those of the reactants. In the Diels-Alder reaction (Sec. 8.15.1), for example, the diene and dienophile are usually localized, whereas the transition state is aromatic. If the reactants carry substituents, there may be interactions between these in the transition state that are absent in the reactants; interactions of this kind may lead to reaction rates different from those that would be expected if the effects of the substituents were additive.

Consider for example the Diels-Alder reaction of 2-methoxybutadiene (L) with

‡ Reactions leading to seven-membered rings should be able to take place under photochemical conditions; see the last paragraph of Sec. 8.19.

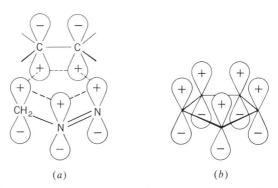

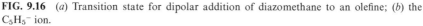

(a)   (b)

FIG. 9.16 (a) Transition state for dipolar addition of diazomethane to an olefine; (b) the $C_5H_5^-$ ion.

acrolein (LI). Methoxyl is a $-E$ substituent, formyl a $+E$ one. We know (Sec. 9.15) that if these are attached to atoms of opposite parity in an even alternant system, there will be mutual conjugation between them. Since the transition state is an even alternant system, being isoconjugate with benzene, it will be correspondingly stabilized if the methoxyl and formyl groups occupy positions of opposite parity in it. This condition is met if the reactants combine to form the "*para*" product (LII), but not if they combine to form the "*meta*" product (LIII). In accordance with this prediction, the reaction does in fact lead almost exclusively to LII.

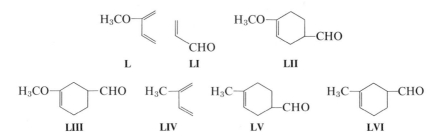

The arguments in Sec. 9.15 show that the same type of interaction should be observed, to a lesser extent, if the two substituents are of $-I$ and $+E$ type, or $+I$ and $-E$ type. The products formed in Diels-Alder reactions are consistent with this. Thus isoprene (LIV) and acrolein (LI) combine to form predominantly the "*para*" isomer (LV) rather than the "*meta*" isomer (LVI).

Another example of the same kind is provided by the radical-catalyzed polymerization of vinyl derivatives. In the transition state for propagation, a radical adds to the double bond of the monomer. If we regard the latter as a substituted ethylene, the transition state will then have a disubstituted odd alternant system isoconjugate with allyl; i.e.

$$\overset{R}{\underset{|}{\sim\!\!\sim\!CH}}\cdot + \overset{S}{\underset{|}{CH_2\!\!=\!\!CH}} \rightarrow \overset{R}{\underset{|}{\sim\!\!\sim\!CH}}\text{---}\overset{S}{\underset{|}{CH_2\!\!=\!\!=\!\!CH}} \rightarrow$$

$$\overset{R}{\underset{|}{\sim\!\!\sim\!CH}}\text{---}CH_2\text{---}\overset{S}{\underset{|}{CH}}\cdot \quad \text{etc.} \quad (9.109)$$

Now the rules for mutual conjugation for odd systems are just the opposite of those for even ones (Sec. 9.15); here mutual conjugation occurs only if a positive substituent and a negative substituent are attached to atoms of the *same* parity. This condition is clearly met in the transition state of Eq. (9.109). If then we copolymerize a mixture of two vinyl derivatives, one containing a positive substituent (e.g. —COOCH$_3$ or —CN) and the other a negative one (e.g. acetoxyl or *p*-methoxyphenyl), the transition state for cross propagation [Eq. (9.109) with $R \neq S$] will be stabilized by mutual conjugation, whereas the transition states for homopropagation [Eq. (9.109) with $R = S$] will not. The different monomer groups will therefore tend to alternate in the polymer, and in extreme cases we might expect the polymer to have a structure in which no two units of the same monomer are directly linked. This effect has indeed been known for a long time experimentally (*alternating effect*); no convincing explanation could be given in terms of resonance theory.

The arguments outlined above should apply quite generally; however the effect is most pronounced in nonionic reactions, during which there is no net transfer of formal charge; for if charges develop, or are destroyed, during a reaction, substituents will commonly exercise first-order effects on the rates which are much larger than the second-order effects considered in this section. Mutual conjugation in the transition state therefore makes itself felt most clearly in the case of electrocyclic reactions, and reactions involving free radicals.

9.19 THE ROLE OF *d* AOs in *π* SYSTEMS

So far we have considered only bonds formed (in our orbital picture) from *s* and *p* AOs; however elements other than those in the first row of the periodic table have *d* AOs in their valence shells, and these can also be used to form bonds. Here we shall consider certain aspects of *d* bonding in so far as it affects organic chemistry.

We shall omit any reference to the chemistry of transition metals, confining our attention solely to organic compounds containing nonmetals such as sulfur and phosphorus. It is true that the chemistry of transition metals in general, and of their organometallic derivatives in particular, is dominated by the behavior of the *d* AOs in them; this, however, is a very large area which could not be treated adequately here without undue expenditure of space, and which has in any case been more than adequately covered in a number of recent monographs.

We can also ignore the contributions of *d* AOs to *σ* bonds, given that very few

organic compounds contain bonds of this type.   [Such exceptions include compounds of pentacovalent phosphorus of the type $(RO)_5P$, of quadricovalent sulfur such as $PhSF_3$, and of trivalent iodine such as $PhICl_2$.]   We shall therefore
confine our attention to the role of π bonds involving the participation of d AOs,
in particular π bonds formed by interaction of a d AO of some atom such as
phosphorus or sulfur with a p AO of a first-row element.   Bonds of this type are
termed $p\pi$-$d\pi$ bonds.

A very clear example of such bonding is provided by the phosphonitrile chlorides.   These are compounds containing the polymeric system $(PNCl_2)_n$, either
in the form of a ring (compare LVII and LVIII), or as an open chain with appropriate terminal groups (e.g. LIX).   X ray structure determinations have shown
that the PN bonds in LVII and LVIII are of equal length, and considerably
shorter than would be expected if they were single.   This must imply that the
phosphorus and nitrogen atoms are linked by π bonds; since the phosphorus
atoms use all their $3s$ and $3p$ AOs in forming σ bonds to four neighboring atoms,
the π bonds must be of $p\pi$-$d\pi$ type.

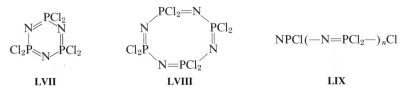

| LVII | LVIII | LIX |

There is an obvious resemblance between the "normal" uncharged resonance
structures LVII and LVIII for the cyclic trimer and tetramer on the one hand
and benzene and cyclooctatetraene on the other; this analogy at once suggests
the possibility that compounds of this type might be aromatic, the more so in
view of the equality of PN bond lengths in each ring.   As we shall now see, however, this analogy is misleading; it arises only because in writing or printing
chemical structures, we use the same symbol (i.e. a line) for bonds of all types.
There is a qualitative difference between the $p\pi$-$d\pi$ bonds in LVII or LVIII and
the $p\pi$-$p\pi$ bonds in a cyclic polyene such as benzene or cyclooctatetraene.

A σ bond formed by an s AO would show no directional properties, since s AOs
are spherically symmetrical.   A σ bond formed by a p AO is, however, strongest
if the nucleus of the other atom lies along the axis of the p AO.   In the localized-
bond model of Sec. 4.11, this directionality carries over to bonds formed by sp^n
hybrid AOs and so accounts for the observed geometries of molecules containing only bonds of this type.   Such localized bonds overlap poorly with one another; following the localized-bond principle (Sec. 4.12), we deduce, correctly,
that the bonds in such molecules should be "localized."

Now p AOs forming π bonds show a lack of directionality analogous to that of
s AOs forming σ bonds.   A p AO has axial symmetry and can overlap equally well
with the p AO of another atom regardless of direction, provided of course that

the other atom lies in the nodal plane of the first p AO and that the axes of the AOs are parallel. A given p AO can therefore form several π bonds simultaneously to other atoms provided they fulfil these conditions (Fig. 9.17a).

This, however, is not true of a d AO. Consider for example a d_{xy} AO. Seen from the side, along the z axis, this looks like Fig. 9.17b. Since the xz plane is a node of this AO, it can form π bonds to atoms lying in that plane. Seen from above, however, i.e. along the y axis, it looks like Fig. 9.17c. Clearly such an AO will form efficient π bonds only to atoms lying along the direction of its lobes, i.e. along the x axis. In other words, a d AO forming a π bond shows the same kind of directionality as a p AO forming a σ bond. In each case, the AO can be used to bind two other atoms simultaneously only if the three atoms lie in a

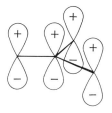

(a)

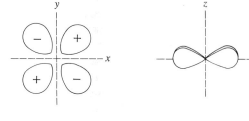

(b)   (c)

(d)

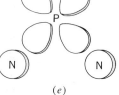

(e)

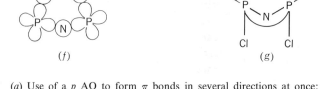

(f)   (g)

FIG. 9.17 (a) Use of a p AO to form π bonds in several directions at once; (b) d_{xy} AO, seen along the z axis; (c) d_{xy} AO, seen along the y axis; (d) a $p\pi$-$d\pi$ bond; (e) phosphorus can form two separate $p\pi$-$d\pi$ bonds to adjacent nitrogen atoms by using different d AOs; (f) MOs in LVII; (g) bonding in LVII, the curved lines representing three-center $d\pi$-$p\pi$-$d\pi$ bonds.

straight line.   Since a linear geometry of this kind is rarely observed, we may expect π bonds formed by d AOs to show the same kind of localization as σ bonds formed by p AOs.   The apparent analogy between LVII and benzene is there-fore entirely misleading; for a phosphorus atom in LVII cannot form satisfactory $d\pi$-$p\pi$ bonds to both the neighboring nitrogen atoms simultaneously, using a single d AO.   If a phosphorus atom in a phosphonitrile chloride is to form effi-cient π bonds to both the neighboring nitrogen atoms simultaneously, it must use two different d AOs, one for each $p\pi$-$d\pi$ bond.‡   Since phosphorus is linked to four neighboring atoms by σ bonds formed through its $3s$ and $3p$ AOs, its geometry should be tetrahedral; the NPN bond angle should therefore be about 109°.   This is close to the angle (90°) between different d AOs; two such AOs can consequently be used to form very good π bonds to the two neighboring nitrogen atoms (Fig. 9.17e).   Each nitrogen, on the other hand, can form π bonds to both adjacent phosphorus atoms via the same $2p$ AO.   According to this pic-ture, the π MOs in a phosphonitrile chloride should split up into three-atom seg-ments (compare Fig. 9.17f), each formed by overlap of a nitrogen $2p$ AO with $3d$ AOs of the two neighboring phosphorus atoms.   Each of these three-center π systems is isoconjugate with allyl.   Furthermore, since the d AOs of phospho-rus are empty, and the p AO of nitrogen doubly occupied, there are just two electrons to be accommodated in each allyl segment; these can fit into the one strongly bonding allyl-type MO.

The π system in a phosphonitrile chloride is therefore not delocalized like the π systems in certain "normal" conjugated molecules; it consists of localized three-center π bonds (Fig. 9.17g).   The stability of such a molecule should therefore be independent of ring size; there should be nothing here correspond-ing to Hückel's rule for cyclic polyenes.   Indeed, there should be no significant difference in stability between the cyclic and open-chain polymers (compare LVII to LIX).

These conclusions agree very well with experiment.   Heating a given phos-phonitrile chloride gives a mixture of cyclic and open-chain species in which no particular members predominate.   The amount of a given polymer at equilibrium is less, the greater the degree of polymerization; this, however, would be expected if the heats of formation per $PNCl_2$ unit were the same in all cases.§   The only exception to this rule is the trimer (LVII), which seems to have a smaller heat of formation than the higher members.   This difference indeed led Craig[38] to suggest that the stabilities of the phosphonitrile chlorides are determined by the same kind of factors that apply in the annulenes, the trimer (LVII) being anti-aromatic because the π system in it contains an odd number of d AOs (see Fig. 8.29a).   However there is a very simple reason why LVII should be less stable

---

‡ For a more detailed discussion, see Ref. 37.

§ Dissociation of $(PNCl_2)_{m+n}$ into $(PNCl_2)_m$ + $(PNCl_2)_n$ leads to an increase in translational entropy; this factor favors the lower polymers.

than the higher polymers, independent of its electronic structure. Since the phosphorus atoms in these compounds tend to a tetrahedral geometry, LVII should be conformationally analogous to cyclohexane. It should therefore be most stable, other things being equal, in an analogous chair conformation. In LVII, however, such a conformation (LX) would be sterically unacceptable, be-cause it would contain three axial chlorine atoms. The repulsions between these must inevitably tend to flatten out the molecule into a less favorable, more or less planar, form. Crystallographic studies have indeed shown LVII to be planar, or almost planar, in contrast to LVIII, which has a zigzag geometry like that of cyclooctane.

The localized-bond picture of the phosphonitrile chlorides accounts of course for the equal bond lengths; for each PNP unit has the same symmetry as the isoconjugate allyl cation. Since phosphorus uses different d AOs to form π bonds to its neighbors, and since these AOs can be chosen at will from an extensive set of $3d$ AOs, there are no necessary correlations between the directions of the two PN π bonds. The π bonds therefore confer no rigidity on the molecule, the geometry of which should accordingly be determined by the skeleton of σ bonds; the chain $(PNCl_2)_n$ should be geometrically similar to, and at least as flexible as, the analogous chain of saturated carbon atoms in polyisobutene (LXI), the *gem*-dimethyl groups in LXI playing the same steric role as the *gem*-dichloro groups in $(PNCl_2)_n$. Both polymers have similar physical properties, forming soft rub-bery solids.

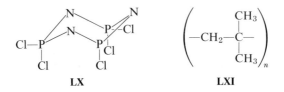

LX   LXI

And finally, since the bonds in the phosphonitrile chlorides are localized, compounds of this type should show no peculiar magnetic effects (e.g. "ring currents"). Craig and his collaborators[39] have themselves confirmed this obvi-ous consequence of the localized-bond picture[37] outlined above.

The same argument can be applied to other compounds in which elements such as phosphorus or sulfur form $d\pi$-$p\pi$ bonds to two or more neighbors. Thus the apparent formal analogy between the groups $>C{=}O$ and $>S{=}O$ or $>S{<}^O_O$ is quite misleading in that whereas direct π interactions with adjacent groups or atoms are possible in the former case (compare the ion $O^-{-}CH{=}O$), they are not in the other two. Conjugative effects cannot be transmitted directly through atoms such as phosphorus or sulfur by $d\pi$-$p\pi$ bonding.

It is true that the methyl group in phenyl methyl sulfone, $PhSO_2CH_3$ (LXII), is acidic, just like that in acetophenone, $PhCOCH_3$; the reason for this acidity is not, however, the same in both cases.   In acetophenone, loss of a proton leaves a mesomeric ion $PhCOCH_2^-$, containing a delocalized π system analogous to that in the allyl anion.   In the case of LXII, the ion has three localized π bonds between sulfur and oxygen or CH_2 (LXIII), formed through different $3d$ AOs of sulfur.

$$PhSO_2CH_3 \qquad \left[Ph-\overset{\overset{O}{\|}}{\underset{\underset{O}{\|}}{S}}=CH_2 \right]^- \qquad PhSCH_3$$

LXII	**LXIII**	**LXIV**

Why then is the methyl group in LXII so very much more acidic than that in phenyl methyl sulfide (LXIV)?   There are two main factors contributing to this. In the first place, the sulfur atom in LXII is sexivalent; in the localized-bond picture, molecules of this type are derived from a promoted form of sulfur of the type $(1s)^2(2s)^2(2p)^6(3s)(3p_x)(3p_y)(3p_z)(3d_1)(3d_2)$, where d_1 and d_2 are the AOs used to form the SO π bonds.   Now $3d$ AOs, being of higher energy, are consequently larger in size than $3s$ or $3p$ AOs; $3d$ electrons are therefore less efficient at screening other electrons in the valence shell of sulfur than are $3s$ or $3p$ electrons.   In other words, the electron affinity at the empty $3d$ AOs of sulfur is greater in this promoted form than it is in the usual bivalent ground state, $(1s)^2(2s)^2(2p)^6(3s)^2(3p)^4$; consequently the sulfur atom in LXII is far readier to use its empty $3d$ AOs to form acceptor π bonds to an adjacent group (i.e. $-CH_2^-$) than is that in LXIV.   Secondly, the S=O bonds in LXII will be very polar in the sense $S^{\delta+}=O^{\delta-}$; the resulting positive charge on sulfur will still further increase its acceptor strength.

One final problem in this area is concerned with the role of sulfur in aromatic compounds such as thiophene.   Does this in any way depend on the presence of $3d$ AOs in the valence shell?   Thiophene is certainly much less reactive than furan or pyrrole, suggesting that it is more "aromatic," and Longuet-Higgins[40] has attributed this difference to the fact that sulfur alone can use d AOs to assist in π bonding.   On the other hand all three compounds are isoconjugate with the aromatic ion $C_5H_5^-$, being derived from it by a perturbation involving an increase in electronegativity of one atom and leading to a consequent decrease in mesomeric stabilization; since electronegativity decreases in the order $O > N > S$, we might on this basis expect the chemical stabilities of these compounds to increase in the order furan $<$ pyrrole $<$ thiophene, as indeed they do.   There is therefore no reason to suppose on the basis of stability alone that the contributions of d AOs are significant, and the same unfortunately applies to other physical and chemical properties that have been studied in the hope of resolving this point. On the whole, the available evidence at present suggests that the contributions of d AOs are small, presumably because in ordinary divalent sulfur their energies are too high.

One case is known, however, in which sulfur probably does use d AOs for π bonding in an aromatic ring, i.e. the thiabenzene derivatives (LXV to LXVIII).[41]

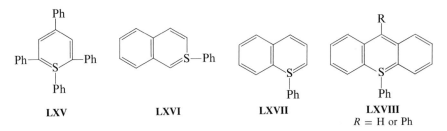

| LXV | LXVI | LXVII | LXVIII |

LXVIII
R = H or Ph

Here there are too many electrons to be accommodated in a π system constructed solely out of p AOs; d AOs must therefore certainly play a role. This, however, would not be surprising, even if they play no part in thiophene; for the sulfur atom in LXVI is in a promoted quadrivalent state. The $3d$ AOs in this should have a much lower energy than those of the unpromoted bivalent sulfur atom in thiophene and they should interact correspondingly more strongly with the adjacent π system. The exact nature of this d participation is, however, still uncertain. Price and his collaborators supposed that one d AO was involved, following the model proposed by Longuet-Higgins[40] for thiophene; however the arguments given earlier in this section make it more likely that the sulfur uses two different d AOs, as does phosphorus in a phosphonitrile chloride.

Further progress in this area will probably have to await the development of better methods for including d AOs in MO calculations. Most of the calculations so far reported have either been based on the HMO approximation or have used SCF treatments in which the parameters have been guessed or chosen to fit spectroscopic data. None of these calculations can be regarded as a reliable guide to the structures of ground states.

9.20 CHOICE OF PARAMETERS IN SCF MO CALCULATIONS FOR ATOMS OTHER THAN C, N, AND O

The earlier sections of this chapter described Pople calculations for heteroconjugated molecules containing carbon, nitrogen, and oxygen, based on the procedures previously developed for hydrocarbons. In order to extend this approach to conjugated systems containing other elements, the necessary parameters must first be estimated. Now there is no difficulty in applying the same methods as before to the estimation of the one-electron parameters W_i and (ii,ii), and the two-center repulsion integrals (ii,jj) could probably be estimated with sufficient accuracy by using Eq. (9.21). Problems arise, however, in estimating the σ-bond energies and one-electron resonance integrals as a function of bond length; for the thermocycle method cannot be used in the absence of data for the properties of the corresponding pure double bonds. For this reason, no quantitative calculations have as yet been reported for the ground states of systems of this kind. The only attempts in this direction have been based on guesses for the parameters, and have been intended primarily to provide qualitative predictions concerning the chemical behavior of certain specific molecules[10] (e.g. Ref. 42).

One particular case where some progress has recently been made[43] has been for fluorine. Since fluorine is so extremely electronegative, the π bonds formed by it are extremely weak (compare Sec. 9.10). The lengths of such bonds, e.g. the CF bonds in aryl fluorides, should not therefore vary much; one can therefore reasonably assume a constant value for the σ-bond energy, and the one-electron resonance integral, for such a bond occurring in different molecules. The values for the CF bond were deduced from ^{19}F nmr data for a wide range of aryl fluorides, and from thermochemical data for fluoro derivatives of ethylene and benzene; these appear to give a consistent interpretation of the limited data available at present.

In the case of boron, of second- and third-row elements forming $p\pi$-$p\pi$ bonds, and of $p\pi$-$d\pi$ binding, some other approach will be necessary. One hopeful line is based on the Mulliken approximation for resonance integrals, which can be written

$$\beta^c = \beta_0 S \qquad\qquad (9.110)$$

where β_0 is a constant characteristic of the bond in question, and S is the overlap integral. This expression has been used for many years in SCF MO calculations, without any real justification. Certainly Eq. (9.110) should hold as a first approximation, but there has been no reason to suppose that it could lead to results of any great accuracy. However it now appears[44] that the values calculated for β^c by the thermocycle method, in cases where this is applicable, e.g. for CC and CN bonds, do follow Eq. (9.110) closely, so it may be possible to estimate β^c in this way in cases where the thermocycle method cannot be used. To do this, one would need to determine only a single parameter β_0; this could be done from suitable thermochemical data for a single molecule.

The extension of the Pople method to conjugated systems of other kinds therefore seems feasible; whether it will prove profitable depends very much on the success of the more general approach described in the next chapter and the speed with which it can be extended to heavier atoms.

PROBLEMS

9.1   Deduce the π-electron densities in pyridine by perturbation theory, with $\alpha_N = \alpha_C + \beta_{CC}$, using the atom-atom polarizabilities for benzene from Prob. 6.3. Compare the results with Fig. 9.2.

9.2 Nitration of quinoline (A) gives a mixture of the 5 and 8 isomers, but nitration of acridine (B) gives a mixture of the 6 (or 3) and 8 (or 1) isomers. Explain this.

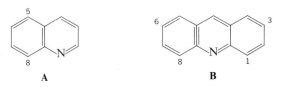

A   **B**

9.3 In an alternant hydrocarbon, the bonds, like the atoms, can be divided into two types, such that no two bonds of a given type have an atom in common. (*a*) Show that the bond-bond polarizability between two bonds of the same type is negative and between two bonds of opposite type is positive. (*b*) Given that $-\beta_{CO} \gg -\beta_{CC}$, how will the bond orders in the ion $[CH_2\text{---}CH\_CH\text{---}CH\_O]^-$ compare with those in $[CH_2\text{---}CH\text{---}CH\_\text{-}CH\text{-}CH_2]^-$?

9.4 Derive expressions for the atom-bond polarizability in (*a*) an odd-AH radical; (*b*) an odd-AH anion.

9.5 Given that oxygen is much more electronegative than carbon, and using the results of Prob. 9.4, deduce the effect of this on the relative bond orders in the two ions discussed in Prob. 9.3.

9.6 Derive an expression in terms of PMO theory relating the pK_A of an aromatic amine ArNH$_2$, where ArH is an even AH, to the NBMO coefficients in the odd AH ArCH$_2$.

9.7 (*a*) Pyridine *N*-oxide undergoes both electrophilic substitution and nucleophilic substitution more readily than benzene. Explain this. (*b*) Explain why nitrosobenzene behaves likewise.

9.8 Deduce the conditions for mutual conjugation in a substituted odd-AH radical.

REFERENCES

1 Orgel, L. E.: "An Introduction to Transition Metal Chemistry," Meuthen & Co., Ltd., London, 1960; J. S. Griffith: "The Theory of Transition Metal Ions," Cambridge University Press, New York, 1961; C. J. Ballhausen: "Introduction to Ligand Field Theory," McGraw-Hill Book Company, New York, 1962.

2 Hinze, J., and H. H. Jaffé: *J. Am. Chem. Soc.* **84**, 540 (1962). Hinze, J.: Ph.D. Thesis, Carnegie Institute of Technology.

3 Dewar, M. J. S., and G. J. Gleicher: *J. Chem. Phys.* **44**, 759 (1966).

4 Chung, A. L. H., and M. J. S. Dewar: *J. Chem. Phys.* **42**, 756 (1965); M. J. S. Dewar and G. J. Gleicher: *J. Am. Chem. Soc.* **87**, 685, 692 (1965).

5   Dewar, M. J. S., and T. Morita: unpublished work.

6   Hinze, J., M. A. Whitehead, and H. H. Jaffé: *J. Am. Chem. Soc.* **85**, 148 (1963); M. A. Whitehead, N. C. Baird, and M. Kaplansky: *Theoret. Chim. Acta* **3**, 135 (1965).

7   Pople, J. A., W. G. Schneider, and H. J. Bernstein: "High-resolution Nuclear Magnetic Resonance," McGraw-Hill Book Company, New York, 1959.

8   Dewar, M. J. S., G. J. Gleicher, and B. P. Robinson: *J. Am. Chem. Soc.* **86**, 5698 (1964).

9   Dewar, M. J. S., and R. Jones: *J. Am. Chem. Soc.* **90**, 2137 (1968).

10 Dewar, M. J. S., and C. G. Venier: unpublished work.

11 Nozoe, T., et al.: *Proc. Japan Acad.* **30**, 473 (1954); *Chem. Ind.* (*London*) **1954**, 1356, 1357; *J. Am. Chem. Soc.* **76**, 3352 (1954).

12 Bamford, C. H., W. G. Barb, A. D. Jenkins, and P. F. Onyon: "Kinetics of Vinyl Polymerization by Radical Mechanisms," Butterworth Scientific Publications, London, 1958; J. C. Bevington: "Radical Polymerization," Academic Press Inc., New York, 1961.

13 Dewar, M. J. S., and V. P. Kubba: *Tetrahedron* **7**, 293 (1959); Dewar, M. J. S., R. Jones, and R. H. Logan, Jr.: *J. Org. Chem.* **33**, 1353 (1968).

14 Dewar, M. J. S.: unpublished work.

15 Szwarc, M.: *Proc. Roy. Soc.* (*London*) **A194**, 267 (1949).

16 Kurita, Y., S. Seto, T. Nozoe, and M. Kubo: *Bull. Chem. Soc. Japan* **26**, 272 (1953).

17 Doering, W. E., and F. L. Detert: *J. Am. Chem. Soc.* **73**, 877 (1951).

18 Coulson, C. A., and H. C. Longuet-Higgins: *Proc. Roy. Soc.* (*London*) **A191**, 39 (1947); **A192**, 16 (1947); **A193**, 447, 456 (1948); **A195**, 188 (1948).

19 Wepster, B. M.: *Rec. Trav. Chim.* **71**, 1171 (1952); S. M. H. van der Krogt and B. M. Wepster, *ibid.* **74**, 161 (1955).

20 Emsley, J. W., J. Feeney, and L. H. Sutcliffe: "High Resolution Nuclear Magnetic Resonance Spectroscopy," p. 556, Pergamon Press, New York, 1965.

21 Lide, D. R.: *Ann. Rev. Phys. Chem.* **15**, 245 (1964).

22 Streitwieser, A., W. C. Langworthy, and J. I. Braumann: *J. Am. Chem. Soc.* **85**, 1761 (1963).

23 Bak, B., D. Christensen, L. Hansen, and J. Rastrop-Andersen: *J. Chem. Phys.* **24**, 720 (1956).

24 Dewar, M. J. S.: *J. Am. Chem. Soc.* **74**, 3350 (1952).

25 Dewar, M. J. S.: *J. Am. Chem. Soc.* **74**, 3350, 3353 (1952).

26 Robinson, R.: "Outline of an Electrochemical (Electronic) Theory of the Course of Organic Reactions," Institute of Chemistry, London, 1932.

27 Kirkwood, J. G., and F. H. Westheimer: *J. Chem. Phys.* **6**, 506 (1938); F. H. Westheimer and J. G. Kirkwood: *ibid.,* 513.

28 Dewar, M. J. S., and P. J. Grisdale: *J. Am. Chem. Soc.* **84**, 3548 (1962).

29 Bekkum, H. van, P. E. Verkade, and B. M. Wepster: *Rec. Trav. Chim.* **78**, 815 (1959).

30 Price, C. C.: *Chem. Rev.* **29**, 37 (1941).

31   Wells, P. R., and W. Adcock: *Australian J. Chem.* **18,** 1365 (1965).

32   Adcock, W., and M. J. S. Dewar: *J. Am. Chem. Soc.* **89,** 379 (1967).

33   Brown, H. C., and W. A. Murphey: *J. Am. Chem. Soc.* **73,** 3308 (1951).

34   Brown, D. A., and M. J. S. Dewar: *J. Chem. Soc.* **1953,** 2406.

35   Adcock, W., and M. J. S. Dewar: *J. Am. Chem. Soc.* **89,** 379 (1967).

36   Huisgen, R.: *Proc. Chem. Soc.* **1961,** 357; *Angew. Chem. Intern. Ed. Engl.* **2,** 565 (1963); Aromaticity, *Chem. Soc. Spec. Publ.* 21, p. 51, 1967.

37   Dewar, M. J. S., E. A. C. Lucken, and M. A. Whitehead: *J. Chem. Soc.* **1960,** 2423.

38   Craig, D. P.: in "Theoretical Organic Chemistry (Kekulé Symposium)," p. 20, Butterworth Scientific Publications, London, 1959; see also *Chem. Soc. Spec. Publ.* 12, p. 343, 1958; *J. Chem. Soc.* **1959,** 997.

39   Craig, D. P., M. L. Heffernan, R. Mason, and N. L. Paddock: *J. Chem. Soc.* **1961,** 1376.

40   Longuet-Higgins, H. C.: *Trans. Faraday Soc.* **45,** 173 (1949).

41   Price, C. C., and G. Suld: *J. Am. Chem. Soc.* **83,** 1770 (1961); **84,** 2094 (1962); C. C. Price, M. Hori, T. Parasaran, and M. Polk, *ibid.* **85,** 2278 (1963).

42   Chalvet, O., R. Daudel, and J. J. Kaufman: in K. Niedenzu (ed.), Boron-Nitrogen Chemistry, *Advan. Chem. Ser.* **42,** 251 (1964); J. J. Kaufman and J. R. Hamann, *ibid.,* 273.

43   Dewar, M. J. S., and J. Kelemen: *J. Chem. Phys.* **49,** 499 (1968).

44   Dewar, M. J. S., and J. Kelemen: unpublished work.

CALCULATIONS INCLUDING σ ELECTRONS

10.1 INTRODUCTION

The localized-bond model provides a very good description of the collective properties of unconjugated molecules, and also (Secs. 5.5 and 6.7) of classical conjugated molecules. The first and most important problem in quantum chemistry is therefore the provision of some treatment for molecules that are conjugated and for which more than one classical structure can be written; the four preceding chapters have outlined a treatment of this kind which seems very satisfactory.

However there are many chemically important situations where this general approach is inadequate. Consider for example the problem of transition states. As we have seen, transition states normally contain delocalized systems of other than π type; the energies of such systems cannot be estimated by the localized-bond model, nor can the delocalized electrons in them be treated by the methods of Chaps. 5 to 9. Since the rate of a chemical reaction is determined by the difference in energy between the reactants and the transition state, this is a serious limitation. The analysis of chemical reactivity in Chap. 7 had consequently to be based on a rather unsatisfactory expedient, i.e. use of an empirical relationship between energies of activation and energies of reaction. If we could calculate the energies of transition states directly, by a quantum-mechanical procedure in which all the valence electrons in a molecule were explicitly included, this difficulty would be avoided. Moreover we would be able to predict the geometries of transition states, and to distinguish between various possible mechanisms for a given reaction by comparing the energies of the corresponding transition states. Other problems that could be treated by an approach of this kind include molecules with three-center bonds (e.g. π complexes, Sec. 8.24), steric hindrance (e.g. in molecules such as o-di-tert-butylbenzene), and ring strain (e.g. in cyclopropane).

The inclusion of σ electrons in our MO treatment admittedly presents many problems. First, there is the sheer magnitude of the calculations, given that the total number of valence electrons in a molecule is very much greater than that of π electrons in a conjugated system of comparable size; benzene for example contains only 6 π electrons, out of a total of 30 valence electrons. Secondly, the MOs no longer have the symmetry of those in a π system, being three-dimensional. Thirdly, in the simple Pople SCF MO treatment, there is the problem of invariance in choice of coordinate axes (Sec. 3.4). And finally, there is the problem of predicting molecular geometry. In the π calculations, this was determined primarily by the stiff skeleton of localized σ bonds, the π electrons representing only a minor perturbation; in a complete valence-shell treatment, we no longer have such an aid.

Consequently calculations of this kind have only recently been attempted in a serious manner, and the best of these still fall short of the success achieved in the π calculations. Nevertheless the results already obtained have been en-couraging enough to virtually ensure ultimate success, and progress in this field is likely to be rapid in the near future. Here we shall give only a brief outline of the present position; for the situation will inevitably change significantly even during the period it takes for this book to get into print.

10.2   THE EXTENDED HÜCKEL METHOD
The first serious attack on the general problem of treating valence-shell electrons in a quantitative manner came from an application of the HMO method. This approach had of course been used for many years in a qualitative or semiquan-titative way, e.g. to discuss the problem of bond localization in classical mole-cules (see Chap. 4); however virtually no attempts had been made to carry out detailed calculations for large molecules. This omission was probably due to two factors. First, such calculations require the use of digital computers of types which have only recently become generally available; secondly, by the time such computers became available, the deficiencies of the HMO method had be-come so apparent that it seemed extremely unlikely that it could prove useful for σ-bonded systems.

As we have seen (Sec. 6.20), the HMO treatment of π electrons is moderately successful only for alternant aromatic hydrocarbons; it fails for systems contain-ing heteroatoms or subject to significant bond alternation. Since the molecules we are now considering inevitably contain atoms of different kinds, and since the bonds in them are localized, they should be almost perfectly unsuitable for treatment by the HMO method.

An approach of this kind has nevertheless been attempted by Hoffmann,[1] who has termed it the *extended Hückel method*. This is based on the HMO method with inclusion of overlap; the secular equation and equations for orbital coefficients are, in our usual notation,

$$|H_{ij} - ES_{ij}| = 0 \tag{10.1}$$

$$\sum_j a_{\mu j}(H_{ij} - E_\mu S_{ij}) = 0 \qquad i = 1, 2, \ldots, n \tag{10.2}$$

the summation being over all the valence-shell AOs. The matrix elements H_{ij} are defined by:

$$H_{ij} = \int \phi_i \mathbf{H} \phi_j \, d\tau \tag{10.3}$$

where the hamiltonian **H** represents motion in the field of a core composed of the nuclei and inner-shell electrons (e.g. in the case of a carbon atom, an ion C^{4+} consisting of the nucleus and two $1s$ electrons) and of the valence electrons. The diagonal matrix elements are set equal to the corresponding valence-state ionization potentials; in this case the valence state is one in which the electrons occupy real s, p, d, etc., AOs rather than hybrid AOs, since there is no need to introduce hybridization in a treatment where the MOs occupied by all the valence electrons are calculated explicitly. The off-diagonal elements are estimated by the Mulliken approximation, i.e.

$$H_{ij} = CS_{ij}(H_{ii} + H_{jj}) \tag{10.4}$$

where C is an empirical constant. Off-diagonal matrix elements are included between all pairs of AOs, irrespective of the atoms to which they belong. The total energy of the molecule is set equal to a sum of the orbital energies of the valence electrons, as in the usual HMO treatment [Eq. (3.73)]; the heat of atomization is estimated by subtracting from this the total energy of the atoms, this likewise being set equal to a sum of the energies of the valence-shell electrons in them (i.e. to a sum of the corresponding valence-shell ionization potentials, H_{ii}).

Such a treatment is obviously open to all the criticisms applying to the usual HMO method (Sec. 3.7); it is therefore not surprising that it gives hopelessly inaccurate results, the calculated heats of atomization being in error by huge amounts and the predicted charge distributions being entirely unrealistic. Such a calculation may have limited applications in certain special areas, e.g. to obtain rough estimates of coupling constants in nmr and esr spectra; it is worthless as a procedure for predicting the structures or chemical behavior of molecules, and the results of such calculations, many of which have unfortunately found their way into print, must be regarded as meaningless.

10.3 APPROXIMATIONS TO THE HARTREE-FOCK TREATMENT

The expected failure of the extended Hückel method makes it clear that our approach must be based on some version of the Hartree-Fock SCF MO method. Very good approximations to this can apparently be obtained by the Roothaan method; however the calculations are so very difficult that they can as yet be applied only to very simple molecules, even using the largest available digital computers. Furthermore, the results obtained in this way are of little or no chemical value since they are far too inaccurate; even an exact Hartree-Fock method is too crude for chemical purposes, because of its neglect of electron correlation, and the resulting heats of atomization are consequently quite unreliable.‡

‡ A good example is provided by fluorine. According to accurate SCF MO calculations, this should be monatomic, the bond energy in F_2 being negative!

Similar criticisms of course apply to attempts to get approximations to the results that would be given by an exact Hartree-Fock treatment. These have fallen into two main categories. First, the full Roothaan treatment has been applied to polyatomic molecules, the computational complexities being reduced to a manageable form by using limited basis sets, and by using gaussian functions instead of SZOs so that the electron repulsion integrals can be calculated more simply (e.g. Ref. 2). Secondly, semiempirical LCAO MO methods have been used, the parameters in them being chosen to give the best agreement with the results of exact SCF MO treatments in cases where these are available (e.g. Refs. 3 to 5). For reasons indicated above, neither of these approaches can represent a satisfactory solution to the problems of chemistry.

10.4 SEMIEMPIRICAL SCF MO METHODS BASED ON THE POPLE APPROXIMATION

If we are concerned with chemistry, our primary aim must be to calculate the heats of formation and geometries of molecules with "chemical" accuracy. The only conceivable way of doing this now or in the foreseeable future lies in some kind of semiempirical SCF LCAO MO approach, in which the parameters are chosen to give the best possible fit to ground-state properties, rather than to reproduce the (hopelessly inaccurate) results of an exact Hartree-Fock treatment. The goal in an approach of this kind is of course to use the simplest possible treatment that can be coaxed into giving adequate results by appropriate parameterization. Consequently our first choice is the Pople SCF MO method, the more so in view of the success of the corresponding π calculations for conjugated molecules. We assume the valence electrons to move in a core composed of the nuclei and inner-shell electrons (compare Sec. 10.2), the MOs being written as linear combinations of all the valence-shell AOs of the contributing atoms, and we neglect overlap and three- and four-center integrals. The remaining integrals can be treated as parameters, subject to the restrictions that the total number of parameters must be kept within bounds, and that their values must be physically reasonable.

As we have seen (Sec. 3.4), a naïve application of the Pople method to problems of this kind runs into difficulties, in that the results are liable to prove sensitive to the choice of coordinate axes. Two solutions of this problem were pointed out in Sec. 3.4.

In the first (CNDO) approximation, we assume all orbitals to be spherically symmetrical in calculating electron repulsion integrals, while the one-electron resonance integrals $\beta_{ij}{}^c$ are given by

$$\beta_{ij}{}^c = \beta_0 S_{ij} \tag{10.5}$$

where β_0 is a constant for the type of bond in question. The effect of orbital shape thus appears only through these resonance integrals, the value of the overlap integral S_{ij} between a p AO ϕ_i and some other AO ϕ_j depending on the orientation of ϕ_i relative to ϕ_j.

The second (NDDO) approximation solves the problem in a more complicated way, by retaining all three- and four-orbital integrals of the type (ij,kk) and (ij,kl) in which the overlap (that is $\phi_i\phi_j$ or $\phi_k\phi_l$) is between AOs of the same atom. Integrals involving overlap between AOs of different atoms [for example (ij,ij) or (ij,kk) when ϕ_i and ϕ_j are AOs of two different atoms] are still set equal to zero.

Most of the published calculations in this field have so far made use of the CNDO approximation, but they have not been concerned with heats of atomization and so the parameters have not been chosen with this end in view.[3] The NDDO model is much more complicated, involving as it does a large number of three- and four-orbital integrals; to apply this method to molecules of reasonable size involves the use of a very powerful digital computer. No calculations of this kind have as yet been reported.

The number of integrals in the NDDO method can be minimized by the following procedure.[6] Consider two atoms, i and j, each of which has an sp^3 valence shell. Denote the corresponding s, p_x, p_y, and p_z AOs by (s_i,x_i,y_i,z_i) and (s_j,x_j,y_j,z_j). Suppose now that we rotate the coordinates used to specify the molecule into the orientation indicated in Fig. 10.1. The valence-shell AOs of atoms i and j in this new coordinate system will be (s_i,x'_i,y'_i,z'_i) and (s_j,x'_j,y'_j,z'_j), the (spherical) s AOs being of course invariant to rotation. Now p AOs transform like vectors; we can therefore express the original p AOs $(x_i,y_i,z_i,x_j,y_j,z_j)$ as linear combinations of the transformed sets; e.g.

$$x_i = lx'_i + my'_i + nz'_i \tag{10.6}$$

where l, m, and n are the direction cosines of the new set of axes relative to the old. Any repulsion integral (ij,kl) involving the original set of AOs can therefore be expressed in terms of the corresponding AOs of Fig. 10.1.

In this coordinate system, most of the three- and four-orbital integrals vanish through symmetry. Consider for example the integral $(s'_iy'_i,s'_js'_j)$. Since this integral represents the mutual repulsion of two charge distributions, its value must

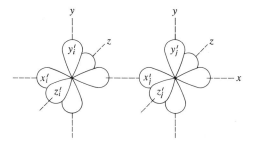

FIG. 10.1 Choice of coordinate axes for calculating repulsion integrals between atoms i and j in the NDDO and PNDO methods.

be independent of the coordinate system used to calculate it. Since the orbitals in question have two planes of symmetry (the xz and yz planes in Fig. 10.1), the integral must in particular be invariant for reflection in these planes. Since reflection in the xz plane leaves s_i and s_j unchanged, but reverses the sign of y_i, our integral changes sign if we reflect the system in the xz plane. It follows that the integral $(s_i'y_i',s_j's_j')$ must vanish.

Extending this argument, we see that only the following integrals survive, assuming of course that we can neglect all overlap between any AO of atom i, and any AO of atom j:

1 All two-orbital integrals of the type (ii,kk)

2 All integrals involving s-$p\sigma$ overlap; for example $(s_i'x_i',s_j'x_j')$
  or $(s_i'x_i',y_j'y_j')$ (10.7)

3 The three specific integrals $(x_i'y_i',x_j'y_j')$, $(x_i'z_i',x_j'z_j')$, and $(y_i'z_i',y_j'z_j')$

The last three integrals survive because although any of the p AOs is antisymmetric for reflection in its nodal plane, the product of two parallel p AOs (for example $y_i'y_j'$) is symmetric.

Following this line of approach, we have written a program for the NDDO method; preliminary results obtained with this have been encouraging,[7] and a brief outline of the procedures we are using will be given presently. Most of our work has, however, been carried out using simpler methods,[6] intermediate between the CNDO and NDDO approximations.

Consider an integral of the type $(sp,\phi\phi)$ when s and p are an s AO and a p AO of a given atom. If we rotate the coordinate axes, this integral will be replaced by a sum of integrals of the type $(sp',\phi\phi)$ when p' is one of the new p AOs of the atom in question. If therefore we neglect overlap between the s AO s and any p AO of the same atom, *all* these integrals will vanish. Such neglect will therefore have no effect on the invariance to rotation, since their net contribution will always be identically equal to zero. This suggests that we could simplify the NDDO approximation greatly by simply neglecting integrals of this type, i.e. those listed in part 2 of Eq. (10.7). Furthermore, the three integrals in part 3 of (10.7) are all very small. If we calculate them by direct integration, using SZOs of a pair of carbon atoms at an internuclear distance of 1.5 Å, we find that they are all approximately equal to 0.1 ev. Since their magnitudes are moreover similar, and since changes in their contributions arise only from the small differences between them, it seems very likely that we could neglect them without significantly affecting the rotational invariance of our calculations. Taken together, these approximations form the basis of the *PNDO* (*partial neglect of differential overlap) approximation.*[6] It clearly represents a very great simplification in comparison with the full NDDO treatment since the repulsion integrals appearing in it can now all be expressed in terms of simple two-orbital, two-center integrals of the type (ii,kk).

One further approximation has recently been introduced by Pople et al.[5] and by us.[8] This differs from CNDO only by the inclusion of one-center electron repulsion integrals involving differential overlap.   Most such integrals vanish through symmetry, the only ones to be considered being of the type (ij,ij) when ϕ_i and ϕ_j are two different AOs of a given atom.   In the case of second-row elements, there are just two such integrals, ϕ_i being a $2s$ or $2p$ AO, and ϕ_j a $2p$ AO different from ϕ_i.

Pople et al. evaluated these integrals theoretically, following the general philosophy adopted[3] by them in calculations of this kind.   Their object was to estimate geometries and dipole moments of molecules, not heats of formation; they also used an open-shell version of this INDO (intermediate neglect of differential overlap) approximation to calculate spin coupling constants in the esr spectra of radicals.   We[8] on the other hand have used a simpler version of this general approach to calculate heats of formation.   In our treatment, the various integrals are estimated in a manner similar to that used in the π approximation (Chaps. 5 and 9), the parameters being chosen to fit the observed heats of formation of selected molecules.   To distinguish this treatment from INDO, we have termed it MINDO (modified INDO).

In all Pople treatments of σ-bonded systems, the orbital coefficients are given by similar sets of equations, viz.

$$\sum_j a_{\mu j}(F_{ij} - E\delta_{ij}) = 0 \tag{10.8}$$

where, as usual, E_μ is one root of the secular equation:

$$|F_{ij} - E\delta_{ij}| = 0 \tag{10.9}$$

Note that the basis-set functions (i.e. the valence-shell AOs of the contributing atoms) are all mutually orthogonal; for the orbitals of a given atom form an orthogonal set, and we neglect all overlap between AOs of different atoms.

The elements of the F matrix in the CNDO approximation can be written down very easily, from intuition; a rigorous derivation is left to the reader as an exercise.   In this approach, where all overlap is neglected,

$$F_{ii}^{(m)} = W_i^{(m)} + \tfrac{1}{2}q_i(ii,ii) + \sum_{j \neq i} q_j(ii,jj) + \sum_{n \neq m} V_{in} \tag{10.10}$$

$$F_{ij} = \beta_{ij}^c - \tfrac{1}{2}p_{ij}(ii,jj) \tag{10.11}$$

Here $W_i^{(m)}$ represents the energy of an electron occupying the AO ϕ_i and moving in the field of the core of its own atom m; in the case of carbon, this would include a term representing the attraction between the electron in ϕ_i and the quadruply charged core C^{4+}. V_{in} likewise represents the attraction between an electron in the AO ϕ_i and the core of atom n.   The remaining terms in Eq. (10.10) represent the repulsion between an electron in the AO ϕ_i and the other valence electrons.

In the NDDO or PNDO approximations, the F matrix is given by the full Roothaan expression,

$$F_{ii}{}^{(m)} = W_i{}^{(m)} + \sum_{n \neq m} V_{in} + \sum_k \sum_l P_{kl}[(ii,kl) - \tfrac{1}{2}(ik,il)] \qquad (10.12)$$

$$F_{ij} = \beta_{ij}{}^c + \sum_k \sum_l P_{kl}[(ij,kl) - \tfrac{1}{2}(ik,jl)] \qquad (10.13)$$

with the proviso that the three- and four-orbital integrals vanish if they involve overlap between AOs of different atoms.

10.5   CHOICE OF PARAMETERS

10.5.1   INTRODUCTION   The parameters appearing in Pople valence-shell calculations are of four main types.

First, there are the "atomic" parameters $W_i{}^{(m)}$ and (ij,kl), where ϕ_i, ϕ_j, ϕ_k, and ϕ_l are AOs of the same atom; these will have the same value for an isolated atom m and so we can estimate them empirically from spectroscopic data for atoms.   From our point of view, these quantities do not need to be regarded as parameters; for our problem is to calculate the changes in energy when atoms combine to form molecules, not the changes in energy when nuclei and electrons combine to form atoms.   We can legitimately treat any results derived from the study of atoms as free information.

Secondly, there are the electron repulsion integrals (ij,kl); these we may hope to estimate by some simple empirical scheme analogous to that used in the π calculations (see Sec. 5).

Thirdly, there are the core resonance integrals $\beta_{ij}{}^c$.   These must be treated as pure parameters, because they do not correspond to any simple physical quantity.   This point was emphasized in Sec. 3.2.   The integrals $\beta_{ij}{}^c$ are not "true" one-electron resonance integrals $(\beta_{ij}{}^c)_t$, defined by

$$(\beta_{ij}{}^c)_t = \int \phi_i \mathbf{H}^c \phi_j \, d\tau \qquad (10.14)$$

They represent differences between the "true" values and those given by a simple Mulliken approximation, i.e.

$$\beta_{ij}{}^c = (\beta_{ij}{}^c)_t - \tfrac{1}{2} S_{ij}(I_i + I_j) \qquad (10.15)$$

where I_i and I_j are the valence-state ionization potentials of the AOs ϕ_i and ϕ_j. Since, however, $(\beta_{ij}{}^c)_t$ should itself be very nearly proportional to S_{ij}, we should choose for $\beta_{ij}{}^c$ a function of the form

$$\beta_{ij}{}^c = (\beta_{ij}{}^c)_0 S_{ij} \qquad (10.16)$$

where $(\beta_{ij}{}^c)_0$ is a quantity characteristic of the AOs ϕ_i and ϕ_j but independent of their positions in space.   A function of this kind is in any case necessary if our calculations are to be invariant for rotation of the coordinate axes (Sec. 3.2).

Fourthly, there are the core attraction integrals V_{in}, and terms V_{mn} representing mutual repulsions between different cores. Since the cores in this treatment consist of nuclei together with inner-shell electrons, the cores should be small compared with the valence-shell AOs. This condition suggests that V_{in} and V_{mn} might be calculated by a point-charge model, replacing the core by an equivalent point charge at its center; a procedure such as this is not, however, generally feasible in treatments of this type. The following reason explains this infeasibility.

Consider a simple molecule, say H_2. Each electron moves in a potential field due to the attractions by two nuclei, each of charge $+e$, and the repulsion of the other electron. The arguments of Sec. 2.5 tell us that the average interelectronic repulsion must be less than the average attraction of each electron to either nucleus. The electrons therefore move in an average potential field which is stronger than that in an isolated hydrogen atom, and the bonding MO in H_2 is correspondingly smaller. This can be seen in an LCAO MO treatment, where the bonding MO is composed of $1s$ AOs of the two atoms, if we treat the nuclear charges Z as parameters and determine their best values by a variation method. The optimum value found in this way is about 1.2. If therefore we follow the simple LCAO MO approximation, of assuming that MOs can be expressed in terms of AOs of the individual atoms, we shall arrive at an AO for H_2 which is too diffuse, being composed of hydrogenlike AOs with $Z = 1$ instead of $Z = 1.2$. The energy we calculate for H_2 will of course be correspondingly too high and the estimated heat of atomization correspondingly too low. The same situation occurs quite generally in molecules, as is shown by rigorous Roothaan calculations in which the effective nuclear charges of the basis-set AOs are allowed to vary. In an LCAO approximation, the AOs used should be ones appropriate to atoms in molecules, not to atoms in isolation.

In a complete Roothaan treatment, where all the integrals are evaluated theoretically, the appropriate AOs can be found by the variation method. In our semiempirical approach, this is no longer the case; for the variation theorem applies only if the energy is evaluated by direct integration, using the correct hamiltonian for the system in question. If therefore we are to allow for the effects of orbital contraction, as we must do if we are to get results of the accuracy we require, we can proceed in one of two different ways. First, we could treat the orbital contraction as a parameter to be determined empirically. This would be the best solution in principle, but difficult in practice; as yet, no calculations of this kind have been reported. The other alternative is to allow for the changes in energy of the AOs by an appropriate modification of some other part of the expression for the total energy of the molecule; this permits us to use "normal" AOs in our treatment, with the advantage that the corresponding "atomic" parameters can be evaluated from experimental data for atoms. The latter approach has been followed up till now in all attempts to calculate accurately heats of atomization of σ-bonded molecules.

10.5.2 ATOMIC PARAMETERS; KLOPMAN'S METHOD Consider an atom with an sp^3 valence shell, e.g. carbon. It is very easily seen that the only repulsion integrals that do not vanish from symmetry are of two types, (ii,kk) and (ik,ik). From the symmetric relationship of the set of three p AOs, it follows that there are just six distinct integrals to be considered, viz.

$$(ss,ss) \qquad (ss,pp) \qquad (sp,sp) \qquad (xx,xx) \qquad (xx,yy) \qquad (xy,xy) \quad (10.17)$$

where p is any of the three p AOs and x and y are respectively the p_x and p_y AOs. Integrals involving the third p AO (p_z) have similar values, e.g.

$$(xz,xz) = (yz,yz) = (xy,xy) \tag{10.18}$$

The other atomic integrals to be determined are the core energies W_s and W_p of an electron occupying an s AO, or a p AO, respectively. There are thus eight quantities to be determined from experimental data for the atom. Carrying through this program would clearly be a difficult task; up till now, attempts to calculate ground-state energies accurately have been based on the following simplification, due to Klopman[9] (see also Ref. 6).

Klopman assumes that the repulsion between two valence-shell electrons of a given atom is the same, no matter what orbitals they occupy. The repulsion can then have one of just two possible values A^+ and A^-, depending on whether the spins of the electrons are the same (A^+) or opposite (A^-). Since the repulsion between two electrons of opposite spin in the AOs ϕ_i and ϕ_j is given by the integral (ii,jj), while the repulsion between two electrons of parallel spin is less than this by an exchange term (ij,ij), it follows from Eqs. (10.17) and (10.18) that:

$$(ss,ss) = (pp,pp) = (ss,pp) = (xx,yy) = (xx,zz) = (yy,zz) = A^- \tag{10.19}$$
$$(sp,sp) = (xy,xy) = (xz,xz) = (yz,yz) = A^- - A^+ \tag{10.20}$$

Consider the states of carbon of the type $(1s)^2(2s)^2(2p)^2$. As we have seen, there are 15 distinct configurations of this kind (Sec. 9.2), 9 singlets and 6 triplets. In Klopman's approximation, the total binding energy of the four valence electrons is the same (^1E) for each singlet configuration, being given by:

$$^1E = 2W_s + 2W_p + 2A^+ + 4A^- \tag{10.21}$$

where W_s represents a sum of the kinetic energy of an electron occupying the $2s$ AO and its potential energy due to attraction by the core (i.e. C^{4+}), while W_p represents the corresponding quantity for a $2p$ electron. There are six repulsions to be taken into account between the four electrons taken in pairs; four of these are repulsions between pairs of electrons of opposite spin, two between electrons of parallel spin. Likewise the energies of each of the triplet configurations are the same (^3E), being given by:

$$^3E = 2W_s + 2W_p + 3A^+ + 3A^- \tag{10.22}$$

If therefore we can estimate ^1E and ^3E from experimental data for the atom, we shall have two equations to determine the four unknowns W_s, W_p, A^+, and A^-. The necessary additional equations can be found from similar analyses of configurations representing other states of neutral carbon, for example $(1s)^2(2s)(2p)^3$, or of ions such as C^+, for example $(1s)^2(2s)^2(2p)$ or $(1s)^2(2s)(2p)^2$.

The argument of Sec. 9.2 shows that each such set of configurations of the type $(1s)^2(2s)^2(2p)^2$ corresponds to a set of real states of the atom. In this particular instance, the states in question are the five substates of a ^1D state, the three substates of a $3p$ state with $S_z = 0$, and a ^1S state. The real states of the atom are represented by linear combinations of the nine singlet configurations. Now it is easily shown that in a situation of this kind, the sum of the energies of the nine individual configurations must be equal to the sum of the energies of the nine linear combinations representing real states of the atom; the argument is precisely the same as that used in Sec. 4.10 in our proof that the mutual interaction of a set of filled MOs leads to no net change in energy. Consequently,

$$9^1E = 5E(^1D) + 3E(^3P) + E(^1S)$$

or
$$^1E = \tfrac{1}{9}[5E(^1D) + 3E(^3P) + E(^1S)] \tag{10.23}$$

when $E(^1D)$, $E(^3P)$, and $E(^1S)$ are the energies of the ^1D, ^3P, and ^1S states respectively. The energy of the singlet configuration thus appears as a weighted mean or *barycenter* of the energies of real states of the atom, which of course can be estimated directly from spectroscopic data. Likewise,

$$^3E = E(^3P) \tag{10.24}$$

since the triplet configurations all correspond to substates of a single state of carbon, that is ^3P.

This procedure may seem rather primitive; in practice, however, it works surprisingly well. Many more states of carbon are known than are required to determine the quantities W_s, W_p, A^+, and A^-; the energies of the additional states provide a stringent test of Klopman's scheme, from which it emerges with flying colors. Moreover the same is true of all other atoms for which adequate spectroscopic data are available; we may therefore use Klopman's approximation with some confidence in valence-shell calculations. Table 10.1 shows the values of the parameters for several first-row elements.

TABLE 10.1   Klopman[a] parameters, in electron volts, for C, N, and O

Atom	W_s	W_p	A^+	A^-
C	−49.884	−42.696	10.144	11.144
N	−69.593	−58.669	10.718	11.975
O	−96.247	−80.591	12.149	13.707

[a] G. Klopman, *J. Am. Chem. Soc.* **86,** 1463 (1964).

10.5.3   ELECTRON REPULSION INTEGRALS   The electron repulsion integrals occurring in the various Pople treatments have been approximated in two distinct ways.

In the first, the integrals are calculated directly; programs for estimating them are now generally available, having been developed in the course of various a priori calculations. One cannot, however, use standard SZOs for this purpose, for reasons indicated in our discussion of the corresponding integrals in the Pople π approximation; use of standard SZOs gives values for the one-center integrals that are very much greater than those found empirically from Eqs. (10.19) and (10.20). The differences could be reduced by using SCF AOs in the calculations; however this would not only be very laborious but it would also fail to allow for the effects of electron correlation (see Sec. 5.3). An obvious solution is to apply empirical corrections to the integrals, such as to make them approximate to the empirical one-center values as the internuclear distances tend to zero. One way to do this is to modify the effective nuclear charges Z in the expressions for the SZOs; we used this approach in our preliminary NDDO calculations.[7]

A second alternative is to use some purely empirical expression, analogous to that employed in the π approximation [see Eq. (5.17)]. This can be done quite easily in the case of the MINDO and PNDO treatments, where only two-orbital integrals of the type (ii,kk) are taken into account. As in the π calculations, these must obey two boundary conditions. As the internuclear separation r_{ik} tends to zero, (ii,kk) must tend to the one-center integral A^-, while as r_{ik} tends to infinity, (ii,kk) must tend to e^2/r_{ik}. In the MINDO approximation, where repulsion integrals depend only on the internuclear separation and not on orbital orientation, one can use an expression identical in form with that [Eq. (5.17)] in the π approximation, viz.

$$(ii,kk) = e^2[r_{ik}^2 + (\rho_i + \rho_k)^2]^{-1/2} \tag{10.25}$$

where ρ_i and ρ_k are defined by:

$$\rho_i = \frac{e}{2A_i^-} \qquad \rho_k = \frac{e}{2A_k^-} \tag{10.26}$$

In the PNDO approximation, different values must be used for integrals involving p AOs in different orientations. In the terminology of Fig. 10.1, there are 10 distinct integrals to be considered, viz.

$$
\begin{array}{cccc}
(s_i's_i',s_j's_j') & (x_i'x_i',x_j'x_j') & (y_i'y_i',y_j'y_j') & (y_i'y_i',z_j'z_j') \\
(s_i's_i',x_j'x_j') & (x_i'x_i',s_j's_j') & (s_i's_i',y_j'y_j') & (y_i'y_i',s_j's_j') \\
(x_i'x_i',y_j'y_j') & (y_i'y_i',x_j'x_j') & &
\end{array} \tag{10.27}
$$

If the values of these are calculated for carbon, using standard SZOs ($Z = 3.25$) and an internuclear distance of 1.55 Å, the integrals are seen to fall into three

TABLE 10.2 Comparison of values for repulsion integrals found by direct quadrature with those given by Eqs. (10.26) to (10.28) for carbon atoms at 1.55 Å

Group	Integral	Calculated value, ev	
		From SZOs	From Eqs. (10.26) to (10.28)
I	$(s_i s_i, s_j s_j)$	9.28	7.13
	$(s_i s_i, y_j y_j)$	9.12	7.13
	$(y_i y_i, y_j y_j)$	8.98	7.13
	$(y_i y_i, z_j z_j)$	8.98	7.13
II	$(x_i x_i, s_j s_j)$	9.61	7.81
	$(x_i x_i, y_j y_j)$	9.41	7.81
III	$(x_i x_i, x_j x_j)$	9.99	8.45

distinct groups (Table 10.2). This pattern has been reproduced in published PNDO calculations by the following modification[6] of Eq. (10.23):

Group I:
$$(ii,kk) = e^2[r_{ik}^2 + (\rho_i + \rho_k)^2]^{-1/2} \qquad (10.28a)$$

Group II:
$$(ii,kk) = e^2[r_{ik}^2 + (\rho_i T_{ik} + \rho_k)^2]^{-1/2} \qquad (10.28b)$$

(here ϕ_i is the $\rho\sigma$-type AO)

Group III:
$$(ii,kk) = e^2[r_{ik}^2 + (\rho_i + \rho_k)^2 T_{ik}^2]^{-1/2} \qquad (10.28c)$$

Here:

$$T_{ik} = e^{-\alpha_{ik}r_{ik}} \qquad (10.29)$$

where α_{ik} is a parameter appearing in the expression from the internuclear repulsion [see below, Eq. (10.40)]. These expressions obey the boundary conditions, and, as the last column of Table 10.2 shows, they reproduce quite well the pattern indicated by the values found by direct quadrature from SZOs.

10.5.4   CORE RESONANCE INTEGRALS   In the Roothaan treatment, the core resonance integral $(\beta_{ij}^c)_\tau$ represents the energy of the overlap cloud between the AOs ϕ_i and ϕ_j due to attraction by the core; intuitively one might expect this to run parallel to the magnitude of the overlap cloud (i.e. to S_{ij}), and to the binding energies of the two AOs ϕ_i and ϕ_j (i.e. the valence-state ionization potentials I_i and I_j). This of course is the basis of the Mulliken approximation for such integrals, viz.

$$(\beta_{ij}^c)_\tau \approx \beta S_{ij}(I_i + I_j) \qquad (10.30)$$

As we have seen, the corresponding integral β_{ij}^c in the Pople treatment has no direct significance; it represents [Eq. (10.15)] the difference between the "true" resonance integral $(\beta_{ij})_t$ and a mean of the two valence-state ionization potentials. If then we accept the Mulliken approximation [Eq. (10.30)], for the "true" resonance integral, we find

$$\beta_{ij}{}^c = BS_{ij}(I_i + I_j) - \tfrac{1}{2}(I_i + I_j) = B'S_{ij}(I_i + I_j) \tag{10.31}$$

On this basis, we can still use the Mulliken approximation for integrals of this kind, with a suitable choice of the constant B'. This is the approach which has so far been followed in attempts to calculate heats of atomization accurately by the Pople method. In this treatment, it is in any case necessary to set $\beta_{ij}{}^c$ proportional to S_{ij}, or at least to some function with the same angular dependence, in order that the results of the calculations should be independent of the choice of coordinate axes; extensive trials[6,10] have also shown the need for the factor $I_i + I_j$, at least in the MINDO and PNDO approximations; for its omission leads to MOs in the wrong order of orbital energy.‡

In our preliminary studies[6,8,10] we found it necessary to modify Eq. (10.31) further, by introducing a distance-dependent factor, since otherwise it was impossible to account satisfactorily for the heats of formation of paraffins, olefines, and acetylenes with a single set of parameters. Such a factor seems intuitively reasonable since the core energy of the overlap cloud between the AOs ϕ_i and ϕ_j should depend on its distance from the nuclei concerned, and so on the internuclear separation r_{ij}. In the PNDO method, the final expression[6] for $\beta_{ij}{}^c$ had the form:

$$\beta_{ij}{}^c = B_{ij}S_{ij}(I_i + I_j)[r_{ij}{}^2 + (p_i + p_j)^2]^{-1/2} \tag{10.32}$$

where p_i and p_j are the quantities defined by Eq. (10.25). In the MINDO approximation, where there are no "molecular" parameters other than those in the expression for $\beta_{ij}{}^c$, it was found[8] necessary to introduce an additional parameter into this expression, i.e.

$$\beta_{ij}{}^c = S_{ij}(I_i + I_j)\left(A_{ij} + \frac{B_{ij}}{r_{ij}}\right) \tag{10.33}$$

In the preliminary work[6,10] on hydrocarbons, using the PNDO method, it was assumed that the parameter B_{ij} for the integral between dissimilar atoms i and j could be expressed as a mean of the values B_{ii} and B_{jj} for integrals between pairs of like atoms [compare Eq. (10.41) below]. Later this simplifying assumption was found to be unsatisfactory, and the results reported in the following section were obtained[8] using a different parameter B_{ij} for each kind of bond.

Obviously there are a number of alternative expressions that could be used for β_{ij}, based on alternative views of its physical significance. For example Lipscomb and his collaborators[4] have suggested that Eq. (10.30) should apply

---

‡ Leading for example to a situation where the lowest unoccupied MO of ethylene is of σ type instead of π type.

only to the terms representing the potential energy of the overlap cloud due to attraction by the core, whereas the core resonance integral, defined by

$$(\beta_{ij}{}^c)_\tau = \int \phi_i \mathbf{H}^c \phi_j \, d\tau \tag{10.34}$$

also contains kinetic-energy terms, the core operator $\mathbf{H}^c$ containing a term $-(\hbar^2/2m)\nabla^2$, representing kinetic energy. They suggest for $(\beta_{ij}{}^c)_\tau$ an expression of the form:

$$(\beta_{ij}{}^c)_\tau = \int \phi_i \left(-\frac{\hbar^2}{2m} \nabla^2 \right) \phi_j \, d\tau + C(I_i' + I_j') \tag{10.35}$$

where I_i' and I_j' are the parts of the valence-state ionization potentials representing potential energy only; these can be deduced by subtracting from I_i and I_j the corresponding kinetic-energy terms, e.g.

$$I_i' = I_i - \int \phi_i \left(-\frac{\hbar^2}{2m} \nabla^2 \right) \phi_i \, d\tau \tag{10.36}$$

The kinetic-energy integrals are evaluated directly, using SZOs. There are, however, obvious objections to this approach, in so far as the Pople method is concerned. In the first place, integrals of the type occurring in Eq. (10.33) are very sensitive to the expressions used for the AOs ϕ_i and ϕ_j, especially for resonance integrals between nonbonded atoms; SZOs are very poor approximations to Hartree-Fock AOs in regions remote from the nucleus. Even the analytical approximations to Hartree-Fock AOs given by the Roothaan method are likely to prove deficient in this respect; for AOs of this type are chosen to minimize the total energy of the atom in question, and this is determined by the parts of the AOs close to the nucleus. Secondly, the Pople resonance integrals are not the same as the ones appearing in the Roothaan method, and the difference between them [Eq. (10.14)] contains a kinetic-energy term [i.e. the parts of the quantities I_i and I_j that arise from kinetic-energy terms; compare Eq. (10.36)]. However this general argument indicates very clearly ways in which Eq. (10.30) may have to be modified in the future to give good heats of atomization for arbitrary molecules.

10.5.5 CORE-ELECTRON ATTRACTION AND CORE REPULSION   The attraction between an electron in an AO ϕ_i and the core of atom j is a quantity that enters directly into the SCF MO treatment [V_{in} in Eq. (10.11)]. This could be estimated theoretically, but attempts to do so have not in our experience proved satisfactory. Indeed, it would perhaps be illogical to adopt theoretical values for V_{in}, given that we use for the interelectronic repulsions empirical values less than those given by direct quadrature; both these quantities are likely to be affected by similar factors.

This can be seen very clearly from the following argument. Consider the interactions between an electron in the AO ϕ_i of atom m and the core and electrons of some other atom n.   If atom n is neutral overall (i.e. has on average enough valence electrons to exactly balance the core charge), the coulomb inter-action between our electron and atom n should vanish.‡   This will be true only if we assume the core-electron attraction between the electron in ϕ_i and the core of atom n to be equal and opposite to the repulsion between the electron in ϕ_i and electrons in the valence-shell AOs of atom n, a condition which will cer-tainly not be met if we use a theoretical value for the former and empirical values for the latter.   For this reason, all valence-shell calculations by the Pople method have hitherto used the approximation of setting the core-electron attrac-tion V_{in} equal and opposite to the net interelectronic repulsion between the elec-tron in ϕ_i and electrons in atom n corresponding to the assumed occupation of AOs in its valence state.   Thus if atom n is a carbon atom, when the valence state has one electron in each valence-shell AO (s, x, y, or z),

$$-V_{in} = (ii,ss) + (ii,xx) + (ii,yy) + (ii,zz) \tag{10.37}$$

Note that this is the same approximation that was used in the π calculations.

The core-core repulsion presents a more difficult problem.   The simplest solution would be to set this equal to the total electron-electron repulsion, as was done in the π calculations; here, however, such an assumption leads to pre-dicted bond lengths that are much too short.   The reason for this is easily seen. If we accept Eq. (10.37) for the core-electron attraction, and an analogous ex-pression for the core-core repulsion, then the net classical coulomb potential be-tween two neutral atoms in a molecule vanishes for all internuclear distances; for the electron-electron and core-core repulsions are exactly balanced by the core-electron attractions.   Now the electron-electron repulsion is in fact less than that calculated classically, because of the "exchange" correction to the repulsions between pairs of electrons with similar spins, while the core-electron attraction is greater than that calculated classically, because of the quantum-mechanical effect embodied in the one-electron integrals (see Sec. 3.1).   Both these corrections moreover increase as the internuclear separation decreases, and so the potential between our atoms decreases steadily as they approach and is a minimum when the internuclear separation is zero.§   This difficulty did not arise in the π calculations, because there we assumed a stiff framework of localized σ bonds whose rigidity was mainly responsible for establishing the molecular geometry.   Here there is nothing to prevent the molecule from collapsing.

In view of this, an obvious alternative would be to use the "correct" form

---

‡ The interaction is equal to a sum of the penetration integrals between ϕ_i and atom n, which we neglect [see Eq. (3.55)].

§ Complete collapse is prevented only by a decrease in the one-electron resonance integrals β^c; thus β^c for an s AO of one atom, and a p AO of a second, tends to zero as the nuclear separation tends to zero, an s AO and a p AO of a given atom being orthogonal to one another.

$C_m C_n e^2 / r_{mn}$ for the core-core repulsion between atoms m and n, $C_m e$ and $C_n e$ being their respective core charges; for this is much greater than the electron-electron repulsion, and the difference between the two increases as r_{mn} decreases. Attempts to use this expression have, however, been unsatisfactory, since it leads to calculated repulsions which are too large to be compensated by adjustment of the parameters in the core resonance integrals. The trouble here is probably due to two major contributing factors. In the first place, the calculated core-electron attractions are numerically much greater than the corresponding electron-electron repulsions; if therefore we use the theoretical value for the core-core repulsion, thus making it much larger than the electron-electron repulsion, we cannot set the core-electron attraction equal to *minus* the electron-electron repulsion without greatly overestimating the net coulomb repulsions between pairs of atoms. Secondly, our neglect of orbital contraction (Sec. 10.5.1) leads to an underestimate of the total energy, and this error increases as the internuclear separation decreases; in order to allow for it, we must in some way introduce a corresponding correction elsewhere. A convenient way to do this is to use a value for the core-core repulsion smaller than the theoretical one calculated for point charges.

In the PNDO calculations,[6,10] the core-core repulsion $V_{mn}{}^c$ between atoms m and n was accordingly treated as a parametric function of the internuclear separation r_{mn}. Such a function must clearly obey two boundary conditions. In order that the net forces between neutral atoms at large internuclear separations should vanish, and in view of our assumption that the core-electron attraction is equal to minus the electron-electron repulsion, V_{mn} must also approach the electron-electron repulsion $V_{mn}{}^E$ as r_{mn} becomes large; i.e.

$$V_{mn}{}^c \rightarrow \sum_i^m \sum_j^n n_i n_j (ii,jj) \equiv V_{mn}{}^E \qquad \text{as } r_{mn} \rightarrow \infty \qquad (10.38)$$

where the first sum is over the valence-shell AOs of atom m, the second over the valence-shell AOs of atom n, and n_k is the number of electrons in the AO ϕ_k when the atom in question is in its standard valence state. Secondly, since the internuclear repulsion becomes enormously greater than any other term in the total energy when r_{mn} is very small,

$$V_{mn}{}^c \rightarrow \frac{C_m C_n e^2}{r_{mn}} \qquad \text{as } r_{mn} \rightarrow 0 \qquad (10.39)$$

where $C_m e$, $C_n e$ are the respective core charges of atoms m and n. In the calculations so far reported,[6,10] the following one-parameter relation was accordingly used for $V_{mn}{}^c$:

$$V_{mn}{}^c = V_{mn}{}^E + \left(\frac{C_m C_n e^2}{r_{mn}} - V_{mn}{}^E \right) e^{-\alpha_{mn} r_{mn}} \qquad (10.40)$$

where α_{mn} is a parameter characteristic of atoms m and n. In order to reduce the number of parameters, it was further assumed that

$$\alpha_{mn} = (\alpha_{mm}\alpha_{nn})^{1/2} \tag{10.41}$$

Although the use of this potential function avoids the problem of molecular collapse, it has not as yet been found possible to reproduce experimental bond lengths exactly; heats of atomization have therefore so far been calculated using assumed molecular geometries, which do not correspond to those that would be found theoretically by minimizing the total energy. If we are willing to do this, i.e. abandon attempts to calculate bond lengths and concentrate solely on reproducing heats of atomization for assumed geometries, then the problem of molecular collapse becomes unimportant and we can simply set $V_{mn}{}^c$ and $V_{mn}{}^E$ equal. This is the approach that has been followed in calculations[8] using the MINDO approximation. The objection to any such treatment is that it can be applied only to "normal" molecules; for unless our calculations can reproduce bond lengths as well as total energy, they cannot be expected to work for systems containing abnormal bonds (e.g. transition states in reactions or nonclassical structures such as π complexes). The calculations described in the following section must therefore be regarded as a stopgap until the problem of calculating bond lengths has been solved.

10.6 HEATS OF ATOMIZATION OF HYDROCARBONS

In the rest of this chapter, we shall outline the results of calculations that had been carried out at the time it was written. Since the field is progressing extremely rapidly, the situation will inevitably have changed significantly by the time this book gets into print; nevertheless the results already obtained make it seem almost certain that the problem of estimating heats of atomization of molecules in general, and of transition states in particular, will be effectively solved in the near future.

All attempts to estimate heats of atomization accurately have been based on one of the procedures indicated at the end of the preceding section, using either the PNDO or MINDO approximations and with assumed molecular geometries. Calculations have so far been carried out for hydrocarbons[6,8,10] and for organic compounds containing nitrogen and oxygen;[8] since the subject is in such a state of rapid flux, it will be sufficient here to summarize the results for hydrocarbons, to show the potentialities of this kind of approach. The necessary integrals were calculated by the procedures indicated in Sec. 10.5, the values of the parameters α_{mn}, A_{mn}, and B_{mn} being found by fitting the observed heats of atomization of a few simple unstrained molecules (H_2, CH_4, C_2H_6, C_2H_4, and C_3H_8).

Table 10.3 compares heats of atomization calculated by both procedures for a wide range of hydrocarbons with values determined experimentally. The calculations were carried out using "standard" geometries, i.e. with standard values

TABLE 10.3 Calculated and observed heats of formation, in kilocalories per mole, of hydrocarbons from elements in their standard states[10]

Compound	ΔH_f obs.[a]	PNDO approximation		MINDO approximation	
		ΔH_f calc.[a]	Difference	ΔH_f calc.[a]	Difference
CH$_4$	−17.9	−17.9	0.0	−17.9	0.0
C$_2$H$_6$	−20.2	−22.1	−1.9	−20.2	0.0
(structure)	−24.8	−26.8	−2.0	−24.9	−0.1
(structure)	−30.2	−31.5	−1.3	−29.4	+0.7
(structure)	−32.2	−31.9	+0.3	−31.8	+0.4
(structure)	−35.0	−36.2	−1.2	−34.0	+1.0
(structure)	−36.9	−35.5	+1.4	−37.1	−0.2
C(CH$_3$)$_4$	−39.7	−37.6	+2.3	−40.6	−0.9
(structure)	−29.4	−30.0	−0.6	−26.4	+3.0
(structure, H—CH$_3$)	−37.0	−35.3	+1.7	−34.9	+2.1
C$_2$H$_4$	+12.5	+12.5	0.0	+13.8	+1.3
(structure)	+4.9	+4.5	−0.4	+5.2	+0.3
(structure)	0.0	−0.4	−0.4	+0.8	+0.8
(structure)	−2.7	−2.9	−0.2	−3.0	−0.3
(structure)	−1.7	+0.3	+2.0		
(structure)	−4.0	−3.8	+0.2	−5.9	−1.9
(structure)	+26.3	+26.1	−0.2	+25.7	−0.6
(structure)	+28.5	+27.2	−1.3		
BENZENE	+19.8	+19.9	+0.1	+20.2	+0.4
TOLUENE	+12.0	+11.7	−0.3	+10.2	−1.8
o-XYLENE	+4.5	+4.3	−0.2	−0.3	−4.8
m-XYLENE	+4.1	+3.6	−0.5	+0.2	−3.9
p-XYLENE	+4.3	+3.5	−0.8	0.0	−4.3
STYRENE	+35.2	+34.3	−0.9	+32.9	−2.3
(structure)	+12.7	+12.1	−0.6	+16.4	+3.7
(structure)	+39.7	+40.5	+0.8	+31.0	−8.7

TABLE 10.3 (*continued*)

Compound	ΔH_f obs.[a]	PNDO approximation		MINDO approximation	
		ΔH_f calc.[a]	Difference	ΔH_f calc.[a]	Difference
	+44.2	+46.3	+2.1	+42.2	−2.0
trans-	+31.0	+36.1	+5.1	+39.5	+8.4
	+39.4	+40.2	+0.8		
	+36.1	+37.6	+1.5		
	+66.6	+58.7	−7.9	+66.6	0.0
	+46.4	+42.4	−4.0	+43.4	−3.0
	+6.4	+6.4	0.0	+11.3	+4.9
CUBANE	+148.7	+116.9	−31.8	+116.9	−31.8
	+35.0	+35.1	0.0	+40.9	+5.9
	+22.4	+18.0	−4.4	+19.6	−3.8
	−18.5	−24.9	−6.4	−19.2	−0.7
	−25.5	−30.0	−4.5	−26.2	−0.7
	+7.7	+3.3	−4.4	+8.1	+0.4
	+32.4	+27.8	−4.6	+30.2	−2.2
	+31.0	+27.6	−3.4	+19.6	−11.4
	−1.7	+3.2	+4.9	+3.6	−4.9
NAPHTHALENE	+36.3	+37.9	+1.6	+27.5	+8.8
AZULENE	+68.9	+72.1	+3.2		

[a] See Refs. 6, 8, and 10.

for bond lengths (C—C, 1.535 Å; C=C, 1.338 Å; C≡C, 1.210 Å; —$\overset{|}{\underset{|}{C}}$—H, 1.093 Å; =$\overset{|}{C}$—H, 1.083 Å; ≡C—H, 1.059 Å) and assuming all bond angles to be tetrahedral, or 120° or 180°, except for small rings, where their values were estimated on the assumption of minimum distortion from equilibrium.

The agreement is evidently excellent. It is particularly noteworthy that our procedure gives very good estimates for the heats of formation of molecules with small strained rings; this provides a direct test of the method, since no mention of ring strain as such appears anywhere in the theoretical treatment or in the choice of parameters. Table 10.4 lists strain energies, estimated from the calculated and observed[9] PNDO heats of atomization by comparing them with values deduced for equivalent unstrained molecules by Franklin's group-additivity

TABLE 10.4 Strain energies in microcyclic hydrocarbons calculated[8,10] by the PNDO method

Compound	Strain energy, kcal/mole		
	Obs.	Calc.	Difference
△	27.5	26.9	−0.6
◇	62.8	64.8	+2.0
△=	37.2	38.7	+1.5
△	52.6	44.7	−7.9
△	47.0	43.0	−4.0
⋈	61.4	63.5	+2.1
□	26.1	26.1	0.0
□	26.0	26.0	0.0
⊟	27.9	23.5	−4.4
CUBANE	156.4	124.6	−31.8
TETRAHEDRANE		137.3	
BICYCLOBUTADIENE		99.2	

method;‡ estimated values are also included for several systems which are as yet unknown. Some amusing predictions follow from these results. For example, if the strain energy of tetrahedrane (I) is as great as that predicted, I should not exist as a stable species except perhaps at very low temperatures; for it should undergo spontaneous disruption via the diradical (II) into cyclobutadiene (III) with extreme ease. On the other hand the unlikely looking molecule bicyclobutadiene (IV) should be quite stable at room temperature, the energy required to break any bond in it being more than 45 kcal/mole; indeed the calculated heat of atomization is greater than that observed for the isomeric diacetylene (V). Perhaps these predictions[7,10] will have been tested by the time this book reaches print! Of course IV should be extremely reactive, undergoing polymerization very exothermically; however it should be stable if isolated in a suitable matrix.

| I | II | III | IV | V |

Table 10.5 shows comparisons of the energies of various pairs of isomers; in each case, the calculated heats of atomization lead to correct predictions as to their relative stabilities. Admittedly the calculated differences in energy are not too good, percentagewise; this, however, is not surprising, given that their absolute values are so small.

‡ This is an extension of the usual empirical scheme of additive bond energies, in which allowance is effectively made for the secondary changes in bond energy both with hybridization (Sec. 4.5) and with the other groups attached to the atoms forming the bond. See Ref. 11.

TABLE 10.5   Heats of isomerization calculated by the PNDO method[10]

Reaction	ΔH, kcal/mole	
	Calc.	Obs.
ETHANE staggered → eclipsed[a]	+0.9	+2.9
BUTANE normal → iso	−0.4	−2.0
PENTANE normal → neo	−1.4	−4.7
CYCLOHEXANE chair → boat	+2.6	+5.3
METHYLCYCLOHEXANE equatorial → axial	+2.3	+1.9
ETHYLENE planar → perpendicular[a]		
BUTADIENE trans → cis	+1.1	+2.2
2-BUTENE trans → cis	+3.2	+1.0
PROPENE CH eclipsed → staggered[a]		+2.0
TOLUENE CH eclipsed → staggered[a]	+0.005	~0.0
CYCLOOCTATETRAENE tub → planar with alternating single and double bonds	+12.2	+12.8–15.4

[a] Barrier to rotation.

10.7 COMPARISON OF THE VALENCE-SHELL METHOD
AND THE π APPROXIMATION; VALIDITY OF THE
HÜCKEL APPROXIMATION

Another interesting comparison can be made between the MOs calculated by the valence-shell method and the π MOs given by the earlier π calculations (Chap. 5). Table 10.6 shows this comparison for several conjugated hydrocarbons.[12] The agreement between the calculated orbital energies for the π MOs is quite remarkable, the more so when one considers that the parameters in the two treatments were chosen by entirely different procedures. Moreover this agreement also extends to other properties of the π electrons (e.g. π-bond orders).

One of the problems in calculations based on the Hückel σ-π approximation has been the uncertainty concerning its accuracy; various arguments have shown that it should hold to a first approximation, but there has been no evidence to indicate the kind of errors that might be involved through neglect of σ-π interactions. The results in Table 10.6 suggest that it is in fact a remarkably good approximation for planar conjugated molecules, very much better indeed than could possibly have been anticipated on theoretical grounds.

10.8 DIPOLE MOMENTS; LONE PAIRS

Yet another comparison with experiment would be provided by dipole moments; here, however, a complication arises.

The dipole moment μ of a molecule is equal to a vector sum of the moments of the individual particles in it about the origin; in the case of electrons, the moments are averaged over all positions of the electron. Thus in a classical picture,

$$\mu = \sum_m Z_m e \mathbf{r}_m - e \sum_i \langle \mathbf{r}_i \rangle \qquad (10.42)$$

where $\mathbf{r}$ is the radius vector of a given particle from the origin, Z_m is the nuclear charge of atom m, and the first sum is over the nuclei m and the second over the electrons i. The symbol $\langle \mathbf{r}_i \rangle$ implies the time-averaged radius vector of electron i.

In a quantum-mechanical treatment, μ is given by a similar expression in which the average positions of the electrons are calculated as expectation values for the corresponding position vector operators. Since the radius vector is a function of the position coordinates, it is represented in the Schrödinger representation by the same expression as in classical mechanics. If then electron i occupies the MO ψ_ν,

$$\langle \mathbf{r}_i \rangle = \frac{\int \psi_\nu \mathbf{r} \psi_\nu \, d\tau}{\int \psi_\nu^2 \, d\tau} \qquad (10.43)$$

where $\mathbf{r}$ is the radius vector of the volume element $d\tau$.

TABLE 10.6   Energy levels in hydrocarbons, in electron volts[12]

Molecule	Level type	Energy level		Difference
		From valence-shell theory	From SCF π theory	
ETHYLENE	π	10.965	10.855	+0.110
	σ	13.000		
trans-BUTADIENE	π	10.139	10.070	+0.069
	σ	11.850		
	π	11.994	12.060	−0.066
	σ	12.723		
FULVENE	π	10.076	10.008	+0.068
	π	10.321	10.428	−0.107
	σ	11.543		
	σ	11.893		
	σ	12.061		
	π	12.968	12.899	+0.069
	σ	13.029		
BENZENE	π	10.184	10.287[d]	−0.103
	σ	11.634		
	σ	13.060		
	π	13.100	13.037	+0.063
	σ	13.659		
STYRENE	π	9.788	9.804	−0.016
	π	10.217	10.293	−0.076
	σ	11.234		
	π	11.428	11.506	−0.078
	σ	11.555		
	σ	12.707		
	σ	12.732		
	π	13.300	13.215	+0.085
	σ	13.503		
NAPHTHALENE	π	9.309	9.274	+0.035
	π	9.965	10.068	−0.103
	σ	11.008		
	π	11.011	11.110	−0.099
	σ	11.336		
	π	12.022	12.042	−0.020
	σ	12.151		
	σ	12.715		
	σ	13.000		
	σ	13.317		
	σ	13.552		
	π	13.788	13.627	+0.161
	σ	15.019		

TABLE 10.6   (*continued*)

Molecule	Level type	Energy level		Difference
		From valence-shell theory	From SCF π theory	
AZULENE	π	8.851	8.666	+0.185
	π	9.476	9.432	+0.044
	π	11.256	11.489	−0.233
	σ	11.385		
	σ	11.404		
	σ	11.929		
	σ	12.078		
	π	12.137	12.107	+0.030
	σ	12.589		
	σ	13.009		
	π	13.688	13.577	+0.111
	σ	14.407		
CYCLOBUTADIENE	π	9.428	9.525	−0.097
	σ	11.251		
	σ	12.191		
	σ	12.566		
	π	12.574	12.612	−0.038
	σ	16.042		

Expanding ψ_ν in terms of AOs, we find:

$$\langle \mathbf{r}_i \rangle = \frac{\int \left(\sum_i a_{\nu i}\phi_i \right) \mathbf{r} \left(\sum_j a_{\nu j}\phi_j \right) d\tau}{\int \left(\sum_i a_{\nu i}\phi_i \right) \left(\sum_j a_{\nu j}\phi_j \right) d\tau}$$

$$\equiv \frac{\sum_i \sum_j a_{\nu i} a_{\nu j} r_{ij}}{\sum_i \sum_j a_{\nu i} a_{\nu j} S_{ij}} \tag{10.44}$$

where $r_{ij} = \phi_i \mathbf{r} \phi_j \, d\tau$ (10.45)

Since the integrand will be significant only in the small region of space common to the AOs ϕ_i and ϕ_j, we may reasonably replace $\mathbf{r}$ in Eq. (10.45) by a mean value ρ_{ij}. In that case

$$r_{ij} = \int \phi_i \rho_{ij} \phi_j \, d\tau = \rho_{ij} S_{ij} \tag{10.46}$$

Moreover the mean radius vector ρ_{ij} of the overlap cloud between the AOs ϕ_i and ϕ_j is likely to be close to the mean of those for the two individual orbitals; i.e.

$$\rho_{ij} \approx \tfrac{1}{2}(\rho_{ii} + \rho_{jj}) \tag{10.47}$$

If we introduce these approximations into Eq. (10.44), we find

$$\langle \mathbf{r}_i \rangle \frac{\sum_i a_{\nu i}^2 \rho_{ii}}{\sum_i a_{\nu i}^2} \qquad (10.48)$$

This is identical with the expression that would be obtained in a treatment where differential overlap is neglected, so that

$$\rho_{ij} = S_{ij} = 0 \qquad i \neq j \qquad (10.49)$$

The argument is the same as that used to justify the neglect of differential overlap in the Pople method (Sec. 3.4); it applies so long as the basis-set AOs are all AOs of different atoms, as of course was the case in the π calculations. Since the mean radius vector ρ_{ij} of an AO of atom m is clearly the same as that of the corresponding nucleus, that is $\mathbf{r}_m$ [Eq. (10.42)], it follows that in this approximation,

$$\mu = \sum_m Q_m \mathbf{r}_m \qquad (10.50)$$

where Q_m is the net formal charge on atom m, i.e. the difference between the core charge $Z_m e$ and the total charge $-q_m e$ of the q_m electrons occupying its AOs. This is the expression used to calculate the contribution of π electrons to the dipole moment of a conjugated molecule in the π approximation, Z_m in this case being equal to the effective core charge c_m.

In the valence-shell method, however, each atom may contribute more than one orbital; if so, the simplifying assumptions in the above treatment break down. Here the corresponding overlap terms S_{ij} in the denominator of Eq. (10.44) vanish, while the terms r_{ij} in the numerator do not. Consider for example the case where ϕ_i is an s AO of atom m and ϕ_j a p AO of the same atom. The overlap cloud between them is indicated in Fig. 10.2. It consists of two similar parts, of opposite sign; the total overlap, as measured by the integral S_{ij}, therefore vanishes. However the centers of gravity of the two overlap regions do not coin-

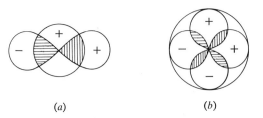

(a)   (b)

FIG. 10.2 Overlap cloud. (*a*) Between an *s* AO and a *p* AO; (*b*) between a pair of *p* AOs. The relative signs of segments of the overlap cloud are distinguished by horizontal and vertical hatching.

cide in space; the corresponding contributions to r_{ij} will therefore differ not only in sign but also in magnitude. Therefore ρ_{ij} does not vanish, and the corresponding contribution to the numerator of Eq. (10.44) must be retained in passing to Eq. (10.48). In other words, we can neglect two-center differential overlap in calculating dipole moments, but *not* one-center overlap. We could do so only if all AOs were spherically symmetrical, so that the corresponding integrals ρ_{ij}, like S_{ij}, vanished.

If therefore we wish to calculate dipole moments of molecules by the valence-shell method, we should, if we wish to be consistent, use an approximation in which the relevant one-center differential overlap is taken into account. Furthermore, it is very easily seen (compare Fig. 10.2) that the only overlap that is significant in this sense is that between an s AO and a p AO; for this alone gives rise to a dipole. Overlap between s AOs gives spherically symmetrical overlap clouds, while that between AOs of other types gives multipoles whose contributions to the dipole moments of molecules will be very small. We should therefore use an approximation in which differential overlap between s and p AOs of a given atom is explicitly taken into account; consequently the only logical way to calculate dipole moments is to use the NDDO approximation.

Since, however, the PNDO and CNDO methods can apparently give good estimates of heats of atomization, it seems not unreasonable to hope that they may lead to orbitals similar to those that would be given by the more elaborate NDDO approach. Both these methods may therefore be used to estimate dipole moments; however if we do this, we must be careful to include the one-center overlap terms, between s and p AOs, even though these are otherwise neglected. Thus with the usual rules for normalization,

$$\mu = \sum_m \left(Q_m \mathbf{r}_m + \sum_{i,j}^m \int \phi_i \mathbf{r} \phi_j \, d\tau \right) \tag{10.51}$$

where the integral is over all pairs of valence-shell AOs, ϕ_i and ϕ_j, of atom m.

One very important corollary emerges in the case of molecules containing atoms with unshared pairs of electrons, e.g. nitrogen or oxygen. In the simple localized-bond picture, we suppose such electrons to occupy a hybrid AO; since AOs of this type are not symmetrical, the electrons occupying such an AO have a large dipole moment (Sec. 4.13). Indeed, the dipole moments of molecules such as ammonia or water are due mainly to the unshared electrons in them, the polarity of the σ bonds being relatively insignificant. The polarity of unshared pairs has extremely important chemical consequences; in particular it is responsible for the behavior of such molecules as donors in forming hydrogen bonds. Now in the SCF MO treatment, these dipole moments arise entirely from integrals of the type r_{ij} between an s AO and a p AO of the atom in question. If therefore we wish to take account of intramolecular interactions in which such dipoles play a part, we must include them implicitly in our treatment or, in other words, use the full NDDO approximation.

10.9   SUMMARY

In this chapter we have given only a very brief outline of the Pople valence-shell method for two reasons; first, because very little work has as yet been done in this area, and secondly, because progress is likely to be so rapid that anything written at this time will soon be out of date.   The principles involved are, however, straightforward, and the reader should have no difficulty in following future work in this field.

Forty years ago Dirac remarked that the development of quantum theory had reduced chemistry to a theorem in applied mathematics; for any chemical problems could in principle be solved by solving the appropriate Schrödinger equation.   While any a priori program of this kind lies far in the unforeseeable future, the work described in this book raises a real and exciting possibility that a practical solution of the problem may be in sight.   The success of the Pople method when applied to the π electrons of conjugated systems, and the results of preliminary valence-shell calculations, seem to suggest very strongly that this approach will before long lead to results of sufficient accuracy to make it a major chemical tool.   The prospects for the future are moreover unlimited; for the rapid growth and increasing availability of computers should bring progressively more sophisticated treatments within the scope of this semiempirical approach.   In short, quantum chemistry seems on the verge of a major leap forward, and the days when chemists could get by with a smattering of resonance theory, or even of HMO theory, are probably numbered.

10.10   POSTSCRIPT (ADDED IN PROOF)

When this chapter was written, the one-center integrals in the MINDO method were calculated by Klopman's method;[6,9] however it was subsequently found[8] that problems arise concerning the invariance of the results to choice of coordinate axes, so in the published version[8] the one-center integrals were estimated by the method used by Pople et al.[5] in their INDO approximation.

A further recent development has been the use of an empirical core-repulsion function [compare Eq. (10.40)] in the MINDO method; in the case of hydrocarbons this has already led[13] to a procedure which allows CC and CH bond lengths to be estimated to ± 0.02 Å, and at the same time gives heats of formation with an accuracy almost equal to that of the original MINDO treatment (Table 10.3). The predictions in Sec. 10.9 are therefore certainly not overly optimistic.

PROBLEMS

10.1   In the CNDO method, it is assumed that two-center repulsion integrals (ii, jj) have values that are independent of the orientation of the AOs ϕ_i and ϕ_j.   Under these conditions, *all* differential overlap can be neglected. The neglect of differential overlap is, however, merely permissive; examine the conditions under which integrals involving differential overlap could be admitted into the CNDO method without destroying the invariance of the results to choice of coordinate axes.

10.2   Prove that one-center repulsion integrals involving sp overlap can be neglected in the NDDO method without destroying the invariance of the results to choice of coordinate axes.

10.3   Derive Eqs. (10.10) and (10.11).

10.4   Examine the validity of Klopman's treatment of energy states of atoms by applying it to oxygen, using the following experimental values for various barycenters of the oxygen atom and ions derived from it.

System	Barycenter	$S_z{}^a$	Energy, ev^b
O^{++}	$(2s)(2p)^3$	2	56.235
	$(2s)^2(2p)^2$	0	50.75
	$(2s)^2(2p)^2$	1	48.76
O$^+$	$(2s)(2p)^4$	$\frac{3}{2}$	28.48
	$(2s)^2(2p)^3$	$\frac{1}{2}$	17.132
	$(2s)^2)(2p)^3$	$\frac{3}{2}$	13.614
O	$(2s)(2p)^5$	1	15.656
	$(2s)^2(2p)^4$	0	1.558
	$(2s)^2(2p)^4$	1	0
O$^-$	$(2s)^2(2p)^5$	$\frac{1}{2}$	-1.465

^{a} Component of spin along the z-axis, in units of h; thus $S_z = 2$ corresponds to a state with four unpaired electrons with parallel spins.
^{b} Relative to the "ground-state" barycenter, $(2s)^2(2p)^2(2p)(2p)$, with two unpaired electrons with parallel spins.

REFERENCES

1   Hoffmann, R.: *J. Chem. Phys.* **39**, 1397 (1963).

2   Csizmadia, I. G., M. C. Harrison, J. W. Moskowitz, and B. T. Sutcliffe: *Theoret. Chim. Acta* **6**, 191 (1966); J. M. Schulman and J. W. Moskowitz: *J. Chem. Phys.* **43**, 3287 (1965).

3   Pople, J. A., and G. A. Segal: *J. Chem. Phys.* **43**, 5136 (1965); **44**, 3289 (1966).

4   Newton, M. D., F. P. Boer, and W. N. Lipscomb: *J. Am. Chem. Soc.* **88**, 2353, 2361, 2367 (1966).

5   Pople, J. A., D. L. Beveridge, and P. A. Dobosh: *J. Chem. Phys.* **47**, 2026 (1967).

6   Dewar, M. J. S., and G. Klopman: *J. Am. Chem. Soc.* **89**, 3089 (1967).

7   Dewar, M. J. S., and R. Sustmann: unpublished work.

8   Baird, N. C., and M. J. S. Dewar: *J. Chem. Phys.* In press.

9   Klopman, G.: *J. Am. Chem. Soc.* **86**, 1463, 4550 (1964); **87**, 3300 (1965).

10   Baird, N. C., and M. J. S. Dewar: *J. Am. Chem. Soc.* **89,** 3966 (1967).

11   Franklin, J. L.: *Ind. Eng. Chem.* **41,** 1070 (1949).

12   Baird, N. C., and M. J. S. Dewar: *Theoret. Chim. Acta* (*Berlin*) **9,** 1 (1967).

13   Dewar, M. J. S., and E. Hasselbach: unpublished work.